PEARSON

ALWAYS LEARNING

Allen R. Angel • Dennis C. Runde

Elementary Algebra for College Students

Custom Edition for Pima Medical Institute

Taken from:
Elementary Algebra for College Students, Eighth Edition
by Allen R. Angel and Dennis C. Runde

PIMA
MEDICAL
INSTITUTE

Front Cover Photo Credit: Photo by Bill Cronin, Copyright Pima Medical Institute.
Back Cover Photo Credit: Image from *Anatomie normale du corps humain* courtesy of the National Library of Medicine, illustration by Sigismond Balicki.

Taken from:

Elementary Algebra for College Students, Eleventh Edition
by Allen R. Angel and Dennis C. Runde
Copyright © 2011, 2007, 2004 by Pearson Education
Published by Prentice Hall
Boston, Massachusetts 02116

This special edition published in cooperation with Pearson Learning Solutions.

Pearson Learning Solutions, 501 Boylston Street, Suite 900, Boston, MA 02116
A Pearson Education Company
www.pearsoned.com

Printed in the United States of America

21   18

000200010271802121

CW

ISBN 10: 1-269-45487-0
ISBN 13: 978-1-269-45487-2

To my wife, Kathy,
and my sons, Robert and Steven
Allen R. Angel

To my wife, Kristin,
and our sons, Alex, Nick, and Max
Dennis C. Runde

Brief Contents

1 Real Numbers   1

2 Solving Linear Equations and Inequalities   91

3 Applications of Algebra   171

4 Exponents and Polynomials   221

5 Factoring   281

6 Rational Expressions and Equations   337

7 Graphing Linear Equations   403

Contents

Preface   xi

To the Student   xvi

1 Real Numbers   1

1.1 Study Skills for Success in Mathematics 2
1.2 Problem Solving 7
1.3 Fractions 20
1.4 The Real Number System 31
1.5 Inequalities 36
    Mid-Chapter Test: Sections 1.1–1.5 41
1.6 Addition of Real Numbers 42
1.7 Subtraction of Real Numbers 50
1.8 Multiplication and Division of Real Numbers 59
1.9 Exponents, Parentheses, and the Order of Operations 67
1.10 Properties of the Real Number System 76
    Chapter 1 Summary 83
    Chapter 1 Review Exercises 88
    Chapter 1 Practice Test 90

2 Solving Linear Equations and Inequalities   91

2.1 Combining Like Terms 92
2.2 The Addition Property of Equality 101
2.3 The Multiplication Property of Equality 107
2.4 Solving Linear Equations with a Variable on Only One Side of the Equation 114
    Mid-Chapter Test: Sections 2.1–2.4 122
2.5 Solving Linear Equations with the Variable on Both Sides of the Equation 123
2.6 Formulas 132
2.7 Ratios and Proportions 144
2.8 Inequalities in One Variable 156
    Chapter 2 Summary 163
    Chapter 2 Review Exercises 167
    Chapter 2 Practice Test 169
    Cumulative Review Test 170

3 Applications of Algebra   171

3.1 Changing Application Problems into Equations   172
3.2 Solving Application Problems   186
    Mid-Chapter Test: Sections 3.1–3.2   196
3.3 Geometric Problems   197
3.4 Motion, Money, and Mixture Problems   203
    Chapter 3 Summary   215
    Chapter 3 Review Exercises   216
    Chapter 3 Practice Test   219
    Cumulative Review Test   220

4 Exponents and Polynomials   221

4.1 Exponents   222
4.2 Negative Exponents   233
4.3 Scientific Notation   242
    Mid-Chapter Test: Sections 4.1–4.3   251
4.4 Addition and Subtraction of Polynomials   251
4.5 Multiplication of Polynomials   258
4.6 Division of Polynomials   268
    Chapter 4 Summary   275
    Chapter 4 Review Exercises   277
    Chapter 4 Practice Test   279
    Cumulative Review Test   280

5 Factoring   281

5.1 Factoring a Monomial from a Polynomial   282
5.2 Factoring by Grouping   289
5.3 Factoring Trinomials of the Form $ax^2 + bx + c, a = 1$ 294
5.4 Factoring Trinomials of the Form $ax^2 + bx + c, a \neq 1$ 302
    Mid-Chapter Test: Sections 5.1–5.4   312
5.5 Special Factoring Formulas and a General Review of Factoring   313
5.6 Solving Quadratic Equations Using Factoring   320
5.7 Applications of Quadratic Equations   324
    Chapter 5 Summary   331
    Chapter 5 Review Exercises   334
    Chapter 5 Practice Test   335
    Cumulative Review Test   336

6 Rational Expressions and Equations   337

6.1 Simplifying Rational Expressions   338
6.2 Multiplication and Division of Rational Expressions   345
6.3 Addition and Subtraction of Rational Expressions with a Common Denominator and Finding the Least Common Denominator   352
6.4 Addition and Subtraction of Rational Expressions   359
    Mid-Chapter Test: Sections 6.1–6.4   366
6.5 Complex Fractions   367

6.6 Solving Rational Equations   372

6.7 Rational Equations: Applications and Problem Solving   379

6.8 Variation   390

Chapter 6 Summary   396

Chapter 6 Review Exercises   399

Chapter 6 Practice Test   401

Cumulative Review Test   402

7 Graphing Linear Equations   403

7.1 The Cartesian Coordinate System and Linear Equations in Two Variables   404

7.2 Graphing Linear Equations   411

7.3 Slope of a Line   420

Mid-Chapter Test: Sections 7.1–7.3   430

7.4 Slope-Intercept and Point-Slope Forms of a Linear Equation   431

7.5 Graphing Linear Inequalities   442

7.6 Functions   445

Chapter 7 Summary   455

Chapter 7 Review Exercises   458

Chapter 7 Practice Test   461

Cumulative Review Test   462

Appendices   463

Appendix A   Review of Decimals and Percent   463

Appendix B   Finding the Greatest Common Factor and Least Common Denominator   466

Appendix C   Geometry   469

Answers   A1

Applications Index   I1

Subject Index   I5

Preface

This book was written for college students and other adults who have never been exposed to algebra or those who have been exposed but need a refresher course. Our primary goal was to write a book that students can read, understand, and enjoy. To achieve this goal we have used short sentences, clear explanations, and many detailed, worked-out examples. We have tried to make the book relevant to college students by using practical applications of algebra throughout the text.

The many factors that contributed to the success of the previous editions have been retained. In preparing this revision, we considered the suggestions of instructors and students throughout the country. The *Principles and Standards for School Mathematics*, prepared by the National Council of Teachers of Mathematics (NCTM), and *Beyond Crossroads: Implementing Mathematics Standards in the First Two Years of College,* by the American Mathematical Association of Two-Year Colleges (AMATYC) together with advances in technology, influenced the writing of this text.

New to This Edition

One of the most important features of the text is its readability. The book is very readable for students of all reading skill levels. The Eighth Edition continues this emphasis and has been revised with a focus on improving accessibility and addressing the learning needs and styles of today's students. To this end, the following changes have been made:

Content Changes

- Discussions throughout the text have been thoroughly revised for brevity and accessibility. Whenever possible, a visual example or diagram is used to explain concepts and procedures.
- **Understanding Algebra** is a new feature appearing in the margin throughout the text. Placed at key points, **Understanding Algebra** draws students' attention quickly to the important concepts and facts that they need to master.
- The pedagogical use of color has been enhanced and now includes a color-coded system for variables and notation, to support a more visual approach.
- Exercise sets now begin with new **Warm-Up Exercises** — and include an emphasis on vocabulary. These exercises are great as a warm-up to the homework or as a 5-minute quiz. The Concept/Writing exercises (formerly found at the start of the exercise sets) are now located after the Problem Solving section in the exercise sets.
- Exercises and applications have been updated throughout.

- Using Your Calculator and Using Your Graphing Calculator boxes have been removed from this edition.

Enhancements to Resources

- The Chapter Test Prep Video and Lecture Series Videos are now captioned in both English and Spanish. The videos are available in MyMathLab. The Chapter Test Prep videos are also available on YouTube.
- MyMathLab and MathXL have been significantly updated including:

    1. A substantial increase in exercises coverage
    2. Suggested Assignments in homework builder
    3. Cumulative chapter tests for modular approach

Features of the Text

Full-Color Format

Color is used pedagogically in the following ways:
- Important definitions and procedures are color screened.
- Color screening or color type is used to make other important items stand out.
- Artwork is enhanced and clarified with use of multiple colors.
- The full-color format allows for easy identification of important features by students.
- The full-color format makes the text more appealing and interesting to students.

Accuracy

Accuracy in a mathematics text is essential. To ensure accuracy in this book, math teachers from around the country have read the pages carefully for typographical errors and have checked all the answers.

Connections

Many of our students do not thoroughly grasp new concepts the first time they are presented. In this text we encourage students to make connections. That is, we introduce a concept, then later in the text briefly reintroduce it and build upon it. Often an important concept is used in many sections of the text. Important concepts are also reinforced throughout the text in the Cumulative Review Exercises and Cumulative Review Tests.

Chapter Opening Application

Each chapter begins with a real-life application related to the material covered in the chapter. By the time students complete the chapter, they should have the knowledge to work the problem.

Goal of This Chapter

This feature on the chapter opener page gives students a preview of the chapter and also indicates where this material will be used again in other chapters of the book. This material helps students see the connections among various topics in the book and the connection to real-world situations.

The Use of Icons

At the beginning of each exercise set the icons for MathXL®, *Math XL* , and for MyMathLab, *MyMathLab* , are illustrated to remind students of these homework resources.

Keyed Section Objectives

Each section opens with a list of skills that the student should learn in that section. The objectives are then keyed to the appropriate portions of the sections with blue numbers such as **1**.

Problem Solving

Pólya's five-step problem-solving procedure is discussed in Section 1.2. Throughout the book, problem solving and Pólya's problem-solving procedure are emphasized.

Practical Applications

Practical applications of algebra are stressed throughout the text. Students need to learn how to translate application problems into algebraic symbols. The problem-solving approach used throughout this text gives students ample practice in setting up and solving application problems. The use of practical applications motivates students.

Detailed, Worked-Out Examples

A wealth of examples have been worked out in a step-by-step, detailed manner. Important steps are highlighted in color, and no steps are omitted until after the student has seen a sufficient number of similar examples.

Now Try Exercises

In each section, after each example, students are asked to work an exercise that parallels the example given in the text. These Now Try Exercises make the students *active,* rather than passive, learners and they reinforce the concepts as students work the exercises. Through these exercises, students have the opportunity to immediately apply what they have learned. After each example, Now Try Exercises are indicated in green type such as Now Try Exercise 27. They are also indicated in green type in the exercise sets, such as 27.

Study Skills Section

Students taking this course may benefit from a review of essential study skills. Such study skills are essential for suc-cess in mathematics. Section 1.1, the first section of the text, discusses such study skills. This section should be very beneficial for your students and should help them to achieve success in mathematics.

Understanding Algebra

The new **Understanding Algebra** boxes appear in the margin throughout the text. Placed at key points, **Understanding Algebra** helps students focus on the important concepts and facts that they need to master.

Helpful Hints

The Helpful Hint boxes offer useful suggestions for problem solving and other varied topics. They are set off in a special manner so that students will be sure to read them.

Avoiding Common Errors

Common student errors are illustrated. Explanations of why the shown procedures are incorrect are given. Explanations of how students may avoid such errors are also presented.

Exercise Sets

The exercise sets are broken into three main categories: Warm-Up Exercises, Practice the Skills, and Problem Solving. Many exercise sets also contain Concept/Writing, Challenge Problems, and/or Group Activities. Each exercise set is graded in difficulty. The early problems help develop the student's confidence, and then students are eased gradually into the more difficult problems. A sufficient number and variety of examples are given in each section for the student to successfully complete even the more difficult exercises. The number of exercises in each section is more than ample for student assignments and practice.

Warm-Up Exercises

Exercise sets now begin with new Warm-Up Exercises. These fill-in-the-blank exercises include an emphasis on vocabulary. They serve as a great warm-up to the homework exercises or as 5-minute quizzes.

Problem-Solving Exercises

These exercises help students become better thinkers and problem solvers. Many of these exercises involve real-life applications of algebra. It is important for students to be able to apply what they learn to real-life situations. Many problem-solving exercises help with this.

Concept/Writing Exercises

Most exercise sets include exercises that require students to write out the answers in words. These exercises improve students' understanding and comprehension of the material. Many of these exercises involve problem solving and conceptualization and help develop better reasoning and critical thinking skills. These exercises are located following the Problem-Solving exercises within the end-of-section exercise sets.

Challenge Problems

These exercises, which are part of many exercise sets, provide a variety of problems. Many were written to stimulate student thinking. Others provide additional applications of algebra or present material from future sections of the book so that students can see and learn the material on their own before it is covered in class. Others are more challenging than those in the regular exercise set.

Video Lecture Exercises

The exercises that are worked out in detail on the Lecture Videos are marked with the video icon, ◄. This will prove helpful for your students.

Cumulative Review Exercises

All exercise sets (after the first two) contain questions from previous sections in the chapter and from previous chapters. These Cumulative Review Exercises will reinforce topics that were previously covered and help students retain the earlier material, while they are learning the new material. For the students' benefit, Cumulative Review Exercises are keyed to the section where the material is covered, using brackets, such as [3.4].

Group Activities

Many exercise sets have group activity exercises that lead to interesting group discussions. Many students learn well in a cooperative learning atmosphere, and these exercises will get students talking mathematics to one another.

Mid-Chapter Tests

In the middle of each chapter is a Mid-Chapter Test. Students should take each Mid-Chapter Test to make sure they understand the material presented in the chapter up to that point. In the student answers, brackets such as [2.3] are used to indicate the section where the material was first presented.

Chapter Summary

At the end of each chapter is a comprehensive chapter summary that includes important chapter facts and examples illustrating these important facts.

Chapter Review Exercises

At the end of each chapter are review exercises that cover all types of exercises presented in the chapter. The review exercises are keyed using color numbers and brackets, such as [1.5], to the sections where the material was first introduced.

Chapter Practice Tests

The comprehensive end-of-chapter practice test will enable the students to see how well they are prepared for the actual class test. The section where the material was first introduced is indicated in brackets in the student answers.

Cumulative Review Tests

These tests, which appear at the end of each chapter after the first, test the students' knowledge of material from the beginning of the book to the end of that chapter. Students can use these tests for review, as well as for preparation for the final exam. These exams, like the Cumulative Review Exercises, will serve to reinforce topics taught earlier. In the answer section, after each answer, the section where that material was covered is given using brackets.

Answers

The *odd answers* are provided for the exercise sets. *All answers* are provided for the Cumulative Review Exercises, Mid-Chapter Test, Chapter Review Exercises, Chapter Practice Tests, and Cumulative Review Tests. Answers are not provided for the Group Activity exercises since we want students to reach agreement by themselves on the answers to these exercises.

Prerequisite

This text assumes no prior knowledge of algebra. However, a working knowledge of arithmetic skills is important. Fractions are reviewed early in the text, and decimals and percent are reviewed in Appendix A.

Modes of Instruction

The format and readability of this book lend it to many different modes of instruction. The constant reinforcement of concepts will result in greater understanding and retention of the material by your students.

The features of the text and the large variety of supplements available make this text suitable for many types of instructional modes, including

- lecture
- hybrid or blended courses
- distance learning
- self-paced instruction
- modified lecture
- cooperative or group study
- learning laboratory

Student and Instructor Resources

STUDENT RESOURCES

Student Solutions Manual Provides complete worked-out solutions to • the odd-numbered section exercises • all exercises in the Mid-Chapter Tests, Chapter Reviews, Chapter Practice Tests, and Cumulative Review Tests	**Worksheets for Classroom or Lab Practice** • Extra practice exercises for every section of the text with ample space for students to show their work
Lecture Videos • For each section of the text, there are about 20 minutes of lecture. Exercises in the text that are worked on the videos are identified in the text by the ☛ icon. • Captioned in English and Spanish • Available in MyMathLab®	**Chapter Test Prep Videos** • Step-by-step solutions to every exercise in each Chapter Practice Test • Available in MyMathLab® • Available on YouTube (search "Angel Elementary Algebra" and click on "Channels")

INSTRUCTOR RESOURCES

Annotated Instructor's Edition Contains all the content found in the student edition, plus the following: • Answers to exercises on the same text page with graphing answers in the Graphing Answer section at the back of the text • Instructor Example provided in the margin paired with each student example	**Instructor's Resource Manual with Tests and Mini-Lectures** • Mini-lectures for each text section • Several forms of test per chapter (free response and multiple choice) • Answers to all items • Available for download from the IRC and in MyMathLab®
	TestGen® • Available for download from the IRC
Instructor's Solutions Manual • Available for download from the IRC and in MyMathLab®	**Online Resources** • MyMathLab® (access code required) • MathXL® (access code required)

Acknowledgments

We thank our spouses, Kathy Angel and Kris Runde, for their support and encouragement throughout the project. We are grateful for their wonderful support and understanding while we worked on the book.

We also thank our children: Robert and Steven Angel and Alex, Nick, and Max Runde. They also gave us support and encouragement and were very understanding when we could not spend as much time with them as we wished because of book deadlines. Special thanks to daughter-in-law, Kathy; mother-in-law, Patricia; and father-in-law, Scott. Without the support and understanding of our families, this book would not be a reality.

We would like to thank Lawrence Gilligan and Donna Petrie for their conscientiousness and attention to detail in reviewing pages, artwork, and answers. Special thanks to Larry who has been involved in all aspects of the project.

We want to thank Rafiq Ladhani and his team at Edumedia for accuracy reviewing the pages and checking all answers.

Many people at Pearson deserve thanks, including all those listed on the copyright page. In particular, we thank Paul Murphy, Editor in Chief; Mary Beckwith, Sponsoring Editor; Joanna Doxey, Associate Editor; Marketing Managers, Michelle Renda and Adam Goldstein; Debbie Meyer, Project Editor; Patty Bergin, Production Supervisor; Karen Wernholm, Senior Managing Editor; and Barbara Atkinson, Senior Designer.

We would like to thank the following reviewers and focus group participants for their thoughtful comments and suggestions:

Darla Aguilar, *Pima Community College, AZ*
Frances Alvarado, *University of Texas–Pan American, TX*
Jose Alvarado, *University of Texas–Pan American, TX*
Ben Anderson, *Darton College, GA*
Mary Lou Baker, *Columbia State Community College, TN*
Sharon Berrian, *Northwest Shoals Community College, AL*
Dianne Bolen, *Northeast Mississippi Community College, MS*
Julie Bonds, *Sonoma State University, CA*
Clark Brown, *Mojave Community College, AZ*
Connie Buller, *Metropolitan Community College, NE*
Marc D. Campbell, *Daytona Beach Community College, FL*
Julie Chesser, *Owens Community College, OH*
Kim Christensen, *Maple Woods Community College, MO*
Barry Cogan, *Macomb Community College, MI*
Pat C. Cook, *Weatherford College, TX*
Lisa DeLong Cuneo, *Pennsylvania State University–Dobois, PA*
Stephan Delong, *Tidewater Community College, VA*
Deborah Doucette, *Erie Community College (North), NY*

William Echols, *Houston Community College, TX*
Dale Felkins, *Arkansas Technical University, AR*
Reginald Fulwood, *Palm Beach Community College, FL*
Susan Grody, *Broward Community College, FL*
Abdollah Hajikandi, *State University of New York–Buffalo, NY*
Olga Cynthia Harrison, *Baton Rouge Community College, LA*
Richard Hobbs, *Mission College, CA*
Joe Howe, *St. Charles Community College, MO*
Laura L. Hoye, *Trident Technical College, SC*
Barbara Hughes, *San Jacinto Community College (Central), TX*
Mary Johnson, *Inver Hills Community College, MN*
Jane Keller, *Metropolitan Community College, NE*
Mike Kirby, *Tidewater Community College, VA*
William Krant, *Palo Alto College, TX*
Gayle L. Krzemine, *Pikes Peak Community College, CO*
Mitchel Levy, *Broward Community College, FL*
Mitzi Logan, *Pitt Community College, NC*
Jason Mahar, *Monroe Community College, NY*
Kimberley A. Martello, *Monroe Community College, NY*
Constance Meade, *College of Southern Idaho, ID*
Lynnette Meslinsky, *Erie Community College, NY*
Elizabeth Morrison, *Valencia Community College, FL*
Elsie Newman, *Owens Community College, OH*
Charlotte Newsom, *Tidewater Community College, VA*
Charles Odion, *Houston Community College, TX*
Jean Olsen, *Pikes Peak Community College, CO*
Jearme Pirie, *Erie Community College (North), NY*
Behnaz Rouhani, *Athens Technical College, GA*
Brian Sanders, *Modesto Junior College, CA*
Glenn R. Sandifer, *San Jacinto Community College (Central), TX*
Rebecca Schantz, *Prairle State College, IL*
Cristela Sifuentez, *University of Texas–Pan American, TX*
Fereja Tahir, *Illinois Central College, IL*
Burnette Thompson, Jr., *Houston Community College, TX*
Mary Vachon, *San Joaquin Delta College, CA*
Andrea Vorwark, *Maple Woods Community College, MO*
Ronald Yates, *Community College of Southern Nevada, NY*

Focus Group Participants

Linda Barton, *Ball State, IN*
Karen Egedy, *Baton Rouge Community College, LA*
Daniel Fahringer, *Harrisburg Area Community College, PA*
Sharon Hamsa, *Longview Community College, MO*
Cynthia Harrison, *Baton Rouge Community College, LA*
Judy Kasabian, *El Camino College, CA*
Christopher Yarish, *Harrisburg Area Community College, PA*

To the Student

Algebra is a course that requires active participation. You must read the text and pay attention in class, and, most importantly, you must work the exercises. The more exercises you work, the better.

The text was written with you in mind. Short, clear sentences are used, and many examples are given to illustrate specific points. The text stresses useful applications of algebra. Hopefully, as you progress through the course, you will come to realize that algebra is not just another math course that you are required to take, but a course that offers a wealth of useful information and applications.

This text makes full use of color. The different colors are used to highlight important information. Important procedures, definitions, and formulas are placed within colored boxes.

The boxes marked **Understanding Algebra** should be studied carefully. They emphasize concepts and facts that you need to master to succeed. **Helpful Hints** should be studied carefully, for they stress important information. Be sure to study **Avoiding Common Errors** boxes. These boxes point out common errors and provide the correct procedures for doing these problems.

After each example you will see a Now Try Exercise reference, such as Now Try Exercise 27. The exercise indicated is very similar to the example given in the book. You may wish to try the indicated exercise after you read the example to make sure you truly understand the example. In the exercise set, the Now Try exercises are written in green, such as 27.

In the exercise sets, the exercises with a video, ▄ indicate that these exercises are worked out on the Lecture Videos.

Some questions you should ask your professor early in the course include: What supplements are available for use? Where can help be obtained when the professor is not available? Supplements that may be available include: the Student Solutions Manual; the Lecture Series Videos; the Chapter Test Prep Video; *Math XL*; and *MyMathLab*. All these items are discussed under the heading of Supplements in Section 1.1 and listed in the Preface.

You may wish to form a study group with other students in your class. Many students find that working in small groups provides an excellent way to learn the material. By discussing and explaining the concepts and exercises to one another, you reinforce your own understanding. Once guidelines and procedures are determined by your group, make sure to follow them.

One of the first things you should do is to read Section 1.1, Study Skills for Success in Mathematics. Read this section slowly and carefully, and pay particular attention to the advice and information given. Occasionally, refer back to this section. This could be the most important section of the book. Pay special attention to the material on doing your homework and on attending class.

At the end of all exercise sets (after the first two) are **Cumulative Review Exercises.** You should work these problems on a regular basis, even if they are not assigned. These problems are from earlier sections and chapters of the text, and they will refresh your memory and reinforce those topics. If you have a problem when working these exercises, read the appropriate section of the text or study your notes that correspond to that material. The section of the text where the Cumulative Review Exercise was introduced is indicated in brackets, [ ], to the left of the exercise. After reviewing the material, if you still have a problem, make an appointment to see your professor. Working the Cumulative Review Exercises throughout the semester will also help prepare you to take your final exam.

Near the middle of each chapter is a **Mid-Chapter Test.** You should take each Mid-Chapter Test to make sure you understand the material up to that point. The section where the material was first introduced is given in brackets after the answer in the answer section of the book.

At the end of each chapter are a **Chapter Summary, Chapter Review Exercises,** a **Chapter Practice Test,** and a **Cumulative Review Test.** Before each examination you should review this material carefully and take the Chapter Practice Test (you may want to review the *Chapter Test Prep Video* also). If you do well on the Chapter Practice Test, you should do well on the class text. The questions in the Review Exercises are marked to indicate the section in which that material was first introduced. If you have a problem with a Review Exercise question, reread the section indicated. You may also wish to take the Cumulative Review Test that appears at the end of every chapter (starting with Chapter 2).

In the back of the text there is an **answer section** that contains the answers to the *odd-numbered* exercises, including the Challenge Problems. Answers to *all* Cumulative Review Exercises, Mid-Chapter Tests, Chapter Review Exercises, Chapter Practice Tests, and Cumulative Review Tests are provided. Answers to the Group Activity exercises are not provided, for we wish students to reach agreement by themselves on answers to these exercises. The answers should be used only to check your work. For the Mid-Chapter Tests, Chapter Practice Tests, and Cumulative Review Tests, after each answer the section number where that type of exercise was covered is provided.

We have tried to make this text as clear and error free as possible. No text is perfect, however. If you find an error in the text, or an example or section that you believe can be improved, we would greatly appreciate hearing from you. If you enjoy the text, we would also appreciate hearing from you. You can submit comments to math@pearson.com, subject for Allen Angel and Dennis Runde.

Allen R. Angel
Dennis C. Runde

1 Real Numbers

1.1 Study Skills for Success in Mathematics

1.2 Problem Solving

1.3 Fractions

1.4 The Real Number System

1.5 Inequalities

Mid-Chapter Test: Sections 1.1–1.5

1.6 Addition of Real Numbers

1.7 Subtraction of Real Numbers

1.8 Multiplication and Division of Real Numbers

1.9 Exponents, Parentheses, and the Order of Operations

1.10 Properties of the Real Number System

Chapter 1 Summary

Chapter 1 Review Exercises

Chapter 1 Practice Test

Goals of This Chapter

This chapter will provide you with the foundation that you need in order to succeed in this course and all other mathematics courses you will take. Learning proper study skills is the first step in building this foundation. *Please read Section 1.1 carefully and follow the advice given*. The emphasis of this chapter is to provide you with an understanding of the real number system.

In this chapter, you will learn a five-step problem-solving procedure that will be used throughout the book. Once you have learned the material in this chapter, you will be able to tackle the subsequent chapters in the book with confidence.

© Andrew Rich/iStockphoto

A college education is worth money! The amount of average annual income increases dramatically as one's education increases. For example, in 2007 someone with a bachelor's degree earned more than twice as much as a person without a high school diploma. In Exercise 43 on page 19, we will see how to analyze pictorial data to calculate the financial advantages of a college education.

1.1 Study Skills for Success in Mathematics

1 Recognize the goals of this text.

2 Learn proper study skills.

3 Prepare for and take exams.

4 Learn to manage time.

This section is extremely important. Take the time to read it carefully and follow the advice given.

Most of you taking this course fall into one of three categories: (1) those who did not take algebra in high school, (2) those who took algebra in high school but did not understand the material, or (3) those who successfully completed algebra in high school but have been out of school for some time and need to take the course again. Whichever the case, you will need to acquire study skills for mathematics courses.

Before we discuss study skills, we will present the goals of this text. These goals may help you realize why certain topics are covered in the text and why they are covered as they are.

1 Recognize the Goals of This Text

The goals of this text include:

1. Presenting traditional algebra topics
2. Preparing you for more advanced mathematics courses
3. Building your confidence in, and your enjoyment of, mathematics
4. Improving your reasoning and critical thinking skills
5. Increasing your understanding of how important mathematics is in solving real-life problems
6. Encouraging you to think analytically, so that you will feel comfortable translating real-life problems into mathematical equations, and then solving the problems.

In addition to teaching you the mathematical content, our goals are to teach you to be more *mathematically literate*, which is also called *quantitatively literate*. We wish to teach you to *communicate mathematically*, to teach you to *understand and interpret data* in a variety of formats, to teach you measurement and geometric concepts, to teach you to *reason more logically*, and to teach you to be able to represent real world applications mathematically, which is called *modeling*. Throughout the book we will strive to increase your mathematical understanding to help you become more successful in mathematics, in your future job, and throughout life.

We also realize that some of you may have some mathematics anxiety. We have written the book to try to help you overcome that anxiety by building your confidence in mathematics.

It is important to realize that this course is the foundation for more advanced mathematics courses. A thorough understanding of algebra will make it easier for you to succeed in later mathematics courses and in life.

2 Learn Proper Study Skills

Have a Positive Attitude You may be thinking to yourself, "I hate math," or "I wish I did not have to take this class." You may have heard of "math anxiety" and feel you fit this category. The first thing to do to be successful in this course is to change your attitude to a more positive one. You must be willing to give this course, and yourself, a fair chance.

Based on past experiences in mathematics, you may feel that this is difficult. However, mathematics is something you need to work at. Many of you are more mature now than when you took previous mathematics courses. Your maturity and desire to learn are extremely important and can make a tremendous difference in your ability to succeed in mathematics. I believe you can be successful in this course, but you also need to believe it.

Prepare for and Attend Class To be prepared for class, you need to do your homework assignments completely. If you have difficulty with the homework, or some of the concepts, write down questions to ask your instructor. If you were given a reading assignment, read the appropriate material carefully before class.

After the material is explained in class, read the corresponding sections of the text slowly and carefully, word by word.

You should plan to attend every class. Generally, the more absences you have, the lower your grade will be. Every time you miss a class, you miss important information. If you must miss a class, contact your instructor ahead of time, and get the reading assignment and homework. If possible, before the next class, try to copy a friend's notes to help you understand the material you missed.

In algebra and other mathematics courses, the material you learn is cumulative. The new material is built on material that was presented previously. You must understand each section before moving on to the next section, and each chapter before moving on to the next chapter. Therefore, do not let yourself fall behind. Seek help as soon as you need it—do not wait! You will greatly increase your chance of success in this course by following the study skills presented in this section.

While in class, pay attention to what your instructor is saying. If you don't understand something, ask your instructor to repeat the material. If you don't ask questions, your instructor will not know that you have a problem understanding the material.

In class, take careful notes. Write numbers and letters clearly, so that you can read them later. Make sure your x's do not look like y's and vice versa. It is not necessary to write down every word your instructor says. Copy the major points and the examples that do not appear in the text. You should not be taking notes so frantically that you lose track of what your instructor is saying.

Read the Text   Mathematics textbooks should be read slowly and carefully, word by word. If you do not understand something, reread that material. It is a good idea to read with a pencil in your hand, making notes as you proceed.

Don't panic! As you read the examples, notice that the "flow" is basically downward. It is a challenge but try to understand the reasons for each step. This downward movement is a sequence of steps that takes a problem from statement toward its solution. Each step is important to understand. If you have trouble with the rationale for a step, you should ask your instructor for clarification.

When you come across a new concept or definition, you may wish to underline or highlight it so that it stands out. Then it will be easier to find later. Also, work the **Now Try Exercises** that appear in the text following each example. The Now Try Exercises are designed so that you have the opportunity to immediately apply new ideas. Make notes of things you do not understand to ask your instructor.

There are numerous boxes in the left margin marked **Understanding Algebra**. These boxes give alternative wording and additional illustration of important concepts. You may want to give these special attention as you read and see how they help with topics in the text and examples.

This textbook has other special features to help you. I suggest that you pay particular attention to these highlighted features, including the **Avoiding Common Errors** boxes, the **Helpful Hint** boxes, and important procedures and definitions identified by color. The Avoiding Common Errors boxes point out the most common errors made by students. Read and study this material very carefully and make sure that you understand what is explained. If you avoid making these common errors, your chances of success in this and other mathematics classes will be increased greatly. The Helpful Hints offer many valuable techniques for working certain problems. They may also present some very useful information or show an alternative way to work a problem.

Do the Homework   *Two very important commitments that you must make to be successful in this course are attending class and doing your homework regularly.* Your assignments must be worked conscientiously and completely. Do your homework as soon as possible, so the material presented in class will be fresh in your mind. It is through doing homework that you truly learn the material. While working homework you will become aware of the types of problems that you need further help with. If you do not work the assigned exercises, you will not know what questions to ask in class.

When you do your homework, make sure that you write it neatly and carefully. Pay particular attention to copying signs and exponents correctly.

Don't forget to check the answers to your homework assignments. This book contains the answers to the odd-numbered exercises in the back of the book. In addition, the answers to all the Cumulative Review Exercises, Mid-Chapter Tests, Chapter Review Exercises, Chapter Practice Tests, and Cumulative Review Tests are in the back of the book. The section number where the material is first introduced is provided next to the exercises for the Cumulative Review Exercises and Chapter Review Exercises. The section number where the material is first introduced is provided with the answers in the back of the book for the Mid-Chapter Tests, Chapter Practice Tests, and Cumulative Review Tests. Answers to the Group Activity Exercises are not provided because we want you to arrive at the answers as a group.

Ask questions in class about homework problems you don't understand. You should not feel comfortable until you understand all the concepts needed to work every assigned problem successfully.

Study for Class Study in the proper atmosphere, in an area where you will not be constantly disturbed, so that your attention can be devoted to what you are reading. The area where you study should be well ventilated and well lit. You should have sufficient desk space to spread out all your materials. Your chair should be comfortable. You should try to minimize distractions while you are studying. You should not study for hours on end. Short study breaks are a good idea.

Before you begin studying, make sure that you have all the materials you need (pencils, markers, calculator, etc.). You may wish to highlight the important points covered in class or in the book.

It is recommended that students study and do homework for at least two hours for each hour of class time. Some students require more time than others. It is important to spread your studying time out over the entire week rather than studying during one large block of time.

When studying, you should not only understand how to work a problem but also know *why* you follow the specific steps you do to work the problem. If you do not have an understanding of why you follow the specific process, you will not be able to transfer the process to solve similar problems.

This book has Mid-Chapter Tests in the middle of each chapter. These exercises reinforce material presented in the first half of the chapter. They will also help you determine if you need to go back and review the topics covered in the first half of the chapter. For any of the Mid-Chapter Test questions that you get incorrect, turn to the section provided with the answers in the back of the book and review that section. This book also has Cumulative Review Exercises at the end of every section after Section 1.2. These exercises reinforce material presented earlier in the course, and you will be less likely to forget the material if you review it repeatedly throughout the course. The exercises will also help prepare you for the final exam. Even if these exercises are not assigned for homework, I urge you to work them as part of your studying process.

3 Prepare for and Take Exams

If you study a little bit each day you should not need to cram the night before an exam. Begin your studying early. If you wait until the last minute, you may not have time to seek the help you may need if you find you cannot work a problem.

To prepare for an exam:

1. Read your class notes.
2. Review your homework assignments.
3. Study formulas, definitions, and procedures you will need for the exam.
4. Read the Avoiding Common Errors boxes and Helpful Hint boxes carefully.
5. Read the summary at the end of each chapter.
6. Work the Chapter Review Exercises at the end of each chapter. If you have difficulties, restudy those sections. If you still have trouble, seek help.

7. Work the Mid-Chapter Test and the Chapter Practice Test.

8. Rework quizzes previously given if the material covered in the quizzes will be included on the test.

9. If your exam is a cumulative exam, work the Cumulative Review Test.

10. Now, if you can arrange it, you may want to consider a session of study with a partner or group from your class. With a partner, you can construct a sample test to take to simulate your actual test and help alleviate test anxiety. Try these steps:

    a) Using three-by-five-inch index cards, go through the text and select representative problems—writing the question on one side of the card and the answer or page reference on the other. Choose questions you think will most likely be asked; don't choose easy problems. Have your study partner do the same thing. Probably 20 to 25 good, representative questions should do it.

    b) Here is the key: *shuffle the cards*. One thing that makes tests more difficult than homework is that homework problems are often of the same type and knowing how to start the problem is not too difficult. But test questions are all mixed up and to simulate that, shuffle the cards.

    c) You take your partner's test—be sure to give yourself the same amount of time your instructor will give you—and your partner takes your test. Try to avoid distractions (music, food, etc.). Grade your partner's test and have your partner grade your test. Then study weak areas and repeat the process if necessary.

Prepare for Midterm and Final Exam When studying for a comprehensive midterm or final exam follow the procedures discussed for preparing for an exam. However, also:

1. Study all your previous tests and quizzes carefully. Make sure that you have learned to work the problems that you may have previously missed.

2. Work the Cumulative Review Test at the end of each chapter. These tests cover the material from the beginning of the book to the end of that chapter.

3. If your instructor has given you a worksheet or practice exam, make sure that you complete it. Ask questions about any problems you do not understand.

4. Begin your studying process early so that you can seek all the help you need in a timely manner.

Take an Exam Make sure you get sufficient sleep the night before the test. Arrive at the exam site early so that you have a few minutes to relax before the exam. If you rush into the exam, you will start out nervous and anxious. After you are given the exam, you should do the following:

1. Carefully write down any formulas or ideas that you want to remember.

2. Look over the entire exam quickly to get an idea of its length. Also make sure that no pages are missing.

3. Read the test directions carefully.

4. Read each question carefully. Show all of your work. Answer each question completely, and make sure that you have answered the specific question asked.

5. Work the questions you understand best first; then go back and work those you are not sure of. Do not spend too much time on any one problem or you may not be able to complete the exam. Be prepared to spend more time on problems worth more points.

6. Attempt each problem. You may get at least partial credit even if you do not obtain the correct answer. If you make no attempt at answering the question, you will lose full credit.

7. Work carefully step by step. Copy all signs and exponents correctly when working from step to step, and make sure to copy the original question from the test correctly.

8. Write clearly so that your instructor can read your work. If your instructor cannot read your work, you may lose credit. When appropriate, make sure that your final answer stands out by placing a box around it.

9. If you have time, check your work and your answers.

10. Do not be concerned if others finish the test before you or if you are the last to finish. Use any extra time to check your work.

Stay calm when taking your test. Do not get upset if you come across a problem you can't figure out right away. Go on to something else and come back to that problem later.

4 Learn to Manage Time

As mentioned earlier, it is recommended that students study and do homework for at least two hours for each hour of class time. Finding the necessary time to study is not always easy. The following are some suggestions that you may find helpful.

1. Plan ahead. Determine when you will study and do your homework. Do not schedule other activities for these periods. Try to space these periods evenly over the week.

2. Be organized, so that you will not have to waste time looking for your books, your pencil, your calculator, or your notes.

3. If you are allowed to use a calculator, use it for tedious calculations.

4. When you stop studying, clearly mark where you stopped in the text.

5. Try not to take on added responsibilities. You must set your priorities. If your education is a top priority, as it should be, you may have to reduce time spent on other activities.

6. If time is a problem, do not overburden yourself with too many courses.

Use Supplements This text comes with a large variety of supplements. Find out from your instructor early in the semester which supplements are available and might be beneficial for you to use. Supplements should not replace reading the text, but should be used to enhance your understanding of the material. If you miss a class, you may want to review the video on the topic you missed before attending the next class.

The supplements available are: the Student Solutions Manual which works out the odd section exercises as well as all the end-of-chapter exercises; the Lecture Series Videos, which show about 20 minutes of lecture per section and include the worked out solutions to the exercises marked with this icon ◀; the Chapter Test Prep Video, which works out every problem in every Chapter Practice Test; *Math*XL MathXL®, a powerful online tutorial and homework system; *MyMathLab* MyMathLab, the online course which houses MathXL. The Lecture Series Videos and Chapter Test Prep Videos are available through MyMathLab. The Chapter Test Prep Videos are also available on YouTube (search Angel "Elementary Algebra" and click on "Channels").

Seek Help Be sure to get help as soon as you need it! Do not wait! In mathematics, one day's material is usually based on the previous day's material. So, if you don't understand the material today, you may not be able to understand the material tomorrow.

Where should you seek help? There are often a number of resources on campus. Try to make a friend in the class with whom you can study. Often, you can help one another. You may wish to form a study group with other students in your class. Discussing the concepts and homework with your peers will reinforce your own understanding of the material.

You should know your instructor's office hours, and you should not hesitate to seek help from your instructor when you need it. Make sure you read the assigned material and attempt the homework before meeting with your instructor. Come prepared with specific questions to ask.

There are often other sources of help available. Many colleges have a mathematics lab or a mathematics learning center where tutors are available. Ask your instructor early in the semester where and when tutoring is available. Arrange for a tutor as soon as you need one.

A Final Word   You can be successful at mathematics if you attend class regularly, pay attention in class, study your text carefully, do your homework daily, review regularly, and seek help as soon as you need it. Good luck in your course and remember: *Mathematics is not a spectator sport!*

EXERCISE SET 1.1

Do you know:

1. your professor's name and office hours?

2. your professor's office location and telephone number?

3. where and when you can obtain help if your professor is not available?

4. the name and phone number of a friend in your class?

5. what supplements are available to assist you in learning?

6. if your instructor is recommending the use of a particular calculator?

7. when you can use your calculator in this course?

8. if your instructor is requiring the use of MyMathLab?

If you do not know the answers to questions 1–8, you should find out as soon as possible.

9. What are your goals for this course?

10. What are your reasons for taking this course?

11. List the things you need to do to prepare properly for class.

---

indicates an exercise worked out on the Lecture Series Videos.

12. Are you beginning this course with a positive attitude? It is important that you do!

13. For each hour of class time, how many hours outside of class are recommended for studying and doing homework?

14. Explain how a mathematics text should be read.

15. Two very important commitments that you must make to be successful in this course are **a)** doing homework regularly and completely and **b)** attending class regularly. Explain why these commitments are necessary.

16. When studying, you should not only understand how to work a problem, but also why you follow the specific steps you do. Why is this important?

17. Have you given any thought to studying with a friend or a group of friends? Can you see any advantages in doing so? Can you see any disadvantages in doing so?

18. Write a summary of the steps you should follow when taking an exam.

1.2 Problem Solving

1 Learn the five-step problem-solving procedure.

2 Solve problems involving bar, line, and circle graphs.

3 Solve problems involving statistics.

1 Learn the Five-Step Problem-Solving Procedure

One of the main reasons we study mathematics is to use it to solve real-life problems. To solve most real-life problems mathematically, we need to be able to express the problem in mathematical symbols. We will spend a great deal of time explaining how to express real-life applications mathematically.

You can approach any problem using the general five-step **problem-solving procedure** developed by George Pólya (1887–1985) in his book *How to Solve It*.

Guidelines for Problem Solving

1. **Understand the problem.**
   - Read the problem *carefully* at least twice. In the first reading, get a general overview of the problem. In the second reading, determine (*a*) exactly what you are being asked to find and (*b*) what information the problem provides.
   - Make a list of the given facts. Determine which are pertinent to solving the problem.
   - Determine whether you can substitute smaller or simpler numbers to make the problem more understandable.
   - If it will help you organize the information, list the information in a table.
   - If possible, make a sketch to illustrate the problem. Label the information given.

2. **Translate the problem to mathematical language.**
   - This will generally involve expressing the problem in terms of an algebraic expression or equation. (We will explain how to express application problems as equations in Chapter 3.)
   - Determine whether there is a formula that can be used to solve the problem.

3. **Carry out all necessary calculations.**

4. **Check the answer obtained in step 3.**
   - Ask yourself, "Does the answer make sense?" "Is the answer reasonable?" If the answer is not reasonable, recheck your method for solving the problem and your calculations.
   - Check the solution in the original wording of the problem if possible.

5. **Make sure you have answered the question.**
   - State the answer clearly.

> **Understanding Algebra**
>
> An *expression* is a collection of numbers, letters, grouping symbols, and operations.

In step 2 we use the words *algebraic expression*. An **algebraic expression**, sometimes simply referred to as an **expression**, is a general term for any collection of numbers, letters (called variables), grouping symbols such as parentheses ( ) or brackets [ ], and **operations** (such as addition, subtraction, multiplication, and division). In this section we will not be using variables, so we will discuss their use later.

Examples of Expressions

$$3 + 4, \qquad 6(12 \div 3), \qquad (2)(7)$$

The following examples show how to apply the guidelines for problem solving. In some problems it may not be possible or necessary to list every step in the procedure. If you need to review procedures for adding, subtracting, multiplying, or dividing decimal numbers, or if you need a review of percents, read Appendix A before proceeding.

EXAMPLE 1 **Buying Games** Georgia May is deciding which would be less expensive, buying her son's birthday presents on eBay or buying them at a local toy store. Founded in 1995, eBay is The World's Online Marketplace® for the sale of goods and services by a diverse community of individuals and small businesses. The eBay community includes more than 100 million registered members from around the world. The local toy store is only minutes from Georgia's house. Therefore, the cost of gasoline for her car will not factor into her decision. On eBay, the three games Georgia would like to purchase cost $5.99, $9.95, and $19.95. Shipping costs for the games would total $11.10. There would be no sales tax on this purchase. At the local toy store, the total cost for the same three games would be $57.89 plus 8.25% sales tax.

a) Which would be less expensive for Georgia, purchasing the games on eBay or at the local toy store?

b) How much would Georgia save by making the less expensive purchase?

Solution

a) Understand the problem A careful reading of the problem shows that the task is to determine if it would be less expensive for Georgia to purchase the games on eBay or at the local toy store. Make a list of all the information given and determine which information is needed to solve the problem.

Information Given	Pertinent to Solving the Problem?
eBay includes more than 100 million registered members	no
$5.99, $9.95, and $19.95 cost of the games on eBay	yes
$11.10 shipping costs on eBay	yes
no sales tax on the eBay purchase	yes
cost of gasoline not a factor in Georgia's decision	yes
$57.89 cost of the games at the local toy store	yes
8.25% sales tax at the local toy store	yes

To determine whether eBay or a local store would be the better choice for purchasing the games, it is *not* necessary to know that eBay includes more than 100 million registered members. Solving this problem involves:

- calculating the total cost of games on eBay (including shipping)
- calculating the total cost of games at local store (including sales tax)

To calculate sales tax, you need to determine 8.25% of the cost of the games at the local toy store. When performing calculations, numbers given as percents are changed to decimal numbers. So we will use 0.0825 for 8.25%.

Translate the problem into mathematical language

total cost of games on eBay = cost of each individual game + shipping costs

total cost of games at local toy store = total cost of games + 8.25% sales tax

Carry out the calculations

total cost of games on eBay = $5.99 + $9.95 + $19.95 + $11.10 = $46.99

total cost of games at local toy store = $57.89 + 0.0825($57.89)

= $57.89 + $4.78 = $62.67

Check the answer The total costs of $46.99 and $62.67 are reasonable based on the information given.

Answer the question asked It would be less expensive for Georgia to purchase the games on eBay.

b) Understand To determine how much Georgia would save by making the less expensive purchase, you need to subtract the total cost of the games on eBay from the total cost of the games at the local toy store.

Translate

total cost at toy store − total cost on eBay = amount Georgia would save

Carry Out $62.67 − $46.99 = $15.68

Check The answer $15.68 seems reasonable.

Answer Georgia would save $15.68 by purchasing the games on eBay.

Now Try Exercise 27

EXAMPLE 2 Processor Speed In April 2008, IBM began shipping its fastest processor, the Power6, that could perform 5.0 billion operations per second (5.0 gigahertz, symbolized 5.0 GHz). How many operations could it perform in 0.4 second?

Solution Understand We are given the name of the processor, a speed of about 5.0 billion (5,000,000,000) operations per second, and 0.4 second. To determine the answer to this problem, the name of the processor, Power6, is not needed.

To obtain the answer, will we need to multiply or divide? Often a fairly simple problem seems more difficult because of the numbers involved. When very large or very small numbers make the problem confusing, try substituting commonly used numbers in the problem to determine your problem-solving strategy. Suppose the problem said the processor can perform 6 operations per second. How many operations can it perform in 2 seconds? Simply multiply 6 × 2 to get 12. Since we multiplied to obtain this answer, we also will need to multiply to obtain the answer to the given problem.

Understanding Algebra

When solving word problems, it is often helpful to solve a simpler problem first.

Translate
  number of operations in 0.4 second = 0.4(number of operations per second)

Carry Out   = 0.4(5,000,000,000)

                                   = 2,000,000,000

Understanding Algebra

Notice that the answer to the problem in Example 2 is a complete English sentence, not simply a number, and the number has a unit, operations.

Check The answer, 2,000,000,000 operations, is less than the 5,000,000,000 operations per second, which makes sense because the processor is operating for less than a second.

Answer In 0.4 second, the processor can perform about 2,000,000,000 operations.

Now Try Exercise 21

EXAMPLE 3 Medical Insurance Brook Matthews' medical insurance policy is similar to that of many workers. Her policy requires that she pay the first $100 of medical expenses each calendar year (called a deductible). After the deductible is paid, she pays 20% of the medical expenses (called a co-payment) and the insurance company pays 80%. (There is a maximum co-payment of $600 that she must pay each year. After that, the insurance company pays 100% of the fee schedule.) On January 1, Brook sprained her ankle playing tennis. She went to the doctor's office for an examination and X rays. The total bill of $325 was sent to the insurance company.

a) How much of the bill will Brook be responsible for?

b) How much will the insurance company be responsible for?

Solution **a)** Understand First we list all the *relevant* given information.

Given Information

$100 deductible

20% co-payment after deductible

80% paid by insurance company after deductible

$325 doctor bill

All the other information is not needed to solve the problem. Brook will be responsible for the first $100 and 20% of the remaining balance. The insurance company will be responsible for 80% of the balance after the deductible. Before we can find what Brook owes, we need to first find the balance of the bill after the deductible. The balance of the bill after the deductible is $325 − $100 = $225.

Translate
Brook's responsibility = deductible + 20% of balance of bill after the deductible

Carry Out   Brook's responsibility $= 100 + 20\%(225)$

$$= 100 + 0.20(225)$$

$$= 100 + 45$$

$$= 145$$

Check and Answer   The answer appears reasonable. Brook will be responsible for $145.

b) The insurance company will be responsible for 80% of the balance after the deductible.

insurance company's responsibility $= 80\%$ of balance after deductible

$$= 0.80(225)$$

$$= 180$$

Thus, the insurance company is responsible for $180. This checks because the sum of Brook's responsibility and the insurance company's responsibility is equal to the doctor's bill.

$$\$145 + \$180 = \$325$$

We could have also found the answer to part **b)** by subtracting Brook's responsibility from the total amount of the bill, but to give you more practice with percents we decided to show the solution as we did.

Now Try Exercise 33

2 Solve Problems Involving Bar, Line, and Circle Graphs

Problem solving often involves understanding and reading graphs and sets of data (or numbers). To work Example 4, you must interpret a bar graph and work with data.

EXAMPLE 4 **Walking It Off** Experts suggest that people walk 10,000 steps daily. Depending on stride length, each mile ranges between 2000 and 2500 steps. **Figure 1.1** is a **bar graph** that shows the number of steps it takes to burn off calories from a garden salad with fat-free dressing, a 12-ounce can of soda, a doughnut, and a cheeseburger.

a) Using the bar graph in **Figure 1.1**, estimate the number of steps it takes to burn off calories from a cheeseburger.

b) If Cliff Jackson can walk a mile in 2000 steps, how many miles will he have to walk in order to burn off the calories from the cheeseburger he ate for lunch?

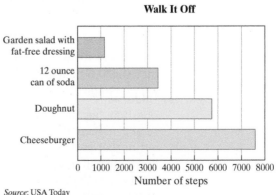

Walk It Off

FIGURE 1.1   *Source*: USA Today

Solution

a) Using the bar to the right of Cheeseburger in **Figure 1.1**, we estimate that the number of steps it takes to burn off calories from a cheeseburger is about 7600.

b) Understand Since it takes Cliff 2000 steps to walk a mile, it follows that he would need to take 4000 steps to walk 2 miles, 6000 steps to walk 3 miles, and so on. To determine how many miles Cliff will have to walk in order to burn off the calories from the cheeseburger, we need to divide as follows.

Translate $\text{miles to walk} = \dfrac{\text{number of steps to burn off calories}}{2000}$

Carry Out $\text{miles to walk} = \dfrac{7600}{2000} = 3.8$

Check and Answer   The answer appears reasonable. Cliff will need to walk 3.8 miles in order to burn off the calories from the cheeseburger that he ate for lunch.

Now Try Exercise 35

In Example 5, we will use the symbol $\approx$, which is read "**is approximately equal to.**" If, for example, the answer to a problem is 34.12432, we may write the answer as ≈ 34.1.

Super Bowl 30-second Commercial Cost

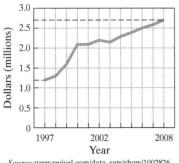

Source: www.swivel.com/data_sets/show/1002826

FIGURE 1.2

EXAMPLE 5 The Super Bowl The **line graph** in **Figure 1.2** shows the cost of a 30-second commercial during Super Bowls from 1997 to 2008. The advertising prices are set by the TV network.

a) Estimate the cost of 30-second commercials in 1997 and 2008.

b) How much more was the cost for a 30-second commercial in 2008 than in 1997?

c) How many times greater was the cost of a 30-second commercial in 2008 than in 1997?

Solution

a) When reading a line graph where the line has some thickness, as in **Figure 1.2**, we will use the center of the line to make our estimate. By observing the dashed lines on the graph, we can estimate that the cost of a 30-second commercial was about $1.2 million (or $1,200,000) in 1997 and about $2.7 million (or $2,700,000) in 2008.

b) We use the problem-solving procedure to answer the question.

Understand   To determine how much more the cost of a 30-second commercial was in 2008 than in 1997, we need to subtract.

Translate   difference in cost = cost in 2008 − cost in 1997

Carry Out   = \$2,700,000 − \$1,200,000 = \$1,500,000

Check and Answer   The answer appears reasonable. The cost was $1,500,000 more in 2008 than in 1997.

c) Understand   If you examine parts **b)** and **c)**, they may appear to ask the same question, but they do not. In Section 1.1, we indicated that it is important to read a mathematics problem carefully, word by word. The two parts are different in that part **b)** asks "how much more was the cost" whereas part **c)** asks "how many <u>times</u> greater." To determine the number of times greater the cost was in 2008 than in 1997, we need to divide the cost in 2008 by the cost in 1997, as shown below.

Translate   number of times greater $= \dfrac{\text{cost in 2008}}{\text{cost in 1997}}$

Carry Out   number of times greater $= \dfrac{2,700,000}{1,200,000} \approx 2.25$

Check and Answer   By observing the graph, we see that the answer is reasonable. The cost of a 30-second commercial during the Super Bowl in 2008 was about 2.25 times the cost in 1997.

Now Try Exercise 37

EXAMPLE 6 Stay-at-Home Parents **Figure 1.3** is a **circle graph** that shows the reasons why married mothers with children under the age of 15 have stayed out of the labor force for the past year. Use **Figure 1.3** to determine the number of married mothers with children under the age of 15 who have stayed out of the labor force for the following reasons: to care for home and family, ill/disabled, retired, going to school, could not find work, and other.

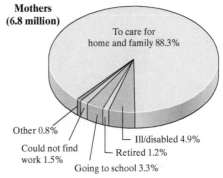

Reasons for Married Mothers with Children Under Age 15 Staying Out of the Labor Force for the Past Year

FIGURE 1.3   *Source*: U.S. Census Bureau

Solution   Understand There were 6.8 million married mothers with children under the age of 15 who were out of the labor force. Of these mothers, 88.3% were out of the labor force to care for home and family. To determine the number of married mothers with children under the age of 15 out of the labor force to care for home and family, we need to find 88.3% of the total number of mothers. To do this, we multiply as follows.

Translate

$$\begin{pmatrix} \text{to care for home} \\ \text{and family} \end{pmatrix} = \begin{pmatrix} \text{percent out of the labor force} \\ \text{to care for home and family} \end{pmatrix}\begin{pmatrix} \text{total number out} \\ \text{of the labor force} \end{pmatrix}$$

Carry Out

to care for home and family $= 0.883(6.8 \text{ million})$

$= 6.0044 \text{ million}$

Thus, 6.0044 million married mothers with children under the age of 15 were out of the labor force to care for home and family.

To find the number who were out of the labor force for being ill/disabled, we do a similar calculation.

ill/disabled $= 0.049(6.8 \text{ million})$

$= 0.3332 \text{ million}$

We do similar calculations to find the number who were retired, going to school, could not find work, or for other reasons were out of the labor force.

$$\text{retired} = 0.012(6.8 \text{ million})$$
$$= 0.0816 \text{ million}$$
$$\text{going to school} = 0.033(6.8 \text{ million})$$
$$= 0.2244 \text{ million}$$
$$\text{could not find work} = 0.015(6.8 \text{ million})$$
$$= 0.102 \text{ million}$$
$$\text{other reasons} = 0.008(6.8 \text{ million})$$
$$= 0.0544 \text{ million}$$

Check   If we add the six amounts, we obtain the 6.8 million total. Therefore, our answer is correct.

$$6.0044 \text{ million} + 0.3332 \text{ million} + 0.0816 \text{ million} + 0.2244 \text{ million}$$
$$+ 0.102 \text{ million} + 0.0544 \text{ million} = 6.8 \text{ million}$$

Answer   The number of married mothers with children under the age of 15 who were out of the labor force were as follows: 6.0044 million to care for home and family; 0.3332 million were ill/disabled; 0.0816 million were retired; 0.2244 million were going to school; 0.102 million could not find work; for other reasons, 0.0544 million.

Now Try Exercise 39

3 Solve Problems Involving Statistics

Because understanding statistics is so important in our society, we will now discuss certain statistical topics and use them in solving problems.

The *mean* and *median* are two **measures of central tendency**, which are also referred to as *averages*. An average is a value that is representative of a set of data (or numbers).

The **mean** of a set of data is determined by adding all the values and dividing the sum by the number of values. For example, to find the mean of 6, 9, 3, 12, 12, we do the following.

$$\text{mean} = \frac{6 + 9 + 3 + 12 + 12}{5} = \frac{42}{5} = 8.4$$

> **Understanding Algebra**
>
> The *mean* is found by dividing the sum of the data by the number of data points. The *median* is the middle score of the ranked data.

We divided the sum by 5 since there are five values. The mean is the most commonly used average and it is generally what is thought of when we use the word *average*.

Another average is the median. The **median** is the value in the middle of a set of **ranked data**. The data may be ranked from smallest to largest or largest to smallest. To find the median of 6, 9, 3, 12, 12, we can rank the data from smallest to largest as follows.

$$3, 6, 9, 12, 12$$
$$\uparrow$$
$$\text{Middle value}$$

The value in the middle of the ranked set of data is 9. Therefore, the median is 9. Note that half the values will be above the median and half will be below the median.

If there is an even number of pieces of data, the median is halfway between the two middle pieces. For example, to find the median of 3, 12, 5, 12, 17, 9, we can rank the data as follows.

$$3, 5, 9, 12, 12, 17$$
$$\uparrow$$
$$\text{Middle values}$$

Since there are six pieces of data (an even number), we find the value halfway between the two middle pieces, the 9 and the 12. To find the median, we add these values and divide the sum by 2.

$$\text{median} = \frac{9 + 12}{2} = \frac{21}{2} = 10.5$$

Thus, the median is 10.5. Note that half the values are above and half are below 10.5.

EXAMPLE 7 The Mean Grade Alfonso Ramirez's first six exam grades are 90, 87, 76, 84, 78, and 62.

a) Find the mean for Alfonso's six grades.

b) If one more exam is to be given, what is the minimum grade that Alfonso can receive to obtain at least a B average (a mean average of 80 or better)?

c) If there is only one more exam, is it possible for Alfonso to obtain an A average (90 or better)? Explain.

Solution

a) To obtain the mean, we add the six grades and divide by 6.

$$\text{mean} = \frac{90 + 87 + 76 + 84 + 78 + 62}{6} = \frac{477}{6} = 79.5$$

b) We will show the problem-solving steps for this part of the example.

Understand   For the mean average of seven exams to be 80, the total points for the seven exams must be 7(80) or 560. The minimum grade needed can be found by subtracting the sum of the first six grades from 560.

Translate

$$\text{minimum grade needed} = 560 - \text{sum of first six exam grades}$$

Carry Out

$$= 560 - (90 + 87 + 76 + 84 + 78 + 62)$$
$$= 560 - 477$$
$$= 83$$

Check   We can check to see that a seventh grade of 83 gives a mean of 80 as follows.

$$\text{mean} = \frac{90 + 87 + 76 + 84 + 78 + 62 + 83}{7} = \frac{560}{7} = 80$$

Answer   A seventh grade of 83 or higher will result in at least a B average.

c) We can use the same reasoning as in part **b)**. For a 90 average, the total points that Alfonso will need to attain is $90(7) = 630$. Since his total points are 477, he will need $630 - 477$ or 153 points to obtain an A average. Since the maximum number of points available on most exams is 100, Alfonso would not be able to obtain an A in the course.

Now Try Exercise 41

EXERCISE SET 1.2

Math XL   MyMathLab
MathXL®   MyMathLab

Warm-Up Exercises

Fill in the blanks with the appropriate word, phrase, or symbol(s) from the following list.

expression	~~measures of central tendency~~	mean	median
~~equation~~	~~approximately equal to~~	~~grouping symbols~~	~~problem solving~~
~~checking~~	circle graphs	~~understanding the problem~~	

1. The ___median___ of the data 2, 4, 7, 8, 9 is 7.

2. A general collection of numbers, symbols, and operations is called a(n) ___equation___.

3. The symbol ≈ means ___approx equal to___.

4. The ___mean___ of the data 2, 4, 7, 8, 9 is 6.

5. One of the five important steps in problem solving, seeing if your answer makes sense, is referred to as ___checking___ a problem.

6. The mean and median are types of averages, also called _measures of central tendancy_

7. Graphical representation of data includes bar graphs, line graphs, and _circle graphs_.

8. Parentheses and brackets are examples of _grouping symbols_

9. In this book we use Pólya's five-step approach for _problem solving_

10. Reading a problem at least twice, making a list of facts, and making a sketch are the problem-solving step called _understanding the problem_

Practice the Skills

11. Test Grades Jenna Webber's test grades are 78, 97, 59, 74, and 74. For Jenna's grades, determine the **a)** mean and **b)** median.

12. Bowling Scores William Krant's bowling scores for five games were 161, 131, 187, 163, and 145. For William's games, determine the **a)** mean and **b)** median.

13. Electric Bills The Malones' electric bills for January through June, 2006, were $96.56, $108.78, $87.23, $85.90, $79.55, and $65.88. For these bills, determine the **a)** mean and **b)** median.

14. Grocery Bills Antoinette Payne's monthly grocery bills for the first five months of 2006 were $204.83, $153.85, $210.03, $119.76, and $128.38. For Antoinette's grocery bills, determine the **a)** mean and **b)** median.

15. Dry Summers The following figure shows the 10 driest summers in the Southeast from 1895 through 2004. Determine the **a)** mean and **b)** median inches of rainfall for the 10 years shown.

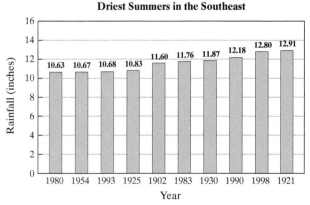

Driest Summers in the Southeast

Bar graph of Rainfall (inches) vs. Year:
- 1980: 10.63
- 1954: 10.67
- 1993: 10.68
- 1925: 10.83
- 1902: 11.60
- 1983: 11.76
- 1930: 11.87
- 1990: 12.18
- 1998: 12.80
- 1921: 12.91

Source: Gloria Forthun, Southeast Regional Climate Center
Records are from 1895 through 2004. The Southeast is Va., N.C., S.C., Ga., Fla., and Ala.

16. Homes for Sale Eight homes are for sale in a community. The sale prices are $124,100, $175,900, $142,300, $164,800, $146,000, $210,000, $112,200, and $153,600. Determine the **a)** mean and **b)** median sale price of the eight homes.

Problem Solving

17. Commissions Barbara Riedell earns a 5% commission on appliances she sells. Her sales last week totaled $9400. Find her week's earnings.

18. Empire State Building May 1, 1931, was the opening day of the Empire State Building. It stands 1454 feet or 443 meters high. Use this information to determine the approximate number of feet in a meter.

19. Sales Tax   a) The sales tax in Jefferson County is 8%. What was the sales tax that Scott Reed paid on a used car that cost $16,700 before tax?

b) What is the total cost of the car including tax?

20. Checking Account The balance in Debbie Ogilvie's checking account is $312.60. She purchased five DVDs at $17.11 each including tax. If she pays by check, what is the new balance in her checking account?

21. Computer Processor Suppose a computer processor can perform about 2.3 billion operations per second. How many operations can it perform in 0.7 second?

22. Buying a Computer Pat Sullivan wants to purchase a computer that sells for $950. He can either pay the total amount at the time of purchase or agree to pay the store $200 down and $33 per month for 24 months.

a) If he pays the down payment and monthly charge, how much will he pay for the computer?

b) How much money can he save by paying the total amount at the time of purchase?

23. Energy Values The following table gives the approximate energy values of some foods and the approximate energy consumption of some activities, in kilojoules (kJ). Determine how long it would take for you to use up the energy from the following.

a) a hamburger by running

b) a chocolate milkshake by walking

c) a glass of skim milk by cycling

Energy Value, Food	(kJ)	Energy Consumption, Activity	(kJ/min)
Chocolate milkshake	2200	Walking	25
Fried egg	460	Cycling	35
Hamburger	1550	Swimming	50
Strawberry shortcake	1440	Running	80
Glass of skim milk	350		

A green numbered exercise, such as 21 indicates a Now Try Exercise.

24. Jet Ski The rental cost of a jet ski from Don's Ski Rental is $20 per half-hour, and the rental cost from A. J.'s Ski Rental is $50 per hour. Suppose you plan to rent a jet ski for 3 hours.

a) Which is the better deal?

b) How much will you save?

25. Gas Mileage When the odometer in Tribet LaPierre's car reads 16,741.3, he fills his gas tank. The next time he fills his tank it takes 10.5 gallons, and his odometer reads 16,935.4. Determine the number of miles per gallon that his car gets.

26. Income Taxes The federal income tax rate schedule for a *joint return* in 2007 is illustrated in the following table.

Adjusted Gross Income	Taxes
$0–$15,650	10% of income
$15,650–$63,700	$1565 + 15% in excess of $15,650
$63,700–$128,500	$8772.50 + 25% in excess of $63,700
$128,500–$195,850	$24,972.50 + 28% in excess of $128,500
$195,850–$349,700	$43,830 + 33% in excess of $195,850
$349,700 and up	$94,601 + 35% in excess of $349,700

Source: www.irs.gov

a) If the Donovins' adjusted gross income in 2007 was $34,612, determine their taxes.

b) If the Ortegas' 2007 adjusted gross income was $75,610, determine their taxes.

27. Buying Tires Eric Weiss purchased four tires through the Internet. He paid $62.30 plus $6.20 shipping and handling per tire. There was no sales tax on this purchase. When he received the tires, Eric had to pay $8.00 per tire for mounting and balancing. At a local tire store, his total cost for the four tires with mounting and balancing would have been $425 plus 8% sales tax. How much did Eric save by purchasing the tires through the Internet?

28. Baseball Salaries Jason Giambi, of the New York Yankees, was the highest paid professional baseball player in 2007, according to *USA Today*. He earned $23.4 million. Bartolo Colon, then of the Los Angeles Angels, was the highest paid pitcher, earning $16 million. In 2007, Giambi batted 254 times and Colon pitched 99 innings. Determine approximately how much more Colon received per inning pitched than Giambi did per at bat.

29. Balance Consider the figure shown. Assuming the green and red blocks have the same weight, where should a single green block, ■, be placed to make the scale balanced? Explain how you determined your answer.

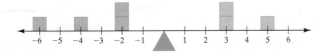

30. Taxi Ride A taxicab charges $2 upon a customer's entering the taxi, then 30 cents for each $\frac{1}{4}$ mile traveled and 20 cents for each 30 seconds stopped in traffic. David Lopez takes a taxi ride for a distance of 3 miles where the taxi spends 90 seconds stopped in traffic. Determine David's cost of the taxi ride.

31. Leaky Faucet A faucet that leaks 1 ounce of water per minute wastes 11.25 gallons in a day.

a) How many gallons of water are wasted in a (non-leap) year?

b) If water costs $5.20 per 1000 gallons, how much additional money per year is being spent on the water bill?

32. Conversions a) What is 1 mile per hour equal to in feet per hour? One mile contains 5280 feet.

b) What is 1 mile per hour equal to in feet per second?

c) What is 60 miles per hour equal to in feet per second?

33. Medical Insurance Mel LeBar's medical insurance policy requires that he pay a $150 deductible each calendar year. After the deductible is paid, he pays 20% of the medical expenses and the insurance company pays 80%. On January 1, Mel's daughter accidentally closed the car door on his finger. He went to the doctor's office for an examination and X rays. The total bill of $365 was sent to the insurance company. If Mel had not as yet paid any of the deductible,

a) how much of the bill will Mel be responsible for?

b) how much will the insurance company be responsible for?

34. Insurance Drivers under the age of 25 who pass a driver education course generally have their auto insurance premium decreased by 10%. Most insurers will offer this 10% deduction until the driver reaches 25. A particular driver education course costs $70. Don Beville, who just turned 18, has auto insurance that costs $630 per year.

a) Excluding the cost of the driver education course, how much would Don save in auto insurance premiums, from the age of 18 until the age of 25, by taking the driver education course?

b) What would be his net savings after the cost of the course?

35. Math Scores The bar graph below shows some 2006 scores from the Program for International Student Assessment, a test for 15-year-olds. The scale was constructed so that an average score is 500.

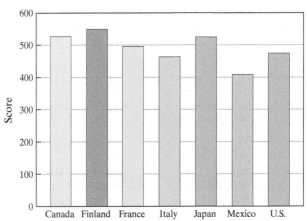

Source: New York Times

a) Which country had the highest math score shown? Estimate the score.

b) Which country had the lowest math scores shown? Estimate the score.

c) Estimate the difference between the scores for Finland and Mexico.

36. Commercial Airlines The bar graph shows the total scheduled passengers on U.S. commercial airlines from 1999 to 2007 with the forecasted totals through 2016. From the bar graph, estimate

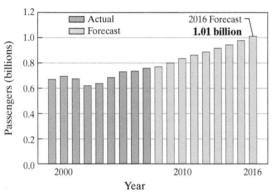

**Total Scheduled Passengers
on U.S. Commercial Airlines**

Source: Federal Aviation Administration

a) the total number of scheduled passengers on U.S. commercial airlines in 2000.

b) the forecasted total number of scheduled passengers on U.S. commercial airlines in 2015.

c) how many times greater is the forecasted total number of scheduled passengers on U.S. commercial airlines in 2015 than in 2000?

37. Motorcycle Sales The line graph below shows the U.S. sales of new motorcycles from 1992 to 2007.

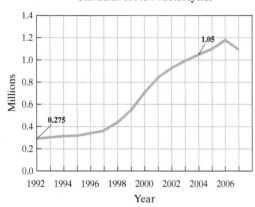

U.S. Sales of New Motorcycles

Source: Motorcycle Industry Council

a) Estimate the number of new motorcycles sold in the U.S. in 1992 and in 2004.

b) How many more new motorcycles were sold in the U.S. in 2004 than in 1992?

c) How many times greater was the number of new motorcycles sold in 2007 than in 1992?

38. SAT Math Scores The line graph below shows the number of freshmen students at the College of Applied Science with high school math SAT scores over 700.

a) During which consecutive years did the number of students remain constant?

During which consecutive years did the number of freshmen with high school math SAT scores over 700

b) increase the most?

c) decrease the most?

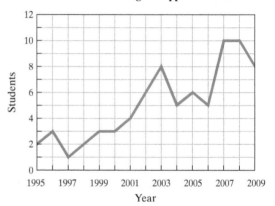

**Number of College Freshman with SAT Math Scores
over 700 — College of Applied Science**

39. Adoption Approximately 1.7 million U.S. households included adopted children. The circle graph below shows the percent of these households that had one adopted child, two adopted children, and three or more adopted children. Estimate the number of U.S. households that had

a) one adopted child.

b) two adopted children.

c) three or more adopted children.

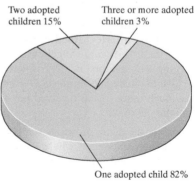

**U.S. Households with Adopted Children
(1.7 million households)**

Source: www.census.gov

40. Jeopardy! As of this writing, Ken Jennings, a software engineer from Salt Lake City, Utah, is the second highest record holder for the most money ever won on a television game show. The circle graph on the next page shows the outcome of the 160 Daily Doubles that Ken attempted on his *Jeopardy!* run. Use the circle graph to determine

a) the number of Daily Doubles Ken answered correctly.

b) the number of Daily Doubles Ken answered incorrectly.

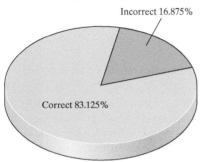

Ken Jennings's Jeopardy Daily Doubles
(160 Total)

Incorrect 16.875%

Correct 83.125%

Source: www.tvgameshows.net/jenningswinnings.htm

41. Test Grades A mean of 60 on all exams is needed to pass a course. On his first five exams Lamond Paine's grades are 50, 59, 67, 80, and 56.

a) What is the minimum grade that Lamond can receive on the sixth exam to pass the course?

b) An average of 70 is needed to get a C in the course. Is it possible for Lamond to get a C? If so, what is the minimum grade that Lamond can receive on the sixth exam?

© Shutterstock

42. Test Grades A mean of 80 on all exams is needed to earn a B in a course. On her first four exams, Heather Feldman's grades are 95, 88, 82, and 85.

a) What is the minimum grade that Heather can receive on the fifth exam to earn a B in the course?

b) A mean of 90 is needed to earn an A in the course. Is it possible for Heather to get an A? If so, what is the minimum grade that Heather can receive on the fifth exam?

43. Level of Education The following bar graph shows the median annual earnings by level of education in 2007 in the United States. Which degree has median annual earnings that are approximately 2.2 times the median annual earnings of someone with less than a high school diploma?

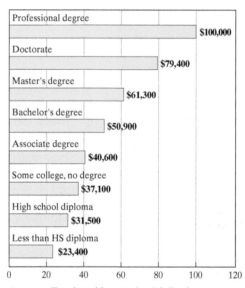

Median Annual Earnings
by Level of Education

Professional degree	$100,000
Doctorate	$79,400
Master's degree	$61,300
Bachelor's degree	$50,900
Associate degree	$40,600
Some college, no degree	$37,100
High school diploma	$31,500
Less than HS diploma	$23,400

Earnings (thousands of dollars)

Source: College Board

44. Exams Mike Ambrosino's mean average on six exams is 78. Find the sum of his scores.

45. Construct Data Construct a set of five pieces of data with a mean of 70 and no two values the same.

Concept/Writing Exercises

46. Suppose a set of data of 10 numbers has a mean of 6. An 11th number is added to the data and it has a value of 5. Will the mean of the new data set increase or decrease? Explain.

47. Consider the set of data 2, 3, 5, 6, 70. Without doing any calculations, can you determine whether the mean or the median is greater? Explain your answer.

Challenge Problem

48. Reading Meters The figure shows how to read an electric meter.

Step 1. Start with the dial on the right. If the arrow falls between two numbers, use the smaller number on the

dial (except when the dial is between 9 and 0, then use the 9). Notice the arrows above the meters indicate the direction the dial is moving (clockwise, then counterclockwise).

Step 2. If the pointer is directly on a number, check the dial to the *right* to make sure it has passed 0 and is headed toward 1. If the dial to the right has not passed 0, use the next lower number. The number on the meters on the right is 16064.

Source: Southern California Edison, Understanding Your Electricity Bill

Suppose your previous month's reading was as shown on the left, and this month's meter reading is as shown below.

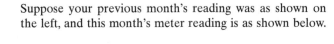

a) Determine this month's meter reading.

b) Determine your electrical cost for this month by first subtracting last month's meter reading from this month's meter reading (measured in kilowatt hours), and then multiplying the difference by the cost per kilowatt hour of electricity. Assume electricity costs 24.3 cents per kilowatt hour.

1.3 Fractions

1 Learn multiplication symbols and recognize factors.

2 Simplify fractions.

3 Multiply fractions.

4 Divide fractions.

5 Add and subtract fractions.

6 Change mixed numbers to fractions and vice versa.

What is the difference between arithmetic and algebra? When doing arithmetic, all the quantities used in the calculations are known. In algebra, however, one or more of the quantities are unknown and must be found. Consider the following:

Mr. Piersma has 1 gallon of paint. In order to paint his bedroom, he needs 3 gallons of paint. How many additional gallons does he need?

This is an example of an algebraic problem. The *unknown* quantity is the number of additional gallons of paint needed. Mr. Piersma needs 2 more gallons of paint.

An understanding of decimal numbers (see Appendix A) and fractions is essential to success in algebra. You will need to know how to simplify a fraction and how to add, subtract, multiply, and divide fractions.

1 Learn Multiplication Symbols and Recognize Factors

In algebra we often use letters called **variables** to represent numbers. Letters commonly used as variables are *x*, *y*, and *z*, but other letters can be used as variables. Variables are usually shown in italics. So that we do not confuse the variable *x* with the multiplication sign × we often use different notation to indicate multiplication.

Multiplication Symbols

If *a* and *b* represent any two mathematical quantities, then each of the following may be used to indicate the product of *a* and *b* ("*a* times *b*").

$$ab \quad a \cdot b \quad a(b) \quad (a)b \quad (a)(b)$$

Examples

3 times 4 may be written:	3 times *x* may be written:	*x* times *y* may be written:
	$3x$	xy
$3(4)$	$3(x)$	$x(y)$
$(3)4$	$(3)x$	$(x)y$
$(3)(4)$	$(3)(x)$	$(x)(y)$

Now we will introduce the term *factors*, which we shall be using throughout the text.

Understanding Algebra

A *factor* is a number or expression that is multiplied by another number or expression.

Factors

The numbers or variables that are multiplied in a multiplication problem are called **factors**.

If $a \cdot b = c$, then a and b are *factors* of c.

For example, in $3 \cdot 5 = 15$, the numbers 3 and 5 are factors of the product 15. In $2 \cdot 15 = 30$, the numbers 2 and 15 are factors of the product 30. Note that 30 has many other factors. Since $5 \cdot 6 = 30$, the numbers 5 and 6 are also factors of 30. Since $3x$ means 3 times x, both the 3 and the x are factors of $3x$.

2 Simplify Fractions

Now we have the necessary information to discuss **fractions**. The top number of a fraction is called the **numerator**, and the bottom number is called the **denominator**. In the fraction $\frac{3}{5}$, the 3 is the numerator and the 5 is the denominator.

Understanding Algebra

The fraction $\frac{3}{5}$ means the same as 3/5 or 3 ÷ 5

Helpful Hint

Consider the fraction $\frac{3}{5}$. There are equivalent methods of expressing this fraction, as illustrated below.

$$\frac{3}{5} = 3/5 = 3 \div 5 = 5\overline{)3}$$

In general, $\frac{a}{b} = a/b = a \div b = b\overline{)a}$

Understanding Algebra

GCF stands for "greatest common factor." It is the largest number that divides evenly into the two given numbers. The GCF of 12 and 18 is 6.

A fraction is **simplified**, or **reduced to its lowest terms**, when the numerator and denominator have no common factors other than 1. To simplify a fraction, follow these steps.

To Simplify a Fraction

1. Find the largest number that will divide (without remainder) both the numerator and the denominator. This number is called the **greatest common factor** (GCF).
2. Then divide both the numerator and the denominator by the greatest common factor.

If you do not remember how to find the greatest common factor of two or more numbers, read Appendix B.

EXAMPLE 1 Simplify **a)** $\frac{10}{25}$ **b)** $\frac{6}{18}$.

Solution

a) The largest number that divides both 10 and 25 is 5. Therefore, 5 is the greatest common factor. Divide both the numerator and the denominator by 5 to simplify the fraction.

$$\frac{10}{25} = \frac{10 \div 5}{25 \div 5} = \frac{2}{5}$$

b) The largest number that divides both 6 and 18 is 6. Divide both the numerator and the denominator by 6.

$$\frac{6}{18} = \frac{6 \div 6}{18 \div 6} = \frac{1}{3}$$

Note in part **b)** that both the numerator and denominator could have been written with a factor of 6. Then the common factor 6 could be divided out.

$$\frac{6}{18} = \frac{1 \cdot \cancel{6}}{3 \cdot \cancel{6}} = \frac{1}{3}$$

Now Try Exercise 11

When you work with fractions you should always simplify your answers.

3 Multiply Fractions

To multiply two or more fractions, multiply their numerators together and multiply their denominators together.

To Multiply Fractions

$$\frac{a}{b} \cdot \frac{c}{d} = \frac{ac}{bd}$$

EXAMPLE 2 Multiply $\frac{3}{13}$ by $\frac{5}{11}$.

Solution $\dfrac{3}{13} \cdot \dfrac{5}{11} = \dfrac{3 \cdot 5}{13 \cdot 11} = \dfrac{15}{143}$

Now Try Exercise 39

Before multiplying fractions, to help avoid having to simplify an answer, we often divide both a numerator and a denominator by a common factor.

EXAMPLE 3 Multiply **a)** $\dfrac{8}{17} \cdot \dfrac{5}{16}$ **b)** $\dfrac{27}{40} \cdot \dfrac{16}{9}$.

Solution

a) Since the numerator 8 and the denominator 16 can both be divided by the common factor 8, we divide out the 8 first. Then we multiply.

$$\frac{8}{17} \cdot \frac{5}{16} = \frac{\overset{1}{\cancel{8}}}{17} \cdot \frac{5}{\underset{2}{\cancel{16}}} = \frac{1 \cdot 5}{17 \cdot 2} = \frac{5}{34}$$

b)
$$\frac{27}{40} \cdot \frac{16}{9} = \frac{\overset{3}{\cancel{27}}}{40} \cdot \frac{16}{\underset{1}{\cancel{9}}} \qquad \text{Divide both 27 and 9 by 9.}$$

$$= \frac{\overset{3}{\cancel{27}}}{\underset{5}{\cancel{40}}} \cdot \frac{\overset{2}{\cancel{16}}}{\underset{1}{\cancel{9}}} \qquad \text{Divide both 40 and 16 by 8.}$$

$$= \frac{3 \cdot 2}{5 \cdot 1} = \frac{6}{5}$$

Now Try Exercise 41

Understanding Algebra

When we write 1, 2, 3, 4, ..., the three dots, called an *ellipsis,* indicate the pattern continues indefinitely.

The numbers 0, 1, 2, 3, 4, ... are called **whole numbers**. The whole numbers continue indefinitely. Thus, the numbers 468 and 5043 are also whole numbers. To multiply a whole number by a fraction, write the whole number with a denominator of 1 and then multiply.

EXAMPLE 4 **Lawn Mower Engine** Some engines run on a mixture of gas and oil. A particular lawn mower engine requires a mixture of $\frac{5}{64}$ gallon of oil for each gallon of gasoline used. A lawn care company wishes to make a mixture for this engine using 12 gallons of gasoline. How much oil must be used?

Solution We must multiply 12 by $\frac{5}{64}$ to determine the amount of oil that must be used. First we write 12 as $\frac{12}{1}$, then we divide both 12 and 64 by their greatest common factor, 4, as follows.

$$12 \cdot \frac{5}{64} = \frac{12}{1} \cdot \frac{5}{64} = \frac{\overset{3}{\cancel{12}}}{1} \cdot \frac{5}{\underset{16}{\cancel{64}}} = \frac{3 \cdot 5}{1 \cdot 16} = \frac{15}{16}$$

Thus, $\frac{15}{16}$ gallon of oil must be added to the 12 gallons of gasoline to make the proper mixture.

Now Try Exercise 89

4 Divide Fractions

Understanding Algebra

To divide $\frac{1}{3} \div \frac{5}{7}$

we convert to multiplication:

$\frac{1}{3} \cdot \frac{7}{5} = \frac{7}{15}$

To divide one fraction by another, invert the divisor (the second fraction if written with $\div$) and proceed as in multiplication.

> **To Divide Fractions**
>
> $$\frac{a}{b} \div \frac{c}{d} = \frac{a}{b} \cdot \frac{d}{c} = \frac{ad}{bc}$$

Sometimes, rather than being asked to add, subtract, multiply, or divide, you may be asked to *evaluate* an expression. To **evaluate** an expression means to obtain the answer to the problem using the operations given.

EXAMPLE 5 Evaluate **a)** $\frac{3}{5} \div \frac{5}{6}$ **b)** $\frac{3}{8} \div 12.$

Solution

a) $\frac{3}{5} \div \frac{5}{6} = \frac{3}{5} \cdot \frac{6}{5} = \frac{3 \cdot 6}{5 \cdot 5} = \frac{18}{25}$

b) Write 12 as $\frac{12}{1}$. Then invert the divisor and multiply.

$$\frac{3}{8} \div 12 = \frac{3}{8} \div \frac{12}{1} = \frac{\overset{1}{\cancel{3}}}{8} \cdot \frac{1}{\underset{4}{\cancel{12}}} = \frac{1}{32}$$

Now Try Exercise 47

5 Add and Subtract Fractions

Understanding Algebra

To add or subtract fractions, they need to first have a common denominator. The smallest number that is divisible by two or more denominators is called the *least common denominator* or *LCD*.

Fractions that have the same (or a *common*) *denominator can be added or subtracted.* To add or subtract fractions with the same denominator, add or subtract the numerators and keep the common denominator.

> **To Add and Subtract Fractions**
>
> $$\frac{a}{c} + \frac{b}{c} = \frac{a+b}{c} \quad \text{or} \quad \frac{a}{c} - \frac{b}{c} = \frac{a-b}{c}$$

EXAMPLE 6 **a)** Add $\dfrac{6}{15} + \dfrac{2}{15}$.   **b)** Subtract $\dfrac{8}{13} - \dfrac{5}{13}$.

Solution

a) $\dfrac{6}{15} + \dfrac{2}{15} = \dfrac{6+2}{15} = \dfrac{8}{15}$ **b)** $\dfrac{8}{13} - \dfrac{5}{13} = \dfrac{8-5}{13} = \dfrac{3}{13}$

Now Try Exercise 55

To add (or subtract) fractions with unlike denominators, we must first rewrite each fraction with a common denominator. The smallest number that is divisible by two or more denominators is called the **least common denominator** or **LCD**. *If you have forgotten how to find the least common denominator, review Appendix B now.*

EXAMPLE 7 Add $\dfrac{1}{2} + \dfrac{1}{5}$.

Solution We cannot add these fractions until we rewrite them with a common denominator. Since the lowest number that both 2 and 5 evenly divide into is 10, we will first rewrite both fractions with the least common denominator of 10.

$$\frac{1}{2} = \frac{1}{2} \cdot \frac{5}{5} = \frac{5}{10} \quad \text{and} \quad \frac{1}{5} = \frac{1}{5} \cdot \frac{2}{2} = \frac{2}{10}$$

Now we add.

$$\frac{1}{2} + \frac{1}{5} = \frac{5}{10} + \frac{2}{10} = \frac{7}{10}$$

Now Try Exercise 63

Multiplying both the numerator and denominator by the same number is the same as multiplying by 1. Thus, the value of the fraction does not change.

EXAMPLE 8 How much larger is $\dfrac{3}{4}$ inch than $\dfrac{2}{3}$ inch?

Solution To find the difference, we need to subtract $\dfrac{2}{3}$ inch from $\dfrac{3}{4}$ inch.

$$\frac{3}{4} - \frac{2}{3}$$

The least common denominator is 12. Therefore, we rewrite both fractions with a denominator of 12.

$$\frac{3}{4} = \frac{3}{4} \cdot \frac{3}{3} = \frac{9}{12} \quad \text{and} \quad \frac{2}{3} = \frac{2}{3} \cdot \frac{4}{4} = \frac{8}{12}$$

Now we subtract.

$$\frac{3}{4} - \frac{2}{3} = \frac{9}{12} - \frac{8}{12} = \frac{1}{12}$$

Thus, $\dfrac{3}{4}$ inch is $\dfrac{1}{12}$ inch greater than $\dfrac{2}{3}$ inch.

Now Try Exercise 75

It is important to remember that dividing out a common factor in the numerator of one fraction and the denominator of a different fraction can be performed only when multiplying fractions. *This process cannot be performed when adding or subtracting fractions.*

CORRECT MULTIPLICATION PROBLEMS	INCORRECT ADDITION PROBLEMS

$$\frac{\overset{1}{\cancel{3}}}{5} \cdot \frac{1}{\cancel{3}_{1}} \qquad\qquad \frac{\overset{1}{\cancel{3}}}{5} + \frac{1}{\cancel{3}_{1}}$$

$$\frac{\overset{2}{\cancel{8}} \cdot 3}{\underset{1}{\cancel{4}}} \qquad\qquad \frac{\overset{2}{\cancel{8}} + 3}{\underset{1}{\cancel{4}}}$$

The mixed number $2\frac{3}{4}$ means $2 + \frac{3}{4}$.

6 Change Mixed Numbers to Fractions and Vice Versa

Consider the number $5\frac{2}{3}$. This is an example of a **mixed number**. A mixed number consists of a whole number followed by a fraction. The mixed number $5\frac{2}{3}$ means $5 + \frac{2}{3}$. We can change $5\frac{2}{3}$ to a fraction as follows.

$$5\frac{2}{3} = \boxed{5} + \frac{2}{3} = \boxed{\frac{15}{3}} + \frac{2}{3} = \frac{15 + 2}{3} = \frac{17}{3}$$

Notice that we expressed the whole number, 5, as a fraction with a denominator of 3, then added the fractions.

EXAMPLE 9 Change $7\frac{3}{8}$ to a fraction.

Solution

$$7\frac{3}{8} = \boxed{7} + \frac{3}{8} = \boxed{\frac{56}{8}} + \frac{3}{8} = \frac{56 + 3}{8} = \frac{59}{8}$$

Now Try Exercise 25

Now consider the fraction $\frac{17}{3}$. We convert it to a mixed number as follows.

$$\frac{17}{3} = \boxed{\frac{15}{3}} + \frac{2}{3} = \boxed{5} + \frac{2}{3} = 5\frac{2}{3}$$

Notice we wrote $\frac{17}{3}$ as a sum of two fractions, each with the denominator of 3. The first fraction being added, $\frac{15}{3}$, is the equivalent of the largest integer that is less than $\frac{17}{3}$.

EXAMPLE 10 Change $\frac{43}{6}$ to a mixed number.

Solution $\quad \dfrac{43}{6} = \boxed{\dfrac{42}{6}} + \dfrac{1}{6} = \boxed{7} + \dfrac{1}{6} = 7\dfrac{1}{6}$

Now Try Exercise 31

Notice in Example 10 the fraction $\frac{43}{6}$ is simplified because the greatest common divisor of the numerator and denominator is 1. Do not confuse simplifying a fraction with changing a fraction with a value greater than 1 to a mixed number. The fraction $\frac{43}{6}$ can be converted to the mixed number $7\frac{1}{6}$. However, $\frac{43}{6}$ is a simplified fraction.

Now we will work examples that contain mixed numbers.

FIGURE 1.4

EXAMPLE 11 **Plumbing** To repair a plumbing leak, a coupling $\frac{1}{2}$ inch long is glued to a piece of plastic pipe. After the gluing, the piece of plastic pipe showing is $2\frac{9}{16}$ inches, as shown in **Figure 1.4**. How long is the combined length?

Solution   Understand and Translate   We need to add $2\frac{9}{16}$ inches and $\frac{1}{2}$ inch to obtain the combined length. After we write both fractions with a common denominator, we add the numbers.

Carry Out

$$
\text{original numbers}\left\{\begin{array}{c} 2\frac{9}{16} \\ +\ \frac{1}{2} \\ \hline \end{array} \quad\rightarrow\quad \begin{array}{c} 2\frac{9}{16} \\ +\ \frac{8}{16} \\ \hline 2\frac{17}{16} \end{array}\right\} \text{fractions rewritten with common denominator of 16}
$$

Since $2\frac{17}{16} = 2 + \frac{17}{16} = 2 + 1\frac{1}{16} = 3\frac{1}{16}$, the sum is $3\frac{1}{16}$.

Check and Answer   The answer appears reasonable. Thus, the total length is $3\frac{1}{16}$ inches.

Now Try Exercise 93

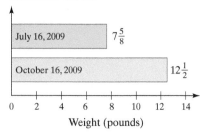

FIGURE 1.5

EXAMPLE 12 **Gaining Weight** The graph in **Figure 1.5** shows the weight of the Smallwoods' baby boy, Jonathan, on July 16, 2009, and on October 16, 2009. How much weight did Jonathan gain during this time period?

Solution   Understand and Translate   To find the increase, we need to subtract Jonathan's weight on July 16, 2009, from his weight on October 16, 2009. We will subtract vertically.

Carry Out

$$
\begin{array}{c} 12\frac{1}{2} \\ -\ 7\frac{5}{8} \\ \hline \end{array} \quad\rightarrow\quad \begin{array}{c} 12\frac{4}{8} \\ -\ 7\frac{5}{8} \\ \hline \end{array}
$$

Since we wish to subtract $\frac{5}{8}$ from $\frac{4}{8}$, and $\frac{5}{8}$ is greater than $\frac{4}{8}$, we write $12\frac{4}{8}$ as $11\frac{12}{8}$. To get $11\frac{12}{8}$, we take 1 unit from the number 12 and write it as $\frac{8}{8}$. This gives $11 + 1 + \frac{4}{8} = 11 + \frac{8}{8} + \frac{4}{8} = 11 + \frac{12}{8} = 11\frac{12}{8}$. Now we subtract as follows.

$$
\begin{array}{c} 12\frac{1}{2} \\ -\ 7\frac{5}{8} \\ \hline \end{array} \quad\rightarrow\quad \begin{array}{c} 12\frac{4}{8} \\ -\ 7\frac{5}{8} \\ \hline \end{array} \quad\rightarrow\quad \begin{array}{c} 11\frac{12}{8} \\ -\ 7\frac{5}{8} \\ \hline 4\frac{7}{8} \end{array}
$$

Check and Answer   By examining the graph, we see that the answer is reasonable. Thus, Jonathan gained $4\frac{7}{8}$ pounds during this time period.

Now Try Exercise 85

Although it is not necessary to change mixed numbers to fractions when adding or subtracting mixed numbers, it is necessary to change mixed numbers to fractions when multiplying or dividing mixed numbers. We illustrate this procedure in Example 13.

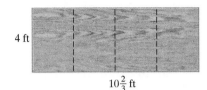

4 ft

$10\frac{2}{3}$ ft

FIGURE 1.6

EXAMPLE 13 **Cutting Wood** A carpenter is cutting a rectangular piece of wood 4 feet wide by $10\frac{2}{3}$ feet long into four equal strips, as shown in **Figure 1.6**. Find the dimensions of each strip.

Solution   Understand and Translate   We know from **Figure 1.6** that one side will have a width of 4 feet. To find the length of the strips, we need to divide $10\frac{2}{3}$ by 4.

Carry Out

$$10\frac{2}{3} \div 4 = \frac{32}{3} \div \frac{4}{1} = \frac{\overset{8}{\cancel{32}}}{3} \cdot \frac{1}{\underset{1}{\cancel{4}}} = \frac{8}{3} = 2\frac{2}{3}$$

Check and Answer   If you multiply $2\frac{2}{3}$ by 4 you obtain the original length, $10\frac{2}{3}$.

Thus, the calculation is correct. The dimensions of each strip will be 4 feet by $2\frac{2}{3}$ feet.

Now Try Exercise 87

EXERCISE SET 1.3

MathXL®   *MyMathLab*

Warm-Up Exercises

Fill in the blanks with the appropriate word, phrase, or symbol(s) from the following list.

~~variables~~	factors	~~LCD~~	~~added or subtracted~~
~~GCF~~	~~mixed number~~	~~ellipsis~~	$\frac{1}{6}$
$\frac{2}{3}$	~~denominator~~	$\frac{3}{2}$	

1. When two fractions are being _added or subtracted_ we rewrite them so that they both have the same (common) denominator.

2. $5 + \frac{1}{3}$ is usually written as $5\frac{1}{3}$, which is called a _mixed #_.

3. Letters that represent numbers are called _variables_.

4. In the expression 2, 4, 6, 8, …, the three dots, called an _ellipsis_, signify the sequence continues indefinitely.

5. $\frac{1}{3} \div \frac{1}{2} =$ _2/3_ .

6. Numbers or variables that are multiplied together are called _factors_.

7. In the fraction $\frac{3}{4}$, 4 is called the _denominator_.

8. 15 is the _LCD_ of 30 and 75.

9. To perform the division $\frac{4}{7} \div \frac{2}{3}$ we rewrite it as $\frac{4}{7} \cdot$ _3/2_ .

10. 40 is the _GCF_ of the fractions $\frac{3}{8}$ and $\frac{7}{10}$.

Practice the Skills

Simplify each fraction. If a fraction is already simplified, so state.

11. $\frac{10}{15}$ $\frac{2}{3}$ 12. $\frac{40}{10}$ 13. $\frac{6}{24}$ $\frac{1}{4}$ 14. $\frac{19}{25}$ 15. $\frac{36}{76}$ $\frac{9}{19}$ 16. $\frac{16}{72}$

17. $\frac{18}{42}$ $\frac{3}{7}$ 18. $\frac{60}{105}$ 19. $\frac{18}{49}$ simplified   20. $\frac{100}{144}$ 21. $\frac{12}{25}$ simplified   22. $\frac{42}{138}$

Convert each mixed number to a fraction.

23. $2\frac{13}{15}$ $\frac{43}{15}$ **24.** $15\frac{1}{3}$ **25.** $7\frac{2}{3}$ $\frac{23}{3}$ **26.** $14\frac{3}{4}$ **27.** $3\frac{5}{18}$ $\frac{59}{18}$ **28.** $2\frac{2}{9}$ **29.** $9\frac{6}{17}$ $\frac{159}{17}$ **30.** $3\frac{3}{32}$

Write each fraction as a mixed number.

31. $\frac{7}{4}$ $1\frac{3}{4}$ **32.** $\frac{18}{7}$ **33.** $\frac{13}{4}$ $3\frac{1}{4}$ **34.** $\frac{9}{2}$ **35.** $\frac{32}{7}$ $4\frac{4}{7}$ **36.** $\frac{110}{20}$ **37.** $\frac{86}{14}$ $\frac{43}{7}$ **38.** $\frac{72}{14}$

Find each product or quotient. Simplify the answer.

39. $\frac{1}{3}\cdot\frac{4}{5}$ $\frac{4}{15}$ **40.** $\frac{6}{13}\cdot\frac{7}{17}$ **41.** $\frac{5}{12}\cdot\frac{4}{15}$ $\frac{20}{180}=\frac{1}{9}$ **42.** $\frac{36}{48}\cdot\frac{16}{45}$

43. $\frac{1}{2}\frac{3}{4}\div\frac{1}{2}$ $=\frac{3}{8}$ **44.** $\frac{15}{16}\cdot\frac{4}{3}$ **45.** $\frac{3}{8}\div\frac{3}{4}$ $\frac{12}{24}=\frac{1}{2}$ **46.** $\frac{3}{8}\cdot\frac{10}{11}$

47. $\frac{10}{3}\div\frac{5}{9}$ $\frac{90}{15}$ $\frac{30}{5}=6$ **48.** $\frac{5}{9}\div30$ **49.** $\frac{15}{4}\cdot\frac{2}{3}$ $=\frac{30}{12}=\frac{5}{2}$ **50.** $\frac{5}{12}\div\frac{4}{3}$

51. $5\frac{3}{8}\div1\frac{1}{4}$ **52.** $\left(2\frac{1}{5}\right)\left(\frac{7}{8}\right)$ **53.** $\frac{28}{13}\cdot\frac{2}{7}$ $\frac{56}{91}$ **54.** $4\frac{4}{5}\div\frac{8}{15}$

Add or subtract. Simplify each answer.

55. $\frac{3}{8}+\frac{2}{8}$ $\frac{5}{8}$ **56.** $\frac{18}{36}-\frac{5}{36}$ **57.** $\frac{3}{14}-\frac{1}{14}$ **58.** $\frac{1}{4}+\frac{3}{4}$

59. $\frac{4}{35}+\frac{6}{15}$ $\frac{12}{15}=\frac{18}{15}=\frac{6}{5}$ **60.** $\frac{7}{8}-\frac{5}{6}$ **61.** $\frac{9}{17}+\frac{2}{34}$ **62.** $\frac{3}{7}+\frac{17}{35}$

63. $\frac{1}{3}+\frac{1}{4}$ **64.** $\frac{1}{6}-\frac{1}{18}$ **65.** $\frac{7}{12}-\frac{2}{9}$ **66.** $\frac{3}{7}+\frac{5}{12}$

67. $3\frac{1}{8}-\frac{5}{12}$ **68.** $5\frac{6}{7}+4\frac{5}{8}$ **69.** $6\frac{1}{3}-3\frac{1}{2}$ **70.** $2\frac{3}{8}+3\frac{3}{4}$

71. $9\frac{2}{5}-6\frac{1}{2}$ **72.** $4\frac{5}{9}-\frac{7}{8}$ **73.** $5\frac{9}{10}+3\frac{1}{3}$ **74.** $8\frac{2}{7}-3\frac{1}{3}$

75. How much larger is $\frac{5}{6}$ mile than $\frac{3}{8}$ mile? $\frac{5}{6}\ \frac{20}{24}$ $-\frac{3}{8}\ \frac{9}{24}$ $\boxed{\frac{11}{24}}$

76. How much larger is $\frac{1}{5}$ meter than $\frac{1}{7}$ meter?

Problem Solving

77. **Height Gain** The following graph shows Rebecca Bersagel's height, in inches, on her 8th and 12th birthdays. How much had Rebecca grown in the 4 years?

Rebecca Bersagel's Height

$55\frac{3}{16}$ $\frac{883}{16}$ $\frac{883}{16}$ $\frac{143}{16}$
$-46\frac{1}{4}$ $\frac{185}{4}$ $\frac{740}{16}=\frac{143}{16}$

$8\frac{15}{16}$ 10

78. **Road Paving** The following graph shows the progress of the Davenport Paving Company in paving the Memorial Highway. How much of the highway was paved from June through August?

Highway Paved in Selected Months

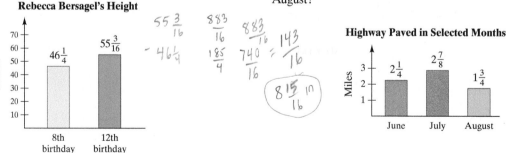

In many problems you will need to subtract a fraction from 1, where 1 represents "the whole" or the "total amount." Exercises 79–82 are answered by subtracting the given fraction from 1.

79. **Putting Success** Lamont is a local golf pro and last year he made $\frac{46}{55}$ of all his putts from within six feet. What fraction of his putts from within six feet did he miss?

80. **Global Warming** The probability that an event does not occur may be found by subtracting the probability that the event does occur from 1. If the probability that global warming is occurring is $\frac{7}{9}$, find the probability that global warming is not occurring.

81. Time to BS Degree A recent study by the non-profit Education Trust found that $\frac{37}{100}$ of first-time freshmen at four-year schools earned their bachelor's degrees in four years. What fraction of freshmen did not finish their bachelor's degree in 4 years?

Freshman Finishing Bachelor's Degree

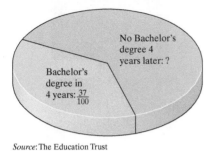

Source: The Education Trust

82. Home Heating The following circle graph shows the fraction of U.S. homes that used electricity to heat their homes. Determine the fraction of U.S. homes that did not use electricity.

How Americans Heat Their Homes

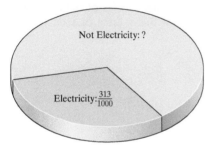

Source: www.census.gov

In Exercises 83–98, answer the questions asked.

83. Python's Growth An albino python at Cypress Gardens, Florida, was 3 feet, $3\frac{1}{4}$ inches when born. Its present length is 15 feet, $2\frac{1}{2}$ inches. How much has it grown since birth?

Albino python

84. Cream Pie A Boston cream pie weighs $1\frac{5}{16}$ pounds. If the pie is to be divided equally among 6 people, how much will each person get?

85. Running Denise started a running program in January when she could run a mile in $10\frac{1}{2}$ minutes. After 6 months, Denise could run a mile in $8\frac{1}{5}$ minutes. By how many minutes did Denise improve in 6 months? $\frac{21}{2} - \frac{41}{5} = \frac{105}{10} - \frac{82}{10} = \frac{23}{10}$

$2\frac{3}{10}$ min.

86. Baking Turkey The instructions on a turkey indicate that a 12- to 16-pound turkey should bake at 325°F for about 22 minutes per pound. Josephine Nickola is planning to bake a $13\frac{1}{2}$-pound turkey. Approximately how long should the turkey be baked?

87. Wood Cut Debbie Anderson cuts a piece of wood measuring $3\frac{1}{8}$ inches into two equal pieces. How long is each piece? $\frac{25}{8} \times \frac{1}{2} = \frac{25}{16} = 1\,9/16$ in

88. Pants Inseam The inseam on a new pair of pants is 32 inches. If Don O'Neal's inseam is $29\frac{3}{8}$ inches, by how much will the pants need to be shortened?

89. Drug Amount A nurse must give $\frac{1}{16}$ milligram of a drug for each kilogram of patient mass. If Mr. Krisanda has a mass of 80 kilograms, find the amount of the drug Mr. Krisanda should be given. $x = 5\,mg$ $\frac{1}{16} \times \frac{80}{x}$

90. Chopped Onions A recipe for pot roast calls for $\frac{1}{4}$ cup chopped onions for each pound of beef. For $5\frac{1}{2}$ pounds of beef, how many cups of chopped onions are needed?

91. Shampoo A bottle of shampoo contains 15 fluid ounces. If Tierra Bentley uses $\frac{3}{8}$ of an ounce each time she washes her hair, how many times can Tierra wash her hair using this bottle? 40 times

92. Fencing Matt Mesaros wants to fence in his backyard as shown. The three sides to be fenced measure $16\frac{2}{3}$ yards, $22\frac{2}{3}$ yards, and $14\frac{1}{8}$ yards.

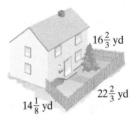

a) How much fence will Matt need?

b) If Matt buys 60 yards of fence, how much will be left over?

93. Windows An insulated window for a house is made up of two pieces of glass, each $\frac{1}{4}$-inch thick, with a 1-inch space between them. What is the total thickness of this window?

94. Truck Weight A flatbed tow truck weighing $4\frac{1}{2}$ tons is carrying two cars. One car weighs $1\frac{1}{6}$ tons, the other weighs $1\frac{3}{4}$ tons. What is the total weight of the tow truck and the two cars?

95. Cutting Wood A 28-inch length of wood is to be cut into $4\frac{2}{3}$ inch strips. How many whole strips can be made? Disregard loss of wood due to cuts made.

96. Fasten Bolts A mechanic wishes to use a bolt to fasten a piece of wood $4\frac{1}{2}$ inches thick to a metal tube $2\frac{1}{3}$ inches thick. If the thickness of the nut is $\frac{1}{8}$ inch, find the length of the shaft of the bolt so that the nut fits flush with the end of the bolt (see the figure below).

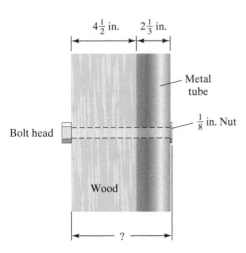

97. Entertainment Center Scott Morningstar just bought a high definition television that will sit atop his entertainment credenza. The TV measures $36\frac{1}{2}$ inches high. Its stand is $14\frac{1}{8}$ inches high and the credenza is $31\frac{3}{4}$ inches high.

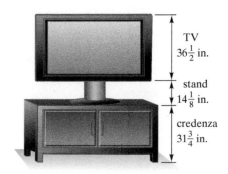

a) If Scott has 8-foot ceilings in his house, will there be sufficient room for this purchase?

b) Find the total height of the TV, the stand, and the credenza.

98. Soda If five 2-liter bottles of soda are split evenly among 30 people, how many liters of soda will each person get?

Concept/Writing Exercises

99. Another way of saying "find the LCD of the 3 fractions $\frac{1}{6}, \frac{2}{3}, \frac{7}{10}$" is to say "find the least common multiple (LCM) of 6, 3, and 10." Write a few sentences to describe how to go about finding the LCM of 6, 3, and 10.

100. Explain how to simplify a fraction.

Challenge Problems

101. Add or subtract the following fractions using the rule discussed in this section. Your answer should be a single fraction, and it should contain the symbols given in the exercise.

a) $\dfrac{*}{a} + \dfrac{?}{a}$ **b)** $\dfrac{\odot}{?} - \dfrac{\square}{?}$

c) $\dfrac{\triangle}{\square} + \dfrac{4}{\square}$ **d)** $\dfrac{x}{3} - \dfrac{2}{3}$

e) $\dfrac{12}{x} - \dfrac{4}{x}$

102. Multiply the following fractions using the rule discussed in this section. Your answer should be a single fraction and it should contain the symbols given in the exercise.

a) $\dfrac{\triangle}{a} \cdot \dfrac{\square}{b}$ **b)** $\dfrac{6}{3} \cdot \dfrac{\triangle}{\square}$

c) $\dfrac{x}{a} \cdot \dfrac{y}{b}$ **d)** $\dfrac{3}{8} \cdot \dfrac{4}{y}$

e) $\dfrac{3}{x} \cdot \dfrac{x}{y}$

103. Drug Dosage An allopurinol pill comes in 300-milligram doses. Dr. Muechler wants a patient to get 450 milligrams each day by cutting the pills in half and taking one-half pill three times a day. If he wants to prescribe enough pills for a 6-month period (assume 30 days per month), how many pills should he prescribe?

Group Activity

Discuss and answer Exercise 104 as a group.

104. Potatoes The following table gives the amount of each ingredient recommended to make 2, 4, and 8 servings of instant mashed potatoes.

Servings	2	4	8
Water	$\frac{2}{3}$ cup	$1\frac{1}{3}$ cups	$2\frac{2}{3}$ cups
Milk	2 tbsp	$\frac{1}{3}$ cup	$\frac{2}{3}$ cup
Butter*	1 tbsp	2 tbsp	4 tbsp
Salt†	$\frac{1}{4}$ tsp	$\frac{1}{2}$ tsp	1 tsp
Potato flakes	$\frac{2}{3}$ cup	$1\frac{1}{3}$ cup	$2\frac{2}{3}$ cups

*or margarine

†Less salt can be used if desired.

Determine the amount of potato flakes and milk needed to make 6 servings by the different methods described. When working with milk, 16 tbsp = 1 cup.

a) Group member 1: Determine the amounts of potato flakes and milk needed to make 6 servings by multiplying the amounts for 2 servings by 3.

b) Group member 2: Determine the amounts by adding the amounts for 2 servings to the amounts for 4 servings.

c) Group member 3: Determine the amounts by finding the average (mean) of 4 and 8 servings.

d) As a group, determine the amounts by subtracting the amounts for 2 servings from the amounts for 8 servings.

e) As a group, compare your answers from parts **a)** through **d)**. Are they all the same? If not, can you explain why?

Cumulative Review Exercises

[1.1] **105.** What is your instructor's name and office hours?

[1.2] **106.** What is the mean of 9, 8, 15, 32, 16?

107. What is the median of 9, 8, 15, 32, 16?

[1.3] **108.** What are variables?

1.4 The Real Number System

1 Identify sets of numbers.

2 Know the structure of the real numbers.

This section introduces you to different sets of numbers and to the structure of the real number system.

1 Identify Sets of Numbers

A **set** is a collection of **elements** listed within braces. The set $\{a, b, c, d, e\}$ consists of five elements, namely $a, b, c, d,$ and e. A set that contains no elements is called an **empty set** (or **null set**). The symbols $\{\ \}$ or $\emptyset$ are used to represent the empty set.

Two important sets are the natural numbers and the whole numbers. The whole numbers were introduced earlier.

> Natural numbers: $\{1, 2, 3, 4, 5, \ldots\}$
>
> Whole numbers: $\{0, 1, 2, 3, 4, 5, \ldots\}$

An aid in understanding sets of numbers is a number line (**Fig. 1.7**).

FIGURE 1.7

The number line continues indefinitely in both directions. The numbers to the right of 0 are positive and those to the left of 0 are negative. Zero is neither positive nor negative (**Fig. 1.8**).

FIGURE 1.8

Understanding Algebra

A *set* is a collection of elements—in this book, usually numbers. The set of natural numbers less than 6, for example, is {1, 2, 3, 4, 5}.

Figure 1.9 illustrates the natural numbers marked on a number line. The natural numbers are also called the **counting numbers** or the **positive integers**.

FIGURE 1.9

Another important set of numbers is the integers.

$$\text{Integers:}\quad \{\ldots,-5,-4,-3,-2,-1,\underbrace{}_{\text{Negative integers}},0,\underbrace{1,2,3,4,5,\ldots}_{\text{Positive integers}}\}$$

The integers consist of the negative integers, 0, and the positive integers. The integers are marked on the number line in **Figure 1.10**.

FIGURE 1.10

Fractions and certain decimal numbers do not belong to the set of integers but they do belong to the set of rational numbers. The set of **rational numbers** consists of all the numbers that can be expressed as a quotient (or a ratio) of two integers, with the denominator not 0.

Rational numbers: {quotient of two integers, denominator not 0}

All integers are rational numbers since they can be written with a denominator of 1. For example, $3 = \dfrac{3}{1}$, $-12 = \dfrac{-12}{1}$, and $0 = \dfrac{0}{1}$. All fractions containing integers in the numerator and denominator (with the denominator not 0) are rational numbers. For example, the fraction $\dfrac{3}{5}$ is a quotient of two integers and is a rational number.

When a fraction that is a ratio of two integers is converted to a decimal number by dividing the numerator by the denominator, the quotient will always be either a *terminating decimal number,* such as 0.3 and 3.25, or a *repeating decimal number* such as 0.3333... and 5.2727.... The three dots at the end of a number indicate that the numbers continue to repeat in the same manner indefinitely. All terminating decimal numbers and all repeating decimal numbers are rational numbers and can be expressed as a quotient of two integers. For example, $0.3 = \dfrac{3}{10}$, $3.25 = \dfrac{325}{100}$, $0.3333... = \dfrac{1}{3}$, and $5.2727... = \dfrac{522}{99}$. Some rational numbers are illustrated on the number line in **Figure 1.11**.

FIGURE 1.11

Some numbers are not rational. Numbers such as the square root of 2, written $\sqrt{2}$, are not rational numbers. Any number that can be represented on the number line that is not a rational number is called an **irrational number**. Irrational numbers are non-terminating, non-repeating decimal numbers. For example, $\sqrt{2}$ cannot be expressed exactly as a decimal number. Irrational numbers can only be *approximated* by decimal numbers. $\sqrt{2}$ is *approximately* 1.41. Thus, we may write $\sqrt{2} \approx 1.41$. Some irrational numbers are illustrated on the number line in **Figure 1.12**.

FIGURE 1.12

2 Know the Structure of the Real Numbers

Any number that is either rational or irrational is called a **real number** and the number line is often referred to as a **real number line.**

The symbol $\mathbb{R}$ is used to represent the set of real numbers. The natural numbers, the whole numbers, the integers, the rational numbers, and the irrational numbers are all real numbers. **Figure 1.13** illustrates the relationships between the various sets of numbers within the set of real numbers.

Consider the natural number 5. If we follow the branches in **Figure 1.13a** upward, we see that the number 5 is also a whole number, an integer, a rational number, and a real number. Now consider the number $\frac{1}{2}$. It belongs to the noninteger rational numbers. If we follow the branches upward, we can see that $\frac{1}{2}$ is also a rational number and a real number.

Understanding Algebra

A *real number* is any number that is either rational or irrational.

The set of all real numbers is denoted by the symbol $\mathbb{R}$

Understanding Algebra

$\sqrt{2}$ and $\sqrt{5}$ are examples of irrational numbers but $\sqrt{16}$ is rational because it is exactly 4.

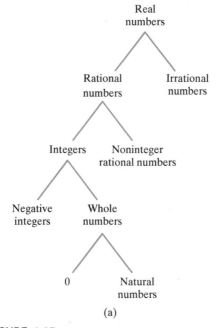

Real Numbers	
Rational numbers	Irrational numbers
(Integers and noninteger rational numbers)	(Certain* square roots and other special numbers)
−12 4 0	$\sqrt{2}$ $\sqrt{5}$
$\frac{3}{8}$ $\frac{1}{3}$ −1.24	π $\sqrt{12}$
$-1\frac{3}{5}$ −2.463	

*Other higher roots like $\sqrt[3]{2}$ and $\sqrt[4]{5}$ are also irrational numbers.

(a)   (b)

FIGURE 1.13

EXAMPLE 1   Consider the following set of numbers.

$$\left\{ \sqrt{11}, -\frac{3}{8}, -0.6, -4, 7\frac{1}{2}, 12, 0, \sqrt{5}, -48, 3.9, -\sqrt{7} \right\}$$

List the elements of the set that are

a) natural numbers.   **b)** whole numbers.   **c)** integers.
d) rational numbers.   **e)** irrational numbers.   **f)** real numbers.

Solution   We will list the elements from left to right as they appear in the set. However, the elements may be listed in any order.

a) 12   **b)** 12, 0   **c)** −4, 12, 0, −48

d) $-\frac{3}{8}, -0.6, -4, 7\frac{1}{2}, 12, 0, -48, 3.9$ **e)** $\sqrt{11}, \sqrt{5}, -\sqrt{7}$

f) $\sqrt{11}, -\frac{3}{8}, -0.6, -4, 7\frac{1}{2}, 12, 0, \sqrt{5}, -48, 3.9, -\sqrt{7}$

Now Try Exercise 51

EXERCISE SET 1.4   *MathXL*   MathXL®   *MyMathLab*   MyMathLab

Warm-Up Exercises

Fill in the blanks with the appropriate word, phrase, or symbol(s) from the following list.

set	irrational numbers	rational numbers	the empty set
$\{1, 2, 3\}$	counting numbers	whole numbers	real numbers line
integers	$\{\ldots, -3, -2, -1\}$	π	$\dfrac{1}{2}$

1. $\sqrt{5}$ and $\sqrt{7}$ are examples of _____ .

2. The set of negative integers is _____ .

3. Another name for the positive integers is the set of _____ .

4. The set $\{\ldots, -2, -1, 0, 1, 2, 3, \ldots\}$ is more commonly referred to as the set of _____ .

5. The set of real numbers can be displayed pictorially as a _____ .

6. The symbol $\varnothing$ is used to denote _____ .

7. $\{0, 1, 2, 3, \ldots\}$ is called the set of _____ .

8. Numbers that can be expressed as a fraction having integer numerator and non-zero integer denominator are called _____ .

9. An example of a real number that is not a rational number is _____ .

10. In general, a collection of elements is called a _____ .

Practice the Skills

In Exercises 11–16, list each set of numbers.

11. Integers

12. Counting numbers

13. Whole numbers

14. Positive integers

15. Negative integers

16. Natural numbers

In Exercises 17–48, indicate whether each statement is true or false.

17. 0 is a whole number.

18. -1 is a negative integer.

19. -7.3 is a real number.

20. $\dfrac{3}{5}$ is an integer.

21. 0.6 is an integer.

22. 0 is a natural number.

23. $\sqrt{2}$ is a rational number.

24. $\sqrt{3}$ is a real number.

25. $-\dfrac{1}{5}$ is a rational number.

26. $-2\dfrac{1}{3}$ is a rational number.

27. 0 is a rational number.

28. 9.2 is a rational number.

29. $4\dfrac{5}{8}$ is an irrational number.

30. 0 is not a positive number.

31. $-\sqrt{5}$ is an irrational number.

32. Every counting number is a rational number.

33. The symbol $\varnothing$ is used to represent the empty set.

34. Every integer is negative.

35. Every real number is a rational number.

36. Every negative integer is a real number.

37. Every rational number is a real number.

38. When zero is added to the set of counting numbers, the set of whole numbers is formed.

39. Some real numbers are not rational numbers.

40. Some irrational numbers are not real numbers.

41. Every negative number is a negative integer.

42. All real numbers can be represented on a number line.

43. The symbol $\mathbb{R}$ is used to represent the set of real numbers.

44. Any number to the left of zero on a number line is a negative number.

45. Every number greater than zero is a positive integer.

46. Irrational numbers cannot be represented on a number line.

47. When the negative integers, the positive integers, and 0 are combined, the integers are formed.

48. The natural numbers, counting numbers, and positive integers are different names for the same set of numbers.

49. **Hotels** Some buildings in Europe have elevators that list negative numbers for floors below the ground level. For example, a floor might be designated as -2. In many countries, floor number 13 is omitted because of superstition. Considering the numbers -2 and 13, list those that are

   a) positive integers.

   b) rational numbers.

   c) real numbers.

   d) whole numbers.

50. **Address** We generally think of house addresses as being integers greater than 0. Have you ever seen a house number that was not an integer greater than 0? There are quite a few such addresses in cities and towns across America. The house

numbers 0 and $2\frac{1}{2}$ appear on Legare Street in Charleston, SC.
Considering the numbers 0 and $2\frac{1}{2}$, list those that are

© Allen R. Angel

a) integers

b) rational numbers

c) real numbers

51. Consider the following set of numbers.

$$\left\{ -\frac{5}{7}, 0, -2, 3, 6\frac{1}{4}, \sqrt{7}, -\sqrt{3}, 1.63, 77 \right\}$$

List the numbers that are

a) positive integers.

b) whole numbers.

c) integers.

d) rational numbers.

e) irrational numbers.

f) real numbers.

52. Consider the following set of numbers.

$$\left\{ -6, 7, 12.4, -\frac{9}{5}, -2\frac{1}{4}, \sqrt{3}, 0, 9, \sqrt{7}, 0.35, \frac{22}{7} \right\}$$

List the numbers that are

a) positive integers.

b) whole numbers.

c) integers.

d) rational numbers.

e) irrational numbers.

f) real numbers.

Problem Solving

Give three examples of numbers that satisfy the given conditions.

53. An integer but not a negative integer.

54. A real number but not an integer.

55. An irrational number and a negative number.

56. A real number and a rational number.

57. A rational number but not a natural number.

58. An integer and a rational number.

59. A negative integer and a rational number.

60. A negative integer and a real number.

61. A real number but not a positive rational number.

62. A rational number but not a negative number.

63. A real number but not an irrational number.

64. A negative number but not a negative integer.

Three dots inside a set indicate that the set continues in the same manner. For example, $\{1, 2, 3, \ldots, 84\}$ is the set of natural numbers from 1 up to and including 84. In Exercises 65 and 66, determine the number of elements in each set.

65. $\{8, 9, 10, 11, \ldots, 94\}$

66. $\{-4, -3, -2, -1, 0, 1, \ldots, 64\}$

Challenge Problems

*The diagrams in Exercises 67 and 68 are called **Venn diagrams**. Venn diagrams are used to illustrate sets. For example, in the diagrams, circle A contains all the elements in set A, and circle B contains all the elements in set B. For each diagram, determine **a)** set A, **b)** set B, **c)** the set of elements that belong to both set A and set B, and **d)** the set of elements that belong to either set A or set B.*

67.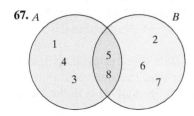

68.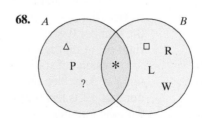

69. Consider the sets $A = \{1, 2, 3, 4\}$ and $B = \{1, 2, 3, 4, \ldots\}$.

    a) Explain the difference between set A and set B.

    b) How many elements are in set A?

    c) How many elements are in set B?

    d) Set A is an example of a *finite set*. Can you guess the name given to a set like set B?

70. How many decimal numbers are there

    a) between 1.0 and 2.0?

    b) between 1.4 and 1.5? Explain your answer.

71. How many fractions are there

    a) between 1 and 2?

    b) between $\frac{1}{3}$ and $\frac{1}{5}$? Explain your answer.

Group Activity

Discuss and answer Exercise 72 as a group.

72. Set A **union** set B, symbolized $A \cup B$, consists of the set of elements that belong to set A or set B (or both sets). Set A **intersection** set B, symbolized $A \cap B$, consists of the set of elements that both set A and set B have in common. Note that the elements that belong to both sets are listed only once in the union of the sets.

    Consider the pairs of sets below.

        Group member 1: $A = \{2, 3, 4, 6, 8, 9\}$ $B = \{1, 2, 3, 5, 7, 8\}$

        Group member 2: $A = \{a, b, c, d, g, i, j\}$ $B = \{b, c, d, h, m, p\}$

        Group member 3: $A = \{\text{red, blue, green, yellow}\}$ $B = \{\text{pink, orange, purple}\}$

    a) Group member 1: Find the union and intersection of the sets marked Group member 1.

    b) Group member 2: Find the union and intersection of the sets marked Group member 2.

    c) Group member 3: Find the union and intersection of the sets marked Group member 3.

    d) Now as a group, check each other's work. Correct any mistakes.

    e) As a group, using group member 1's sets, construct a Venn diagram like those shown in Exercises 67 and 68.

Cumulative Review Exercises

[1.3] **73.** Convert $5\frac{4}{5}$ to a fraction.

      74. Write $\frac{16}{3}$ as a mixed number.

75. Subtract $\frac{7}{8} - \frac{1}{3}$.

76. Divide $\frac{3}{5} \div 6\frac{3}{4}$.

1.5 Inequalities

1 Determine which is the greater of two numbers.

2 Find the absolute value of a number.

1 Determine Which Is the Greater of Two Numbers

The number line, which shows numbers increasing from left to right, can be used to explain inequalities (see **Fig. 1.14**). When comparing two numbers, *the number to the right on the number line is the greater number, and the number to the left is the lesser number.* The symbol $>$ is used to represent the words "is greater than." The symbol $<$ is used to represent the words "is less than."

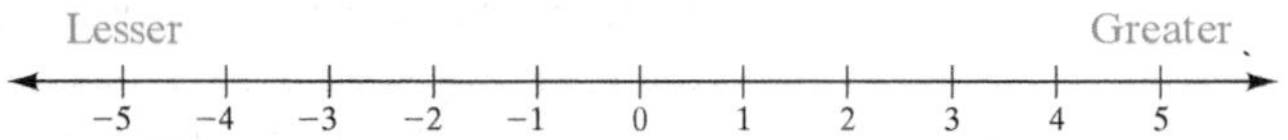

FIGURE 1.14

    The statement that the number 3 is greater than the number 2 is written $3 > 2$. Notice that 3 is to the right of 2 on the number line in **Figure 1.14**. The statement that the number 0 is greater than the number -1 is written $0 > -1$. Notice that 0 is to the right of -1 on the number line.

    Instead of stating that 3 is greater than 2, we could state that 2 is less than 3, written $2 < 3$. Notice that 2 is to the left of 3 on the number line. The statement that the number -1 is less than the number 0 is written $-1 < 0$. Notice that -1 is to the left of 0 on the number line.

EXAMPLE 1 Insert either $>$ or $<$ in the shaded area between each pair of numbers to make a true statement.

a) -4 ▢ -2 **b)** $-\dfrac{3}{2}$ ▢ 2.5 **c)** $\dfrac{1}{2}$ ▢ $\dfrac{1}{4}$ **d)** -2 ▢ 4

Solution   The points given are shown on the number line (**Fig. 1.15**).

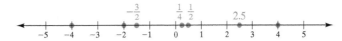

FIGURE 1.15

a) $-4 < -2$; notice that -4 is to the left of -2.

b) $-\dfrac{3}{2} < 2.5$; notice that $-\dfrac{3}{2}$ is to the left of 2.5.

c) $\dfrac{1}{2} > \dfrac{1}{4}$; notice that $\dfrac{1}{2}$ is to the right of $\dfrac{1}{4}$.

d) $-2 < 4$; notice that -2 is to the left of 4.

Now Try Exercise 35

EXAMPLE 2 Insert either $>$ or $<$ in the shaded area between each pair of numbers to make a true statement.

a) -3 ▢ 3 **b)** -3 ▢ -4 **c)** -4 ▢ 0 **d)** -1.08 ▢ -1.8

Solution   The numbers given are shown on the number line (**Fig. 1.16**).

FIGURE 1.16

a) $-3 < 3$; notice that -3 is to the left of 3.

b) $-3 > -4$; notice that -3 is to the right of -4.

c) $-4 < 0$; notice that -4 is to the left of 0.

d) $-1.08 > -1.8$; notice that -1.08 is to the right of -1.8.

Now Try Exercise 43

2 Find the Absolute Value of a Number

The **absolute value** of a number can be considered the distance between the number and 0 on a number line. Thus, the absolute value of 3, written $|3|$, is 3 since it is 3 units from 0 on a number line. Similarly, the absolute value of -3, written $|-3|$, is also 3 since -3 is 3 units from 0. See **Figure 1.17**.

$$|3| = 3 \quad \text{and} \quad |-3| = 3$$

FIGURE 1.17

Since the absolute value of a number measures the distance (without regard to direction) of a number from 0 on the number line, *the absolute value of every number will be either positive or zero.*

Number	Absolute Value of Number
6	$\lvert 6 \rvert = 6$
-6	$\lvert -6 \rvert = 6$
0	$\lvert 0 \rvert = 0$
$-\dfrac{1}{2}$	$\left\lvert -\dfrac{1}{2} \right\rvert = \dfrac{1}{2}$

Understanding Algebra

The absolute value of a real number will always be either zero or positive.

The negative of the absolute value of a nonzero number will always be a negative number. For example,

$$-\lvert 2 \rvert = -(2) = -2 \quad \text{and} \quad -\lvert -3 \rvert = -(3) = -3$$

EXAMPLE 3 Insert either $>, <,$ or $=$ in each shaded area to make a true statement.

a) $\lvert 3 \rvert \;=\; 3$ **b)** $\lvert -2 \rvert \;=\; \lvert 2 \rvert$ **c)** $-2 \;<\; \lvert -4 \rvert$

d) $\lvert -2 \rvert \;<\; \lvert -4 \rvert$ **e)** $\left\lvert -\dfrac{2}{5} \right\rvert \;<\; \lvert -0.42 \rvert$

Solution

a) $\lvert 3 \rvert = 3.$ **b)** $\lvert -2 \rvert = \lvert 2 \rvert$, since both $\lvert -2 \rvert$ and $\lvert 2 \rvert$ equal 2.

c) $-2 < \lvert -4 \rvert$, since $\lvert -4 \rvert = 4.$

d) $\lvert -2 \rvert < \lvert -4 \rvert$, since $\lvert -2 \rvert = 2$ and $\lvert -4 \rvert = 4.$

e) When an absolute value contains a fraction, we can compare it to an absolute value containing a decimal number by rewriting the fraction as a decimal number and comparing the absolute values of the decimal numbers.

$$\left\lvert -\dfrac{2}{5} \right\rvert = \lvert -0.40 \rvert = 0.40$$

$$\lvert -0.42 \rvert = 0.42$$

Therefore, $\left\lvert -\dfrac{2}{5} \right\rvert < \lvert -0.42 \rvert$ because $0.40 < 0.42.$

Now Try Exercise 57

The concept of absolute value is very important in higher-level mathematics courses.

EXERCISE SET 1.5   *Math XL*   *MyMathLab*
MathXL®   MyMathLab

Warm-Up Exercises

Fill in the blanks with the appropriate word, phrase, or symbol(s) from the following list.

$\lvert -4 \rvert$	0	$\lvert 6 - (-4) \rvert$	distance
is greater than	-4	is less than	$\lvert a \rvert$
positive number	negative number	True	False

1. Regardless of the value of a, the value of $\lvert a \rvert - \lvert a \rvert$ is ____0____ .

2. The symbol $<$ means __less than__ .

3. The absolute value of the number a is expressed as ____$\lvert a \rvert$____ .

4. If we write $x > 0$, alternatively we could say that x is a __positive #__ .

5. (True or False) If a and b are real numbers and $a < b$, then $b > a$. __True__ .

6. The symbol $>$ means __greater than__ .

7. The distance between 6 and –4 on the number line can be expressed as _____ .

8. The distance the number –4 is from zero can be expressed as _____ .

9. The negative of the absolute value of a nonzero number will always be a _____ .

10. The absolute value of a number represents its _____ from 0 on a real number line.

Practice the Skills

Evaluate.

11. $|7|$ –7

12. $|-6|$ 6

13. $|-15|$ 15

14. $|0|$ 0

15. $-|0|$ 0

16. $|54|$ 54

17. $-|-5|$ –5

18. $-|92|$ 92

19. $-|26|$ 26

20. $-|-34|$ –34

Insert either $<$ or $>$ in each shaded area to make a true statement.

21. $36 > 24$

22. $4 > -2$

23. $-4 < 0$

24. $-6 < -4$

25. $\dfrac{1}{2} > -\dfrac{2}{3}$

26. $\dfrac{3}{5} < \dfrac{4}{5}$

27. $0.7 < 0.8$

28. $-0.2 > -0.4$

29. $-\dfrac{1}{2} > -1$

30. $-0.14 > -0.92$

31. $-5 < 5$

32. $-\dfrac{3}{4} > -1$

33. $-2.1 < -2$

34. $-1.83 < -1.82$

35. $\dfrac{4}{5} > -\dfrac{4}{5}$

36. $-9 > -12$

37. $-\dfrac{3}{8} < \dfrac{3}{8}$

38. $-4.09 > -5.3$

39. $0.49 > 0.43$

40. $-1.0 < -0.7$

41. $-0.086 > -0.095$

42. $\dfrac{1}{2} > -\dfrac{1}{2}$

43. $0.001 \quad 0.002$

44. $-0.006 > -0.007$

45. $\dfrac{5}{8} > 0.6$ $\dfrac{6}{10}$ $\dfrac{24}{40}$

46. $2.7 < \dfrac{10}{3}$

47. $-\dfrac{4}{3} \quad -\dfrac{2}{3}$

48. $\dfrac{19}{2} > \dfrac{17}{2}$

49. $-0.8 < -\dfrac{3}{5}$ $\dfrac{6}{10}$ $\dfrac{}{10}$

50. $-0.7 < -0.2$

51. $0.3 \quad \dfrac{1}{3}$

52. $\dfrac{9}{20} > 0.42$ $\dfrac{}{100}$

53. $-\dfrac{17}{30} > -\dfrac{16}{20}$

54. $\dfrac{13}{15} < \dfrac{8}{9}$

55. $-(-6) < -(-5)$

56. $-\left(-\dfrac{12}{13}\right) < \dfrac{7}{8}$

Insert either $<$, $>$, or $=$ in each shaded area to make a true statement.

57. $5 > |-2|$

58. $|-12| < |-13|$

59. $\dfrac{3}{4} < |-4|$

60. $|-4| > -3$

61. $|0| < |-4|$

62. $|-2.1| > |-1.8|$

63. $4 < \left|-\dfrac{9}{2}\right|$

64. $|-5| > -|-6|$

65. $\left|-\dfrac{4}{5}\right| < \left|-\dfrac{5}{4}\right|$

66. $\left|\dfrac{2}{5}\right| = |-0.40|$ $\dfrac{}{100}$

67. $|-4.6| = \left|-\dfrac{23}{5}\right|$ $\dfrac{46}{10}$

68. $\left|-\dfrac{8}{3}\right| \quad |-3.5|$ $\dfrac{35}{10}$ $\dfrac{}{10}$

Insert either $>$, $<$, or $=$ in each shaded area to make a true statement.

69. $\dfrac{2}{3} + \dfrac{2}{3} + \dfrac{2}{3} + \dfrac{2}{3} < 4 \cdot \dfrac{2}{3}$ $\dfrac{8}{3}$

70. $\dfrac{3}{4} + \dfrac{3}{4} > \dfrac{3}{4} \cdot \dfrac{3}{4}$ $\dfrac{9}{16}$

71. $\dfrac{1}{2} \cdot \dfrac{1}{2} < \dfrac{1}{2} \div \dfrac{1}{2}$ $\dfrac{2}{1}$ $\dfrac{2}{2}$ $\dfrac{29}{15}$

72. $5 \div \dfrac{2}{3} > \dfrac{2}{3} \div \dfrac{1}{5}$ $\dfrac{2}{15}$ $\dfrac{15}{3} \cdot \dfrac{2}{2}$

73. $\dfrac{7}{8} - \dfrac{4}{8} < \dfrac{7}{8} \div \dfrac{1}{2}$ $\dfrac{2}{1}$ $\dfrac{14}{8}$

74. $3\dfrac{1}{5} + \dfrac{1}{3} > 3\dfrac{1}{5} \cdot \dfrac{1}{3}$

$\dfrac{24}{15}\dfrac{8}{5}$ $\dfrac{1}{3}\dfrac{5}{15}$ $\dfrac{9}{5}\cdot\dfrac{1}{3} = \dfrac{9}{15}$

Arrange the numbers from smallest to largest.

75. $0.46, \dfrac{4}{9}, |-5|, -|-1|, \dfrac{3}{7}$ $-|-1|, \dfrac{23}{50}, \dfrac{4}{9}, \dfrac{3}{7}, |-5|$

76. $-\dfrac{3}{4}, -|0.6|, -\dfrac{5}{9}, -1.74, |-1.9|$ $-1.74, -\dfrac{5}{9}, -\dfrac{3}{4}, -|0.6|, |-1.9|$

77. $\dfrac{2}{3}, 0.6, |-2.6|, \dfrac{19}{25}, \dfrac{5}{12}$ $\dfrac{19}{25}, \dfrac{5}{12}, 0.6, \dfrac{2}{3}, |-2.6|$

78. $-|-5|, |-9|, \left|-\dfrac{12}{5}\right|, 2.7, \dfrac{7}{12}$ $-|-5|, \dfrac{7}{12}, 2.7, |-\dfrac{12}{5}|, |-9|$

Problem Solving

79. What numbers are 4 units from 0 on a number line?

–4, 4

80. What numbers are 100 units from 0 on the number line?

–100, 100

In Exercises 81–88, give three real numbers that satisfy all the stated criteria. If no real numbers satisfy the criteria, so state and explain why.

81. less than 4 and greater than 8

82. greater than 4 and less than 6

83. less than −2 and greater than −6

84. greater than −5 and greater than −9

85. greater than −3 and greater than 3

86. less than −3 and less than 3

87. greater than $|-2|$ and less than $|-6|$

88. greater than $|-3|$ and less than $|3|$

89. a) Consider the word *between*. What does this word mean?

   b) List three real numbers between 4 and 6

   c) Is the number 4 between the numbers 4 and 6? Explain.

   d) Is the number 5 between the numbers 4 and 6? Explain.

   e) Is it true or false that the real numbers between 4 and 6 are the real numbers that are both greater than 4 and less than 6? Explain.

90. Property Crime Rates The following line graph shows the U.S. property crime rates per 1000 households from 1973 to 2005.

Property Crime Rates

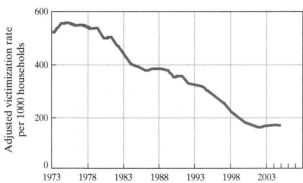

Note: Property crimes include burglary, theft, and motor vehicle theft.

Source: www.ojp.usdoj.gov

Estimate the year(s) when the property crime rate was

a) first less than 400 per 1000 households.

b) first less than 200 per 1000 households.

c) greater than 400 per 1000 households and less than 600 per 1000 households.

91. Peanuts The following bar graph shows the percent of the recommended daily allowance of certain nutrients in 1 ounce of dry-roasted, salted peanuts. Use the bar graph to determine which nutrients provide

Nutrients in Peanuts

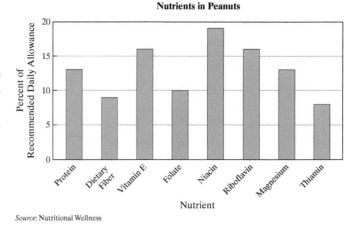

Source: Nutritional Wellness

a) less than 10% of the recommended daily allowance.

b) greater than 15% of the recommended daily allowance.

Concept/Writing Exercises

92. Are there any real numbers whose absolute value is not a positive number? Explain your answer.

93. Will $|a| - |a| = 0$ always be true for any real number a? Explain.

94. Suppose a and b represent any two real numbers. Suppose $a > b$ is true. Will $|a| > |b|$ also be true? Explain and give an example to support your answer.

95. Suppose a and b represent any two real numbers. Suppose $|a| > |b|$ is true. Will $a > b$ also be true? Explain and give an example to support your answer.

Challenge Problems

96. A number greater than 0 and less than 1 (or between 0 and 1) is multiplied by itself. Will the product be less than, equal to, or greater than the original number selected? Explain why this is always true.

97. A number between 0 and 1 is divided by itself. Will the quotient be less than, equal to, or greater than the original number selected? Explain why this is always true.

98. What two numbers can be substituted for x to make $|x| = 3$ a true statement?

99. Are there any values for x that would make $|x| = -5$ a true statement? Explain.

100. a) To what is $|x|$ equal if x represents a real number greater than or equal to 0?

   b) To what is $|x|$ equal if x represents a real number less than 0?

   c) Fill in the following shaded areas to make a true statement.

$$|x| = \begin{cases} \rule{1cm}{0.4cm} & , x \geq 0 \\ \rule{1cm}{0.4cm} & , x < 0 \end{cases}$$

Group Activity

Discuss and answer Exercise 101 as a group.

101. a) Group member 1: Draw a number line and mark points on the line to represent the following numbers.

$$|-2|, \qquad -|3|, \qquad -\left|\frac{1}{3}\right|$$

b) Group member 2: Do the same as in part **a)**, but on your number line mark points for the following numbers.

$$|-4|, \qquad -|2|, \qquad \left|-\frac{3}{5}\right|$$

c) Group member 3: Do the same as in parts **a)** and **b)**, but mark points for the following numbers.

$$|0|, \qquad \left|\frac{16}{5}\right|, \qquad -|-3|$$

d) As a group, construct one number line that contains all the points listed in parts **a)**, **b)**, and **c)**.

Cumulative Review Exercises

[1.3] **102.** Add $2\frac{3}{5} + 3\frac{1}{3}$.

[1.4] **103.** List the set of integers.

104. List the set of whole numbers.

105. Consider the following set of numbers.

$$\left\{ 5, -2, 0, \frac{1}{3}, \sqrt{3}, -\frac{5}{9}, 2.3, \pi \right\}$$

List the numbers that are

a) natural numbers.

b) whole numbers.

c) integers.

d) rational numbers.

e) irrational numbers.

f) real numbers.

Mid-Chapter Test: 1.1–1.5

To find out how well you understand the chapter material to this point, take this brief test. The answers, and the section where the material was initially discussed, are given in the back of the book. Review any questions that you answered incorrectly.

1. For each hour of class time, how many hours outside of class are recommended for studying and doing homework?

2. Phone Bills Jason Wisely's monthly phone bills for the first six months of 2009 were $78.83, $96.57, $62.23, $88.79, $101.75, and $55.62. For Jason's phone bills, determine the **a)** mean and **b)** median.

3. Checking Account The balance in Elizabeth Mater's checking account is $652.70. She deposited $230.75 and then purchased three books at $19.62 each, including tax. If she pays by check, what is the new balance in her checking account?

4. Boat Rental The rental cost of a boat from Natwora's Boat Rental is $7.50 per 15 minutes, and the rental cost from Gurney's Boat Rental is $18 per half hour. Suppose you plan to rent a boat for 4 hours.

a) Which is the better deal?

b) How much will you save?

5. Water Rate The water rate in Livingston County is $1.85 per 1000 gallons of water used. What is the water bill for a resident of Livingston County who uses 33,700 gallons of water?

Perform the indicated operation.

6. $\frac{3}{7} \cdot \frac{7}{18}$

7. $\frac{9}{16} \div \frac{13}{13}$

8. $\frac{5}{8} + \frac{3}{5}$

9. $6\frac{1}{4} - 3\frac{1}{5}$

10. Garden Justin Calhoun wants to fence in his rectangular garden to keep out deer. His garden measures $14\frac{2}{3}$ feet by $12\frac{1}{2}$ feet. How much fence will Justin need?

© Sarah Joos/Shutterstock

In Exercises 11–15, indicate whether each statement is true or false.

11. 0 is a natural number.

12. -8.6 is a real number.

13. $3\frac{2}{3}$ is an irrational number.

14. Every integer is a real number.

15. Every whole number is a counting number.

16. Evaluate $-\left|-\frac{7}{10}\right|$.

Insert either <, >, or = in each shaded area to make a true statement.

17. -0.005 ⬜> -0.006 **18.** $\dfrac{7}{8}$ ⬜> $\dfrac{5}{6}$

$\dfrac{21}{24}$ $\dfrac{20}{24}$

19. $|-9|$ ⬜< $|-19|$ **20.** $\left|-\dfrac{3}{8}\right|$ ⬜< $|-0.375|$

$\dfrac{75}{200}$ $\dfrac{15}{40}$ $\dfrac{3}{5}$

1.6 Addition of Real Numbers

1. Add real numbers using a number line.
2. Add fractions.
3. Identify opposites.
4. Add using absolute values.

There are many practical uses for negative numbers. A submarine diving below sea level, a bank account that has been overdrawn, a business spending more than it earns, and a temperature below zero are some examples.

The four basic **operations** of arithmetic are addition, subtraction, multiplication, and division. Both positive and negative numbers can be added, subtracted, multiplied, and divided. In this section, we discuss the operation of addition.

1 Add Real Numbers Using a Number Line

> **Understanding Algebra**
>
> With the exception of 0, *any number without a sign in front of it is positive.* For example, 3 means +3 and 5 means +5.

To add numbers, we make use of a number line. Represent the first number to be added (first *addend*) by an arrow starting at 0. The arrow is drawn to the right if the number is positive. If the number is negative, the arrow is drawn to the left. From the tip of the first arrow, draw a second arrow to represent the second addend. The second arrow is drawn to the right or left, as just explained. The sum of the two numbers is found at the tip of the second arrow.

EXAMPLE 1 Evaluate $3 + (-4)$ using a number line. ——

Solution   *Always begin at 0.* Since the first addend, the 3, is positive, the first arrow starts at 0 and is drawn 3 units to the right (**Fig. 1.18**).

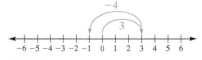

FIGURE 1.18   FIGURE 1.19

> **Understanding Algebra**
>
> When adding a positive number and a negative number, the result may be either positive or negative.
>
> $3 + (-4) = -1$
>
> $6 + (-1) = 5$

The second arrow starts at 3 and is drawn 4 units to the left, since the second addend is negative (**Fig. 1.19**). The tip of the second arrow is at -1. Thus,

$$3 + (-4) = -1$$

Now Try Exercise 27

EXAMPLE 2 Evaluate $-4 + 2$ using a number line. ——

Solution   Begin at 0. Since the first addend is negative, -4, the first arrow is drawn 4 units to the left. From there, since 2 is positive, the second arrow is drawn 2 units to the right. The second arrow ends at -2 (**Fig. 1.20**).

FIGURE 1.20

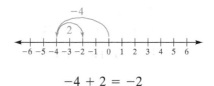

$$-4 + 2 = -2$$

Now Try Exercise 37

EXAMPLE 3 Evaluate $-3 + (-2)$ using a number line. ────

Solution   Start at 0. Since both numbers being added are negative, both arrows will be drawn to the left (**Fig. 1.21**).

FIGURE 1.21
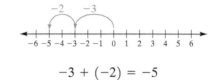

$$-3 + (-2) = -5$$

Now Try Exercise 39

In Example 3, we can think of the expression $-3 + (-2)$ as combining a *loss* of 3 and a *loss* of 2 for a total *loss* of 5, or -5.

EXAMPLE 4 Add $5 + (-5)$ using a number line. ────

Solution   The first arrow starts at 0 and is drawn 5 units to the right. The second arrow starts at 5 and is drawn 5 units to the left. The tip of the second arrow is at 0. Thus, $5 + (-5) = 0$ (**Fig. 1.22**).

FIGURE 1.22
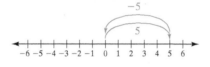

$$5 + (-5) = 0$$

Now Try Exercise 31

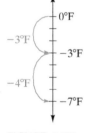

FIGURE 1.23

EXAMPLE 5 **Below-Zero Temperatures** At the beginning of the five o'clock news broadcast on a winter day in Rochester, New York, the chief meteorologist reported that the temperature was three degrees below zero Fahrenheit. During the weather segment twenty minutes later, the chief meteorologist stated that the temperature had dropped four degrees since the beginning of the news broadcast. Find the temperature at 5:20 P.M.

Solution   A vertical number line (**Fig. 1.23**) may help you visualize this problem.

$$-3 + (-4) = -7°F$$

Now Try Exercise 117

2 Add Fractions

To add fractions, where one or more of the fractions is negative, we use the same general procedure discussed in Section 1.3. Whenever the denominators are not the same, we will find the least common denominator (LCD) and then we obtain the answer by adding the numerators while keeping the LCD.

For example, suppose after obtaining a common denominator, we have $-\dfrac{19}{29} + \dfrac{13}{29}$.

To obtain the numerator of the answer, we may add $-19 + 13$ on the number line to obtain -6. The denominator of the answer is the common denominator, 29. Thus, the answer is $-\dfrac{6}{29}$.

$$-\frac{19}{29} + \frac{13}{29} = \frac{-19 + 13}{29} = \frac{-6}{29} = -\frac{6}{29}$$

Understanding Algebra

Notice that when you add two negative numbers, the result is negative: $(-3) + (-4) = -7$.

Let's look at one more example. Suppose after obtaining the LCD, we have $-\frac{7}{40} + \left(-\frac{5}{40}\right)$. We add $-7 + (-5)$ on the number line to obtain -12. The denominator of the answer is 40. Thus, the answer before being simplified is $-\frac{12}{40}$. The final answer simplifies to $-\frac{3}{10}$. We show these calculations as follows:

$$-\frac{7}{40} + \left(-\frac{5}{40}\right) = \frac{-7 + (-5)}{40} = \frac{-12}{40} = -\frac{3}{10}$$

EXAMPLE 6 Add $\frac{7}{16} + \left(-\frac{2}{3}\right)$.

Solution The LCD is 48. Changing each fraction to a fraction with a denominator of 48 yields

$$\frac{7}{16} \cdot \frac{3}{3} + \left(-\frac{2}{3}\right) \cdot \frac{16}{16}$$

$$\text{or} \quad \frac{21}{48} + \left(-\frac{32}{48}\right)$$

To add these fractions, we keep the LCD and add the numerators to get

$$\frac{7}{16} + \left(-\frac{2}{3}\right) = \frac{21}{48} + \left(-\frac{32}{48}\right) = \frac{21 + (-32)}{48}$$

Now we add $21 + (-32)$ on a number line to get the numerator of the fraction, -11; see **Figure 1.24**.

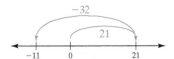

FIGURE 1.24

$$\text{Thus, } \frac{7}{16} + \left(-\frac{2}{3}\right) = \frac{21}{48} + \left(-\frac{32}{48}\right) = \frac{21 + (-32)}{48} = -\frac{11}{48}.$$

Now Try Exercise 77

EXAMPLE 7 Add $-\frac{7}{8} + \left(-\frac{3}{40}\right)$.

Solution The LCD is 40. Rewriting the first fraction with the LCD gives the following.

$$-\frac{7}{8} + \left(-\frac{3}{40}\right) = -\frac{7}{8} \cdot \frac{5}{5} + \left(-\frac{3}{40}\right)$$

$$= -\frac{35}{40} + \left(-\frac{3}{40}\right) = \frac{-35 + (-3)}{40}$$

Now we add $-35 + (-3)$ to get the numerator of the fraction, -38; see **Figure 1.25**

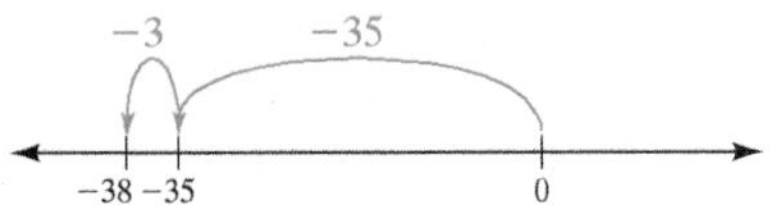

FIGURE 1.25

$$\text{Thus, } -\frac{7}{8} + \left(-\frac{3}{40}\right) = \frac{-35}{40} + \left(\frac{-3}{40}\right) = \frac{-35 + (-3)}{40} = -\frac{38}{40} = -\frac{19}{20}.$$

Now Try Exercise 85

> **Helpful Hint**
>
> When the numbers being added are large, you are not expected to actually mark and count the units. For example, when determining $21 + (-32)$ you will not need to count 32 units to the left from 21 to obtain the answer -11.
>
> In objective 3, we will show you how to obtain $21 + (-32) = -11$ without having to draw number lines. We present adding on a number line here to help you understand the concept of addition of signed numbers, and to help you in determining, without doing any calculations, whether the sum of two signed numbers will be a positive number, a negative number, or zero.

3 Identify Opposites

Now let's consider **opposites**, or **additive inverses**.

> **Opposites (or Additive Inverses)**
>
> Any two numbers whose sum is zero are said to be **opposites**, or **additive inverses**, of each other. In general, if we let a represent any real number, then its opposite is $-a$ and $a + (-a) = 0$.

In Example 4, the sum of 5 and -5 is 0. Thus, -5 is the opposite of 5 and 5 is the opposite of -5.

EXAMPLE 8 Find the opposite of each number.

a) 3   **b)** -4 **c)** $-\dfrac{7}{8}$

Solution

a) The opposite of 3 is -3, since $3 + (-3) = 0$.

b) The opposite of -4 is 4, since $-4 + 4 = 0$.

c) The opposite of $-\dfrac{7}{8}$ is $\dfrac{7}{8}$, since $-\dfrac{7}{8} + \dfrac{7}{8} = 0$.

Now Try Exercise 15

> **Understanding Algebra**
>
> The *additive inverse* of a number has the property that the sum of the number and its additive inverse is 0. So, (-5) is the additive inverse, or *opposite,* of 5 because $(-5) + 5 = 0$.

4 Add Using Absolute Values

Recall that the absolute value of a nonzero number will always be positive.

> **Adding Real Numbers with the Same Sign**
>
> To add real numbers with the same sign (either both positive or both negative), add their absolute values. The sum has the same sign as the numbers being added.

EXAMPLE 9 Add $4 + 8$.

Solution   Since both numbers have the same sign, both positive, we add their absolute values: $|4| + |8| = 4 + 8 = 12$. Since both numbers being added are positive, the sum is positive. Thus, $4 + 8 = 12$.

Now Try Exercise 49

EXAMPLE 10 Add $-6 + (-9)$.

Solution   Since both numbers have the same sign, both negative, we add their absolute values: $|-6| + |-9| = 6 + 9 = 15$. Since both numbers being added are negative, their sum is negative. Thus, $-6 + (-9) = -15$.

Now Try Exercise 51

Understanding Algebra

The sum of two positive numbers will always be positive and the sum of two negative numbers will always be negative.

Adding Two Signed Numbers with Different Signs

To add two signed numbers with different signs, one positive and the other negative, subtract the smaller absolute value from the larger absolute value. The answer has the sign of the number with the larger absolute value.

EXAMPLE 11   Add $10 + (-6)$. ───────

Solution   The two numbers being added have different signs, so we subtract the smaller absolute value from the larger: $|10| - |-6| = 10 - 6 = 4$. Since $|10|$ is greater than $|-6|$ and the sign of 10 is positive, the sum is positive. Thus, $10 + (-6) = 4$.

Now Try Exercise 53

EXAMPLE 12   Add $12 + (-18)$. ───────

Solution   The numbers being added have different signs, so we subtract the smaller absolute value from the larger: $|-18| - |12| = 18 - 12 = 6$. Since $|-18|$ is greater than $|12|$ and the sign of -18 is negative, the sum is negative. Thus, $12 + (-18) = -6$.

Now Try Exercise 55

EXAMPLE 13   Add $-21 + 20$. ───────

Solution   The two numbers being added have different signs, so we subtract the smaller absolute value from the larger: $|-21| - |20| = 21 - 20 = 1$. Since $|-21|$ is greater than $|20|$, the sum is negative. Therefore, $-21 + 20 = -1$.

Now Try Exercise 61

Now let's look at some additional examples that contain fractions and decimal numbers.

EXAMPLE 14   Add $-\dfrac{3}{5} + \dfrac{4}{7}$. ───────

Solution   We can write each fraction with the least common denominator, 35.

$$-\frac{3}{5} + \frac{4}{7} = -\frac{3}{5} \cdot \frac{7}{7} + \frac{4}{7} \cdot \frac{5}{5}$$

$$= \frac{-21}{35} + \frac{20}{35} = \frac{-21 + 20}{35}$$

Since $|-21|$ is greater than $|20|$, the final answer will be negative. In Example 13, we found that $-21 + 20 = -1$. Thus, we can write

$$\frac{-21}{35} + \frac{20}{35} = \frac{-21 + 20}{35} = \frac{-1}{35} = -\frac{1}{35}$$

Thus, $-\dfrac{3}{5} + \dfrac{4}{7} = -\dfrac{1}{35}$.

Now Try Exercise 87

Examples 15 and 16 contain decimal numbers. If you have forgotten how to perform the basic operations of addition, subtraction, multiplication, and division of decimal numbers, read Appendix A now.

EXAMPLE 15 Add $-37.45 + (-26.98)$.

Solution   Since both numbers have the same sign, both negative, we add their absolute values: $|-37.45| + |-26.98| = 37.45 + 26.98$.

$$
\begin{array}{r}
37.45 \\
+\ 26.98 \\
\hline
64.43
\end{array}
$$

Since two negative numbers are being added, the sum is negative. Therefore, $-37.45 + (-26.98) = -64.43$.

Now Try Exercise 67

EXAMPLE 16 **Net Profit or Loss** The B.J. Donaldson Printing Company had a loss of $4005.69 for the first 6 months of the year and a profit of $29,645.78 for the second 6 months of the year. Find the net profit or loss for the year.

Solution   Understand and Translate   This problem can be represented as $-4005.69 + 29,645.78$. Since the numbers have different signs, we subtract the smaller absolute value from the larger.

Carry Out $|29,645.78| - |-4005.69| = 29,645.78 - 4005.69$

$$
\begin{array}{r}
29,645.78 \\
-\ \ \ 4005.69 \\
\hline
25,640.09
\end{array}
$$

Since $|29,645.78|$ is greater than $|-4005.69|$ and the sign of 29,645.78 is positive, the sum is positive. Thus, $-4005.69 + 29,645.78 = 25,640.09$.

Check and Answer   The answer is reasonable. Thus, the net profit for the year was $25,640.09.

Now Try Exercise 121

Understanding Algebra

The sum of two signed numbers with different signs may be either positive or negative. The sign of the sum will be the same as the sign of the number with the larger absolute value.

$$13 + (-45) = -32$$

$$(-17) + 20 = 3$$

Helpful Hint

Architects often make a scale model of a building before starting construction of the building. This model helps them visualize the project and often helps them avoid problems.

Mathematicians also construct models. A *mathematical model* may be a physical representation of a mathematical concept. It may be as simple as using tiles or chips to represent specific numbers. For example, below we use a model to help explain addition of real numbers. This may help some of you understand the concepts better.

We let a red chip represent +1 and a green chip represent −1.

● = +1   ● = −1

If we add +1 and −1, or a red and a green chip, we get 0.
Now consider the addition problem $3 + (-5)$. We can represent this as

● ● ● + ● ● ● ● ●
‾3‾   ‾‾−5‾‾

If we remove 3 red chips and 3 green chips, or three zeros, we are left with 2 green chips, which represents a sum of −2. Thus, $3 + (-5) = -2$,

If we remove 3 red chips and 3 green chips, or three zeros, we are left with 2 green chips, which represents a sum of −2. Thus, $3 + (-5) = -2$,

Now consider the problem $-4 + (-2)$. We can represent this as

● ● ● ● + ● ●
‾‾−4‾‾   ‾−2‾

Since we end up with 6 green chips, and each green chip represents −1, the sum is −6. Therefore, $-4 + (-2) = -6$.

EXERCISE SET 1.6

MathXL   MyMathLab

MathXL®   MyMathLab

Warm-Up Exercises

Fill in the blanks with the appropriate word, phrase, or symbol(s) from the following list.

opposites ~~additive inverse~~ ~~common denominator~~ addends ~~sum~~

absolute value ~~−8~~ numerator negative ~~8~~

positive

1. The sum of two negative numbers is always ___neg___ .

2. Another expression for "opposite" of a real number is ___absolute value___

3. The expression $|x|$ is read "the _____ of x."

4. The sum of two positive numbers is always ___positive___ .

5. In the statement $(-8) + 5 = -3$, the number -3 is called the ___sum___ of -8 and 5.

6. In the statement $(-8) + 5 = -3$, the numbers -8 and 5 are called _____ .

7. $-|-8| =$ ___−8___ .

8. $|-8| =$ ___8___ .

9. When adding two fractions with different signs, we first find the ___CD___ .

10. Two numbers that add up to zero are ___additive inverse___ of each other.

In Exercises 11 and 12, are the calculations shown correct? If not, explain why not.

11. $\dfrac{-5}{12} + \dfrac{9}{12} = \dfrac{-5+9}{12} = \dfrac{4}{12} = \dfrac{1}{3}$

12. $\dfrac{-6}{70} + \left(\dfrac{-9}{70}\right) = \dfrac{-6 + (-9)}{70} = \dfrac{-15}{70} = -\dfrac{3}{14}$

Practice the Skills

Write the opposite of each number.

13. 19 −19

14. −7 , 7

15. −28 , 28

16. 3 , −3

17. 0 0

18. $-3\frac{1}{2}$ 3½

19. $\frac{5}{3}$, −5/3

20. $-\frac{1}{4}$, ¼

21. $2\frac{3}{5}$, −2⅗

22. −1 , 1

23. 3.72 , −3.72

24. −0.721 , 0.721

Add.

25. $5 + 16$ = 21

26. $-8 + 2$ −6

27. $4 + (-3)$ 1

28. $9 + (-12)$ −3

29. $-4 + (-2)$ −6

30. $-3 + (-5)$ −8

31. $6 + (-6)$ 0

32. $-8 + 8$ 0

33. $-4 + 4$ 0

34. $-6 + 6$ 0

35. $-8 + (-2)$ −10

36. $6 + (-5)$ 1

37. $-7 + 3$ −4

38. $-6 + 9$ 3

39. $-8 + (-5)$ −13

40. $0 + (-3)$ −3

41. $0 + 0$ 0

42. $0 + (-0)$ 0

43. $-8 + 0$ −8

44. $-9 + 13$ 4

45. $-18 + (-9)$ −27

46. $-7 + 7$ 0

47. $-33 + (-31)$ −64

48. $-27 + (-9)$ −36

49. $7 + 9$ 16

50. $12 + 3$ 15

51. $-8 + (-4)$ −12

52. $-25 + (-36)$ −61

53. $6 + (-3)$ 3

54. $52 + (-25)$ 27

55. $13 + (-19)$ −6

56. $34 + (-40)$ −6

57. $180 + (-220)$

58. $-452 + 312$

59. $-11 + (-20)$ −31

60. $-33 + (-92)$ −125

61. $-67 + 28$

62. $183 + (-183)$

63. $184 + (-93)$

64. $-19 + 176$ 167

65. $80.5 + (-90.4)$

66. $-24.6 + (-13.9)$

67. $-124.7 + (-19.3)$

68. $106.3 + (-110.9)$

69. $-123.56 + (-18.35)$

70. $-72.79 + 33.47$

71. $-99.36 + 45.71$

72. $-84.15 + (-29.98)$

Add.

73. $\dfrac{3}{5} + \dfrac{1}{7}$

74. $\dfrac{5}{8} + \dfrac{3}{5}$

75. $\dfrac{5}{12} + \dfrac{6}{7}$

76. $\dfrac{2}{9} + \dfrac{3}{10}$

77. $-\dfrac{8}{11} + \dfrac{4}{5}$

78. $-\dfrac{4}{9} + \dfrac{5}{27}$

79. $-\dfrac{7}{10} + \dfrac{11}{90}$

80. $\dfrac{8}{9} + \left(-\dfrac{1}{3}\right)$

81. $-\dfrac{7}{30} + \left(-\dfrac{4}{5}\right)$

82. $-\dfrac{7}{9} + \left(-\dfrac{1}{5}\right)$

83. $\dfrac{9}{25} + \left(-\dfrac{3}{50}\right)$

84. $-\dfrac{1}{15} + \left(-\dfrac{5}{6}\right)$

85. $-\dfrac{4}{5} + \left(-\dfrac{5}{75}\right)$

86. $\dfrac{5}{36} + \left(-\dfrac{5}{24}\right)$

87. $-\dfrac{9}{24} + \dfrac{5}{7}$

88. $-\dfrac{9}{40} + \dfrac{4}{15}$

89. $-\dfrac{5}{12} + \left(-\dfrac{3}{10}\right)$

90. $\dfrac{7}{16} + \left(-\dfrac{5}{24}\right)$

91. $-\dfrac{13}{14} + \left(-\dfrac{7}{42}\right)$

92. $-\dfrac{11}{27} + \left(-\dfrac{7}{18}\right)$

In Exercises 93–108, **a)** *determine by observation whether the sum will be a positive number, zero, or a negative number;* **b)** *find the sum.*

93. $587 + (-197)$ **94.** $-140 + (-629)$ **95.** $-84 + (-289)$ **96.** $-647 + 352$

97. $-947 + 495$ **98.** $762 + (-762)$ **99.** $-496 + (-804)$ **100.** $-354 + 1090$

101. $-375 + 263$ **102.** $1127 + (-84)$ **103.** $-1833 + (-2047)$ **104.** $-426 + 572$

105. $3124 + (-2013)$ **106.** $-9095 + (-647)$ **107.** $-1025 + (-1025)$ **108.** $7513 + (-4361)$

Indicate whether each statement is true or false.

109. The sum of two negative numbers is always a negative number.

110. The sum of a negative number and a positive number is sometimes a negative number.

111. The sum of two positive numbers is never a negative number.

112. The sum of a positive number and a negative number is always a negative number.

113. The sum of a positive number and a negative number is always a positive number.

114. The sum of a number and its opposite is always equal to zero.

Problem Solving

Write an expression that can be used to solve each problem and then solve.

115. Credit Card David Nurkiewicz owed $94 on his credit card. He charged another item costing $183. Find the amount that David owed.

116. Charge Card Mrs. Chu charged $142 worth of goods on her charge card. Find her balance after she made a payment of $87.

117. Football A football team lost 18 yards on one play and then lost 3 yards on the following play. What was the total loss in yardage?

118. Overdrawn Checking Account Mrs. Jahn is unaware that her checking account has been overdrawn by $56. While shopping, she writes a check for $162. Find the total amount by which Mrs. Jahn has overdrawn her account.

119. Drilling for Water A company is drilling a well. During the first week they drilled 27 feet, and during the second week they drilled another 34 feet before they struck water. How deep is the well?

120. Coffee Bar The Frenches opened a coffee bar. Their income and expenses for their first three months of operation are shown in the following graph.

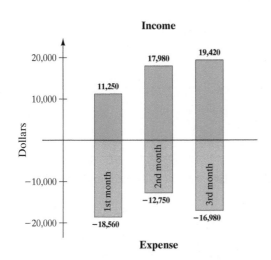

Income

(bar graph, y-axis "Dollars")

1st month: 11,250 / −18,560
2nd month: 17,980 / −12,750
3rd month: 19,420 / −16,980

Expense

a) Find the net profit or loss (the sum of income and expenses) for the first month.

b) Find the net profit or loss for the second month.

c) Find the net profit or loss for the third month.

121. High Mountain The Web site *www.guinnessworldrecords.com* lists Mauna Kea in Hawaii as the tallest mountain in the world when measured from its base to its peak. The base of Mauna Kea is 19,684 feet below sea level. The total height of the mountain from its base to its peak is 33,480 feet. How high is the peak of Mauna Kea above sea level?

© Matthew Browning/Shutterstock

Hawaii's Mauna Kea is the world's highest mountain measured from the seafloor to its peak.

122. Net Profit or Loss The Crafty Scrapbook Company had a loss of $3000 for the first 4 months of the year and a profit of $37,400 for the last 8 months of the year. Find the net profit or loss for the year.

123. Surplus and Deficit The following graph shows the surplus or deficit for Gilmar Publishing Company in Cincinnati, Ohio, for the years 1996 through 2008.

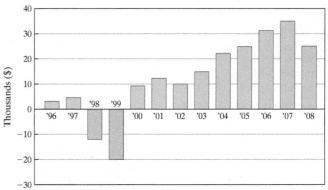

Surplus/Deficit
Gilmar Publishing Company

(bar graph, y-axis "Thousands ($)", x-axis years '96 through '08)

Source: www.gilmarpublishing.com

a) Estimate the surplus or deficit for Gilmar Publishing in 1998.

b) Estimate the surplus or deficit for Gilmar Publishing for each of the years 2006, 2007, and 2008. Then estimate the surplus or deficit from 2006 through 2008 by adding these three estimates.

124. Stocks The following chart shows percent changes from the first quarter of 2007 through the first quarter of 2008 for the mutual fund Fidelity Puritan Fund.

   Determine the percent change for the fund from the first quarter of 2007 through the first quarter of 2008 by adding the individual percents.

Fidelity Puritan Fund	Percent change from previous quarter
1st quarter 2007	4.2%
2nd quarter 2007	5.2%
3rd quarter 2007	0.2%
4th quarter 2007	−13.5%
1st quarter 2008	−3.0%

Challenge Problems

Evaluate each exercise by adding the numbers from left to right. We will discuss problems like this shortly.

125. $(-8) + (-6) + (-12)$ ~26

126. $5 + (-7) + (-8)$

127. $29 + (-46) + 37$

128. $4 + (-5) + 6 + (-8)$ −3

129. $(-12) + (-10) + 25 + (-3)$ 0

130. $(-4) + (-2) + (-15) + (-27)$

131. $\frac{1}{2} + \left(-\frac{1}{3}\right) + \frac{1}{5}$

132. $-\frac{3}{8} + \left(-\frac{2}{9}\right) + \left(-\frac{1}{2}\right)$

Find the following sums. Explain how you determined your answer. (Hint: Pair small numbers with large numbers from the ends inward.)

133. $1 + 2 + 3 + \cdots + 10$

134. $1 + 2 + 3 + \cdots + 20$

Cumulative Review Exercises

[1.3] **135.** Multiply $\left(\frac{4}{7}\right)\left(2\frac{3}{8}\right)$. $\frac{19}{8}$ $\frac{126}{56}$

136. Subtract $3 - \frac{5}{16}$.

[1.4] **137.** True or False: Every number less than zero is a negative integer.   T

[1.5] *Insert either* $<, >,$ *or* $=$ *in each shaded area to make a true statement.*

138. $|-3|$ > 2

139. 8 < $|-12|$

1.7 Subtraction of Real Numbers

1 Subtract numbers.

2 Subtract numbers mentally.

3 Evaluate expressions containing more than two numbers.

Understanding Algebra

We convert a subtraction problem to addition by adding the opposite of the second number to the first number. So, $6 - (-10)$ is rewritten as $6 + 10 = 16$.

1 Subtract Numbers

Any subtraction problem can be rewritten as an addition problem using the additive inverse.

To Subtract Real Numbers

In general, if a and b represent any two real numbers, then
$$a - b = a + (-b)$$

EXAMPLE 1 Evaluate $9 - (+4)$.

Solution   We are subtracting a positive 4 from 9. To accomplish this, we add the opposite of $+4$, which is -4, to 9.

$$9 - (+4) = 9 + (-4) = 5$$

Subtract   Positive 4   Add   Negative 4

We evaluated $9 + (-4)$ using the procedures for *adding* real numbers presented in Section 1.6.

Now Try Exercise 13

Understanding Algebra

The parts of a subtraction problem:

$16 \leftarrow$ minuend
$- \underline{12} \leftarrow$ subtrahend
$4 \leftarrow$ difference

Often in a subtraction problem, when the number being subtracted is a positive number, the + sign preceding the number being subtracted is not shown. For example, in the subtraction $9 - 4$,

$$9 - \boxed{4} \text{ means } 9 - \boxed{(+4)}$$

Thus, to evaluate $9 - 4$, we must add the opposite of 4, which is -4, to 9.

$$9 - 4 = 9 + (-4) = 5$$

Subtract Positive 4 Add Negative 4

This procedure is illustrated in Example 2.

EXAMPLE 2 Evaluate $5 - 3$. ——————————

Solution   We must subtract a positive 3 from 5. To change this problem to an addition problem, we add the opposite of 3, which is -3, to 5.

Subtraction   Addition
problem   problem
$$5 - 3 = 5 + (-3) = 2$$

Subtract Positive 3 Add Negative 3

Now Try Exercise 15

EXAMPLE 3 Evaluate. ——————————

a) $4 - 9$ **b)** $-4 - 2$

Solution

a) Add the opposite of 9, which is -9, to 4.

$$4 - 9 = 4 + (-9) = -5$$

b) Add the opposite of 2, which is -2, to -4.

$$-4 - 2 = -4 + (-2) = -6$$

Now Try Exercise 17

In Example 4, we subtract numbers that contain decimal points.

EXAMPLE 4 Evaluate $16.32 - 18.75$. ——————————

Solution   Add the opposite of 18.75, which is -18.75, to 16.32.

$$16.32 - 18.75 = 16.32 + (-18.75) = -2.43$$

Now Try Exercise 53

In Examples 5 and 6, we will show how to subtract a negative number.

EXAMPLE 5 Evaluate $4 - (-2)$. ——————————

Solution   We are asked to subtract a negative 2 from 4. To do this, we add the opposite of -2, which is 2, to 4.

$$4 - (-2) = 4 + 2 = 6$$

Subtract Negative 2 Add Positive 2

Now Try Exercise 19

Understanding Algebra

Whenever we subtract a negative number, we *always* replace the two negative signs with a plus sign.

$$6 - (-9) = 6 + 9$$

Helpful Hint

By examining Example 5, we see that

$$4 - (-2) = 4 + 2$$

Two negative signs together   Plus

EXAMPLE 6   Evaluate.

a) $7 - (-5)$ **b)** $-15 - (-12)$

Solution

a) Since we are subtracting a negative number, adding the opposite of -5, which is 5, to 7 will result in the two negative signs being replaced by a plus sign.

$$7 - (-5) = 7 + 5 = 12$$

b) $-15 - (-12) = -15 + 12 = -3$

Now Try Exercise 29

Helpful Hint

We will now indicate how we may illustrate subtraction using colored chips. Remember from the preceding section that a red chip represents $+1$ and a green chip -1.

● = +1   ● = −1

Consider the subtraction problem $2 - 5$. If we change this to an addition problem, we get $2 + (-5)$. We can then add, as was done in the preceding section. The figure below shows that $2 + (-5) = -3$.

Now consider $-2 - 5$. This means $-2 + (-5)$, which can be represented as follows:

Thus, $-2 - 5 = -7$.
Now consider the problem $-3 - (-5)$. This can be rewritten as $-3 + 5$, which can be represented as follows:

Thus, $-3 - (-5) = 2$.
Some students still have difficulty understanding why when you subtract a negative number you obtain a positive number. Let's look at the problem $3 - (-2)$. This time we will look at it from a slightly different point of view. Let's start with 3:

● ● ●

From this we wish to subtract a negative 2. To the $+3$ shown above we will add two zeros by adding two $+1 - 1$ combinations. Remember, $+1$ and -1 sum to 0.

+3   0   0

Now we can subtract or "take away" the two -1's as shown:

From this we see that we are left with $3 + 2$ or 5. Thus, $3 - (-2) = 5$.

EXAMPLE 7 Subtract 12 from 3. ————————

Solution

$$3 - 12 = 3 + (-12) = -9$$

Now Try Exercise 57

Helpful Hint

Example 7 asked us to "subtract 12 from 3." The correct way of writing this is $3 - 12$. Notice that the number following the word "from" is our starting point. That is where the calculation begins. For example:

Subtract 2 from 7 **means** $7 - 2$.   From 7, subtract 2 **means** $7 - 2$.

Subtract 5 from -1 **means** $-1 - 5$.   From -1, subtract 5 **means** $-1 - 5$.

Subtract -4 from -2 **means** $-2 - (-4)$.   From -2, subtract -4 **means** $-2 - (-4)$.

Subtract -3 from 6 **means** $6 - (-3)$.   From 6, subtract -3 **means** $6 - (-3)$.

Subtract a from b **means** $b - a$.   From a, subtract b **means** $a - b$.

EXAMPLE 8 Subtract 5 from 5. ————————

Solution

$$5 - 5 = 5 + (-5) = 0$$

Now Try Exercise 59

EXAMPLE 9 Subtract -6.48 from 4.25. ————————

Solution

$$4.25 - (-6.48) = 4.25 + 6.48 = 10.73$$

Now Try Exercise 61

Now we will perform subtraction problems that contain fractions.

EXAMPLE 10 Subtract $\dfrac{5}{9} - \dfrac{13}{15}$. ————————

Solution Begin by changing the subtraction problem to an addition problem.

$$\frac{5}{9} - \frac{13}{15} = \frac{5}{9} + \left(-\frac{13}{15}\right)$$

Now rewrite the fractions with the LCD, 45, and add the fractions as was done in the last section.

$$\frac{5}{9} + \left(-\frac{13}{15}\right) = \frac{5}{9} \cdot \frac{5}{5} + \left(-\frac{13}{15}\right) \cdot \frac{3}{3}$$

$$= \frac{25}{45} + \left(-\frac{39}{45}\right) = \frac{25 + (-39)}{45} = \frac{-14}{45} = -\frac{14}{45}$$

Thus, $\dfrac{5}{9} - \dfrac{13}{15} = -\dfrac{14}{45}$.

Now Try Exercise 85

EXAMPLE 11 Subtract $-\dfrac{7}{18}$ from $-\dfrac{9}{15}$.

Solution   This problem is written $-\dfrac{9}{15} - \left(-\dfrac{7}{18}\right)$.

We can simplify this as follows.

$$-\frac{9}{15} - \left(-\frac{7}{18}\right) = -\frac{9}{15} + \frac{7}{18}.$$

The LCD of 15 and 18 is 90. Rewriting the fractions with a common denominator gives

$$-\frac{9}{15} \cdot \frac{6}{6} + \frac{7}{18} \cdot \frac{5}{5} = -\frac{54}{90} + \frac{35}{90} = \frac{-54 + 35}{90}$$

$$= \frac{-19}{90} = -\frac{19}{90}.$$

Now Try Exercise 87

Let us now look at some applications that involve subtraction.

EXAMPLE 12 **A Gift Card Balance** Brigitte Martineau's gift card indicates a balance of $86.23 before she makes purchases totaling $127.49. Find the amount that Brigitte owes the cashier after she uses her gift card.

Solution   Understand and Translate   We can obtain the amount that Brigitte owes by subtracting 127.49 from 86.23.

Carry Out $86.23 - 127.49 = 86.23 + (-127.49) = -41.26$

Check and Answer   The negative indicates a deficit, which is what we expect. Therefore, Brigitte owes the cashier $41.26.

Now Try Exercise 131

EXAMPLE 13 **Temperature Difference** On January 30, 2008, the high temperature for the day in Laredo, Texas, was 86°F. On the same day, the low temperature in Wahpeton, North Dakota, was −26°F. Find the difference in their temperatures.

Solution   Understand and Translate   The word *difference* in the example title indicates subtraction. We can obtain the difference in their temperatures by subtracting as follows.

Carry Out $86 - (-26) = 86 + 26 = 112$

Check and Answer   Therefore, the high temperature in Laredo is 112°F greater than the low temperature in Wahpeton.

Now Try Exercise 135

Laredo, Texas

EXAMPLE 14 **Measuring Snow** A kindergarten class in Richfield, Minnesota, has a snow gauge placed outside its window that is left untouched for two days. Suppose that on the first day $6\dfrac{3}{8}$ inches of snow falls. On the second day, no snow falls, but $1\dfrac{1}{2}$ inches of the first day's snowfall melts. How much snow remains after the second day?

Solution   Understand and Translate   From the first amount, $6\dfrac{3}{8}$ inches, we must subtract $1\dfrac{1}{2}$ inches.

Carry Out   We begin by changing the subtraction problem to an addition problem. We then change the mixed numbers to fractions, and then rewrite each fraction with the LCD, 8.

$$6\frac{3}{8} - 1\frac{1}{2} = 6\frac{3}{8} + \left(-1\frac{1}{2}\right)$$

$$= \frac{51}{8} + \left(-\frac{3}{2}\right)$$

$$= \frac{51}{8} + \left(-\frac{3}{2}\right) \cdot \frac{4}{4}$$

$$= \frac{51}{8} + \left(-\frac{12}{8}\right)$$

$$= \frac{51 + (-12)}{8} = \frac{39}{8} \quad \text{or} \quad 4\frac{7}{8}$$

Check and Answer   Thus, after the second day there were $4\frac{7}{8}$ inches of snow remaining. Based upon the numbers given in the problem, the answer seems reasonable.

Now Try Exercise 133

EXAMPLE 15 Evaluate. —————

a) $15 + (-4)$ 11
b) $-16 - 3$ -19
c) $19 + (-14)$ 5
d) $7 - (-9)$ 16
e) $-9 - (-3)$ -6
f) $8 - 13$ -5

Solution   Parts **a)** and **c)** are addition problems, whereas the other parts are subtraction problems. We can rewrite each subtraction problem as an addition problem to evaluate.

a) $15 + (-4) = 11$ **b)** $-16 - 3 = -16 + (-3) = -19$
c) $19 + (-14) = 5$ **d)** $7 - (-9) = 7 + 9 = 16$
e) $-9 - (-3) = -9 + 3 = -6$ **f)** $8 - 13 = 8 + (-13) = -5$

Now Try Exercise 31

2 Subtract Numbers Mentally

In the previous examples, we rewrote subtraction problems as addition problems. We did this because we know how to add real numbers. After this chapter, when we work out a subtraction problem, we will not show this step. *You need to practice and thoroughly understand how to add and subtract real numbers. When asked to evaluate an expression like $-4 - 6$, you need to be able to compute the answer mentally.*

Let's evaluate a few subtraction problems without showing the process of changing the subtraction to addition.

EXAMPLE 16 Evaluate. ————
a) $-7 - 5$ **b)** $4 - 12$ **c)** $18 - 25$ **d)** $-20 - 12$
Solution
a) $-7 - 5 = -12$ **b)** $4 - 12 = -8$ **c)** $18 - 25 = -7$ **d)** $-20 - 12 = -32$

Now Try Exercise 33

In Example 16 **a)**, we may have reasoned that $-7 - 5$ meant $-7 + (-5)$, which is -12, but we did not need to show it.

EXAMPLE 17 Evaluate $-\frac{3}{5} - \frac{7}{8}$. —————

Solution   Write each fraction with the LCD, 40.

$$-\frac{3}{5} \cdot \frac{8}{8} - \frac{7}{8} \cdot \frac{5}{5} = -\frac{24}{40} - \frac{35}{40} = \frac{-24 - 35}{40} = -\frac{59}{40} = -1\frac{19}{40}$$

Now Try Exercise 77

Notice in Example 17, when we had $-\dfrac{24}{40} - \dfrac{35}{40}$, we could have written $\dfrac{-24 + (-35)}{40}$, but at this time we elected to write it as $\dfrac{-24 - 35}{40}$. Since $-24 - 35$ is -59, the answer is $-\dfrac{59}{40}$ or $-1\dfrac{19}{40}$.

3 Evaluate Expressions Containing More Than Two Numbers

In evaluating expressions involving more than one addition and subtraction, work from left to right unless parentheses or other grouping symbols appear.

> **Understanding Algebra**
>
> When performing a string of additions and subtractions, always work from left to right.

EXAMPLE 18 Evaluate.

a) $9 - 12 + 3$ **b)** $-7 - 15 - 6$ **c)** $-5 + 1 - 8$

Solution   We work from left to right.

a) $\underline{9 - 12} + 3$
$= -3 + 3$
$= 0$

b) $\underline{-7 - 15} - 6$
$= -22 - 6$
$= -28$

c) $\underline{-5 + 1} - 8$
$= -4 - 8$
$= -12$

Now Try Exercise 119

> **Understanding Algebra**
>
> Whenever we see an expression of the form $a + (-b)$, we can write the expression as $a - b$.
>
> $2 + (-5) = 2 - 5$
>
> Whenever we see an expression of the form $a - (-b)$, we can rewrite it as $a + b$.
>
> $6 - (-8) = 6 + 8$

Rewriting Expressions

In general, for any real numbers a and b,

$$a + (-b) = a - b, \text{ and}$$
$$a - (-b) = a + b$$

Using the given information, the expression $9 + (-12) - (-8)$ may be simplified to $9 - 12 + 8$.

EXAMPLE 19

a) Evaluate $-5 - (-9) + (-12) + (-3)$.

b) Simplify the expression in part **a)**.

c) Evaluate the simplified expression in part **b)**.

Solution

a) We work from left to right. The shading indicates the additions being performed to get to the next step.

$$\begin{aligned}
-5 - (-9) + (-12) + (-3) &= -5 + 9 + (-12) + (-3) \\
&= 4 + (-12) + (-3) \\
&= -8 + (-3) \\
&= -11
\end{aligned}$$

b) The expression simplifies as follows:

$$-5 - (-9) + (-12) + (-3) = -5 + 9 - 12 - 3$$

c) Evaluate the simplified expression from left to right. Begin by adding $-5 + 9$ to obtain 4.

$$\begin{aligned}
-5 + 9 - 12 - 3 &= 4 - 12 - 3 \\
&= -8 - 3 \\
&= -11
\end{aligned}$$

When you come across an expression like the one in Example 19 **a)**, you should simplify it as we did in part **b)** and then evaluate the simplified expression.

Now Try Exercise 129

EXERCISE SET 1.7

MathXL MyMathLab
MathXL® MyMathLab

Warm-Up Exercises

Fill in the blanks with the appropriate word, phrase, or symbol(s) from the following list.

opposite	subtrahend	$-a - b$	$a + b$	difference
zero	left to right	minuend	$a + (-b)$	$a - b$
$-a + b$				

1. In the equation $4 - 7 = -3$, 4 is called the _____ .

2. In the equation $4 - 7 = -3$, 7 is called the _____ .

3. In the equation $4 - 7 = -3$, -3 is called the _____ .

4. $a - b$ could be rewritten as _____ .

5. When subtracting a number, we add its _____ .

6. When a number is subtracted from itself, the result is _____ .

7. When many numbers are being added and subtracted, we always work from _____ .

8. The opposite of the number $a + b$ is _____ .

9. $-a - (-b)$ could be rewritten as _____ .

10. $a - (-b)$ could be rewritten as _____ .

In Exercises 11 and 12, are the following calculations correct? If not, explain why.

11. $\dfrac{4}{9} - \dfrac{3}{7} = \dfrac{28}{63} - \dfrac{27}{63} = \dfrac{28 - 27}{63} = \dfrac{1}{63}$

12. $-\dfrac{5}{12} - \dfrac{7}{9} = -\dfrac{15}{36} - \dfrac{28}{36} = \dfrac{-15 - 28}{36} = -\dfrac{43}{36}$

Practice the Skills

Evaluate.

13. $8 - (+2)$ 6

14. $17 - (+8)$ 9

15. $12 - 5$

16. $9 - 4$

17. $8 - 9$ -1

18. $-6 - 3$ -9

19. $9 - (-3)$

20. $17 - (-5)$

21. $-8 - 8$ -16

22. $-4 - (-3)$ -7

23. $0 - 9$

24. $19 - (-9)$

25. $8 - 8$ 0

26. $10 - 10$ 0

27. $-3 - 1$

28. $-5.7 - (-3.1)$

29. $-8 - (-5)$ -13

30. $4 - 9$ -5

31. $6 - (-3)$

32. $6 - 10$

33. $-9 - 11$ -21

34. $37 - 40$ -3

35. $0 - (-9.8)$

36. $-6.3 - 4.7$

37. $-4.8 - (-5.1)$

38. $-4 - (-4)$ -8

39. $44 - 7$

40. $9 - 9$

41. $-8 - (-12)$

42. $-6 - (-2)$ -8

43. $18 - (-4)$

44. $-25 - 16$

45. $-9 - 2$

46. $-85 - (-8)$ -93

47. $-90.7 - 40.3$

48. $-52.6 - 37.9$

49. $-45 - 39$

50. $-500 - (-400)$ -900

51. $70 - (-70)$

52. $130 - (-90)$

53. $42.3 - 49.7$

54. $81.3 - 92.5$

55. $-7.85 - (-3.92)$

56. $-12.43 - (-9.57)$

57. Subtract 15 from 4.

58. Subtract 7 from 1.   1-7=-6

59. Subtract 21 from 21.   0

60. Subtract 13 from 13.   0

61. Subtract -12.4 from -6.3.   -6.3 + -12.4

62. Subtract 17.3 from -9.8.   -9.8 - 17.3

63. Subtract -7.9 from 10.3.   10.3 - (-7.9)

64. Subtract -23 from -23.   -23 + -23

65. Subtract 24 from 13.   13 - 24

66. Subtract -11.7 from -5.2.   -5.2 - 11.7

67. Subtract 7.8 from -10.3.   -10.3 - 7.8

68. Subtract -9.6 from 3.4.   3.4 + (-9.6)

Evaluate.

69. $\dfrac{5}{9} - \dfrac{1}{8}$

70. $\dfrac{4}{5} - \dfrac{5}{6}$

71. $\dfrac{8}{15} - \dfrac{7}{45}$

72. $\dfrac{5}{12} - \dfrac{7}{8}$

73. $-\dfrac{7}{10} - \dfrac{5}{12}$

74. $-\dfrac{1}{4} - \dfrac{2}{3}$

75. $-\dfrac{4}{15} - \dfrac{3}{20}$

76. $-\dfrac{5}{4} - \dfrac{7}{11}$

77. $-\dfrac{7}{12} - \dfrac{5}{40}$

78. $-\dfrac{5}{6} - \dfrac{3}{32}$

79. $\dfrac{5}{8} - \dfrac{6}{48}$

80. $\dfrac{17}{18} - \dfrac{13}{20}$

81. $-\dfrac{4}{9} - \left(-\dfrac{3}{5}\right)$

82. $\dfrac{5}{20} - \left(-\dfrac{1}{8}\right)$

83. $\dfrac{3}{16} - \left(-\dfrac{5}{8}\right)$

84. $-\dfrac{5}{12} - \left(-\dfrac{3}{8}\right)$

85. Subtract $\dfrac{7}{9}$ from $\dfrac{4}{7}$. $\dfrac{4}{7} - \dfrac{7}{9}$

86. Subtract $\dfrac{7}{15}$ from $\dfrac{5}{8}$. $5/8 - \dfrac{7}{15}$

87. Subtract $-\dfrac{3}{10}$ from $-\dfrac{5}{12}$. $\dfrac{-5}{12} + \dfrac{-3}{10}$

88. Subtract $-\dfrac{5}{16}$ from $-\dfrac{9}{10}$. $\dfrac{-9}{10} + \dfrac{-5}{16}$

In Exercises 89–106, **a)** *determine by observation whether the difference will be a positive number, zero, or a negative number;* **b)** *find the difference; and* **c)** *examine your answer to part* **b)** *to see whether it is reasonable and makes sense.*

89. 378 − 279   **90.** 483 − 569   **91.** −482 − 137   **92.** 178 − (−377)

93. 843 − (−745)   **94.** 864 − (−762)   **95.** −408 − (−604)   **96.** −623 − 111

97. −1024 − (−576)   **98.** −104.7 − 27.6   **99.** 165.7 − 49.6   **100.** −40.2 − (−12.6)

101. Subtract 364 from 295.   **102.** Subtract −433 from −932.   **103.** Subtract 647 from −1023.

104. Subtract 2432 from −4120.   **105.** Subtract −7.62 from −7.62.   **106.** Subtract 36.7 from −103.2.

Evaluate.

107. 7 + 5 − (+8)   **108.** 15 − (+9) − (+5)   **109.** −6 + (−6) + 16   **110.** 9 − 4 + (−2)

111. −13 − (+5) + 3   **112.** 7 − (+4) − (−3)   **113.** −9 − (−3) + 4   **114.** 15 + (−7) − (−3)

115. 5 − (−9) + (−1)   **116.** 12 + (−5) − (−4)   **117.** 17 + (−8) − (+14)   **118.** −7 + 6 − 3

119. −36 − 5 + 9   **120.** 45 − 3 − 7   **121.** −12 + 7 − 9   **122.** −2 − 7 − 13

123. 25 − 19 + 3   **124.** −4 − 1 + 5   **125.** −4 − 6 + 5 − 7   **126.** −9 − 3 − (−4) + 5

127. 17 + (−3) − 9 − (−7)   **128.** 32 + 5 − 7 − 12

129. −9 + (−7) + (−5) − (−3)   **130.** 6 − 9 − (−3) + 12

Problem Solving

131. Lands' End The Lands' End catalog department had 300 ladies' blue cardigan sweaters in stock on December 1. By December 9, the department had taken orders for 343 of the sweaters.

a) How many sweaters were on back order?

b) If the catalog department wanted 100 sweaters in addition to those already ordered, how many sweaters would it need to back order?

© Lya Cattel/istockphoto.com

132. Leadville, Co According to the *Guinness Book of World Records,* the city with the greatest elevation in the United States is Leadville, Colorado, at 10,152 feet. The city with the lowest elevation in the United States, at 184 feet below sea level, is Calipatria, California. What is the difference in the elevation of these cities?

133. Measuring Rainfall At Kim Christensen's house, a rain gauge is placed in the yard and is left untouched for 2 days. Suppose that on the first day, $2\frac{1}{4}$ inches of rain falls. On the second day, no rain falls, but $\frac{3}{8}$ inch of the first day's rainfall evaporates. How much water remains in the gauge after the second day?

134. Death Valley A medical supply package is dropped into Death Valley, California, from a helicopter 1605.7 feet above sea level. The package lands at a location in Death Valley 267.4 feet below sea level. What vertical distance did the package travel?

135. Temperature Change The greatest change in temperature ever recorded within a 24-hour period occurred at Browning, Montana, on January 23, 1916. The temperature fell from 44°F to −56°F. How much did the temperature drop?

136. Going Home Two college students are driving on an expressway, going home for spring break. Shawntoya travels 58.5 miles in 1 hour. Marcelino travels 67.3 miles in 1 hour.

a) If Shawntoya and Marcelino start at the same parking lot and travel in opposite directions, how far apart will they be in 1 hour?

b) If Shawntoya and Marcelino start at the same parking lot and travel in the same direction, how far apart will they be in 1 hour?

137. Golf The chart below shows some final scores at the Masters golf tournament, held in Augusta, Georgia, in 2008.

Golfer	Score (above or below par)
T. Immelman	−8
T. Woods	−5
S. Cink	−4
P. Harrington	−2
M. Jimenez	−1
V. Singh	+1
H. Stenson	+2
A. Cabrera	+4
K. Choi	+10

Source: www.masters.org

a) If par for the Masters is 288 strokes, determine T. Immelman's score in 2008.

b) What was the difference in the strokes between K. Choi and S. Cink in 2008?

138. Inseam Christine Henry purchases a new pair of pants whose inseam is $32\frac{1}{2}$ inches. If $2\frac{3}{4}$ inches are cut from the inseam of the pants, what will be the new inseam of the pants?

Concept/Writing Exercises

139. Your friend is having trouble in algebra class distinguishing among these three expressions: $x - y$, $y - x$, and $x - (-y)$. Using 3 for x and 8 for y, explain in writing why all three expressions are different.

140. Simplify $3 - (-9) + (-4)$ by eliminating two signs next to one another and replacing them with a single sign. Explain how you determined your answer and then evaluate your answer.

Challenge Problems

Find each sum.

141. $1 - 2 + 3 - 4 + 5 - 6 + 7 - 8 + 9 - 10$

142. $1 - 2 + 3 - 4 + 5 - 6 + \cdots + 99 - 100$

143. Consider a number line.

a) What is the distance, in units, between -11 and -3?

b) Write a subtraction problem to represent this distance (the distance is to be positive).

144. Stock Amy Tait buys a stock for $50. Will the stock be worth more if it decreases by 10% and then increases by 10%, or if it increases by 10% and then decreases by 10%, or will the value be the same either way?

145. Rolling Ball A ball rolls off a table and follows the path indicated in the figure. Suppose the maximum height

reached by the ball on each bounce is 1 foot less than on the previous bounce.

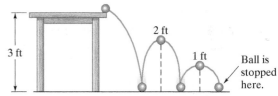

a) Determine the total vertical distance traveled by the ball.

b) If we consider the ball moving in a downward direction as negative, and the ball moving in an upward direction as positive, what was the net vertical distance traveled (from its starting point) by the ball?

Cumulative Review Exercises

[1.4] **146.** List the set of counting numbers.

147. Explain the relationship between the set of rational numbers, the set of irrational numbers, and the set of real numbers.

[1.5] *Insert either* $>$, $<$, *or* $=$ *in each shaded area to make the statement true.*

148. $|-3| \; > \; -5$

149. $-|-9| \; < \; -|-5|$

[1.7] **150.** Subtract $\frac{7}{8}$ from $\frac{5}{6}$.

$$\frac{5}{6} - \frac{7}{8}$$

1.8 Multiplication and Division of Real Numbers

1. Multiply numbers.

2. Divide numbers.

3. Remove negative signs from denominators.

4. Evaluate divisions involving 0.

1 Multiply Numbers

The following rules are used in determining the sign of the product when two numbers are multiplied.

The Sign of the Product of Two Real Numbers

1. The product of two numbers with **like** signs is a **positive** number.

2. The product of two numbers with **unlike** signs is a **negative** number.

The product of two positive numbers or two negative numbers will be a positive number. The product of a positive number and a negative number will be a negative number.

EXAMPLE 1 Evaluate.

a) $4(-5)$ **b)** $(-6)(7)$ **c)** $(-9)(-3)$

Solution

a) Since the numbers have unlike signs, the product is negative.

$$4(-5) = -20$$

b) Since the numbers have unlike signs, the product is negative.

$$(-6)(7) = -42$$

c) Since the numbers have like signs, both negative, the product is positive.

$$(-9)(-3) = 27$$

Now Try Exercise 17

EXAMPLE 2 Evaluate.

a) $(-8)(5)$ **b)** $(-4)(-8)$ **c)** $0(6)$
d) $0(-2)$ **e)** $4.2(-9.7)$ **f)** $(-3.62)(-6.18)$

Solution

a) $(-8)(5) = -40$ **b)** $(-4)(-8) = 32$ **c)** $0(6) = 0$
d) $0(-2) = 0$ **e)** $4.2(-9.7) = -40.74$ **f)** $(-3.62)(-6.18) = 22.3716$

Note that zero multiplied by any real number equals zero.

Now Try Exercise 29

> **Helpful Hint**
>
> At this point some students begin confusing problems like $-2 - 3$ with $(-2)(-3)$ and problems like $2 - 3$ with $2(-3)$. If you do not understand the difference between problems like $-2 - 3$ and $(-2)(-3)$, make an appointment to see your instructor as soon as possible.
>
> | Subtraction Problems | Multiplication Problems |
> |---|---|
> | $-2 - 3 = -5$ | $(-2)(-3) = 6$ |
> | $2 - 3 = -1$ | $(2)(-3) = -6$ |

EXAMPLE 3 Evaluate.

a) $\left(\dfrac{-1}{8}\right)\left(\dfrac{-3}{5}\right)$ **b)** $\left(\dfrac{3}{20}\right)\left(\dfrac{-3}{10}\right)$

Solution

a) $\left(\dfrac{-1}{8}\right)\left(\dfrac{-3}{5}\right) = \dfrac{(-1)(-3)}{8(5)} = \dfrac{3}{40}$ **b)** $\left(\dfrac{3}{20}\right)\left(\dfrac{-3}{10}\right) = \dfrac{3(-3)}{20(10)} = -\dfrac{9}{200}$

Now Try Exercise 41

Sometimes you may be asked to perform more than one multiplication in a given problem. When this happens, the sign of the final product can be determined by counting the number of *negative* numbers being multiplied. *The product of an even number of negative numbers will always be positive. The product of an odd number of negative numbers will always be negative.*

EXAMPLE 4 Evaluate. ─────────────

a) $(-5)(-3)(1)(-4)$ **b)** $(-2)(-4)(-1)(3)(-4)$

Solution

a) Since there are an odd number of negative numbers, the product will be negative, as illustrated.

$$(-5)(-3)(1)(-4) = (15)(1)(-4)$$
$$= (15)(-4)$$
$$= -60$$

b) Since there are an even number of negative numbers, the product will be positive, as illustrated.

$$(-2)(-4)(-1)(3)(-4) = (8)(-1)(3)(-4)$$
$$= (-8)(3)(-4)$$
$$= (-24)(-4)$$
$$= 96$$

Now Try Exercise 35

2 Divide Numbers

The rules for dividing numbers are very similar to those used in multiplying numbers.

> **The Sign of the Quotient of Two Real Numbers**
>
> 1. The quotient of two numbers with **like** signs is a **positive** number.
> 2. The quotient of two numbers with **unlike** signs is a **negative** number.

Therefore, the quotient of two positive numbers or two negative numbers will be a positive number. The quotient of a positive number and a negative number will be a negative number.

EXAMPLE 5 Evaluate. ─────────────

a) $\dfrac{10}{-5}$ **b)** $\dfrac{-45}{5}$ **c)** $\dfrac{-36}{-6}$

Solution

a) Since the numbers have unlike signs, the quotient is negative.

$$\frac{10}{-5} = -2$$

b) Since the numbers have unlike signs, the quotient is negative.

$$\frac{-45}{5} = -9$$

c) Since the numbers have like signs, both negative, the quotient is positive.

$$\frac{-36}{-6} = 6$$

Now Try Exercise 55

Understanding Algebra

In the division problem

$$(24) \div (4) = 6$$

24 is called the *dividend,* 4 is called the *divisor,* and 6 is called the *quotient.*

Understanding Algebra

A fraction is really a division problem:

$$(24) \div (4) = 6$$

is the same as

$$\frac{24}{4} = 6$$

EXAMPLE 6 Evaluate.

a) $-16 \div (-2)$ **b)** $\dfrac{-2}{3} \div \dfrac{-5}{7}$

Solution

a) Since the numbers have like signs, both negative, the quotient is positive.

$$-16 \div (-2) = \frac{-16}{-2} = 8$$

b) Invert the *divisor*, $\dfrac{-5}{7}$, and then multiply.

$$\frac{-2}{3} \div \frac{-5}{7} = \left(\frac{-2}{3}\right)\left(\frac{7}{-5}\right) = \frac{-14}{-15} = \frac{14}{15}$$

Now Try Exercise 77

EXAMPLE 7 Evaluate, rounding your answer to the nearest hundredth when appropriate.

a) $-18.86 \div 4.1$ **b)** $\dfrac{-27.2}{-2.6}$

Solution

a) Since the numbers have unlike signs, the quotient is negative.

$$\frac{-18.86}{4.1} = -4.6$$

b) Since the numbers have like signs, both negative, the quotient is positive.

$$\frac{-27.2}{-2.6} \approx 10.46$$

The answer in part **b)** was rounded to two decimal places, or hundredths. If you have forgotten how to round decimal numbers, review Appendix A now.

Now Try Exercise 69

> **Helpful Hint**
>
> For multiplication and division of two real numbers:
>
> $$(+)(+) = +$$ $$\frac{(+)}{(+)} = +$$
> $$(-)(-) = +$$ $$\frac{(-)}{(-)} = +$$
>
> Like signs give positive products and quotients.
>
> $$(+)(-) = -$$ $$\frac{(+)}{(-)} = -$$
> $$(-)(+) = -$$ $$\frac{(-)}{(+)} = -$$
>
> Unlike signs give negative products and quotients.

3 Remove Negative Signs from Denominators

We now know that the quotient of a positive number and a negative number is a negative number. The fractions $-\dfrac{3}{4}, \dfrac{-3}{4}$, and $\dfrac{3}{-4}$ all represent the same negative number, negative three-fourths.

The Quotient of a Positive Number and a Negative Number

If a and b represent any real numbers, $b \neq 0$, then

$$\frac{a}{-b} = \frac{-a}{b} = -\frac{a}{b}$$

In mathematics we generally do not write a fraction with a negative sign in the denominator. When a negative sign appears in a denominator, we can move it to the numerator or place it in front of the fraction. For example, the fraction $\frac{5}{-7}$ should be written as either $\frac{-5}{7}$ or $-\frac{5}{7}$.

EXAMPLE 8   Evaluate $\frac{3}{7} \div \left(\frac{-12}{35} \right)$.

Solution

$$\frac{3}{7} \div \left(\frac{-12}{35} \right) = \frac{\overset{1}{\cancel{3}}}{\underset{1}{\cancel{7}}} \cdot \left(\frac{\overset{5}{\cancel{35}}}{\underset{4}{\cancel{-12}}} \right) = \frac{1(5)}{1(-4)} = \frac{5}{-4} = -\frac{5}{4}$$

Now Try Exercise 73

The operations on real numbers are summarized in **Table 1.1**.

TABLE 1.1   Summary of Operations on Real Numbers

Signs of Numbers	Addition	Subtraction	Multiplication	Division
Both Numbers Are Positive	Sum Is Always Positive	Difference May Be Either Positive or Negative	Product Is Always Positive	Quotient Is Always Positive
Examples				
6 and 2	$6 + 2 = 8$	$6 - 2 = 4$	$6 \cdot 2 = 12$	$6 \div 2 = 3$
2 and 6	$2 + 6 = 8$	$2 - 6 = -4$	$2 \cdot 6 = 12$	$2 \div 6 = \frac{1}{3}$
One Number Is Positive and the Other Number Is Negative	Sum May Be Either Positive or Negative	Difference May Be Either Positive or Negative	Product Is Always Negative	Quotient Is Always Negative
Examples				
6 and −2	$6 + (-2) = 4$	$6 - (-2) = 8$	$6(-2) = -12$	$6 \div (-2) = -3$
−6 and 2	$-6 + 2 = -4$	$-6 - 2 = -8$	$-6(2) = -12$	$-6 \div 2 = -3$
Both Numbers Are Negative	Sum Is Always Negative	Difference May Be Either Positive or Negative	Product Is Always Positive	Quotient Is Always Positive
Examples				
−6 and −2	$-6 + (-2) = -8$	$-6 - (-2) = -4$	$-6(-2) = 12$	$-6 \div (-2) = 3$
−2 and −6	$-2 + (-6) = -8$	$-2 - (-6) = 4$	$-2(-6) = 12$	$-2 \div (-6) = \frac{1}{3}$

4 Evaluate Divisions Involving 0

What is $\frac{0}{1}$ equal to? Note that $\frac{6}{3} = 2$ because $3 \cdot 2 = 6$. We can follow the same procedure to determine the value of $\frac{0}{1}$. Suppose that $\frac{0}{1}$ is equal to some number, which we will designate by ? .

$$\text{If} \quad \frac{0}{1} = \boxed{?} \quad \text{then} \quad 1 \cdot \boxed{?} = 0$$

Since only $1 \cdot 0 = 0$, the ? must be 0. Thus, $\frac{0}{1} = 0$. Using the same technique, we can show that zero divided by any nonzero number is zero.

> **Zero Divided by a Nonzero Number**
>
> If a represents any real number except 0, then
> $$0 \div a = \frac{0}{a} = 0$$

Now what is $\frac{1}{0}$ equal to?

$$\text{If} \quad \frac{1}{0} = \boxed{?} \quad \text{then} \quad 0 \cdot \boxed{?} = 1$$

But since 0 multiplied by any number will be 0, there is no value that can replace ? . We say that $\frac{1}{0}$ is **undefined**. Using the same technique, we can show that any real number, except 0, divided by 0 is undefined.

> **Division by Zero**
>
> If a represents any real number except 0, then
> $$a \div 0 \quad \text{or} \quad \frac{a}{0} \quad \text{is } \textbf{undefined}$$

What is $\frac{0}{0}$ equal to?

$$\text{If} \quad \frac{0}{0} = \boxed{?} \quad \text{then} \quad 0 \cdot \boxed{?} = 0$$

Since the product of any number and 0 is 0, the ? can be replaced by any real number. Therefore, the quotient $\frac{0}{0}$ cannot be determined, and so there is no answer. Thus, we will not use it in this course.[*]

> **Summary of Division Involving 0**
>
> If a represents any real number except 0, then
> $$\frac{0}{a} = 0 \quad \text{and} \quad \frac{a}{0} \text{ is undefined}$$

EXAMPLE 9 Indicate whether each quotient is 0 or undefined.

a) $\frac{0}{2}$ **b)** $\frac{5}{0}$ **c)** $\frac{0}{-4}$ **d)** $\frac{-2}{0}$

Solution   The answer to parts **a)** and **c)** is 0. The answer to parts **b)** and **d)** is undefined.

Now Try Exercise 95

---

[*]At this level, some professors prefer to call $\frac{0}{0}$ *indeterminate* while others prefer to call $\frac{0}{0}$ *undefined*. In higher-level mathematics courses, $\frac{0}{0}$ is sometimes referred to as an *indeterminate form*.

EXERCISE SET 1.8   MathXL®   MyMathLab

Warm-Up Exercises

Fill in the blanks with the appropriate word, phrase, or symbol(s) from the following list.

positive	negative	infinity	product	indeterminate form
zero	63	undefined	$-\dfrac{a}{b}$	$\dfrac{a}{b}$

−63

1. The product of a positive real number with a negative real number is ___neg___ .

2. 16 divided by 0 is ___0___ .

3. 0 divided by 8 is ___ .

4. The fraction $\dfrac{a}{-b}$ may be rewritten as ___$-9/b$___ .

5. The fraction $-\dfrac{a}{-b}$ may be rewritten as $-\dfrac{9}{b}$.

6. If x is 9 and y is −7 then the value of xy is ___2___ .

7. The product of two negative numbers is a ___pos___ number.

8. 0 divided by 0 is an ___ .

9. If x is 9 and y is −7 then the value of $x(-y)$ is ___neg___ .

10. When two real numbers are multiplied, the result is called the ___product___ of the two numbers.

Determine the sign of each product.

11. $(8)(4)(-5)$ −

12. $(-9)(-12)(20)$ +

13. $(-102)(-16)(24)(19)$ +

14. $(1054)(-92)(-16)(-37)$ −

15. $(-40)(-16)(30)(50)(-13)$ −

16. $(-1)(3)(-462)(-196)(-312)$ +

Practice the Skills

Find each product.

17. $(-5)(-4)$ 20

18. $-4(2)$

19. $5(-3)$

20. $6(-2)$

21. $(-8)(-20)$ 160

22. $(-3)(2)$

23. $-2.1(6)$

24. $-1(8.7)$

25. $6(7)$ 42

26. $-9(-4)$

27. $9(-9)$

28. $(7)(-8)$

29. $(-5)(-6)$ 30

30. $0(-5)$

31. $(-9)(0)(-6)$

32. $5(-4)(2)$

33. $(21)(-1)(4)$ −44

34. $2(8)(-1)(-3)$

35. $-1(-3)(3)(-8)$

36. $(2)(-4)(-5)(-1)$

37. $(-4)(5)(-7)(10)$ 1400

38. $(-3)(2)(5)(3)$

39. $(-1)(3)(0)(-7)$

40. $(-6)(6)(4)(-4)$

Find each product.

41. $\left(\dfrac{-1}{2}\right)\left(\dfrac{3}{5}\right)$ $-\dfrac{3}{10}$

42. $\left(\dfrac{1}{3}\right)\left(\dfrac{-3}{5}\right)$ $-\dfrac{3}{15}$

43. $\left(\dfrac{-5}{9}\right)\left(\dfrac{-7}{15}\right)$ $\dfrac{36}{135}$

44. $\left(\dfrac{4}{5}\right)\left(\dfrac{-3}{10}\right)$ $\dfrac{-12}{50}$ $\dfrac{-6}{25}$

45. $\left(\dfrac{6}{-3}\right)\left(\dfrac{4}{-2}\right)$ $\dfrac{24}{6}$ 4

46. $\left(\dfrac{9}{-10}\right)\left(\dfrac{6}{-7}\right)$ $\dfrac{56}{70}$

47. $\left(\dfrac{3}{4}\right)\left(\dfrac{-2}{15}\right)$ $\dfrac{-6}{60}$ $\dfrac{-1}{10}$

48. $\left(\dfrac{-9}{10}\right)\left(\dfrac{7}{-8}\right)$ $\dfrac{63}{80}$

Find each quotient.

49. $\dfrac{-42}{6}$ −7

50. $25 \div 5$ 5

51. $-16 \div (-4)$ $\dfrac{16-1}{4}$ $\dfrac{16}{4}=4$

52. $\dfrac{-18}{9}$ −2

53. $\dfrac{-36}{-9}$ 4

54. $\dfrac{30}{-6}$ −5

55. $\dfrac{36}{-2}$ −18

56. $\dfrac{-15}{-1}$ 15

57. $\dfrac{-19.8}{-2}$ 9.9

58. $-15.6/(-3)$ 5.2

59. $40/(-4)$ −10

60. $\dfrac{63}{-7}$ −9

61. $\dfrac{-66}{2}$ −33

62. $\dfrac{-25}{-5}$ 5

63. $\dfrac{48}{-12}$ −4

64. $\dfrac{-10}{10}$ −1 $-13\overline{)26}$ −2

65. $-64.8 \div (-4)$

66. $-86.4/(-2)$ 43.2

67. Divide 0 by 4. 0

68. Divide 26 by −13. −3

69. Divide 30.8 by −5.6.

70. Divide −67.64 by 7.6. 9.41 $7.6\overline{)67.64}$ $\dfrac{684}{5}$ $\dfrac{314}{304}$

71. Divide −30 by −5. 6

72. Divide −36 by −6. 6

Find each quotient.

73. $\dfrac{3}{12} \div \left(\dfrac{-5}{8}\right)$ $-\dfrac{8}{5} = \dfrac{-24}{60}$ $-\dfrac{2}{5}$

74. $\dfrac{1}{4} \times \left(\dfrac{-6}{13}\right)$ $-\dfrac{6}{52}$

75. $\dfrac{-5}{12} \times (-3)$ $\dfrac{15}{12}$

76. $\dfrac{6}{15} \div \left(\dfrac{7}{30}\right)$ $\dfrac{30}{7}$ $\dfrac{180}{105}$

77. $\dfrac{-15}{21} \div \left(\dfrac{-15}{21}\right)$ $\dfrac{21}{15} = \dfrac{315}{315} = 1$

78. $\dfrac{-4}{9} \div \left(\dfrac{-6}{7}\right)$ $-\dfrac{7}{6} = \dfrac{28}{56}$

79. $(-12) \div \dfrac{5}{12}$ $\dfrac{12-144}{5}$

80. $\dfrac{-16}{3} \div \left(\dfrac{5}{-9}\right)$ $-\dfrac{9}{5}$ $\dfrac{144}{15}$

Evaluate.

81. −4(8)

82. $\dfrac{-18}{-2}$

83. $\dfrac{-100}{-5}$

84. −50 ÷ (−10)

85. −7(2)

86. 6.4(−8)

87. 27.9 ÷ (−3)

88. Divide 130 by −10.

89. −100 ÷ 5

90. 4(−2)(−1)(−5)

91. Divide −90 by −90.

92. (6)(1)(−3)(4)

Indicate whether each quotient is 0 or undefined.

93. 0 ÷ 8.6

94. $\dfrac{-2.7}{0}$

95. $\dfrac{5}{0}$

96. $\dfrac{0}{1}$

97. 0 ÷ (−7)

98. $\dfrac{6}{0}$

99. 8 divided by 0

100. 0 divided by 12

In Exercises 101–116, **a)** *determine by observation whether the product or quotient will be a positive number, zero, a negative number, or undefined;* **b)** *find the product or quotient if it exists;* **c)** *examine your answer in part* **b)** *to see whether it is reasonable and makes sense.*

101. 92(−38)

102. −168 ÷ 42

103. −240/15

104. 0/12

105. 243 ÷ (−27)

106. (323)(−115)

107. (−49)(−126)

108. (1530)(0)

109. 0 ÷ 5335

110. −86.4 ÷ (−36)

111. 8.2 ÷ 0

112. −37.74 ÷ 0

113. 8 ÷ (2.5)

114. (1.1)(9.72)(6.3)

115. (−3.0)(4.2)(−18)

116. −288.86/1.43

Indicate whether each statement is true or false.

117. The product of two negative numbers is a negative number.

118. The product of a positive number and a negative number is a negative number.

119. The quotient of two numbers with unlike signs is a positive number.

120. The quotient of two negative numbers is a positive number.

121. The product of an even number of negative numbers is a positive number.

122. Zero divided by 1 is 1.

123. The product of an odd number of negative numbers is a negative number.

124. Six divided by 0 is 0.

125. Zero divided by 1 is undefined.

126. The product of 0 and any real number is 0.

127. Five divided by 0 is undefined.

128. Division by 0 does not result in a real number.

Problem Solving

129. Football A high school football team is penalized three times, each time with a loss of 15 yards, or −15 yards. Find the total loss due to penalties.

130. Submarine Dive A submarine is at a depth of −160 feet (160 feet below sea level). It dives to 3 times that depth. Find its new depth.

131. Credit Card Leona De Vito's balance on her credit card is −$520 (she owes $520). She pays back $\dfrac{1}{5}$ of this balance.

  a) How much did she pay back?

  b) What is her new balance?

132. Money Owed Brian Philip owes his Dad $500. After he makes four payments of $40 each, how much will he still owe?

133. Garage Sale Four sisters made a total of $775.40 at a garage sale. After they each give their husbands $50 and split the remaining amount equally, how much will each woman receive?

134. Wind Chill On Monday in Minneapolis the wind chill temperature was −30°F. On Tuesday the wind chill temperature was only $\dfrac{1}{3}$ of what it was on Monday. What was the wind chill temperature on Tuesday?

135. Test Score Because of incorrect work, Josue Nunez lost 4 points on each of the five questions on his math test.

  a) How many points did Josue lose altogether?

  b) If the maximum score possible was 100%, what is Josue's test score?

136. Lab Work Jack's job is to monitor the temperature of a superheated piece of metal for ten hours in the lab. He observed that the metal cooled 15° each hour for ten hours.

  a) What number represents the total drop in temperature?

  b) If the temperature of the metal was originally 678°, what was it at the end of the ten hours?

137. Heart Rate The Johns Hopkins Medical Letter states that to find a person's *target heart rate* in beats per minute, follow this procedure. Subtract the person's age from 220, then multiply this difference by 60% and 75%. The difference multiplied by 60% gives the lower limit and the difference multiplied by 75% gives the upper limit.

  a) Find the target heart rate range of a 50-year-old.

  b) Find your own target heart rate.

Challenge Problems

We will learn in the next section that $2^3 = 2 \cdot 2 \cdot 2$ *and* $x^n = \underbrace{x \cdot x \cdot x \cdots \cdot x}_{n \text{ factors of } x}$.

Use this information to evaluate each expression. (n factors of x)

138. 3^4 **139.** $(-5)^3$ **140.** $\left(\dfrac{2}{3}\right)^3$ **141.** 1^{100} **142.** $(-1)^{81}$

143. Will the product of $(-1)(-2)(-3)(-4)\cdots(-10)$ be a positive number or a negative number? Explain how you determined your answer.

144. Will the product of $(1)(-2)(3)(-4)(5)(-6)\cdots(33)(-34)$ be a positive number or a negative number? Explain how you determined your answer.

Group Activity

Discuss and answer Exercise 145 as a group, according to the instructions.

145. a) Each member of the group is to do this procedure separately. At this time do not share your number with the other members of your group.

  1. Choose a number between 2 and 10. *6*
  2. Multiply your number by 9. *54*
  3. Add the two digits in the product together. *9*
  4. Subtract 5 from the sum. *4*
  5. Now choose the corresponding letter of the alphabet that corresponds with the difference found. For example, 1 is a, 2 is b, 3 is c, and so on. *D*

  6. Choose a *one-word* country that starts with that letter. *Denmark*
  7. Now choose a *one-word* animal that starts with the last letter of the country selected. *Kangaroo*
  8. Finally, choose a color that starts with the last letter of the animal chosen. *Orange*

  b) Now share your final answer with the other members of your group. Did you all get the same answer?

  c) Most people will obtain the answer *orange*. As a group, write a paragraph or two explaining why.

Cumulative Review Exercises

[1.5] **146.** Insert either $<, >,$ or $=$ in the shaded area to make a true statement.

$$|-3.6| \;<\; |-2.7|$$

[1.6] **147.** Add $-\dfrac{7}{12} + \left(-\dfrac{1}{10}\right)$.

[1.7] **148.** Subtract -18 from -20.   *$-20-(-18)$ 2*

149. Evaluate $6 - 3 - 4 - 2$. *1*

150. Evaluate $5 - (-2) + 3 - 7$. *-1*

1.9 Exponents, Parentheses, and the Order of Operations

1 Learn the meaning of exponents.

2 Evaluate expressions containing exponents.

3 Learn the difference between $-x^2$ and $(-x)^2$.

4 Learn the order of operations.

5 Learn the use of parentheses.

6 Evaluate expressions containing variables.

Understanding Algebra

Exponents are simply a shorthand notation for repeated multiplication. For example, 3^4 means $3 \cdot 3 \cdot 3 \cdot 3 = 81$.

1 Learn the Meaning of Exponents

In the expression 4^2, the 4 is called the **base**, and the 2 is called the **exponent**. The number 4^2 is read "4 squared" or "4 to the second power" and means

$$\underbrace{4 \cdot 4}_{2 \text{ factors of } 4} = 4^2 \leftarrow \text{exponent}$$

(base)

The number 4^3 is read "4 cubed" or "4 to the third power" and means

$$\underbrace{4 \cdot 4 \cdot 4}_{3 \text{ factors of } 4} = 4^3$$

In general, the number b to the nth power, written b^n, means

$$\underbrace{b \cdot b \cdot b \cdots \cdot b}_{n \text{ factors of } b} = b^n$$

Thus, $b^4 = b \cdot b \cdot b \cdot b$ or $bbbb$ and $x^3 = x \cdot x \cdot x$ or xxx.

2 Evaluate Expressions Containing Exponents

Let's evaluate some expressions that contain exponents.

EXAMPLE 1   Evaluate.   **a)** 3^2 **b)** 2^5 **c)** 1^5 **d)** $(-6)^2$ **e)** $(-2)^3$ **f)** $\left(\dfrac{2}{3}\right)^2$

Solution

a) $3^2 = 3 \cdot 3 = 9$

b) $2^5 = 2 \cdot 2 \cdot 2 \cdot 2 \cdot 2 = 32$

c) $1^5 = 1 \cdot 1 \cdot 1 \cdot 1 \cdot 1 = 1$ (1 raised to any power equals 1; why?)

d) $(-6)^2 = (-6)(-6) = 36$

e) $(-2)^3 = (-2)(-2)(-2) = -8$

f) $\left(\dfrac{2}{3}\right)^2 = \left(\dfrac{2}{3}\right)\left(\dfrac{2}{3}\right) = \dfrac{4}{9}$

Now Try Exercise 19

> ### Understanding Algebra
>
> If no exponent is written, it is assumed to be 1.
>
> $6^1 = 6$ and $x^1 = x$

It is not necessary to write exponents of 1. For example, when writing xxy, we write x^2y and not x^2y^1. *Whenever we see a variable or number without an exponent, we always assume that the variable or number has an exponent of 1.*

Examples of Exponential Notation

a) $xyxx = x^3y$ **b)** $xyzzy = xy^2z^2$

c) $3aabbb = 3a^2b^3$ **d)** $5xyyyy = 5xy^4$

e) $4 \cdot 4rrs = 4^2r^2s$ **f)** $5 \cdot 5 \cdot 5mmn = 5^3m^2n$

Notice in parts **a)** and **b)** that the order of the factors does not matter.

> **Helpful Hint**
>
> Note that $x + x + x + x + x + x = 6x$ and $x \cdot x \cdot x \cdot x \cdot x \cdot x = x^6$. Be careful that you do not get addition and multiplication confused.

> ### Understanding Algebra
>
> An exponent refers only to the number or variable that directly precedes it unless parentheses are used to indicate otherwise.
>
> No parentheses: Parentheses:
>
> -4^2 $(-5)^2$
>
> $-(4)(4) = -16$ $(-5)(-5) = 25$

3 Learn the Difference Between $-x^2$ and $(-x)^2$

An exponent refers only to the number or variable that directly precedes it unless parentheses are used to indicate otherwise. For example, in the expression $3x^2$, only the x is squared. In the expression $-x^2$, only the x is squared. We can write $-x^2$ as $-1x^2$ because any real number may be multiplied by 1 without affecting its value.

$$-x^2 = -1x^2$$

By looking at $-1x^2$ we can see that only the x is squared, not the -1. If the entire expression $-x$ were to be squared, we would need to use parentheses and write $(-x)^2$. Note the difference in the following two examples:

$$-x^2 = -(x)(x)$$
$$(-x)^2 = (-x)(-x)$$

Consider the expressions -3^2 and $(-3)^2$. How do they differ?

$$-3^2 = -(3)(3) = -9$$
$$(-3)^2 = (-3)(-3) = 9$$

> **Helpful Hint**
>
> The expression $-x^2$ is read "negative x squared," or "the opposite of x squared." The expression $(-x)^2$ is read "negative x, quantity squared."

EXAMPLE 2 Evaluate.   **a)** -5^2 **b)** $(-5)^2$ **c)** -2^3 **d)** $(-2)^3$

Solution

a) $-5^2 = -(5)(5) = -25$ **b)** $(-5)^2 = (-5)(-5) = 25$

c) $-2^3 = -(2)(2)(2) = -8$ **d)** $(-2)^3 = (-2)(-2)(-2) = -8$

Now Try Exercise 11

EXAMPLE 3 Evaluate.   **a)** -2^4 **b)** $(-2)^4$

Solution

a) $-2^4 = -(2)(2)(2)(2) = -16$ **b)** $(-2)^4 = (-2)(-2)(-2)(-2) = 16$

Now Try Exercise 23

4   Learn the Order of Operations

Now that we have introduced exponents we can present the **order of operations**. Can you evaluate $2 + 3 \cdot 4$? Is it 20? Or is it 14? To answer this, you must know the order of operations to follow when evaluating a mathematical expression.

> **Understanding Algebra**
>
> *Grouping symbols* can include combinations of parentheses, brackets, braces, and even fraction bars. For example,
>
> $$\frac{-4(5 + 2) - 8}{19 + 3(-5)}$$
>
> evaluates to $\dfrac{-4(7) - 8}{19 - 15}$ or $\dfrac{-36}{4}$
>
> or simply -9.

> **Order of Operations: To Evaluate Mathematical Expressions, Use the Following Order**
>
> 1. First, evaluate the information within **parentheses** ( ), brackets [ ], or braces { }. These are **grouping symbols**, for they group information together. A fraction bar, $-$, also serves as a grouping symbol. If the expression contains nested grouping symbols (one pair of grouping symbols within another pair), evaluate the information in the innermost grouping symbols first.
> 2. Next, evaluate all **exponents.**
> 3. Next, evaluate all **multiplications** or **divisions** in the order in which they occur, working from left to right.
> 4. Finally, evaluate all **additions** or **subtractions** in the order in which they occur, working from left to right.

Some students remember the word PEMDAS or the phrase "Please Excuse My Dear Aunt Sally" to help them remember the order of operations. PEMDAS helps them remember the order: **P**arentheses, **E**xponents, **M**ultiplication, **D**ivision, **A**ddition, **S**ubtraction. Remember, this does not imply multiplication before division or addition before subtraction.

We can now evaluate $2 + 3 \cdot 4$. Since multiplications are performed before additions,

$$2 + 3 \cdot 4 \quad \text{means} \quad 2 + (3 \cdot 4) = 2 + 12 = 14$$

5   Learn the Use of Parentheses

Grouping symbols may be used (1) to change the order of operations to be followed in evaluating an algebraic expression or (2) to help clarify the understanding of an expression.

To evaluate the expression $2 + 3 \cdot 4$, we would normally perform the multiplication, $3 \cdot 4$, first. If we wished to have the addition performed before the multiplication, we could indicate this by placing parentheses around $2 + 3$:

$$(2 + 3) \cdot 4 = 5 \cdot 4 = 20$$

Sometimes it may be necessary to use more than one set of grouping symbols to indicate the order to be followed when evaluating an expression. When one set of grouping symbols is within another set of grouping symbols, we call these **nested grouping symbols**. Whenever we are given an expression with nested grouping symbols, we always evaluate the numbers in the *innermost grouping symbols first*. Color shading is used in the following examples to indicate the order in which the expression is evaluated.

$$6[2 + 3(\; 4 + 1 \;)] = 6[2 + \; 3(5) \;] = 6[\; 2 + 15 \;] = 6[17] = 102$$

$$4[3(\; 6 - 4 \;) \div 6] = 4[\; 3(2) \; \div 6] = 4[\; 6 \div 6 \;] = \; 4[1] \; = 4$$

$$\{2 + [(\; 8 \div 4 \;)^2 - 1]\}^2 = \{2 + [\; 2^2 \; - 1]\}^2 = \{2 + [\; 4 - 1 \;]\}^2 = \{ \; 2 + 3 \; \}^2 = \; 5^2 \; = 25$$

> **Helpful Hint**
>
> If parentheses are not used to change the order of operations, multiplications and divisions are always performed before additions and subtractions. When a problem has only multiplications and divisions, work from left to right. Similarly, when a problem has only additions and subtractions, work from left to right.

EXAMPLE 4 Evaluate $6 + 3 \cdot 5^2 - 4$.

Solution   Colored shading is used to indicate the order in which the expression is to be evaluated.

$$6 + 3 \cdot \; 5^2 \; - 4 \qquad \text{Exponent}$$
$$= 6 + \; 3 \cdot 25 \; - 4 \qquad \text{Multiply.}$$
$$= \; 6 + 75 \; - 4 \qquad \text{Add.}$$
$$= 81 - 4$$
$$= 77$$

Now Try Exercise 51

EXAMPLE 5 Evaluate $-7 + 2[-6 + (36 \div 3^2)]$.

Solution

$$-7 + 2[-6 + (36 \div \; 3^2 \;)] \qquad \text{Exponent}$$
$$= -7 + 2[-6 + (\; 36 \div 9 \;)] \qquad \text{Divide.}$$
$$= -7 + 2[\; -6 + 4 \;] \qquad \text{Add.}$$
$$= -7 + \; 2[-2] \qquad \text{Multiply.}$$
$$= -7 - 4$$
$$= -11$$

Now Try Exercise 65

EXAMPLE 6 Evaluate $(8 \div 2) + 7(5 - 2)^2$.

Solution

$$\; (8 \div 2) \; + 7(\; 5 - 2 \;)^2 \qquad \text{Parentheses}$$
$$= 4 + 7 \; (3)^2 \qquad \text{Exponent}$$
$$= 4 + \; 7 \cdot 9 \qquad \text{Multiply.}$$
$$= 4 + 63$$
$$= 67$$

Now Try Exercise 71

EXAMPLE 7   Evaluate $-8 - 81 \div 9 \cdot 2^2 + 7$.

Solution

$$-8 - 81 \div 9 \cdot \boxed{2^2} + 7 \qquad \text{Exponent}$$
$$= -8 - \boxed{81 \div 9} \cdot 4 + 7 \qquad \text{Divide.}$$
$$= -8 - \boxed{9 \cdot 4} + 7 \qquad \text{Multiply.}$$
$$= \boxed{-8 - 36} + 7 \qquad \text{Subtract.}$$
$$= -44 + 7$$
$$= -37$$

Now Try Exercise 69

EXAMPLE 8   Evaluate.   **a)** $-4^2 + 6 \div 3$ **b)** $(-4)^2 + 6 \div 3$

Solution

a) $-\boxed{4^2} + 6 \div 3 \qquad \text{Exponent}$
$$= -16 + \boxed{6 \div 3} \qquad \text{Divide.}$$
$$= -16 + 2$$
$$= -14$$

b) $\boxed{(-4)^2} + 6 \div 3 \qquad \text{Exponent}$
$$= 16 + \boxed{6 \div 3} \qquad \text{Divide.}$$
$$= 16 + 2$$
$$= 18$$

Now Try Exercise 75

EXAMPLE 9   Evaluate $\dfrac{3}{8} - \dfrac{2}{5} \cdot \dfrac{1}{12}$.

Solution   First perform the multiplication.

$$\frac{3}{8} - \left(\overset{1}{\frac{2}{5}} \cdot \frac{1}{\underset{6}{12}} \right) \qquad \text{Multiply.}$$

$$= \frac{3}{8} - \frac{1}{30} \qquad \text{Subtract.}$$

$$= \frac{45}{120} - \frac{4}{120}$$

$$= \frac{41}{120}$$

Now Try Exercise 81

EXAMPLE 10   Write the following statements as mathematical expressions using parentheses and brackets and then evaluate: Multiply 12 by 3. Add 8 to this product. Subtract 7 from this sum. Divide this difference by 6.

Solution

$$12 \cdot 3 \qquad \qquad \text{Multiply 12 by 3.}$$
$$(12 \cdot 3) + 8 \qquad \qquad \text{Add 8.}$$
$$[(12 \cdot 3) + 8] - 7 \qquad \qquad \text{Subtract 7.}$$
$$\{[(12 \cdot 3) + 8] - 7\} \div 6 \qquad \qquad \text{Divide the difference by 6.}$$

Now evaluate.

$$\{[(\ 12 \cdot 3\ ) + 8] - 7\} \div 6$$
$$= \{[36 + 8] - 7\} \div 6$$
$$= \{44 - 7\} \div 6$$
$$= 37 \div 6$$
$$= \frac{37}{6}$$

Now Try Exercise 125

As shown in Example 10, sometimes brackets, [ ], and braces, { }, are used in place of parentheses to help avoid confusion. If only parentheses had been used, the preceding expression would appear as $(((12 \cdot 3) + 8) - 7) \div 6$.

6 Evaluate Expressions Containing Variables

Now we will evaluate some expressions for given values of the variables.

EXAMPLE 11 Evaluate $5x - 4$ when $x = 3$.

Solution   Substitute 3 for x in the expression.

$$5x - 4 = 5(3) - 4 = 15 - 4 = 11$$

Now Try Exercise 105

EXAMPLE 12 Evaluate   **a)** x^2 **b)** $-x^2$ and   **c)** $(-x)^2$ when $x = 3$.

Solution   Substitute 3 for x.

a) $x^2 = 3^2 = 3(3) = 9$ **b)** $-x^2 = -3^2 = -(3)(3) = -9$

c) $(-x)^2 = (-3)^2 = (-3)(-3) = 9$

Now Try Exercise 95

EXAMPLE 13 Evaluate   **a)** y^2 **b)** $-y^2$ and   **c)** $(-y)^2$ when $y = -4$.

Solution   Substitute -4 for y.

a) $y^2 = (-4)^2 = (-4)(-4) = 16$ **b)** $-y^2 = -(-4)^2 = -(-4)(-4) = -16$

c) $(-y)^2 = [-(-4)]^2 = (4)^2 = 16$

Now Try Exercise 97

Note that $-x^2$ will always be a negative number for any nonzero value of x, and $(-x)^2$ will always be a positive number for any nonzero value of x.

Understanding Algebra

It is easy to confuse the expressions $(-6)^2$ and -6^2. $(-6)^2$ means $(-6) \cdot (-6) = 36$. The expression -6^2 represents the opposite of 6^2. So, $-6^2 = -36$.

Avoiding Common Errors

The expression $-x^2$ means $-(x^2)$. When asked to evaluate $-x^2$ for any real number x, many students will incorrectly treat $-x^2$ as $(-x)^2$. For example, to evaluate $-x^2$ when $x = 5$,

CORRECT

$$-5^2 = -(5^2) = -(5)(5)$$
$$= -25$$

INCORRECT

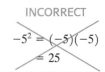

EXAMPLE 14   Evaluate $2x^2 + 4x + 1$ when $x = \dfrac{1}{4}$.

Solution   Substitute $\dfrac{1}{4}$ for each x in the expression, then evaluate using the order of operations.

$$2x^2 + 4x + 1 = 2\left(\frac{1}{4}\right)^2 + 4\left(\frac{1}{4}\right) + 1 \quad \text{Substitute.}$$

$$= 2\left(\frac{1}{16}\right) + 4\left(\frac{1}{4}\right) + 1 \quad \text{Exponent}$$

$$= \frac{1}{8} + 1 + 1 \quad \text{Multiply.}$$

$$= \frac{1}{8} + 2 \quad \text{Add.}$$

$$= 2\frac{1}{8}$$

Now Try Exercise 113

EXAMPLE 15   Evaluate $-y^2 + 3(x + 2) - 5$ when $x = -3$ and $y = -2$.

Solution   Substitute -3 for each x and -2 for each y, then evaluate using the order of operations.

$$-y^2 + 3(x + 2) - 5 = -(-2)^2 + 3(-3 + 2) - 5 \quad \text{Substitute.}$$
$$= -(-2)^2 + 3(-1) - 5 \quad \text{Parentheses}$$
$$= -(4) + 3(-1) - 5 \quad \text{Exponent}$$
$$= -4 - 3 - 5 \quad \text{Multiply.}$$
$$= -7 - 5 \quad \text{Subtract, left to right.}$$
$$= -12$$

Now Try Exercise 121

EXERCISE SET 1.9   Math XL   MyMathLab
MathXL®   MyMathLab

Warm-Up Exercises

Fill in the blanks with the appropriate word, phrase, or symbol(s) from the following list.

~~base~~   ~~exponent~~   ~~grouping symbols~~   ~~innermost~~

~~left to right~~   right to left   exponent expressions

1. When an expression has only additions and subtractions, it is evaluated from ___L to R___ .

2. After evaluating grouping symbols, the next order of operation is to evaluate ___exponent expressions___

3. Parentheses, brackets, and braces are examples of ___grouping symbols___

4. In the expression 7^5, 7 is called the ___base___ .

5. In the expression 7^5, 5 is called the ___exponent___ .

6. When grouping symbols are nested, begin evaluating at the ___innermost___ group.

Practice the Skills

Evaluate.

7. 5^2 25

8. 2^3 8

9. 1^7 7

10. 4^1 4

11. -8^2 −64

12. 7^3 49 / 343

13. $(-3)^2$ 9

14. -6^3 −72

15. $(-1)^3$ −3

16. 2^5 32 / 343

17. -10^2 −100

18. 5^3 125

19. $(-9)^2$ 81

20. $(-3)^3$ −27

21. 3^3 27

22. -7^2 −49

23. $(-4)^4$ 64

24. -4^4 −64

25. -2^4 −16

26. $3^2(4)^2$ 9·16 144

27. $\left(\dfrac{3}{4}\right)^2$ 9/16

28. $\left(\dfrac{5}{8}\right)^3$ $\dfrac{125}{512}$

29. $\left(-\dfrac{1}{2}\right)^5$ $\dfrac{-5}{64}$

30. $\left(-\dfrac{2}{3}\right)^4$ $\dfrac{16}{81}$

31. $5^2 \cdot 3^2$ $25 \cdot 9 = 225$

32. $(-1)^4(2)^4$ -4 16 -64

33. $4^3 \cdot 3^2$ $48 \cdot 9 = 432$

34. $(-2)^3(-1)^9$ -8 -1 8

In Exercises 35–46, **a)** *determine by observation whether the answer should be positive or negative and explain your answer;* **b)** *evaluate the expression; and* **c)** *determine whether your answer in part* **b)** *is reasonable and makes sense.*

35. 7^3

36. 4^6

37. 6^4

38. -2^5

39. $(-3)^5$

40. 10^3

41. $(-5)^4$

42. $(1.3)^3$

43. $-(-9)^2$

44. $(-3.3)^3$

45. $-\left(\dfrac{3}{8}\right)^2$

46. $\left(-\dfrac{3}{4}\right)^3$

Evaluate.

47. $3 + 3 \cdot 6$ $3 + 18 = 21$

48. $7 - 5^2 + 8$

49. $6 - 6 + 8$

50. $(8^2 \div 4) - (20 - 4)$

51. $-7 + 2 \cdot 6^2 - 8$

52. $6 + 2 \cdot 3^2 - 10$

53. $-3^3 + 27$

54. $(-2)^3 + 8 \div 4$

55. $(4 - 5) \cdot (5 - 1)^2$

56. $-10 - 6 - 3 - 2$

57. $3 \cdot 7 + 4 \cdot 2$

58. $4^2 - 3 \cdot 4 - 6$

59. $5 - 2(7 + 5)$

60. $8 + 3(6 + 4)$

61. $-32 - 5(7 - 10)^2$

62. $-40 - 3(4 - 8)^2$

63. $\dfrac{3}{4} + 2\left(\dfrac{1}{5}\right)^2$

64. $-\dfrac{2}{3} - 3\left(\dfrac{3}{4}\right)^2$

65. $-4 + 3[-1 + (12 \div 2^2)]$

66. $-2 + 4[-3 + (48 \div 4^2)]$

67. $(6 \div 3)^3 + 4^2 \div 8$

68. $4 + (4^2 - 13)^4 - 3$

69. $-7 - 48 \div 6 \cdot 2^2 + 5$

70. $-7 - 56 \div 7 \cdot 2^2 + 4$

71. $(9 \div 3) + 4(7 - 2)^2$

72. $(12 \div 4) + 5(6 - 4)^2$

73. $[4 + ((5 - 2)^2 \div 3)^2]^2$

74. $(20 \div 5 \cdot 5 \div 5 - 5)^2$

75. $(-3)^3 + 8 \div 2$

76. $-3^3 + 8 \div 2$

77. $2[1.55 + 5(3.7)] - 3.35$

78. $(8.4 + 3.1)^2 - (3.64 - 1.2)$

79. $\left(\dfrac{2}{5} + \dfrac{3}{8}\right) - \dfrac{3}{20}$

80. $\left(\dfrac{5}{6} \cdot \dfrac{4}{5}\right) + \left(\dfrac{2}{3} \cdot \dfrac{5}{8}\right)$

81. $\dfrac{3}{4} - 4 \cdot \dfrac{5}{40}$

82. $\dfrac{1}{8} - \dfrac{1}{4} \cdot \dfrac{3}{2} + \dfrac{3}{5}$

83. $\dfrac{4}{5} + \dfrac{3}{4} \div \dfrac{1}{2} - \dfrac{2}{3}$

84. $\dfrac{12 - (4 - 6)^2}{6 + 4^2 \div 2^2}$

85. $\dfrac{-4 - [2(9 \div 3) - 5]}{6^2 - 3^2 \cdot 7}$

86. $\dfrac{[(7 - 3)^2 - 4]^2}{9 - 16 \div 8 - 4}$

87. $\dfrac{-[4 - (6 - 12)^2]}{[(9 \div 3) + 4]^2 + 2^2}$

88. $\dfrac{[(5 - (3 - 7)) - 2]^2}{2[(16 \div 2^2) - (8 \cdot 4)]}$

89. $\{5 - 2[4 - (6 \div 2)]^2\}^2$

90. $\{-6 - [3(16 \div 4^2)^2]\}^2$

91. $-\{4 - [-3 - (2 - 5)]^2\}$

92. $3\{4[(3 - 4)^2 - 3]^3 - 1\}$

93. $\{4 - 3[2 - (9 \div 3)]^2\}^2$

94. $2\{5[(4 - 6)^3 - 1]^2 - 3\}$

Evaluate **a)** x^2, **b)** $-x^2$, *and* **c)** $(-x)^2$ *for the following values of x.*

95. 5

96. 8

97. -2

98. -5

99. 6

100. 7

101. $-\dfrac{1}{3}$

102. $\dfrac{3}{4}$

Evaluate each expression for the given value of the variable or variables.

103. $x + 6; x = -2$

104. $2x - 4x + 5; x = 3$

105. $-7z - 3; z = 6$

106. $3(x - 2); x = 5$

107. $a^2 - 6; a = -3$

108. $b^2 - 8; b = 5$

109. $3p^2 - 6p - 4; p = 2$

110. $2r^2 - 5r + 3; r = 1$

111. $-4x^2 - 2x + 1; x = -1$

112. $-t^2 - 4t + 5; t = -4$

113. $-x^2 - 2x + 5; x = \dfrac{1}{2}$

114. $2x^2 - 4x - 10; x = \dfrac{3}{4}$

115. $4(3x + 1)^2 - 6x; x = 5$

116. $3n^2(2n - 1) + 5; n = -4$

117. $r^2 - s^2; r = -2, s = -3$

118. $p^2 - q^2; p = 5, q = -3$

119. $5(x - 6y) + 3x - 7y; x = 1, y = -5$

120. $4(x + y)^2 + 2(x + y) + 3; x = 2, y = 4$

121. $3(x - 4)^2 - (3y - 4)^2; x = -1, y = -2$

122. $6x^2 + 3xy - y^2; x = 2, y = -3$

Problem Solving

Write the following statements as mathematical expressions using parentheses and brackets, and then evaluate.

123. Multiply 6 by 3. From this product, subtract 4. From this difference, subtract 2.

124. Add 4 to 9. Divide this sum by 2. Add 10 to this quotient.

125. Multiply 10 by 4. Add 9 to this product. Subtract 6 from this sum. Divide this difference by 7.

126. Multiply 6 by 3. To this product, add 27. Divide this sum by 8. Multiply this quotient by 10.

127. Add $\frac{4}{5}$ to $\frac{3}{7}$. Multiply this sum by $\frac{2}{3}$.

128. Multiply $\frac{3}{8}$ by $\frac{4}{5}$. To this product, add $\frac{7}{120}$. From this sum, subtract $\frac{1}{60}$.

129. For what value or values of x does $-(x^2) = -x^2$?

130. For what value or values of x does $x = x^2$?

131. Road Trip If a car travels at 65 miles per hour, the distance it travels in t hours is $65t$. Determine how far a car traveling at 65 miles per hour travels in 2.5 hours.

132. Sales Tax If the sales tax on an item is 8%, the sales tax on an item costing d dollars can be found by the expression $0.08d$. Determine the sales tax on a scrapbook that costs $19.99.

133. Projectile Height An object is projected upward with an initial velocity of 48 feet per second from the top of a 70-foot building. The height of the object above the ground at any time t, in seconds, can be found by the expression $-16t^2 + 48t + 70$. Determine the height of the object after 2 seconds.

134. Car Cost If the sales tax on an item is 8%, then the total cost of an item c, including sales tax, can be found by the expression $c + 0.08c$. Find the total cost of a car that costs $17,000.

135. Volume In a gravel pit, gravel often forms the shape of a cone as it comes off of a conveyor belt. The volume of a cone is represented by the expression $\frac{\pi r^2 h}{3}$. If the radius of the cone is 4 feet and its height is 3 feet, what is its volume to the nearest cubic foot?

136. Rework problem 135 for a radius of 10 feet and a height of 9 feet.

Challenge Problems

137. Grass Growth The rate of growth of grass in inches per week depends on a number of factors, including rainfall and temperature. For a certain region of the country, the growth per week can be approximated by the expression $0.2R^2 + 0.003RT + 0.0001T^2$, where R is the weekly rainfall, in inches, and T is the average weekly temperature, in degrees Fahrenheit. Find the amount of growth of grass for a week in which the rainfall is 2 inches and the average temperature is 70°F.

Insert one pair of parentheses to make each statement true.

138. $14 + 6 \div 2 \times 4 = 40$

139. $12 - 4 - 6 + 10 = 24$

140. $24 \div 6 \div 2 + 2 = 1$

Group Activity

*Discuss and answer Exercises 141–144 as a group, according to the instructions. Each question has four parts. For parts **a)**, **b)**, and **c)**, simplify the expression and write the answer in exponential form. Use the knowledge gained in parts **a)**–**c)** to answer part **d)**. (General rules that may be used to solve exercises like these will be discussed in Chapter 6.)*

a) *Group member 1: Do part **a)** of each exercise.*

b) *Group member 2: Do part **b)** of each exercise.*

c) *Group member 3: Do part **c)** of each exercise.*

d) *As a group, answer part **d)** of each exercise. You may need to make up other examples like parts **a)**–**c)** to help you answer part **d)**.*

141. a) $2^2 \cdot 2^3$ **b)** $3^2 \cdot 3^3$ **c)** $2^3 \cdot 2^4$ **d)** $x^m \cdot x^n$

142. a) $\frac{2^3}{2^2}$ **b)** $\frac{3^4}{3^2}$ **c)** $\frac{4^5}{4^3}$ **d)** $\frac{x^m}{x^n}$

143. a) $(2^3)^2$ **b)** $(3^3)^2$ **c)** $(4^2)^2$ **d)** $(x^m)^n$

144. a) $(2x)^2$ **b)** $(3x)^2$ **c)** $(4x)^3$ **d)** $(ax)^m$

Cumulative Review Exercises

[1.2]   **145. Dogs** The graph shows the number of dogs in various houses selected at random in a neighborhood.

Dogs in Selected Houses

a) How many houses have two dogs?

b) Make a chart showing the number of houses that have no dogs, one dog, two dogs, and so on.

c) How many dogs in total are there in all the houses

d) Determine the mean number of dogs in all the houses surveyed.

146. Taxi Cost Yellow Cab charges $2.40 for the first $\frac{1}{2}$ mile plus 20 cents for each additional $\frac{1}{8}$ mile or part thereof. Find the cost of a 3-mile trip.

[1.6]   **147.** Add $-\frac{7}{12} + \frac{4}{9}$.

[1.8]   **148.** Divide $\left(\frac{-5}{7}\right) \div \left(\frac{-3}{14}\right)$.

1.10 Properties of the Real Number System

1 Learn the commutative property.

2 Learn the associative property.

3 Learn the distributive property.

4 Learn the identity properties.

5 Learn the inverse properties.

Here, we introduce various properties of the real number system.

1 Learn the Commutative Property

The **commutative property of addition** states that the order in which any two real numbers are added does not matter.

Commutative Property of Addition

If a and b represent any two real numbers, then
$$a + b = b + a$$

Notice that the commutative property involves a change in *order*. For example,
$$4 + 3 = 3 + 4$$
$$7 = 7$$

The **commutative property of multiplication** states that the order in which any two real numbers are multiplied does not matter.

Commutative Property of Multiplication

If a and b represent any two real numbers, then
$$a \cdot b = b \cdot a$$

For example,
$$6 \cdot 3 = 3 \cdot 6$$
$$18 = 18$$

The commutative property does not hold for subtraction or division. For example, $4 - 6 \neq 6 - 4$ and $6 \div 3 \neq 3 \div 6$.

Understanding Algebra

Two numbers can be added in either order or multiplied in either order. Thus, those operations are *commutative*. Neither subtraction nor division are commutative operations.

2 Learn the Associative Property

The **associative property of addition** states that, in the addition of three or more numbers, parentheses may be placed around any two adjacent numbers without changing the results.

> **Associative Property of Addition**
>
> If *a*, *b*, and *c* represent any three real numbers, then
> $$(a + b) + c = a + (b + c)$$

Notice that the associative property involves a change of *grouping*. For example,

$$(3 + 4) + 5 = 3 + (4 + 5)$$
$$7 + 5 = 3 + 9$$
$$12 = 12$$

In this example, the 3 and 4 are grouped together on the left, and the 4 and 5 are grouped together on the right.

The **associative property of multiplication** states that, in the multiplication of three or more numbers, parentheses may be placed around any two adjacent numbers without changing the results.

> **Associative Property of Multiplication**
>
> If *a*, *b*, and *c* represent any three real numbers, then
> $$(a \cdot b) \cdot c = a \cdot (b \cdot c)$$

For example,

$$(6 \cdot 2) \cdot 4 = 6 \cdot (2 \cdot 4)$$
$$12 \cdot 4 = 6 \cdot 8$$
$$48 = 48$$

Since the associative property involves a change of grouping, when the associative property is used, the content within the parentheses changes.

The associative property does not hold for subtraction or division. For example, $(4 - 1) - 3 \neq 4 - (1 - 3)$ and $(8 \div 4) \div 2 \neq 8 \div (4 \div 2)$.

Often when we add numbers we group the numbers so that we can add them easily. For example, when we add $70 + 50 + 30$ we may first add the $70 + 30$ to get 100. We are able to do this because of the commutative and associative properties.

$$(70 + 50) + 30 = 70 + (50 + 30) \quad \text{Associative property of addition}$$
$$= 70 + (30 + 50) \quad \text{Commutative property of addition}$$
$$= (70 + 30) + 50 \quad \text{Associative property of addition}$$
$$= 100 + 50 \quad \text{Addition facts}$$
$$= 150$$

Notice in the second step that the same numbers remained in parentheses but the order of the numbers changed, $50 + 30$ to $30 + 50$. Since this step involved a change in order (and not grouping), this is the commutative property of addition.

3 Learn the Distributive Property

A very important property of the real numbers is the **distributive property of multiplication over addition**. We often shorten the name to the **distributive property**.

> **Distributive Property**
>
> If a, b, and c represent any three real numbers, then
>
> $$a(b + c) = ab + ac$$

For example, if we let $a = 2$, $b = 3$, and $c = 4$, then

$$2(3 + 4) = (2 \cdot 3) + (2 \cdot 4)$$
$$2 \cdot 7 = 6 + 8$$
$$14 = 14$$

Therefore, we may either add first and then multiply, or multiply first and then add. Another example of the distributive property is

$$2(x + 3) = 2 \cdot x + 2 \cdot 3 = 2x + 6$$

The distributive property can be expanded in the following manner:

$$a\,(b + c + d + \cdots + n) = a\,b + a\,c + a\,d + \cdots + a\,n$$

For example, $3(x + y + 5) = 3x + 3y + 15$.

> **Helpful Hint**
>
> The *commutative property* changes *order*.
>
> The *associative property* changes *grouping*.
>
> The *distributive property* involves *two operations*, usually multiplication and addition.

EXAMPLE 1 Name each property illustrated.

a) $4 + (-2) = -2 + 4$ **b)** $5(r + s) = 5 \cdot r + 5 \cdot s = 5r + 5s$

c) $x \cdot y = y \cdot x$ **d)** $(-12 + 3) + 4 = -12 + (3 + 4)$

Solution

a) Commutative property of addition

b) Distributive property

c) Commutative property of multiplication

d) Associative property of addition

Now Try Exercise 29

> **Helpful Hint**
>
> Do not confuse the distributive property with the associative property of multiplication. Make sure you understand the difference.
>
> Distributive Property   Associative Property of Multiplication
>
> $3(4 + x) = 3 \cdot 4 + 3 \cdot x$ $3(4 \cdot x) = (3 \cdot 4)x$
>
> $= 12 + 3x$ $= 12x$
>
> For the distributive property to be used, there must be two *terms* within parentheses, separated by a plus or minus sign as in $3(4 + x)$.

4 Learn the Identity Properties

Now we will discuss the **identity properties**. When the number 0 is added to any real number, the real number is unchanged. For example, $5 + 0 = 5$ and $0 + 5 = 5$. For this reason we call 0 the **identity element of addition** or **additive identity**. When any real number is multiplied by 1, the real number is unchanged. For example, $7 \cdot 1 = 7$ and $1 \cdot 7 = 7$. For this reason we call 1 the **identity element of multiplication** or **multiplicative identity**.

Identity Properties

If *a* represents any real number, then

$$a + 0 = a \quad \text{and} \quad 0 + a = a \qquad \text{Identity property of addition}$$

and

$$a \cdot 1 = a \quad \text{and} \quad 1 \cdot a = a \qquad \text{Identity property of multiplication}$$

We often use the identity properties without realizing we are using them. For example, when we reduce $\dfrac{15}{50}$, we may do the following:

$$\frac{15}{50} = \frac{3 \cdot 5}{10 \cdot 5} = \frac{3}{10} \cdot \frac{5}{5} = \frac{3}{10} \cdot 1 = \frac{3}{10}$$

When we showed that $\dfrac{3}{10} \cdot 1 = \dfrac{3}{10}$, we used the identity property of multiplication.

5 Learn the Inverse Properties

The last properties we will discuss in this chapter are the **inverse properties**. Numbers like 3 and -3 are *opposites* or *additive inverses* because $3 + (-3) = 0$ and $-3 + 3 = 0$. Any two numbers whose sum is 0 are called *additive inverses* of each other. In general, for any real number *a* its additive inverse is $-a$.

Numbers like 4 and $\dfrac{1}{4}$ are *reciprocals* or *multiplicative inverses* because $4 \cdot \dfrac{1}{4} = 1$ and $\dfrac{1}{4} \cdot 4 = 1$. Any two numbers whose product is 1 are called *multiplicative inverses* of each other. In general, for any real number *a*, its multiplicative inverse is $\dfrac{1}{a}$. The inverse properties are summarized below.

Inverse Properties

If *a* represents any real number, then

$$a + (-a) = 0 \quad \text{and} \quad -a + a = 0 \qquad \text{Inverse property of addition}$$

and

$$a \cdot \frac{1}{a} = 1 \quad \text{and} \quad \frac{1}{a} \cdot a = 1 (a \neq 0) \qquad \text{Inverse property of multiplication}$$

We often use the inverse properties without realizing we are using them. For example, to evaluate the expression $6x + 2$ when $x = \dfrac{1}{6}$, we may do the following:

$$6x + 2 = 6\left(\frac{1}{6}\right) + 2 = 1 + 2 = 3$$

When we multiplied $6\left(\dfrac{1}{6}\right)$ and replaced it with 1, we used the inverse property of multiplication. We will be using both the identity and inverse properties throughout the book, although we may not specifically refer to them by name.

EXAMPLE 2   Name each property illustrated.

a) $2(x + 6) = (2 \cdot x) + (2 \cdot 6) = 2x + 12$

b) $3x \cdot 1 = 3x$

c) $(3 \cdot 6) \cdot 5 = 3 \cdot (6 \cdot 5)$

d) $y \cdot \dfrac{1}{y} = 1$

e) $2a + (-2a) = 0$

f) $3y + 0 = 3y$

Solution

a) Distributive property

b) Identity property of multiplication

c) Associative property of multiplication

d) Inverse property of multiplication

e) Inverse property of addition

f) Identity property of addition

Now Try Exercise 35

EXAMPLE 3   In parts **a)–f)**, the name of a property is given followed by part of an equation. Complete the equation, to the right of the equals sign, to illustrate the given property.

a) Associative property of multiplication
$(5 \cdot 4) \cdot 7 =$

b) Inverse property of addition
$3c + (-3c) =$

c) Identity property of multiplication
$6y \cdot 1 =$

d) Distributive property
$3(x + 5) =$

e) Identity property of addition

$2a + 0 =$

f) Inverse property of multiplication

$b \cdot \dfrac{1}{b} =$

Solution

a) $5 \cdot (4 \cdot 7)$ b) 0 c) $6y$ d) $3x + 15$ e) $2a$ f) 1

Now Try Exercise 55

EXERCISE SET 1.10

MathXL®   MyMathLab

Warm-Up Exercises

Fill in the blanks with the appropriate word, phrase, or symbol(s) from the following list.

associative property of addition

commutative property of addition

additive identity

distributive property of multiplication over addition

multiplicative inverse

associative property of multiplication

commutative property of multiplication

multiplicative identity

additive inverse

zero   undefined

1. $(3 + 4) + 10$ is the same as $3 + (4 + 10)$ illustrates the _____ .

2. $(-7)(-19)$ equals $(-19)(-7)$ illustrates the _____ .

3. A number without a multiplicative inverse is _____ .

4. $(a \cdot b) \cdot c$ is the same as $a \cdot (b \cdot c)$ illustrates the _____ .

5. $-2a$ is the _____ of $2a$.

6. $\dfrac{1}{2}$ is the _____ of 2.

7. When $6(2 + 4)$ is rewritten as $12 + 24$, the _____ is illustrated.

8. $x + y = y + x$ illustrates the _____ .

9. When the number 1 multiplies a number, no change occurs. Thus, 1 is called the _____ .

10. When 0 is added to a number, there is no change. Thus, 0 is called the _____ .

Practice the Skills

In Exercises 11–22, for the given expression, determine **a)** *the additive inverse, and* **b)** *the multiplicative inverse.*

11. 6

12. 5

13. −3

14. −7

15. x

16. z

17. 1.6

18. −0.125

19. $\dfrac{1}{5}$

20. $\dfrac{1}{8}$

21. $-\dfrac{5}{6}$

22. $-\dfrac{2}{9}$

Practice the Skills

Name each property illustrated.

23. $6(x + 7) = 6x + 42$

24. $3 + y = y + 3$

25. $(x + 3) + 5 = x + (3 + 5)$

26. $1(x + 3) = (1)(x) + (1)(3) = x + 3$

27. $5 \cdot y = y \cdot 5$

28. $-4x + 4x = 0$

29. $p \cdot (q \cdot r) = (p \cdot q) \cdot r$

30. $2(x + 4) = 2x + 8$

31. $4(d + 3) = 4d + 12$

32. $3 + (4 + t) = (3 + 4) + t$

33. $3z \cdot 1 = 3z$

34. $0 + 3y = 3y$

35. $2y \cdot \dfrac{1}{2y} = 1$

36. $x \cdot y = y \cdot x$

In Exercises 37–58, the name of a property is given followed by part of an equation. Complete the equation, to the right of the equals sign, to illustrate the given property.

37. commutative property of addition
$-4 + 1 =$

38. inverse property of addition
$(-7a) + 7a =$

39. associative property of multiplication
$-6 \cdot (4 \cdot 2) =$

40. associative property of addition
$-5 + (6 + 8) =$

41. distributive property
$-2(x + y) =$

42. distributive property
$4(x + 3) =$

43. commutative property of multiplication
$x \cdot y =$

44. identity property of multiplication
$(1)\left(-\dfrac{1}{3}b\right) =$

45. commutative property of addition
$4x + 3y =$

46. associative property of multiplication
$-9 \cdot (3 \cdot 8) =$

47. associative property of addition
$(a + b) + 3 =$

48. commutative property of multiplication
$(x + 2)3 =$

49. associative property of addition
$(3x + 4) + 6 =$

50. commutative property of addition
$3(x + y) =$

51. commutative property of multiplication
$3(m + n) =$

52. associative property of multiplication
$(3x)y =$

53. distributive property
$4(x + y + 3)$

54. distributive property
$3(x + y + 2) =$

55. inverse property of addition
$3n + (-3n) =$

56. identity property of addition
$0 + 2x =$

57. identity property of multiplication
$\left(\dfrac{5}{2}n\right)(1) =$

58. inverse property of multiplication
$\left(\dfrac{x}{2}\right)\left(\dfrac{2}{x}\right) =$

Problem Solving

Indicate whether the given processes are commutative. That is, does changing the order in which the actions are done result in the same final outcome? Explain each answer.

59. Putting sugar and then cream in coffee; putting cream and then sugar in coffee.

60. Applying suntan lotion and then sunning yourself; sunning yourself and then applying suntan lotion.

61. Putting your contacts in and then washing your hair; washing your hair and then putting your contacts in.

62. Putting on your sweater and then your coat; putting on your coat and then your sweater.

63. Writing on the chalkboard and then erasing the chalkboard; erasing the chalkboard and then writing on the chalkboard.

64. Getting your hands dirty and then washing your hands; washing your hands and then getting your hands dirty.

In Exercises 65–70, indicate whether the given processes are associative. For a process to be associative, the final outcome must be the same when the first two actions are performed first or when the last two actions are performed first. Explain each answer.

65. Cleaning the kitchen sink, dusting the bedroom furniture, and doing the laundry.

66. In a store, buying cereal, soap, and dog food.

67. Turning on a DVD player, inserting a DVD, and watching the DVD.

68. Putting on a shirt, a tie, and a sweater.

69. Starting a car, moving the shift lever to drive, and then stepping on the gas.

70. Putting cereal, milk, and sugar in a bowl.

71. The commutative property of addition is $a + b = b + a$. Explain why $(3 + 4) + x = x + (3 + 4)$ also illustrates the commutative property of addition.

72. The commutative property of multiplication is $a \cdot b = b \cdot a$. Explain why $(3 + 4) \cdot x = x \cdot (3 + 4)$ also illustrates the commutative property of multiplication.

© Rohit Seth\Shutterstock

Challenge Problems

73. Consider $x + (3 + 5) = x + (5 + 3)$. Does this illustrate the commutative property of addition or the associative property of addition? Explain.

74. Consider $x + (3 + 5) = (3 + 5) + x$. Does this illustrate the commutative property of addition or the associative property of addition? Explain.

75. Consider $x + (3 + 5) = (x + 3) + 5$. Does this illustrate the commutative property of addition? Explain.

76. The commutative property of multiplication is $a \cdot b = b \cdot a$. Explain why $(3 + 4) \cdot (5 + 6) = (5 + 6) \cdot (3 + 4)$ also illustrates the commutative property of multiplication.

Cumulative Review Exercises

[1.3] **77.** Add $2\frac{3}{5} + \frac{2}{3}$.

78. Subtract $3\frac{5}{8} - 2\frac{3}{16}$.

[1.6] **79.** Add $102.7 + (-113.9)$.

80. Write the opposite of $\frac{7}{8}$.

Chapter 1 Summary

IMPORTANT FACTS AND CONCEPTS	EXAMPLES

Section 1.2

Guidelines for Problem Solving

1. **Understand the problem.**
2. **Translate the problem to mathematical language.**
3. **Carry out the mathematical calculations necessary to solve the problem.**
4. **Check the answer obtained in step 3.**
5. **Make sure you have answered the question.**

See page 8 for more details on problem solving.

Jacob Thomas can pay either $725 cash for a desk or pay $300 down and $20 a month for 24 months. How much money can he save by paying cash?

Solution: Understand We need to determine how much he would pay if he paid $300 down and $20 a month for 24 months. This amount would then be compared to $725.

Translate

$$\begin{pmatrix} \text{amount if} \\ \text{paid over 24} \\ \text{months} \end{pmatrix} = \$300 + \begin{pmatrix} \text{additional} \\ \text{amount paid} \\ \text{over 24 months} \end{pmatrix}$$

Carry Out

$$= \$300 + \$20(24)$$
$$= \$300 + \$480$$
$$= \$780$$

The difference in the amounts is $780 - $725 = $55.

Check and Answer

The answer appears reasonable. Jacob can save $55 by paying the total amount at the time of purchase.

An **algebraic expression** is a general term for any collection of numbers, variables, grouping symbols, and operations.

$$8(24 \div 4), 3x - 5, a^2 - 6$$

Bar Graph

Top 10 Community-based Organization Websites by U.S. Marketshare Visits (%) July 2008

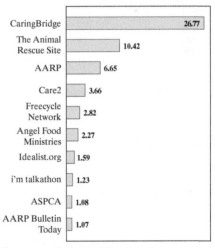

CaringBridge	26.77
The Animal Rescue Site	10.42
AARP	6.65
Care2	3.66
Freecycle Network	2.82
Angel Food Ministries	2.27
Idealist.org	1.59
i'm talkathon	1.23
ASPCA	1.08
AARP Bulletin Today	1.07

Source: www.marketingcharts.com

Line Graph

Indiana SAT Math Scores

Source: www.doe.state.in.us

IMPORTANT FACTS AND CONCEPTS	EXAMPLES

Section 1.2 (continued)

Circle Graph

New Housing Units in the United States
2008

2 or more units: 30%

1 unit: 70%

Source: www.census.gov

The symbol $\approx$ is read **"is approximately equal to."**

$57.91536 \approx 57.92$

Measures of central tendency or **averages** are values that are representative of a set of data.

The **mean** of a set of data is determined by adding all the values and dividing the sum by the number of values.

The **median** is the value in the middle of a set of **ranked data**.

The mean and median are averages.

The mean of Adam Michael's test grades of 82, 95, 76, 92, and 88 is
$$\frac{82 + 95 + 76 + 92 + 88}{5} = \frac{433}{5} = 86.6.$$

The median of Adam's five test grades given above is 88 (circled).
76, 82, 88, 92, 95

Section 1.3

Multiplication Symbols

If a and b represent any two mathematical quantities, then each of the following may be used to indicate the product of a and b ("a times b").

$$ab \quad a \cdot b \quad a(b) \quad (a)b \quad (a)(b)$$

5 times z may be written:

$$5z, \quad 5 \cdot z, \quad 5(z), \quad (5)z \text{ or } (5)(z)$$

The numbers or variables that are multiplied in a multiplication problem are called **factors**.

If $a \cdot b = c$, then a and b are *factors* of c.

In $7 \cdot 9 = 63$, the numbers 7 and 9 are factors of 63.

The numbers $0, 1, 2, 3, 4, \ldots$ are called **whole numbers**.

12, 105, and 0 are whole numbers.

The top number of a fraction is called the **numerator**, and the bottom number is called the **denominator**.

In the fraction $\frac{6}{11}$, the 6 is the numerator and the 11 is the denominator.

To Simplify a Fraction

1. Find the largest number that will divide (without remainder) both the numerator and the denominator. This number is called the **greatest common factor** (GCF).

2. Then divide both the numerator and the denominator by the greatest common factor.

The GCF of 36 and 48 is 12. Therefore,

$$\frac{36}{48} = \frac{36 \div 12}{48 \div 12} = \frac{3}{4}$$

To Multiply Fractions

$$\frac{a}{b} \cdot \frac{c}{d} = \frac{ac}{bd}$$

$$\frac{3}{4} \cdot \frac{3}{5} = \frac{9}{20}$$

To Divide Fractions

$$\frac{a}{b} \div \frac{c}{d} = \frac{a}{b} \cdot \frac{d}{c} = \frac{ad}{bc}$$

$$\frac{9}{7} \div \frac{4}{5} = \frac{9}{7} \cdot \frac{5}{4} = \frac{45}{28}$$

To Add and Subtract Fractions with Like Denominators

$$\frac{a}{c} + \frac{b}{c} = \frac{a + b}{c} \quad \text{or} \quad \frac{a}{c} - \frac{b}{c} = \frac{a - b}{c}$$

1. $\dfrac{3}{13} + \dfrac{7}{13} = \dfrac{3 + 7}{13} = \dfrac{10}{13}$

2. $\dfrac{4}{5} - \dfrac{1}{5} = \dfrac{4 - 1}{5} = \dfrac{3}{5}$

IMPORTANT FACTS AND CONCEPTS	EXAMPLES

Section 1.3 (continued)

The smallest number that is divisible by two or more denominators is called the **least common denominator** or **LCD**.

To add (or subtract) fractions with unlike denominators, first rewrite each fraction with a common denominator.

In the fractions $\frac{7}{9}$ and $\frac{2}{5}$, 45 is the LCD.

Subtract $\frac{7}{9} - \frac{2}{5}$.

$$\frac{7}{9} - \frac{2}{5} = \frac{7}{9} \cdot \frac{5}{5} - \frac{2}{5} \cdot \frac{9}{9}$$
$$= \frac{35}{45} - \frac{18}{45} = \frac{17}{45}$$

A **mixed number** consists of a whole number followed by a fraction.

Change a mixed number to a fraction.

Change a fraction to a mixed number.

$7\frac{4}{5}$ is a mixed number.

$$6\frac{2}{3} = 6 + \frac{2}{3} = \frac{18}{3} + \frac{2}{3} = \frac{20}{3}$$
$$\frac{52}{7} = \frac{49}{7} + \frac{3}{7} = 7 + \frac{3}{7} = 7\frac{3}{7}$$

Section 1.4

A **set** is a collection of **elements** listed within braces.

A set that contains no elements is called an **empty set** (or **null set**).

The set $\{2, 4, 6, 8\}$ consists of four elements, namely 2, 4, 6, and 8.

The set of dogs that can fly is an empty set.

Natural numbers: $\{1, 2, 3, 4, 5, \dots\}$

The natural numbers are also called the **positive integers** or the **counting numbers**.

Whole numbers: $\{0, 1, 2, 3, 4, 5, \dots\}$

Integers: $\{\dots, -3, -2, -1, 0, 1, 2, 3 \dots\}$
$\underbrace{\qquad}_{\text{Negative integers}}$ $\underbrace{\qquad}_{\text{Positive integers}}$

Rational numbers:

$\quad$ {quotient of two integers, denominator not 0}

Irrational numbers: {numbers that can be represented on the number line that are not rational numbers}

Real numbers:
$\quad$ {all numbers that can be represented on a number line}

23, 16, and 1231 are natural numbers.

35, 0, and 257 are whole numbers.

-101, 0, and 236 are integers.

$-3, 2.8, 9\frac{1}{2}, 0, 15, -\frac{9}{13}$, and -3.6 are rational numbers.

$\sqrt{13}$ and $-\sqrt{7}$ are irrational numbers.

$5.7, -\frac{3}{8}, -16, 0, \sqrt{5}, 3\frac{1}{7}, -2.1, -\sqrt{2}$, and 31 are real numbers.

Section 1.5

The symbol $>$ is used to represent the words "is greater than."

The symbol $<$ is used to represent the words "is less than."

1. $3.8 > 3.08$

2. $-7 < -1$

The **absolute value** of a number can be considered the distance between the number and 0 on a number line.

The absolute value of every number will be either *positive* or *zero*.

1. $|12| = 12$

2. $|0| = 0$

3. $|-100| = 100$

Section 1.6

Add Using a Number Line:

Represent the first number to be added (first *addend*) by an arrow starting at 0 on the number line. The arrow is drawn to the right if the number is positive, and to the left if the number is negative. From the tip of the first arrow, draw a second arrow to represent the second addend. The second arrow is drawn to the right or left, as just explained. The sum of the two numbers is found at the tip of the second arrow.

Add $5 + (-7)$.

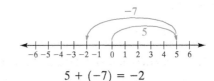

$5 + (-7) = -2$

IMPORTANT FACTS AND CONCEPTS	EXAMPLES

Section 1.6 (continued)

Any two numbers whose sum is zero are said to be **opposites** (or **additive inverses**) of each other.

1. The opposite of 8 is -8.

2. The opposite of $-\dfrac{5}{6}$ is $\dfrac{5}{6}$.

Add Using Absolute Value:

To add real numbers with the same sign, add their absolute values. The sum has the same sign as the numbers being added.

Add $-4 + (-9)$.
$$|-4| + |-9| = 4 + 9 = 13$$
Since both numbers being added are negative, the sum is negative. Thus, $-4 + (-9) = -13$.

To add two signed numbers with different signs, subtract the smaller absolute value from the larger absolute value. The answer has the sign of the number with the larger absolute value.

Add $-25 + 10$.
$$|-25| - |10| = 25 - 10 = 15$$
Since $|-25|$ is greater than $|10|$, the sum is negative. Thus, $-25 + 10 = -15$.

Section 1.7

To Subtract Real Numbers

In general, if a and b represent any two real numbers, then
$$a - b = a + (-b)$$
In evaluating expressions involving more than one addition and subtraction, work from left to right unless parentheses or other grouping symbols appear.

1. $8 - (+4) = 8 + (-4) = 4$

2. $-7 - 5 = -7 + (-5) = -12$

3. $-12 - (-6) = -12 + 6 = -6$

4. $-8 + 5 - 11 = -3 - 11 = -14$

Section 1.8

The Sign of the Product of Two Real Numbers

1. The product of two numbers with **like** signs is a **positive** number.

2. The product of two numbers with **unlike** signs is a **negative** number.

1. $-8(-7) = 56$

2. $5(-6) = -30$

The Sign of the Quotient of Two Real Numbers

1. The quotient of two numbers with **like** signs is a **positive** number.

2. The quotient of two numbers with **unlike** signs is a **negative** number.

1. $\dfrac{-81}{-9} = 9$

2. $\dfrac{-35}{7} = -5$

The Quotient of a Positive Number and a Negative Number

If a and b represent any real numbers, $b \neq 0$, then
$$\frac{a}{-b} = \frac{-a}{b} = -\frac{a}{b}$$

$$\frac{3}{-8} = \frac{-3}{8} = -\frac{3}{8}$$

Summary of Division Involving 0

If a represents any real number except 0, then
$$\frac{0}{a} = 0 \qquad \frac{a}{0} \text{ is undefined}$$

1. $\dfrac{0}{12} = 0$

2. $\dfrac{5}{0}$ is undefined

Section 1.9

In general, the number b to the nth power, written b^n, means
$$\underbrace{b \cdot b \cdot b \cdots b}_{n \text{ factors of } b} = b^n$$

$$x^5 = x \cdot x \cdot x \cdot x \cdot x$$

IMPORTANT FACTS AND CONCEPTS	EXAMPLES

Section 1.9 (continued)

Order of Operations

1. First, evaluate the information within **parentheses** ( ), brackets [ ], or braces { }. These are **grouping symbols**. A fraction bar, $-$, also serves as a grouping symbol. If the expression contains nested grouping symbols, evaluate the information in the innermost grouping symbols first.

2. Next, evaluate all **exponents**.

3. Next, evaluate all **multiplications** or **divisions** in order from left to right.

4. Finally, evaluate all **additions** or **subtractions** in order from left to right.

$$-16 - 3(6 - 8)^2$$
$$= -16 - 3(-2)^2$$
$$= -16 - 3(4)$$
$$= -16 - 12$$
$$= -28$$

Section 1.10

Commutative Property of Addition

If a and b represent any two real numbers, then
$$a + b = b + a$$

$$9 + 6 = 6 + 9$$
$$15 = 15$$

Commutative Property of Multiplication

If a and b represent any two real numbers, then
$$a \cdot b = b \cdot a$$

$$6 \cdot 7 = 7 \cdot 6$$
$$42 = 42$$

Associative Property of Addition

If a, b, and c represent any three real numbers, then
$$(a + b) + c = a + (b + c)$$

$$(1 + 2) + 3 = 1 + (2 + 3)$$
$$3 + 3 = 1 + 5$$
$$6 = 6$$

Associative Property of Multiplication

If a, b, and c represent any three real numbers, then
$$(a \cdot b) \cdot c = a \cdot (b \cdot c)$$

$$(5 \cdot 4) \cdot 3 = 5 \cdot (4 \cdot 3)$$
$$20 \cdot 3 = 5 \cdot 12$$
$$60 = 60$$

Distributive Property

If a, b, and c represent any three real numbers, then
$$a(b + c) = ab + ac$$

$$4(y + 9) = 4 \cdot y + 4 \cdot 9 = 4y + 36$$

Identity Properties

If a represents any real number, then

1. $a + 0 = a$ and $0 + a = a$ Identity property of addition

and

2. $a \cdot 1 = a$ and $1 \cdot a = a$ Identity property of multiplication

1. $15 + 0 = 0 + 15 = 15$

2. $8 \cdot 1 = 1 \cdot 8 = 8$

Inverse Properties

If a represents any real number, then

1. $a + (-a) = 0$ and $-a + a = 0$ Inverse property of addition

and

2. $a \cdot \dfrac{1}{a} = 1$ and $\dfrac{1}{a} \cdot a = 1 (a \neq 0)$ Inverse property of multiplication

a) $9 + (-9) = -9 + 9 = 0$

b) $6 \cdot \dfrac{1}{6} = \dfrac{1}{6} \cdot 6 = 1$

Chapter 1 Review Exercises

[1.2] *Solve.*

1. Final Exam Review Eraj Basnayake bought doughnuts for his math classes for their final exam review sessions. His first class ate 32 doughnuts. His second class ate 29 doughnuts. His third class ate 36 doughnuts, and his fourth class ate 31 doughnuts. If he purchased 13 dozen doughnuts, how many did he have left over?

© debr22pics\Shutterstock

2. Inflation Assume that the rate of inflation for tuition for a course is 7% per year for the next two years. What will tuition for the course cost in two years if the tuition cost is $500 today?

3. Sales Tax The sales tax in Cattaraugus County is 8.25%.
  a) What was the sales tax that Andrew Jacob paid on a laptop computer that cost $899.99 before tax?
  b) What is the total cost of the laptop computer including tax?

4. Plasma TV Dan Marketos wants to purchase a high definition plasma TV for $3000. He can either pay the total amount at the time of purchase, or he can agree to pay the store $400 down and $225 a month for 12 months. How much money can he save by paying the total amount at the time of purchase?

5. Test Grades On Angie Smajstrla's first five exams her grades were 75, 79, 86, 88, and 64. Find the **a)** mean and **b)** median of her grades.

6. Little League The number of points scored by a Little League baseball team in its last six games were 21, 3, 17, 10, 9, and 6. Find the **a)** mean and **b)** median of the points.

7. Commute Times Recently, the U.S. Census Bureau released a report that included the following bar graph. The bar graph shows some of the longest average commute-to-work times

in the United States. Estimate the average one-way commute time in
  a) New York.
  b) Illinois.

Some of the Longest Average Commute-to-Work Times

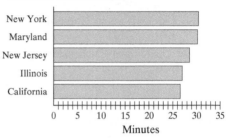

Source: US Census Bureau

8. Freshman Majors The graphs below show the majors of the 2006 and the 2009 freshmen classes at the University of Cincinnati's College of Applied Science.
  a) If there were 900 freshmen in 2006, determine the number of Information Technology majors.
  b) If there were 1100 freshmen in 2009, determine the number of Sports Administration majors.

College of Applied Sciences Major of Entering Freshman

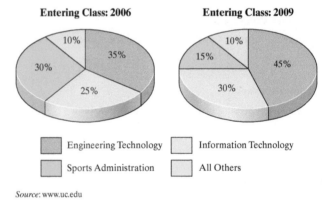

Source: www.uc.edu

[1.3] *Perform each indicated operation. Simplify your answers.*

9. $\dfrac{3}{5} \cdot \dfrac{5}{6}$ **10.** $3\dfrac{5}{7} + 2\dfrac{1}{3}$ **11.** $\dfrac{5}{12} \div \dfrac{3}{5}$ **12.** $\dfrac{5}{6} + \dfrac{1}{3}$ **13.** $3\dfrac{1}{6} - 1\dfrac{1}{4}$ **14.** $7\dfrac{3}{8} \div \dfrac{5}{12}$

[1.4] **15.** List the set of natural numbers.
16. List the set of whole numbers.
17. List the set of integers.
18. Describe the set of rational numbers.
19. Consider the following set of numbers.

$$\left\{ 3, -5, -12, 0, \dfrac{1}{2}, -0.62, \sqrt{7}, 426, -3\dfrac{1}{4} \right\}$$

List the numbers that are
  a) positive integers.
  b) whole numbers.
  c) integers.
  d) rational numbers.
  e) irrational numbers.
  f) real numbers.

20. Consider the following set of numbers.

$$\left\{ -2.3, -8, -9, 1\dfrac{1}{2}, \sqrt{2}, -\sqrt{2}, 1, -\dfrac{3}{17} \right\}$$

List the numbers that are
  a) natural numbers.
  b) whole numbers.
  c) negative integers.
  d) integers.
  e) rational numbers.
  f) irrational numbers.
  g) real numbers.

[1.5]   *Insert either* $<, >,$ *or* $=$ *in each shaded area to make a true statement.*

21. -7 ▨ -5 **22.** -2.6 ▨ -3.6 **23.** 0.50 ▨ 0.509 **24.** 4.6 ▨ 4.06

25. -6.3 ▨ -6.03 **26.** 5 ▨ $|-3|$ **27.** $\left|-\dfrac{9}{2}\right|$ ▨ $|-4.5|$ **28.** $|-10|$ ▨ $|-7|$

[1.6–1.7]   *Evaluate.*

29. $-9 + (-5)$ **30.** $-6 + 6$ **31.** $0 + (-3)$ **32.** $-10 + 4$

33. $-8 - (-2)$ **34.** $-2 - (-4)$ **35.** $4 - (-4)$ **36.** $12 - 12$

37. $2 - 7$ **38.** $7 - (-7)$ **39.** $0 - (-4)$ **40.** $-7 - 5$

41. $\dfrac{4}{3} - \dfrac{3}{4}$ **42.** $\dfrac{1}{2} + \dfrac{3}{5}$ **43.** $\dfrac{5}{9} - \dfrac{3}{4}$ **44.** $-\dfrac{5}{7} + \dfrac{3}{8}$

45. $-\dfrac{5}{12} - \dfrac{5}{6}$ **46.** $-\dfrac{6}{7} + \dfrac{5}{12}$ **47.** $\dfrac{2}{9} - \dfrac{3}{10}$ **48.** $\dfrac{5}{12} - \left(-\dfrac{3}{5}\right)$

Evaluate.

49. $9 - 4 + 9$ **50.** $-8 - 9 + 14$ **51.** $-5 - 4 - 3$ **52.** $-2 + (-3) - 2$

53. $17 - (+4) - (-3)$ **54.** $6 - (-2) + 3$

[1.8]   *Evaluate.*

55. $7(-9)$ **56.** $(-8.2)(-3.1)$ **57.** $(-4)(-5)(-6)$ **58.** $\left(\dfrac{3}{5}\right)\left(\dfrac{-2}{7}\right)$

59. $\left(\dfrac{10}{11}\right)\left(\dfrac{3}{-5}\right)$ **60.** $\left(\dfrac{-5}{8}\right)\left(\dfrac{-3}{7}\right)$ **61.** $0\left(\dfrac{4}{9}\right)$ **62.** $(-4)(-6)(-2)(-3)$

Evaluate.

63. $45 \div (-3)$ **64.** $12 \div (-2)$ **65.** $-14.72 \div 4.6$ **66.** $-37.41 \div (-8.7)$

67. $-88 \div (-11)$ **68.** $-4 \div \left(\dfrac{-4}{9}\right)$ **69.** $\dfrac{28}{-3} \div \left(\dfrac{9}{-2}\right)$ **70.** $\dfrac{14}{3} \div \left(\dfrac{-6}{5}\right)$

Indicate whether each quotient is 0 *or undefined.*

71. $0 \div 5$ **72.** $0 \div (-6)$ **73.** $-12 \div 0$ **74.** $-4 \div 0$ **75.** $\dfrac{8.3}{0}$ **76.** $\dfrac{0}{-9.8}$

[1.6–1.8, 1.9]   *Evaluate.*

77. $-5(3 - 8)$ **78.** $2(4 - 8)$ **79.** $(3 - 6) + 4$

80. $(-4 + 3) - (2 - 6)$ **81.** $[6 + 3(-2)] - 6$ **82.** $(-5 - 3)(4)$

83. $[12 + (-4)] + (6 - 8)$ **84.** $9[3 + (-4)] + 5$ **85.** $-4(-3) + [4 \div (-2)]$

86. $(-3 \cdot 4) \div (-2 \cdot 6)$ **87.** $(-3)(-4) + 6 - 3$ **88.** $[-2(3) + 6] - 4$

[1.9]   *Evaluate.*

89. -6^2 **90.** $(-6)^2$ **91.** 2^4 **92.** $(-3)^3$

93. $(-1)^9$ **94.** $(-2)^5$ **95.** $\left(\dfrac{-4}{5}\right)^2$ **96.** $\left(\dfrac{2}{5}\right)^3$

97. $5^3 \cdot (-2)^2$ **98.** $(-2)^4\left(\dfrac{1}{2}\right)^2$ **99.** $\left(-\dfrac{2}{3}\right)^2 \cdot 3^3$ **100.** $(-4)^3(-2)^2$

Evaluate.

101. $-5 + 3 \cdot 4$ **102.** $4 \cdot 6 + 4 \cdot 2$ **103.** $(3.7 - 4.1)^2 + 6.2$

104. $10 - 36 \div 4 \cdot 3$ **105.** $6 - 3^2 \cdot 5$ **106.** $[6.9 - (3 \cdot 5)] + 5.8$

107. $\dfrac{6^2 - 4 \cdot 3^2}{-[6 - (3 - 4)]}$ **108.** $\dfrac{4 + 5^2 \div 5}{6 - (-3 + 2)}$ **109.** $3[9 - (4^2 + 3)] \cdot 2$

110. $(-3^2 + 4^2) + (3^2 \div 3)$ **111.** $2^3 \div 4 + 6 \cdot 3$ **112.** $(4 \div 2)^4 + 4^2 \div 2^2$

113. $(8 - 2^2)^2 - 4 \cdot 3 + 10$ **114.** $4^3 \div 4^2 - 5(2 - 7) \div 5$ **115.** $-\{-4[27 \div 3^2 - 2(4 - 2)]\}$

116. $2\{4^3 - 6[4 - (2 - 4)] - 3\}$

Evaluate each expression for the given values.

117. $3x - 7; x = 4$ **118.** $6 - 4x; x = -5$ **119.** $2x^2 - 5x + 3; x = 6$

120. $5y^2 + 3y - 2; y = -1$ **121.** $-x^2 + 2x - 3; x = -2$ **122.** $-x^2 + 2x - 3; x = 2$

123. $-3x^2 - 5x + 5; x = 1$ **124.** $-x^2 - 8x - 12y; x = -3, y = -2$

[1.6–1.9]   **a)** *Evaluate each expression, and* **b)** *check to see whether your answer is reasonable.*

125. $278 + (-493)$ **126.** $324 - (-29.6)$ **127.** $\dfrac{-17.28}{6}$

128. $(-62)(-1.9)$ **129.** $(-4)^8$ **130.** $-(4.2)^3$

[1.10]   *Name each indicated property.*

131. $(7 + 4) + 9 = 7 + (4 + 9)$

132. $-5(a + 2) = -5a - 10$

133. $6x + 3x = 3x + 6x$

134. $(x + 4)3 = 3(x + 4)$

135. $4(x + 3) = 4x + 12$

136. $(x + 7) + 4 = x + (7 + 4)$

137. $8b \cdot 1 = 8b$

138. $-8y + 8y = 0$

Chapter 1 Practice Test

Chapter Test Prep Videos provide fully worked-out solutions to any of the exercises you want to review. Chapter Test Prep Videos are available via **MyMathLab** *, or on* **You Tube** *(search "Angel Elementary Algebra" and click on "Channels").*

1. Shopping While shopping, Mia Nguyen purchases two half-gallons of milk for $1.30 each, one Boston cream pie for $4.75, and three 2-liter bottles of soda for $1.10 each.

a) What is her total bill before tax?

b) If there is a 7% sales tax on the bottles of soda, how much is the sales tax?

c) How much is her total bill including tax?

d) How much change will she receive from a $50 bill?

2. TV Commercials The following line graph shows the cost for a 30-second commercial during the same time slot on the same channel for 12 consecutive years. How many times greater was the cost for a 30-second commercial in the twelfth year than in the first year?

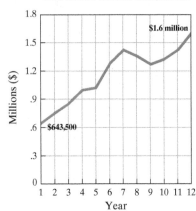

Cost of a 30-Second Commercial

3. Radio The following graph shows the median number of listeners for various radio stations during a specific time.

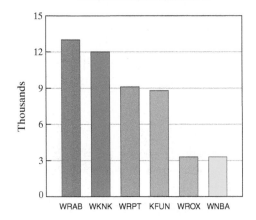

Median Number of Listeners

a) Determine the median number of listeners who listened to WRAB during this time.

b) The median number of listeners who listened to KFUN during this time was approximately 8.8 thousand. Explain what this means.

4. Consider the following set of numbers.

$$\left\{ -6, 42, -3\tfrac{1}{2}, 0, 6.52, \sqrt{5}, \tfrac{5}{9}, -7, -1 \right\}$$

List the numbers that are

a) natural numbers.

b) whole numbers.

c) integers.

d) rational numbers.

e) irrational numbers.

f) real numbers.

Insert either $<$, $>$, or $=$ in each shaded area to make a true statement.

5. -9.9 ▒ -9.09

6. $|-3|$ ▒ $|-2|$

Evaluate.

7. $-7 + (-8)$

8. $-6 - 5$

9. $15 - 12 - 17$

10. $(-4 + 6) - 3(-2)$

11. $(-4)(-3)(2)(-1)$

12. $\left(\dfrac{-2}{9}\right) \div \left(\dfrac{-7}{8}\right)$

13. $\left(-18 \cdot \dfrac{1}{2}\right) \div 3$

14. $-\dfrac{3}{8} - \dfrac{4}{7}$

15. $-6(-2 - 3) \div 5 \cdot 2$

16. $\left(-\dfrac{2}{3}\right)^5$

17. $[6 + ((9 - 3)^2 \div 18)^2]^2$

18. Explain why $-x^2$ will always be a negative value for any nonzero real number selected for x.

Evaluate the expression for the given values.

19. $5x^2 - 8$; $x = -3$

20. $-x^2 - 6x + 3$; $x = -2$

21. $6x - 3y^2 + 4$; $x = 3$, $y = -2$

22. $-x^2 + xy + y^2$; $x = 1$, $y = -2$

Name each indicated property.

23. $x + 3 = 3 + x$

24. $4(x + 9) = 4x + 36$

25. $(2 + x) + 4 = 2 + (x + 4)$

2 Solving Linear Equations and Inequalities

2.1 Combining Like Terms

2.2 The Addition Property of Equality

2.3 The Multiplication Property of Equality

2.4 Solving Linear Equations with a Variable on Only One Side of the Equation

    Mid-Chapter Test: Sections 2.1–2.4

2.5 Solving Linear Equations with the Variable on Both Sides of the Equation

2.6 Formulas

2.7 Ratios and Proportions

2.8 Inequalities in One Variable

    Chapter 2 Summary

    Chapter 2 Review Exercises

    Chapter 2 Practice Test

    Cumulative Review Test

Goals of This Chapter

The major emphasis of this chapter is to teach you how to solve linear equations. *To be successful in solving linear equations, you need to have a thorough understanding of adding, subtracting, multiplying, and dividing real numbers.* This material was discussed in Chapter 1.

The first four sections of this chapter will give you the building blocks you will need for solving linear equations. Section 2.5 combines the material previously presented to teach you how to solve a variety of linear equations. In the last few sections of this chapter, you will learn about formulas, ratios, proportions, and solving linear inequalities.

You will be using principles learned in this chapter throughout the book and in real life.

© dovgan \Shutterstock

There are many algebraic formulas that are very useful in everyday life. For example, we can use algebra to determine the amount we owe on a loan, or to convert dollars to other currencies. Algebraic formulas are also useful in sports and recreation. In Example 7 on page 140, we use algebraic formulas to find the area and circumference of a pizza.

2.1 Combining Like Terms

1　Identify terms.

2　Identify like terms.

3　Combine like terms.

4　Use the distributive property.

5　Remove parentheses when they are preceded by a plus or minus sign.

6　Simplify an expression.

Understanding Algebra

Terms are parts of an expression that get added or subtracted. The expression $2x - 3y - 5$ has 3 terms:

$$2x \quad - \quad 3y \quad - \quad 5$$
$$\uparrow \qquad \uparrow \qquad \uparrow$$
$$\underbrace{\qquad\qquad\qquad}_{\text{terms}}$$

$2x$ is a term, $-3y$ is a term, and -5 is a term.

Understanding Algebra

Terms are added (or subtracted); *factors* are multiplied.

So, in $4x + 7y$, there are two terms (they are $4x$ and $7y$). The 4 and x are factors of the first term and 7 and y are factors of the second.

Understanding Algebra

A *coefficient* is the numerical factor of a term. If none is shown, it is understood that the coefficient is a "1".

1　Identify Terms

In Section 1.3, we indicated that letters called **variables** are used to represent numbers. A variable can represent a variety of different numbers.

As was indicated in Chapter 1, an **expression,** or **algebraic expression,** is a collection of numbers, variables, grouping symbols, and operation symbols.

Examples of Expressions

$$7, \qquad x^2 - 6, \qquad 4x - 3, \qquad 2(x + 5) + 6, \qquad \frac{x + 3}{4}$$

When an algebraic expression consists of several parts, the parts that are *added* are called the **terms** of the expression. Consider the expression $2x - 3y - 5$. The expression can be written as $2x + (-3y) + (-5)$, and so the expression $2x - 3y - 5$ has three terms: $2x$, $-3y$, and -5. The expression $3x^2 + 2xy + 5(x + y)$ also has three terms: $3x^2$, $2xy$, and $5(x + y)$.

When listing the terms of an expression, it is not necessary to list the + sign at the beginning of a term.

Expression	Terms
$-2x + 3y - 8$	$-2x, 3y, -8$
$3y^2 - 2x + \dfrac{1}{2}$	$3y^2, -2x, \dfrac{1}{2}$
$7 + x + 4 - 5x$	$7, x, 4, -5x$
$3(x - 1) - 4x + 2$	$3(x - 1), -4x, 2$
$\dfrac{x + 4}{3} - 5x + 3$	$\dfrac{x + 4}{3}, -5x, 3$

The numerical part of a term is called its **numerical coefficient** or simply its **coefficient.** In the term $6x$, the 6 is the numerical coefficient. Note that $6x$ means the variable x is multiplied by 6.

Term	Numerical Coefficient
$5x$	5
7	7
$-\dfrac{1}{2}x$	$-\dfrac{1}{2}$
$4(x - 3)$	4
$\dfrac{2x}{3}$	$\dfrac{2}{3}$, since $\dfrac{2x}{3}$ means $\dfrac{2}{3}x$
$\dfrac{x + 4}{3}$	$\dfrac{1}{3}$, since $\dfrac{x + 4}{3}$ means $\dfrac{1}{3}(x + 4)$

Whenever a term appears without a numerical coefficient, we assume that the numerical coefficient is 1.

Examples

x means $1x$　　　　　　　　$-x$ means $-1x$

x^2 means $1x^2$　　　　　　$-x^2$ means $-1x^2$

xy means $1xy$　　　　　　　$-xy$ means $-1xy$

$(x + 2)$ means $1(x + 2)$　　$-(x + 2)$ means $-1(x + 2)$

If an expression has a term that is a number (without a variable), we refer to that number as a **constant term**, or simply a **constant**. In the expression $x^2 + 3x - 4$, the -4 is a constant term, or a constant.

2 Identify Like Terms

Like terms are terms that have the same variables with the same exponents, respectively. Constants, such as 4 and -6, are like terms. Some examples of like terms and unlike terms follow. Note that if two terms are like terms, only their numerical coefficients may differ.

<table>
<tr><th>Like Terms</th><th colspan="2">Unlike Terms</th></tr>
<tr><td>$3x, \quad -4x$</td><td>$3x, \quad 2$</td><td>⟵ (One term has a variable, the other is a constant.)</td></tr>
<tr><td>$4y, \quad 6y$</td><td>$3x, \quad 4y$</td><td>⟵ (Variables differ)</td></tr>
<tr><td>$5, \quad -6$</td><td>$x, \quad 3$</td><td>⟵ (One term has a variable, the other is a constant.)</td></tr>
<tr><td>$3(x+1), \quad -2(x+1)$</td><td>$2x, \quad 3xy$</td><td>⟵ (Variables differ)</td></tr>
<tr><td>$3x^2, \quad 4x^2$</td><td>$3x, \quad 4x^2$</td><td>⟵ (Exponents differ)</td></tr>
<tr><td>$5ab, \quad 2ab$</td><td>$4a, \quad 2ab$</td><td>⟵ (Variables differ)</td></tr>
</table>

> ### Understanding Algebra
>
> In the expression $2x - 3y - 8x$, we refer to the $2x$ term and the $-8x$ term as *like terms* because their variable parts are identical.

EXAMPLE 1   Identify any like terms. ────

a) $2x + 3x + 4$ **b)** $2x + 3y + 2$ **c)** $x + 3 + y - \dfrac{1}{2}$ **d)** $x + 3x^2 - 4x^2$

e) $5x - x + 6$ **f)** $3 - (2x + 4x) - 6$ **g)** $12 + x^2 - x + 7$

Solution

a) $2x$ and $3x$ are like terms.

b) There are no like terms.

c) 3 and $-\dfrac{1}{2}$ are like terms.

d) $3x^2$ and $-4x^2$ are like terms.

e) $5x$ and $-x$ (or $-1x$) are like terms.

f) 3 and -6 are like terms; $-2x$ and $4x$ are like terms.

g) 12 and 7 are like terms.

Now Try Exercise 3

3 Combine Like Terms

We often need to simplify expressions by combining like terms. To **combine like terms** means to add or subtract the like terms in an expression. To combine like terms, we can use the procedure that follows.

> #### To Combine Like Terms
>
> 1. Determine which terms are like terms.
> 2. Add or subtract the coefficients of the like terms.
> 3. Multiply the number found in step 2 by the common variable(s).

Examples 2 through 7 illustrate this procedure.

EXAMPLE 2   Combine like terms: $5x + 4x$. ────

Solution $5x$ and $4x$ are like terms with the common variable x. Since $5 + 4 = 9$, then $5x + 4x = 9x$.

Now Try Exercise 9

EXAMPLE 3 Combine like terms: $\dfrac{3}{5}x - \dfrac{2}{3}x$.

Solution   Since $\dfrac{3}{5} - \dfrac{2}{3} = \dfrac{9}{15} - \dfrac{10}{15} = -\dfrac{1}{15}$, then $\dfrac{3}{5}x - \dfrac{2}{3}x = -\dfrac{1}{15}x$.

Now Try Exercise 15

EXAMPLE 4 Combine like terms: $6.47b - 8.39b$.

Solution   Since $6.47 - 8.39 = -1.92$, then $6.47b - 8.39b = -1.92b$.

Now Try Exercise 35

EXAMPLE 5 Combine like terms: $3x + x + 5$.

Solution   The $3x$ and x are like terms.

$$3x + x + 5 = 3x + 1x + 5 = 4x + 5$$

Now Try Exercise 19

Because of the commutative property of addition, the order of the terms in the answer is not critical. Thus, $5 + 4x$ is also an acceptable answer to Example 5. When writing answers, we generally list the terms containing variables in alphabetical order from left to right, and list the constant term last.

The commutative and associative properties of addition will be used to rearrange the terms in Examples 6 and 7.

EXAMPLE 6 Combine like terms: $3b + 6a - 5 - 2a$.

Solution   The only like terms are $6a$ and $-2a$.

$$
\begin{aligned}
3b + 6a - 5 - 2a &= 6a - 2a + 3b - 5 \quad &\text{Rearrange terms.}\\
&= 4a + 3b - 5 \quad &\text{Combined like terms.}
\end{aligned}
$$

Now Try Exercise 21

EXAMPLE 7 Combine like terms: $-2x^2 + 3y - 4x^2 + 3 - y + 5$.

Solution

$$
\begin{aligned}
-2x^2 \quad &\text{and} \quad -4x^2 \quad &\text{are like terms.}\\
3y \quad &\text{and} \quad -y \quad &\text{are like terms}\\
3 \quad &\text{and} \quad 5 \quad &\text{are like terms.}
\end{aligned}
$$

Grouping the like terms together gives

$$
\begin{aligned}
-2x^2 + 3y - 4x^2 + 3 - y + 5 &= -2x^2 - 4x^2 + 3y - y + 3 + 5\\
&= -6x^2 + 2y + 8
\end{aligned}
$$

Now Try Exercise 29

4 Use the Distributive Property

We introduced the distributive property in Section 1.10. Because this property is so important, we will study it again. But before we do, let's briefly review the subtraction of real numbers. Recall from Section 1.7 that

$$6 - 3 = 6 + (-3)$$

In general,

Subtraction of Real Numbers

For any real numbers a and b,

$$a - b = a + (-b)$$

We will use the fact that $a + (-b)$ means $a - b$ in discussing the distributive property.

Distributive Property

For any real numbers a, b, and c,

$$a(b + c) = ab + ac$$

> ## Understanding Algebra
>
> We use the distributive property when combining like terms:
>
> $$5x + 4x = (5 + 4)x = 9x$$
>
> or
>
> $$7y - 3y = (7 - 3)y = 4y$$

EXAMPLE 8 Use the distributive property to remove parentheses.

a) $2(x + 4)$ $\quad 2x + 8$ $\qquad$ **b)** $-5(p + 3)$ $\quad -5p + (-5)(3) = -5p + (-15) = -5p - 15$

Solution

a) $2(x + 4) = 2x + 2(4) = 2x + 8$

b) $-5(p + 3) = -5p + (-5)(3) = -5p + (-15) = -5p - 15$

Note in part **b)** that, instead of leaving the answer $-5p + (-15)$, we wrote it as $-5p - 15$, which is the preferred form of the answer.

Now Try Exercise 61

EXAMPLE 9 Use the distributive property to remove parentheses.

a) $3(x - 2)$ $\quad 3x - 6$ $\qquad$ **b)** $-2(4x - 3)$ $\quad -8x + 6$

Solution

a) By the definition of subtraction, we write $x - 2$ as $x + (-2)$.

$$3(x - 2) = 3[x + (-2)] = 3x + 3(-2)$$
$$= 3x + (-6)$$
$$= 3x - 6$$

b) $-2(4x - 3) = -2[4x + (-3)] = -2(4x) + (-2)(-3) = -8x + 6$

Now Try Exercise 63

The distributive property is very important to the study of algebra. Study the Helpful Hint that follows.

Helpful Hint

With a little practice, you will be able to eliminate some of the intermediate steps when you use the distributive property. When using the distributive property, there are eight possibilities with regard to signs. Study and understand the eight possibilities that follow.

Positive Coefficient

a) $2(x) = 2x$

$2(x +3) = 2x +6$
$2(+3) = +6$

b) $2(x) = 2x$

$2(x -3) = 2x -6$
$2(-3) = -6$

c) $2(-x) = -2x$

$2(-x +3) = -2x +6$
$2(+3) = +6$

d) $2(-x) = -2x$

$2(-x -3) = -2x -6$
$2(-3) = -6$

Negative Coefficient

e) $(-2)(x) = -2x$

$-2(x +3) = -2x -6$
$(-2)(+3) = -6$

f) $(-2)(x) = -2x$

$-2(x -3) = -2x +6$
$(-2)(-3) = +6$

g) $(-2)(-x) = 2x$

$-2(-x +3) = 2x -6$
$(-2)(+3) = -6$

h) $(-2)(-x) = 2x$

$-2(-x -3) = 2x +6$
$(-2)(-3) = +6$

Understanding Algebra

Remember, the distributive property is used for multiplying over a sum of 2 or more terms. This is sometimes referred to as *expanding* an expression. So, $2(x - 3y + 9)$ can be rewritten as $2x - 6y + 18$

The distributive property can be expanded as follows:

$$a(b + c + d + \cdots + n) = ab + ac + ad + \cdots + an$$

Examples of the Expanded Distributive Property

$$3(x + y + z) = 3x + 3y + 3z$$
$$2(x + y - 3) = 2x + 2y - 6$$

EXAMPLE 10 Use the distributive property to remove parentheses.

a) $4(x - 3)$ **b)** $-6(5y - 1)$ **c)** $-\dfrac{1}{2}(4r + 5)$ **d)** $-7(2x + 4y - 9z)$

Solution

a) $4(x - 3) = 4x - 12$

b) $-6(5y - 1) = -30y + 6$

c) $-\dfrac{1}{2}(4r + 5) = -2r - \dfrac{5}{2}$

d) $-7(2x + 4y - 9z) = -14x - 28y + 63z$

Now Try Exercise 79

The distributive property can also be used from the right, as in Example 11.

EXAMPLE 11 Use the distributive property to remove parentheses from the expression $(2x - 8y)4$.

Solution   We distribute the 4 on the right side of the parentheses over the terms within the parentheses.

$$(2x - 8y)4 = 2x(4) - 8y(4)$$
$$= 8x - 32y$$

Now Try Exercise 83

Example 11 could have been rewritten as $4(2x - 8y)$ by the commutative property of multiplication, and then the 4 could have been distributed from the left to obtain the same answer, $8x - 32y$.

> **Helpful Hint**
>
> Students sometimes try to use the distributive property when it cannot be used. For the distributive property to be used, there must be a + or − between the terms *within parentheses* and the terms within parentheses must be *multiplied* by some number or expression. Study the following correct simplifications carefully.
>
> $$4(2xy) = 8xy \qquad \text{(Distributive property is not used)}$$
> $$4(2x + y) = 8x + 4y \qquad \text{(Distributive property is used)}$$
> $$(2x + y) - 4 = 2x + y - 4 \qquad \text{(Distributive property is not used)}$$
> $$(2x + y)(-4) = -8x - 4y \qquad \text{(Distributive property is used)}$$

5 Remove Parentheses When They Are Preceded by a Plus or Minus Sign

In the expression $(4x + 3)$, how do we remove parentheses? Recall that the coefficient of a term is assumed to be 1 if none is shown. Therefore, we may write

$$(4x + 3) = 1(4x + 3)$$
$$= 1(4x) + (1)(3)$$
$$= 4x + 3$$

Understanding Algebra

When no sign or a plus sign precedes parentheses, the parentheses may be removed without having to change the expression inside parentheses.

Other Examples

$$(x + 3) = x + 3$$
$$(2x - 3) = 2x - 3$$
$$+(2x - 5) = 2x - 5$$
$$+(x + 2y - 6) = x + 2y - 6$$

Now consider the expression $-(4x + 3)$. How do we remove parentheses in this expression? Here, the coefficient in front of the parentheses is −1, so each term within the parentheses is multiplied by −1.

$$-(4x + 3) = -1(4x + 3)$$
$$= -1(4x) + (-1)(3)$$
$$= -4x + (-3)$$
$$= -4x - 3$$

Thus, $-(4x + 3) = -4x - 3$. *When a minus sign precedes parentheses, the signs of all the terms within the parentheses are changed when the parentheses are removed.*

Understanding Algebra

Think of the sign preceding a term as being part of that term. So when we rewrite $-(2x - 3)$, we multiply −1 by $2x$ and −1 by −3 to obtain $-2x + 3$.

Examples

$$-(x + 4) = -x - 4$$
$$-(-2x + 3) = 2x - 3$$
$$-(5x - y + 3) = -5x + y - 3$$
$$-(-4c - 3d - 5) = 4c + 3d + 5$$

6 Simplify an Expression

Combining what we learned in the preceding discussions, we have the following procedure for **simplifying an expression.**

> **To Simplify an Expression**
>
> 1. Use the distributive property to remove any parentheses.
> 2. Combine like terms.

EXAMPLE 12 Simplify $6 - (2x + 3)$.

Solution

$$6 - (2x + 3) = 6 - 2x - 3 \quad \text{Use the distributive property.}$$
$$= -2x + 3 \quad \text{Combined like terms.}$$

Note: $3 - 2x$ is the same as $-2x + 3$; however, we generally write the term containing the variable first.

Now Try Exercise 89

EXAMPLE 13 Simplify $-\left(\frac{2}{3}x - \frac{1}{4}\right) + 3x$.

Solution $-\left(\frac{2}{3}x - \frac{1}{4}\right) + 3x = -\frac{2}{3}x + \frac{1}{4} + 3x \quad \text{Distributive property}$

$$= -\frac{2}{3}x + 3x + \frac{1}{4} \quad \text{Rearranged terms.}$$

$$= -\frac{2}{3}x + \frac{9}{3}x + \frac{1}{4} \quad \text{Wrote } x \text{ terms with the LCD, 3.}$$

$$= \frac{7}{3}x + \frac{1}{4} \quad \text{Combined like terms.}$$

Now Try Exercise 101

Notice in Example 13 that $\frac{7}{3}x$ and $\frac{1}{4}$ could not be combined because they are not like terms.

EXAMPLE 14 Simplify $\frac{3}{4}x + \frac{1}{3}(5x - 2)$.

Solution

$$\frac{3}{4}x + \frac{1}{3}(5x - 2) = \frac{3}{4}x + \frac{1}{3}(5x) + \frac{1}{3}(-2) \quad \text{Distributive property}$$

$$= \frac{3}{4}x + \frac{5}{3}x - \frac{2}{3}$$

$$= \frac{9}{12}x + \frac{20}{12}x - \frac{2}{3} \quad \text{Wrote } x \text{ terms with the LCD, 12.}$$

$$= \frac{29}{12}x - \frac{2}{3} \quad \text{Combined like terms.}$$

Now Try Exercise 103

EXAMPLE 15 Simplify $3(2a - 5) - 3(b - 6) - 4a$.

Solution

$$3(2a - 5) - 3(b - 6) - 4a = 6a - 15 - 3b + 18 - 4a \quad \text{Distributive property}$$

$$= 6a - 4a - 3b - 15 + 18 \quad \text{Rearranged terms.}$$

$$= 2a - 3b + 3 \quad \text{Combined like terms.}$$

Now Try Exercise 107

Helpful Hint

Keep in mind the difference between the concepts of *term* and *factor*. When two or more expressions are **multiplied,** each expression is a **factor** of the product. For example, since $4 \cdot 3 = 12$, the 4 and the 3 are factors of 12. Since $3 \cdot x = 3x$, the 3 and the x are factors of $3x$. Similarly, in the expression $5xyz$, the 5, x, y, and z are all factors.

In an expression, the parts that are **added** are the **terms** of the expression. For example, the expression $2x^2 + 3x - 4$ has three terms, $2x^2$, $3x$, and -4. Note that the terms of an expression may have factors. For example, in the term $2x^2$, the 2 and the x^2 are factors because they are multiplied.

EXERCISE SET 2.1

MathXL®   MyMathLab

Warm-Up Exercises

Fill in the blanks with the appropriate word, phrase, or symbol(s) from the following list.

terms $4x - 6y - 18$ ~~like terms~~   ~~unlike terms~~   ~~$-4x + 6y + 18$~~
~~constant~~   factors   ~~coefficient~~   ~~variable~~

1. In the expression $5x - 3y + 17 - 2x$, the 17 is called a _coefficient_ term.

2. When we apply the distributive property to $-2(2x - 3y - 9)$, we obtain _-4x+6y+18_ .

3. In the expression $5x - 3y + 17 - 2x$, the $5x$ and $-2x$ are called _like terms_ .

4. In the expression $5x - 3y + 17 - 2x$, the -3 is called the _constant_ of the second term.

5. In the expression $5x - 3y + 17 - 2x$, the $5x$ and $-3y$ are called _unlike terms_

6. In the expression $12x + 17$, the 12 and x are _factors_ of the first term.

7. In the expression $-4x^2 + 17x - 90$, the $-4x^2, 17x$, and -90 are called _terms_ .

8. In the expression $17x$, the x is called a _variable_ .

Practice the Skills

Combine like terms when possible. If not possible, rewrite the expression as is.

9. $6x + 8x$ $= 14X$
10. $4x - 5x$
11. $3x + 6$

12. $4x + 3y$
13. $y + 3 + 4y$
14. $4x - 7x + 4$

15. $\frac{3}{4}a - \frac{6}{11}a$ $\frac{33}{44}a - \frac{24}{44}a$ $\frac{11}{44}a$ $\frac{1}{4}a$
16. $\frac{3}{4}p - \frac{2}{7}p$
17. $2t - 6x + 5t$

18. $-7 - 4m - 66$
19. $-2w - 3w + 5$
20. $-8y - 4y - 7$

21. $-x + 2 + x - 2$ $-2X-0$
22. $8x - 2y - 1 - 3x$
23. $3 + 6x - 3 - 6x$

24. $y - 2y + 5$
25. $5 + 2t - 4t + 16$
26. $5s - 3s - 2s$

27. $4p + 6 - 16p + 2$ $-12p-8$
28. $-6t + 5 + 2t - 9$
29. $3x^2 - 9y^2 + 7x^2 - 5 - y^2 - 2$

30. $-4x^2 - 6y - 3x^2 + 6 - y - 1$
31. $-2x + 4x - 8$
32. $4 - x + 4x - 8$

33. $b + 4 + \frac{3}{5}$ $b + \frac{20}{5} + \frac{3}{5}$ $b + \frac{23}{5}$
34. $\frac{3}{4}y + 2 + y$
35. $5.1n + 6.42 - 4.3n$

36. $2x^2 + 3y^2 + 14x + 5y^2$
37. $\frac{1}{2}a + 3b + 1$
38. $x + \frac{1}{2}y - \frac{3}{8}y$

39. $13.4x + 1.2x + 8.3$ $14.6X + 8.3$
40. $-4x^2 - 3.1 - 5.2$
41. $-x^2 + 2x^2 + y$

42. $1 + x^2 + 6 - 3x^2$
43. $2x - 7y - 5x + 2y$
44. $3x - 7 - 9 + 4x$

45. $4 - 3n^2 + 9 - 2n$ $13 - 3n^2 - 2n$
46. $9x + y - 2 - 4x$
47. $-19.36 + 40.02x + 12.25 - 18.3x$

48. $52x - 52x - 63.5 - 63.5$
49. $\frac{3}{5}x - 3 - \frac{7}{4}x - 2$
50. $\frac{1}{2}y - 4 + \frac{3}{4}x - \frac{1}{5}y$

51. $5w^3 + 2w^2 + w + 3$ done
52. $4p^2 - 3p^2 + 2p - 5p$
53. $2z - 5z^3 - 2z^3 - z^2$

54. $5ab - 3ab$
55. $6x^2 - 6xy + 3y^2$
56. $x^2 - 3xy - 2xy + 6$

57. $4a^2 - 3ab + 6ab + b^2$ $4a^2 + 3ab + b^2$
58. $4b^2 - 8bc + 5bc + c^2$

Use the distributive property to remove parentheses.

59. $5(x + 2)$ $5X + 10$
60. $2(-y + 5)$
61. $5(x + 4)$ $5X + 20$

62. $-2(y + 8)$
63. $3(x - 6)$ $3X - 18$
64. $-2(x - 4)$

65. $-\frac{1}{2}(2x - 4)$ $-X + 2$
66. $-4(x + 6)$ $-4X - 24$
67. $1(-4 + x)$ $-4 + X$

68. $\frac{2}{3}(m - 18)$
69. $\frac{4}{5}(s - 5)$ $\frac{4}{5}S - 4$
70. $5(x - y + 5)$

71. $-0.3(3x^2 + 5)$
72. $-(x - 3)$
73. $-\frac{1}{3}(3r - 12)$ $-r + 4$

74. $-2(x + y - z)$
75. $0.7(2x + 0.5)$ $1.4X + 0.35$
76. $-(x + 4y)$

77. $-(-x + y)$ $x - y$

78. $(3x + 4y - 6)$

79. $-(2x + 4y - 8)$ $-2x - 4y + 8$

80. $-3(2a + 3b - 7)$

81. $1.1(3.1x - 5.2y + 2.8)$

82. $-4(-2m - 3n + 8)$

83. $(2x - 9y)5$ $10x - 45y$

84. $(8b - 1)7$

85. $(r + 3s - 19)$

86. $(-p + 2q - 3)$

87. $-3(-x + 2y + 4)$ $3x - 6y - 12$

88. $2.3(1.6x + 5.1y - 4.1)$

Simplify.

89. $5 - (3x + 4)$ $5 - 3x + 4$

90. $7 - (2y - 9)$

91. $-2(3 - x) + 7$

92. $-(3t - 3) + 5$

93. $6x + 2(4x + 9)$

94. $3(x + y) + 2y$

95. $2(x - y) + 2x + 3$ $4x - 2y + 3$

96. $6 + (x - 5) + 3x$

97. $4(2c - 3) - 3(c - 4)$

98. $4 + (2y + 2) + y$

99. $8x - (x - 3)$

100. $-(x - 5) - 3x + 4$

101. $-\left(\dfrac{3}{4}x - \dfrac{1}{3}\right) + 2x$

102. $-\left(\dfrac{7}{8}x - \dfrac{1}{2}\right) - 3x$

103. $\dfrac{2}{3}x + \dfrac{1}{2}(5x - 4)$

104. $\dfrac{4}{5}x + \dfrac{1}{7}(3x - 1)$

105. $-(3s + 4) - (s + 2)$

106. $6 - 2(2w + 3) + 5w$

107. $4(x - 1) + 2(3 - x) - 4$

108. $4(3b - 2) - 5(c - 4) - 6b$

109. $4(m + 3) - 4m - 12$

110. $-3(a + 2b) + 3(a + 2b)$

111. $0.4 - (y + 5) + 0.6 - 2$

112. $4 - (2 - x) + 3x$

113. $4 + (3x - 4) - 5$

114. $2y - 6(y - 2) + 3$

115. $4(x + 2) - 3(x - 4) - 5$

116. $6 - (a - 5) - (2b + 1)$

117. $-0.2(6 - x) - 4(y + 0.4)$

118. $-5(2y - 8) - 3(1 + x) - 7$

119. $-6x + 7y - (3 + x) + (x + 3)$

120. $3(t - 2) - 2(t + 4) - 6$

121. $\dfrac{1}{2}(x + 3) + \dfrac{1}{3}(3x + 6)$

122. $\dfrac{2}{3}(r - 2) - \dfrac{1}{2}(r + 4)$

Problem Solving

If $\square + \square + \square + \odot + \odot$ can be represented as $3\square + 2\odot$, write an expression to represent each of the following.

123. $\square + \ominus + \ominus + \square + \ominus$ $3\ominus + 2\square$

124. $\otimes + \bigcirc\!\!\!\bullet + \otimes + \bigcirc\!\!\!\bullet + \bigcirc\!\!\!\bullet + \bigcirc\!\!\!\bullet$

125. $x + y + \triangle + \triangle + x + y + y$ $2x + 3y + 2\triangle$

126. $2 + x + 2 + \ominus + \ominus + 2 + y$

In Exercises 127 and 128, consider the following. The positive factors of 6 are 1, 2, 3, and 6 since

$$1 \cdot 6 = 6$$
$$2 \cdot 3 = 6$$
$$\uparrow \ \uparrow$$
factors

127. List all the positive factors of 18.

128. List all the positive factors of 24.

Concept/Writing Exercises

129. a) When a minus sign precedes an expression within parentheses, explain how to remove parentheses.

b) Write $-(x - 8)$ without parentheses.

$-x + 8$

130. a) What are like terms? Determine whether the following are like terms. If not, explain why.

b) $3x, 4y$

c) $7, -2$

d) $5x^2, 5x$

e) $4x, -5xy$

Challenge Problems

$22x^2 - 25y - 4x + 3$

Simplify. $4x^2 + 5y^2 + 18x^2 - 30y^2 - 4x + 3$

131. $4x^2 + 5y^2 + 6(3x^2 - 5y^2) - 4x + 3$

132. $2x^2 - 4x + 8x^2 - 3(x + 2) - x^2 - 2$

133. $2[3 + 4(x - 5)] - [2 - (x - 3)]$

134. $\dfrac{1}{4}\left[3 - 2(y + 1)\right] - \dfrac{1}{3}\left[2 - (y - 6)\right]$

Cumulative Review Exercises

[1.5]   *Evaluate.*

135. $|-7|$

136. $-|-16|$

[1.7]   **137.** Evaluate $-4 - 13 - (-6)$.

[1.9]   **138.** Write a paragraph explaining the order of operations.

139. Evaluate $-x^2 + 5x - 6$ when $x = -1$.

2.2 The Addition Property of Equality

1. Identify linear equations.
2. Check solutions to equations.
3. Identify equivalent equations.
4. Use the addition property to solve equations.
5. Solve equations by doing some steps mentally.

Understanding Algebra

An *equation* is a statement that two expressions are equal.

$$2x - 3 = 7$$
$$y - 4 = 12 \text{ and}$$
$$6t + 14 = 2.3$$

are all *linear equations in one variable* in which the variable is *x, y,* and *t,* respectively.

Understanding Algebra

A *solution* to an equation is a number that makes the equation a true statement.

Understanding Algebra

We use the symbol $\stackrel{?}{=}$ in the process of checking a solution — we are questioning whether a statement is true.

1 Identify Linear Equations

A statement that shows two algebraic expressions are equal is called an **equation**. For example, $4x + 3 = 2x - 4$ is an equation. In this chapter, we learn to solve **linear equations** in one variable.

> ### Linear Equation
>
> A **linear equation** in one variable is an equation that can be written in the form
>
> $$ax + b = c$$
>
> where *a, b,* and *c* are real numbers $a \neq 0$.

Examples of Linear Equations

$$x + 4 = 7$$
$$2x - 4 = 6$$

2 Check Solutions to Equations

> ### Solution to an Equation
>
> The **solution to an equation** is the number or numbers that when substituted for the variable or variables make the equation a true statement.

The solution to $x + 4 = 7$ is 3 because when *x* is 3, the statement is true: 7 equals 7. A solution can be **checked** by substituting your answer for the variable in the original equation. If the result is true, your solution is correct. If the result is false, then you need to go back and find your error. Try to check all your solutions as this will improve your algebra skills.

To check whether 3 is the solution to $x + 4 = 7$, we substitute 3 for each *x* in the equation.

Check
$$x = 3$$
$$x + 4 = 7$$
$$3 + 4 \stackrel{?}{=} 7$$
$$7 = 7 \quad \text{True}$$

Since the check results in a true statement, 3 is a solution.

EXAMPLE 1 Consider the equation $2x - 4 = 6$. Determine whether 3 is a solution.

Solution   To determine whether 3 is a solution to the equation, we substitute 3 for *x*.

Check
$$x = 3$$
$$2x - 4 = 6$$
$$2(3) - 4 \stackrel{?}{=} 6$$
$$6 - 4 \stackrel{?}{=} 6$$
$$2 = 6 \quad \text{False}$$

Since we obtained a false statement, 3 is not a solution.

Now Try Exercise 11

Now check to see if 5 is a solution to the equation in Example 1. Your check should show that 5 is a solution.

EXAMPLE 2 Determine whether 18 is a solution to the following equation.

$$3x - 2(x + 3) = 12$$

Solution   To determine whether 18 is a solution, we substitute 18 for each x in the equation.

Check

$$x = 18$$
$$3x - 2(x + 3) = 12$$
$$3(18) - 2(18 + 3) \stackrel{?}{=} 12$$
$$3(18) - 2(21) \stackrel{?}{=} 12$$
$$54 - 42 \stackrel{?}{=} 12$$
$$12 = 12 \quad \text{True}$$

Since we obtained a true statement, 18 is a solution.

Now Try Exercise 15

EXAMPLE 3 Determine whether $-\dfrac{3}{2}$ is a solution to the following equation.

$$3(n + 3) = 6 + n$$

Solution   Substitute $-\dfrac{3}{2}$ for each n in the equation.

Check

$$n = -\frac{3}{2}$$
$$3(n + 3) = 6 + n$$
$$3\left(-\frac{3}{2} + 3\right) \stackrel{?}{=} 6 + \left(-\frac{3}{2}\right)$$
$$3\left(-\frac{3}{2} + \frac{6}{2}\right) \stackrel{?}{=} \frac{12}{2} - \frac{3}{2}$$
$$3\left(\frac{3}{2}\right) \stackrel{?}{=} \frac{9}{2}$$
$$\frac{9}{2} = \frac{9}{2} \quad \text{True}$$

Thus, $-\dfrac{3}{2}$ is a solution.

Now Try Exercise 21

3 | Identify Equivalent Equations

Left side of equation = Right side of equation

FIGURE 2.1

To **solve an equation** means to find its solution. *To solve an equation, it is necessary to get the variable alone on one side of the equals sign. When we get an equation in this form, we say that we isolated the variable.* To isolate the variable we make use of two properties: the addition and multiplication properties of equality. Look first at **Figure 2.1.**

Think of an equation as a balanced statement whose left side is balanced by its right side. When solving an equation, we must make sure that the equation remains balanced at all times. *We ensure that an equation always remains balanced by doing the same thing to both sides of the equation.* For example, if we add a number to the left side of the equation, we must add exactly the same number to the right side. If we multiply the right side of the equation by some number, we must multiply the left side by the same number.

When we add the same number to both sides of an equation or multiply both sides of an equation by the same nonzero number, we do not change the solution to the

Understanding Algebra

The strategy for solving a linear equation is to *isolate* the variable on one side of the = sign.

Understanding Algebra

Think of an equation as a balance scale. When a solution checks, the scale balances:

But when a solution doesn't check, the sides are not in balance:

Understanding Algebra

Since we can think of an equation as a scale we are trying to keep in balance, adding the same quantity to both sides preserves the balance.

Now, add 4 to both sides: $x - 4 + 4 = -3 + 4$ or simply $x = 1$.

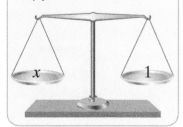

equation. Two or more equations with the same solution are called **equivalent equations.** The equations $2x - 4 = 2, 2x = 6,$ and $x = 3$ are equivalent, since the solution to each is 3.

Check: $x = 3$

$$2x - 4 = 2 \qquad\qquad 2x = 6 \qquad\qquad x = 3$$
$$2(3) - 4 \overset{?}{=} 2 \qquad\quad 2(3) \overset{?}{=} 6 \qquad\quad 3 = 3 \quad \text{True}$$
$$6 - 4 \overset{?}{=} 2 \qquad\qquad 6 = 6 \quad \text{True}$$
$$2 = 2 \quad \text{True}$$

When solving an equation, we use the addition and multiplication properties to express a given equation as equivalent equations until we obtain the solution.

4 Use the Addition Property to Solve Equations

Now we are ready to define the **addition property of equality.**

> **Addition Property of Equality**
>
> If $a = b$ then $a + c = b + c$ for any real numbers a, b, and c.

This property means that the same number can be added to both sides of an equation.

To isolate the variable when solving equations of the form $x + a = b$, *we add* $(-a)$ *to both sides of the equals sign.* This isolates the variable x on the left side of the equation.

Equation	To Solve, Use the Addition Property to Eliminate the Number . . .	. . . By Adding the Opposite to Both Sides
$x - 4 = -3$	-4	4
$x + 5 = 9$	5	-5
$-3 = k + 7$	7	-7
$-5 = x - 4$	-4	4
$-6.25 = y + 12.78$	12.78	-12.78

Now let's work some examples.

EXAMPLE 4 Solve the equation $x - 4 = -3$.

Solution   To isolate the variable, x, we must eliminate the -4 from the left side of the equation. To do this we add 4, the opposite of -4, to *both sides* of the equation.

$$x - 4 = -3$$
$$x - 4 + 4 = -3 + 4 \qquad \text{Add 4 to both sides.}$$
$$x + 0 = 1$$
$$x = 1$$

Note how the process helps to isolate x.

Check $x - 4 = -3$
$$1 - 4 \overset{?}{=} -3$$
$$-3 = -3 \quad \text{True}$$

Now Try Exercise 27

Space limitations prevent us from showing all checks. However, *you should check all of your answers.*

EXAMPLE 5 Solve the equation $x + 5 = 9$. ——————

Solution   To solve this equation, we must eliminate the 5 from the left side of the equation. To do this, we add -5, the opposite of 5, to *both sides* of the equation.

$$x + 5 = 9$$
$$x + 5 + (\boxed{-5}) = 9 + (\boxed{-5}) \quad \text{Add } -5 \text{ to both sides.}$$
$$x + 0 = 4$$
$$x = 4$$

Now Try Exercise 29

Understanding Algebra

"Subtract 5 from both sides" is equivalent to saying "Add (-5) to both sides."

In Example 5, we added -5 to both sides of the equation. We know that $5 + (-5) = 5 - 5$. Thus, adding a negative 5 to both sides of the equation is equivalent to subtracting a 5 from both sides of the equation. *Since subtraction is defined in terms of addition, the addition property also allows us to subtract the same number from both sides of the equation.* Thus, Example 5 could have also been worked as follows:

$$x + 5 = 9$$
$$x + 5 \boxed{- 5} = 9 \boxed{- 5} \quad \text{Subtract 5 from both sides.}$$
$$x + 0 = 4$$
$$x = 4$$

Rather than adding a negative number to both sides of the equation, we will subtract a number from both sides of the equation.

EXAMPLE 6 Solve the equation $-3 = k + 7$. ——————

Solution   We must isolate the variable, k, which is on the right side of the equals sign.

$$-3 = k + 7$$
$$-3 \boxed{- 7} = k + 7 \boxed{- 7} \quad \text{Subtract 7 from both sides.}$$
$$-10 = k + 0$$
$$-10 = k$$

Check

$$-3 = k + 7$$
$$-3 \stackrel{?}{=} -10 + 7$$
$$-3 = -3 \qquad \text{True}$$

Now Try Exercise 25

Helpful Hint

Remember that our goal in solving an equation is to get the variable alone on one side of the equation. To do this, we add or subtract *the number on the same side of the equation as the variable* to or from both sides of the equation.

Equation	Must Eliminate	Number to Add (or Subtract) to (or from) Both Sides of the Equation	Correct Results	Solution
$x - 5 = 8$	-5	add 5	$x - 5 + 5 = 8 + 5$	$x = 13$
$x - 3 = -12$	-3	add 3	$x - 3 + 3 = -12 + 3$	$x = -9$
$2 = x - 7$	-7	add 7	$2 + 7 = x - 7 + 7$	$9 = x$ or $x = 9$
$x + 12 = -5$	$+12$	subtract 12	$x + 12 - 12 = -5 - 12$	$x = -17$
$6 = x + 4$	$+4$	subtract 4	$6 - 4 = x + 4 - 4$	$2 = x$ or $x = 2$
$13 = x + 9$	$+9$	subtract 9	$13 - 9 = x + 9 - 9$	$4 = x$ or $x = 4$

Notice that under the *Correct Results* column, when the equation is simplified by combining terms, the x will become isolated because the sum of a number and its opposite is 0, and $x + 0$ equals x.

EXAMPLE 7   Solve the equation $-5 = x - 4$. ─────

Solution   The variable, x, is on the right side of the equation. By adding 4 to both sides of the equation, we eliminate -4 from the right and x is isolated on the right side:

$$-5 = x - 4$$
$$-5 \;+\; 4 = x - 4 \;+\; 4 \qquad \text{Add 4 to both sides.}$$
$$-1 = x + 0$$
$$-1 = x$$

Thus, the solution is -1.

Now Try Exercise 35

EXAMPLE 8   Solve the equation $-6.25 = y + 12.78$. ─────

Solution   The variable, y, is on the right side of the equation. To isolate the variable, subtract 12.78 from both sides of the equation.

$$-6.25 = y + 12.78$$
$$-6.25 \;-\; 12.78 = y + 12.78 \;-\; 12.78 \qquad \text{Subtract 12.78 from both sides.}$$
$$-19.03 = y + 0$$
$$-19.03 = y$$

Thus, the solution is -19.03.

Now Try Exercise 65

Avoiding Common Errors

When solving an equation, our goal is to isolate the variable on one side of the equals sign. Consider the equation $x + 3 = -4$. How do we solve it?

CORRECT

Remove the 3 from the left side of the equation.

$$x + 3 = -4$$
$$x + 3 \;-\; 3 = -4 \;-\; 3$$
$$x = -7$$

Variable is now isolated.

INCORRECT

Remove the -4 from the right side of the equation.

$$x + 3 = -4$$
$$x + 3 \;+\; 4 = -4 \;+\; 4$$
$$x + 7 = 0$$

Variable is not isolated.

Remember, use the addition property to *remove the number that is on the same side of the equals sign as the variable.*

---

5   Solve Equations by Doing Some Steps Mentally

Consider the following two problems.

a)
$$x \;-\; 5 = 12$$
$$x - 5 + 5 = 12 + 5$$
$$x + 0 = 12 \;+\; 5$$
$$x = 17$$

b)
$$15 = x \;+\; 3$$
$$15 - 3 = x + 3 - 3$$
$$15 \;-\; 3 = x + 0$$
$$12 = x$$

When you feel comfortable using the addition property of equality, you may wish to do some of the steps mentally to reduce some of the written work. For example, the preceding two problems may be shortened as follows:

Shortened Form

a)
$$x - 5 = 12$$
$$x - 5 + 5 = 12 + 5$$ ← Do this step mentally.
$$x = 12 + 5$$
$$x = 17$$

Shortened Form
$$x - 5 = 12$$
$$x = 12 + 5$$
$$x = 17$$

b)
$$15 = x + 3$$
$$15 - 3 = x + 3 - 3$$ ← Do this step mentally.
$$15 - 3 = x$$
$$12 = x$$

Shortened Form
$$15 = x + 3$$
$$15 - 3 = x$$
$$12 = x$$

EXERCISE SET 2.2

Math XL   MyMathLab
MathXL®   MyMathLab

Warm-Up Exercises

Fill in the blanks with the appropriate word, phrase, or symbol(s) from the following list.

~~equation~~   solutions   True   ~~linear~~   ~~2~~   opposite
~~6~~   isolate   ~~equivalent~~   False   ~~check~~

1. To solve the equation $6 = x - 2$, first add _____2_____ to both sides of the equation.

2. Numbers which, when substituted for the variable, make the equation a true statement are called ___Solutions___.

3. The strategy for solving a linear equation in one variable includes a process to ___isolate___ the variable.

4. The symbol $\stackrel{?}{=}$ is used to ___check___ the solution in the given equation.

5. The equation $x - 3 = -19$ is an example of a ___linear___ equation in the variable x.

6. Two equations with the same solutions are called ___equivalent___ equations.

7. A statement of equality between two expressions, like $x + 7 = 19$, is called an ___equation___.

8. To solve the equation $x - 6 = -2$, first add ___6___ to both sides of the equation.

9. When solving the equation $x + a = b$, the ___opposite___ of a is added to both sides.

10. (True or False) The equation $x + 19 = -14$ and $x + 60 = 27$ are equivalent equations. ___True___

Practice the Skills

11. Is $x = 2$ a solution of $4x - 3 = 5$? True

12. Is $x = -6$ a solution of $2x + 1 = x - 5$?

13. Is $x = -3$ a solution of $2x - 5 = 5(x + 2)$? False

14. Is $x = 1$ a solution of $2(x - 3) = -3(x + 1)$?

15. Is $p = -15$ a solution of $2p - 5(p + 7) = 10$? True

16. Is $k = -2$ a solution of $5k - 6(k - 1) = 8$?

17. Is $x = 3.4$ a solution of $3(x + 2) - 3(x - 1) = 9$? True

18. Is $x = \dfrac{3}{4}$ a solution of $x + 5 = 5x + 2$?

19. Is $x = \dfrac{1}{2}$ a solution of $4x - 4 = 2x - 2$? False

20. Is $x = \dfrac{1}{3}$ a solution of $7x + 3 = 2x + 5$?

21. Is $x = \dfrac{11}{2}$ a solution of $3(x + 2) = 5(x - 1)$? True

22. Is $h = 3$ a solution of $-(h - 5) - (h - 6) = 3h - 4$?

Solve each equation and check your solution.

23. $x + 2 = 7$ $x = 5$

24. $x - 4 = 13$

25. $-6 = x + 1$ $x = -7$

26. $-5 = x + 4$

27. $x - 4 = -8$ $x = -4$

28. $x - 16 = -12$

29. $t + 9 = 52$ $t = 43$

30. $x + 8 = 17$

31. $-6 + w = 9$ $w = 15$

32. $3 = 7 + t$

33. $27 = x + 16$ $x = 11$

34. $50 = x - 35$

35. $-18 = x - 14$ $x = -4$

36. $-4 = w + 5$

37. $9 + x = 4$ $x = -5$

38. $x + 29 = -29$

39. $4 + x = -8$ $x = -12$

40. $9 = x - 3$

41. $7 + r = -23$ $r = -30$

42. $a - 5 = -9$

43. $8 = 8 + v$ $v = 0$

44. $9 + x = 12$

45. $7 + x = -50$ $x = -57$

46. $-19 = 8 + t$

47. $12 = 16 + x$ $x = -4$

48. $62 = z - 15$

49. $15 + y = -50$ $y = -65$

50. $-20 = 4 + x$

51. $-15 + x = -15$ $x = 0$ **52.** $8 = 8 + x$ **53.** $5 = x - 12$ $x = 17$ **54.** $-12 = 20 + c$

55. $-50 = x - 24$ $x = -26$ **56.** $-29 + x = -15$ **57.** $43 = 15 + p$ $p = 28$ **58.** $-25 = 74 + x$

59. $40.2 + d = -5.9$ $d = -46.1$ **60.** $-27.23 + x = 9.77$ **61.** $-37 + x = 9.5$ $x = 46.5$ **62.** $7.2 + x = 7.2$

63. $x - 8.77 = -17$ $x = 8.23$ **64.** $6.1 + x = 10.2$ **65.** $9.32 = x + 3.75$ $x = 5.57$ **66.** $-5.62 = y + 11.39$

Problem Solving

67. Do you think the equation $x + 1 = x + 2$ has a real number as a solution? Explain. (We will discuss equations like this in Section 2.5.)

68. Do you think the equation $x + 4 = x + 4$ has more than one real number as a solution? If so, how many solutions does it have? Explain. (We will discuss equations like this in Section 2.5.)

Concept/Writing Exercises

69. To solve a linear equation, we "isolate the variable." Explain what this means.

70. Explain why these three equations are equivalent:
$$2x + 3 = 5, \qquad 2x = 2, \qquad x = 1$$

Challenge Problems

We can solve equations that contain unknown symbols. Solve each equation for the symbol indicated by adding or subtracting a symbol to or from both sides of the equation. Explain each answer. (Remember that to solve the equation you want to isolate the symbol you are solving for on one side of the equation.)

71. $x - \triangle = \square$, for x

72. $\square + ☺ = \triangle$, for ☺

73. ☺ $= \square + \triangle$, for $\square$

74. $\square = \triangle + ☺$, for ☺

Group Activity

Discuss and answer Exercise 75 as a group.

75. Consider the equation $2(x + 3) = 2x + 6$.

  a) Group member 1: Determine whether 4 is a solution to the equation.

  b) Group member 2: Determine whether -2 is a solution to the equation.

  c) Group member 3: Determine whether 0.3 is a solution to the equation.

  d) Each group member: Select a number not used in parts **a)–c)** and determine whether that number is a solution to the equation.

  e) As a group, write what you think is the solution to the equation $2(x + 3) = 2x + 6$ and write a paragraph explaining your answer.

Cumulative Review Exercises

[1.6]   *Add.*

76. $-\dfrac{7}{15} + \dfrac{5}{6}$

77. $-\dfrac{11}{12} + \left(-\dfrac{3}{8}\right)$

[2.1]   *Simplify.*

78. $4x + 3(x - 2) - 5x - 7$

79. $-(2t + 4) + 3(4t - 7) - 3t$

2.3 The Multiplication Property of Equality

1 Identify reciprocals.

2 Use the multiplication property to solve equations.

3 Solve equations of the form $-x = a$.

4 Do some steps mentally when solving equations.

1 Identify Reciprocals

Recall that two numbers are **reciprocals** of each other when their product is 1. Some examples of numbers and their reciprocals follow.

Number	Reciprocal	Product
2	$\dfrac{1}{2}$	$(2)\left(\dfrac{1}{2}\right) = 1$
$-\dfrac{3}{5}$	$-\dfrac{5}{3}$	$\left(-\dfrac{3}{5}\right)\left(-\dfrac{5}{3}\right) = 1$
-1	-1	$(-1)(-1) = 1$

Understanding Algebra

"*Reciprocal*" and "*multiplicative inverse*" are synonyms. The reciprocal of the variable x is $\dfrac{1}{x}$, $x \neq 0$.

The reciprocal of a positive number is a positive number and the reciprocal of a negative number is a negative number. Note that 0 has no reciprocal.

2 Use the Multiplication Property to Solve Equations

In Section 2.2, we used the addition property of equality to solve equations of the form $x + a = b$, where a and b represent real numbers. In this section, we use the multiplication property of equality to solve equations of the form $ax = b$, where a and b represent real numbers.

> **Helpful Hint**
>
> It is important that you recognize the difference between equations like $x + 2 = 8$ and $2x = 8$. In $x + 2 = 8$, the 2 is a *term* that is being added to x, so we use the addition property to solve the equation. In $2x = 8$, the 2 is a *factor* of $2x$. The 2 is the coefficient multiplying the x, so we use the multiplication property to solve the equation.

Multiplication Property of Equality

If $a = b$, then $a \cdot c = b \cdot c$ for any real numbers a, b, and c.

This property means that both sides of an equation can be multiplied by the same nonzero number. *The multiplication property can be used to solve equations of the form $ax = b$.* We can isolate the variable in equations of this form by multiplying both sides of the equation by the reciprocal of a, which is $\dfrac{1}{a}$. Doing so makes the numerical coefficient of the variable, x, become 1.

Understanding Algebra

Since we can think of an equation as a scale we are trying to keep in balance, multiplying the same quantity on both sides preserves the balance.

Now, multiply by $-\dfrac{1}{5}$ on both sides:

$-\dfrac{1}{5}(-5x) = -\dfrac{1}{5}(20)$ or

simply $x = -4$.

Equation	To Solve, Use the Multiplication Property to Change the Term . . .	. . . By Multiplying Both Sides by the Reciprocal
$4x = 9$	$4x$ to $1x$	$\dfrac{1}{4}$
$-5x = 20$	$-5x$ to $1x$	$-\dfrac{1}{5}$
$15 = \dfrac{1}{2}x$	$\dfrac{1}{2}x$ to $1x$	2
$7 = -\dfrac{3}{5}x$	$-\dfrac{3}{5}x$ to $1x$	$-\dfrac{5}{3}$

Now let's work some examples.

EXAMPLE 1 Solve the equation $9x = 63$.

Solution   To isolate the variable, x, we must change the $9x$ on the left side of the equals sign to $1x$. To do this, we multiply both sides of the equation by the reciprocal of 9, which is $\dfrac{1}{9}$.

$$9x = 63$$

$$\frac{1}{9} \cdot 9x = \frac{1}{9} \cdot 63 \qquad \text{Multiply both sides by } \frac{1}{9}.$$

$$\frac{1}{\underset{1}{9}} \cdot \overset{1}{9}x = \frac{1}{\underset{1}{9}} \cdot \overset{7}{63} \qquad \text{Divide out the common factors.}$$

$$1x = 7$$

$$x = 7$$

Now Try Exercise 9

Notice in Example 1 that $1x$ is replaced by x in the last step. Usually we do this step mentally.

EXAMPLE 2 Solve the equation $\dfrac{x}{2} = 4$.

Solution   Since dividing by 2 is the same as multiplying by $\dfrac{1}{2}$, the equation $\dfrac{x}{2} = 4$ is the same as $\dfrac{1}{2}x = 4$. We will therefore multiply both sides of the equation by the reciprocal of $\dfrac{1}{2}$, which is 2.

$$\frac{x}{2} = 4$$

$$\overset{1}{\cancel{2}}\left(\frac{x}{\cancel{2}}\right) = 2 \cdot 4 \qquad \text{Multiply both sides by 2.}$$

$$x = 2 \cdot 4$$

$$x = 8$$

Now Try Exercise 11

> **Understanding Algebra**
>
> $\dfrac{x}{2}$ is the same as $\dfrac{1}{2}x$.

EXAMPLE 3 Solve the equation $\dfrac{2}{3}x = 6$.

Solution   The reciprocal of $\dfrac{2}{3}$ is $\dfrac{3}{2}$. We multiply both sides of the equation by $\dfrac{3}{2}$.

$$\frac{2}{3}x = 6$$

$$\frac{3}{2} \cdot \frac{2}{3}x = \frac{3}{2} \cdot 6 \qquad \text{Multiply both sides by } \frac{3}{2}.$$

$$1x = 9 \qquad \overset{9}{\underset{}{\frac{18}{2}}}$$

$$x = 9$$

We will show a check of this solution.

Check

$$\frac{2}{3}x = 6 \quad \tfrac{3}{1} \; \tfrac{}{2} \; = \; \tfrac{18}{2} \; = 9$$

$$6 = \frac{18}{3} \qquad \frac{2}{3}(9) \overset{?}{=} 6$$

$$6 = 6 \qquad \text{True}$$

Now Try Exercise 49

In Example 1, we multiplied both sides of the equation $9x = 63$ by $\dfrac{1}{9}$ to isolate the variable. We could have also isolated the variable by dividing both sides of the equation by 9, as follows:

$$9x = 63$$

$$\frac{\overset{1}{\cancel{9}}x}{\underset{1}{\cancel{9}}} = \frac{\overset{7}{\cancel{63}}}{\underset{1}{\cancel{9}}} \qquad \text{Divide both sides by 9.}$$

$$x = 7$$

> **Understanding Algebra**
>
> ***Strategy for Equation-Solving:***
>
> 1. Isolate the variable on one side of the equation.
> 2. Be sure the coefficient of the variable is a "1" by multiplying both sides of the equation by the reciprocal of the coefficient of the variable.

We can do this because dividing by 9 is equivalent to multiplying by $\dfrac{1}{9}$. *Since division can be defined in terms of multiplication* $\left(\dfrac{a}{b} \text{ means } a \cdot \dfrac{1}{b}\right)$, *the multiplication property also allows us to divide both sides of an equation by the same nonzero number.*

EXAMPLE 4 Solve the equation $8w = 3$. ────────

Solution   To solve the equation we divide both sides of the equation by 8.

$$8w = 3$$

$$\frac{8w}{8} = \frac{3}{8} \quad \text{Divide both sides by 8.}$$

$$w = \frac{3}{8}$$

Now Try Exercise 33

EXAMPLE 5 Solve the equation $-15 = -3z$. ────────

Solution   To isolate z, we divide both sides of the equation by -3.

$$-15 = -3z$$

$$\frac{-15}{-3} = \frac{-3z}{-3} \quad \text{Divide both sides by }-3.$$

$$5 = z$$

Now Try Exercise 21

EXAMPLE 6 Solve the equation $0.24x = 1.20$. ────────

Solution   Divide both sides of the equation by 0.24 to isolate the variable x.

$$0.24x = 1.20$$

$$\frac{0.24x}{0.24} = \frac{1.20}{0.24} \quad \text{Divide both sides by 0.24.}$$

$$1x = 5$$

$$x = 5$$

Now Try Exercise 35

Helpful Hint

When solving an equation of the form $ax = b$, we can isolate the variable by

1. multiplying both sides of the equation by the reciprocal of a, $\dfrac{1}{a}$, as was done in Examples 1, 2, and 3, or

2. dividing both sides of the equation by a, as was done in Examples 4, 5, and 6.

Either method may be used to isolate the variable. However, if the equation contains a fraction, or fractions, you will arrive at a solution more quickly by multiplying by the reciprocal of a. This is illustrated in Examples 7 and 8.

EXAMPLE 7 Solve the equation $-2x = \dfrac{3}{5}$. ────────

Solution   Since this equation contains a fraction, we will isolate the variable by multiplying both sides of the equation by $-\dfrac{1}{2}$, which is the reciprocal of -2.

$$-2x = \frac{3}{5}$$

$$\left(-\frac{1}{2}\right)(-2x) = \left(-\frac{1}{2}\right)\left(\frac{3}{5}\right) \quad \text{Multiply both sides by }-\frac{1}{2}.$$

$$1x = \left(-\frac{1}{2}\right)\left(\frac{3}{5}\right)$$

$$x = -\frac{3}{10}$$

Now Try Exercise 39

EXAMPLE 8 Solve the equation $-6 = -\dfrac{3}{5}x$.

Solution Since this equation contains a fraction, we will isolate the variable by multiplying both sides of the equation by the reciprocal of $-\dfrac{3}{5}$, which is $-\dfrac{5}{3}$.

$$-6 = -\frac{3}{5}x$$

$$\left(-\frac{5}{3}\right)(-6) = \left(-\frac{5}{3}\right)\left(-\frac{3}{5}x\right) \quad \text{Multiply both sides by } -\frac{5}{3}.$$

$$10 = 1x$$

$$10 = x$$

Now Try Exercise 57

In Example 8, the equation was written as $-6 = -\dfrac{3}{5}x$. This equation is equivalent to the equations $-6 = \dfrac{-3}{5}x$ and $-6 = \dfrac{3}{-5}x$. Can you explain why? All three equations have the same solution, 10.

3 Solve Equations of the Form $-x = a$

When solving an equation, we may obtain an equation like $-x = 7$. This is not a solution since $-x = 7$ means $-1x = 7$. The solution to an equation is of the form $x =$ some number. When an equation is of the form $-x = 7$, we can solve for x by multiplying both sides of the equation by -1, as illustrated in the following example.

EXAMPLE 9 Solve the equation $-x = 7$.

Solution $-x = 7$ means that $-1x = 7$. We are solving for x, not $-x$. We can multiply both sides of the equation by -1 to isolate x on the left side of the equation.

$$-x = 7$$

$$-1x = 7$$

$$(-1)(-1x) = (-1)(7) \quad \text{Multiply both sides by } -1.$$

$$1x = -7$$

$$x = -7$$

Check

$$-x = 7$$

$$-(-7) \overset{?}{=} 7$$

$$7 = 7 \quad \text{True}$$

Thus, the solution is -7.

Now Try Exercise 23

Understanding Algebra

For any real number a, if $-x = a$, then $x = -a$. For example,

if $-x = 7$, then $x = -7$.

If $-x = -2$, then $x = 2$.

Example 9 may also be solved by dividing both sides of the equation by -1. Whenever we have the negative of a variable equal to a quantity, as in Example 9, we can solve for the variable by multiplying or dividing both sides of the equation by -1.

EXAMPLE 10 Solve the equation $-x = -5$.

Solution

$$-x = -5$$

$$-1x = -5$$

$$(-1)(-1x) = (-1)(-5) \quad \text{Multiply both sides by } -1.$$

$$1x = 5$$

$$x = 5$$

Now Try Exercise 25

4 Do Some Steps Mentally When Solving Equations

When you feel comfortable using the multiplication property, you may wish to do some of the steps mentally to reduce some of the written work. Now we present two examples worked out in detail, along with their shortened form.

EXAMPLE 11 Solve the equation $-3t = -21$.

Solution

$$-3t = -21$$

$$\frac{-3t}{-3} = \frac{-21}{-3} \quad \longleftarrow \quad \boxed{\text{Do this step mentally.}}$$

$$t = \frac{-21}{-3}$$

$$\boxed{t = 7}$$

SHORTENED FORM

$$-3t = -21$$

$$t = \frac{-21}{-3}$$

$$t = 7$$

Now Try Exercise 61

EXAMPLE 12 Solve the equation $\frac{1}{5}x = 20$.

Solution

$$\frac{1}{5}x = 20$$

$$5\left(\frac{1}{5}x\right) = 5(20) \quad \longleftarrow \quad \boxed{\text{Do this step mentally.}}$$

$$x = 5(20)$$

$$\boxed{x = 100}$$

SHORTENED FORM

$$\frac{1}{5}x = 20$$

$$x = 5(20)$$

$$x = 100$$

Now Try Exercise 63

> **Helpful Hint**
>
> The **addition property** is used to solve equations of the form $x + a = b$. The *addition property* is used when a number is *added to or subtracted from* a variable.
>
> $$x + 3 = -6$$
> $$x + 3 - 3 = -6 - 3$$
> $$x = -9$$
>
> $$x - 5 = -2$$
> $$x - 5 + 5 = -2 + 5$$
> $$x = 3$$
>
> The **multiplication property** is used to solve equations of the form $ax = b$. It is used when a variable is *multiplied* or *divided by* a number.
>
> $$3x = 6$$
> $$\frac{3x}{3} = \frac{6}{3}$$
> $$x = 2$$
>
> $$\frac{x}{2} = 4$$
> $$2\left(\frac{x}{2}\right) = 2(4)$$
> $$x = 8$$
>
> $$\frac{2}{5}x = 12$$
> $$\left(\frac{5}{2}\right)\left(\frac{2}{5}x\right) = \left(\frac{5}{2}\right)(12)$$
> $$x = 30$$

EXERCISE SET 2.3   Math XL   MyMathLab
MathXL®   MyMathLab

Warm-Up Exercises

Fill in the blanks with the appropriate word, phrase, or symbol(s) from the following list.

$\frac{x}{3}$ $\frac{3}{x}$ $\frac{1}{3}$ 1 check

1 multiplicative inverse 3 isolate $\frac{7}{x}$

1. The expression $\frac{1}{3}x$ can be rewritten as ____$\frac{x}{3}$____ .

2. To solve the equation $3x = 5$, multiply both sides of the equation by ____$1/3$____ .

3. To solve the equation $\frac{x}{3} = 7$, we multiply both sides of the equation by ____$\frac{3}{3}$____ .

4. The strategy for solving a linear equation in one variable includes a process to ____Isolate____ the variable.

5. The symbol $\stackrel{?}{=}$ is used to ____check____ the solution in the given equation.

6. Another way of saying "reciprocal" is ____Multiplicative Inverse____

7. The reciprocal of $\frac{x}{-7}$ is ____$-7/x$____ .

8. Two numbers equal to their own reciprocal are ____1____ and ____-1____ .

Practice the Skills

Solve each equation and check your solution.

9. $5x = 20$ $\frac{20}{5}$ $x=4$ $5(4)=20$

10. $5x = 50$

11. $\frac{x}{3} = 7$

12. $\frac{y}{5} = 3$

13. $4x = 12$ $\frac{x=3}{4}$ $-4(3)=12$

14. $8 = 16y$

15. $\frac{x}{4} = -20$

16. $\frac{x}{3} = -3$

17. $\frac{x}{5} = 4$ $x=20$ $\frac{20}{5}=4$

18. $-7t = 49$

19. $-27n = 81$

20. $\frac{x}{8} = -3$

21. $-7 = 3r$ $r=-\frac{1}{3}$ $3(\frac{7}{3})$

22. $16 = -4y$

23. $-x = 13$

24. $-x = 9$

25. $-x = -8$ $x=8$

26. $-x = -15$

27. $-\frac{w}{3} = -10$

28. $-4 = \frac{c}{7}$

29. $4 = -12x$ $x=-\frac{4}{12}$ $x=-\frac{1}{3}$

30. $12y = -15$

31. $-\frac{x}{3} = -2$

32. $-\frac{a}{8} = -7$

33. $43t = 26$ $t=\frac{26}{43}$

34. $-24x = -18$

35. $-4.2x = -8.4$

36. $-3.88 = 1.94y$

37. $3x = \frac{3}{5}$ $x=\frac{3}{15}$ $x=\frac{1}{5}$

38. $7x = -7$

39. $5x = -\frac{3}{8}$

40. $-2b = -\frac{4}{5}$

41. $16 = -\frac{x}{4}$ $x=-64$

42. $\frac{c}{9} = 0$

43. $-\frac{b}{4} = -60$

44. $-x = -\frac{5}{9}$

45. $\frac{x}{5} = -9$ $x=-45$

46. $-3r = 0$

47. $5 = \frac{x}{4}$

48. $-8 = \frac{x}{-5}$

49. $\frac{3}{5}d = -30$ $d=-50$

50. $\frac{2}{7}x = 7$

51. $\frac{y}{-2} = 0$

52. $-6x = \frac{5}{2}$

53. $\frac{-7}{8}w = 0$ $w=0$

54. $-x = \frac{15}{8}$

55. $\frac{1}{5}x = 4.5$

56. $-\frac{1}{4}x = \frac{3}{4}$

57. $-4 = -\frac{2}{3}z$ $-4=-\frac{2}{3}(6)$ $z=6$

58. $-9 = \frac{-5}{3}n$

59. $-1.4x = 28.28$

60. $-0.42x = -2.142$

Solve each equation by doing some steps mentally. Check your solution.

61. $-8x = -56$ $-8(7)$ $x=7$

62. $-9x = -45$ $-9(5)=45$ $x=5$

63. $\frac{2}{3}x = 6$ $\frac{2}{3}(9)$ $\frac{18}{3}=6$ $x=9$

64. $\frac{1}{3}x = 15$ $\frac{1}{3}(45)$ $\frac{45}{3}=15$ $x=45$

Concept/Writing Exercises

65. a) Explain the difference between $5 + x = 10$ and $5x = 10$.   addition property / multiplication property
   b) Solve $5 + x = 10$. $x=5$
   c) Solve $5x = 10$. $x=2$

66. a) Explain the difference between $3 + x = 6$ and $3x = 6$.
   b) Solve $3 + x = 6$. $x=3$
   c) Solve $3x = 6$. $x=2$

67. Consider the equation $\frac{2}{3}x = 4$. This equation could be solved by multiplying both sides of the equation by $\frac{3}{2}$, the reciprocal of $\frac{2}{3}$, or by dividing both sides of the equation by $\frac{2}{3}$. Which method do you feel would be easier? Explain your answer. Find the solution to the equation. $\frac{12}{2}$

68. Consider the equation $4x = \frac{3}{5}$. Would it be easier to solve this equation by dividing both sides of the equation by 4 or by multiplying both sides of the equation by $\frac{1}{4}$, the reciprocal of 4? Explain your answer. Find the solution to the problem.

69. Consider the equation $\frac{3}{7}x = \frac{4}{5}$. Would it be easier to solve this equation by dividing both sides of the equation by $\frac{3}{7}$ or by multiplying both sides of the equation by $\frac{7}{3}$, the reciprocal of $\frac{3}{7}$? Explain your answer. Find the solution to the equation.

Challenge Problems

70. Consider the equation $\square \odot = \triangle$.

    a) To solve for $\odot$, what symbol do we need to isolate?

    b) How would you isolate the symbol you specified in part **a)**?

    c) Solve the equation for $\odot$.

71. Consider the equation $\odot = \triangle \square$.

    a) To solve for $\square$, what symbol do we need to isolate?

    b) How would you isolate the symbol you specified in part **a)**?

    c) Solve the equation for $\square$.

72. Consider the equation $\# = \dfrac{\odot}{\triangle}$.

    a) To solve for $\odot$, what symbol do we need to isolate?

    b) How would you isolate the symbol you specified in part **a)**?

    c) Solve the equation for $\odot$.

Cumulative Review Exercises

[1.7] **73.** Subtract -4 from -8.

[1.8] **74.** Evaluate $(-3)(-2)(5)(-1)$.

[1.9] **75.** Evaluate $4^2 - 2^3 \cdot 6 \div 3 + 6$.

[1.10] **76.** Name the property illustrated.
$$2 + (4 + y) = (2 + 4) + y$$

[2.2] **77.** Solve the equation $-48 = x + 9$.

2.4 Solving Linear Equations with a Variable on Only One Side of the Equation

1. Solve linear equations with a variable on only one side of the equals sign.

2. Solve equations containing decimal numbers or fractions.

1 Solve Linear Equations with a Variable on Only One Side of the Equals Sign

In this section, we will use *both* the addition and multiplication properties of equality to solve linear equations in which the variable appears on only one side of the equals sign.

No one method is the "best" to solve all linear equations. But the following general procedure can be used to solve linear equations when the variable appears on only one side of the equation.

> **To Solve Linear Equations with a Variable on Only One Side of the Equals Sign**
>
> 1. If the equation contains fractions, multiply *both* sides of the equation by the least common denominator (LCD). This will eliminate the fractions from the equation.
> 2. Use the distributive property to remove parentheses.
> 3. Combine like terms on the same side of the equals sign.
> 4. Use the addition property to obtain an equation with the term containing the variable on one side of the equals sign and a constant on the other side. This will result in an equation of the form $ax = b$.
> 5. Use the multiplication property to isolate the variable.
> 6. Check the solution in the original equation.

Understanding Algebra

As we solve more complicated equations, these six steps will provide the strategy for *isolating the variable*.

When solving an equation you should always check your solution. To conserve space, we will not show all checks.

Consider the equation $2x + 4 = 10$, which contains no fractions, no parentheses, and no like terms on the same side of the equals sign. Therefore, we start with step 4.

$$2x + 4 = 10$$
$$2x + 4 - 4 = 10 - 4 \qquad \text{Addition property (add } (-4) \text{ to both sides).}$$
$$2x = 6 \qquad x\text{-term is now isolated on the left.}$$

Now we use the multiplication property (step 5) to solve for x.

$$2x = 6$$

$$\frac{2x}{2} = \frac{6}{2} \qquad \text{Multiplication property (divide both sides by 2).}$$

$$1x = 3 \qquad \text{We need not write the coefficient ``1.''}$$

$$x = 3 \qquad \text{Final answer}$$

The solution to the equation $2x + 4 = 10$ is 3. Check this solution:

$$2x + 4 = 10$$
$$2(3) + 4 = 10$$
$$6 + 4 = 10$$
$$10 = 10 \qquad \text{True}$$

EXAMPLE 1   Solve the equation $5x - 7 = 13$.

Solution   Since the equation contains no fractions nor parentheses, and since there are no like terms to be combined, we start with step 4.

Step 4
$$5x - 7 = 13$$
$$5x - 7 + 7 = 13 + 7 \qquad \text{Add 7 to both sides.}$$
$$5x = 20$$

Step 5
$$\frac{5x}{5} = \frac{20}{5} \qquad \text{Divide both sides by 5.}$$
$$x = 4$$

Step 6   Check
$$5x - 7 = 13$$
$$5(4) - 7 \stackrel{?}{=} 13$$
$$20 - 7 \stackrel{?}{=} 13$$
$$13 = 13 \qquad \text{True}$$

Since the check is true, the solution is 4. Note that after completing step 4, we obtain $5x = 20$, which is an equation of the form $ax = b$. After completing step 5, we obtain the answer in the form $x = $ some real number.

Now Try Exercise 7

EXAMPLE 2   Solve the equation $-2r - 6 = -3$.

Solution

Step 4
$$-2r - 6 = -3$$
$$-2r - 6 + 6 = -3 + 6 \qquad \text{Add 6 to both sides.}$$
$$-2r = 3$$

Step 5
$$\frac{-2r}{-2} = \frac{3}{-2} \qquad \text{Divide both sides by } -2.$$
$$r = -\frac{3}{2}$$

Step 6   Check
$$-2r - 6 = -3$$
$$-2\left(-\frac{3}{2}\right) - 6 \stackrel{?}{=} -3$$
$$3 - 6 \stackrel{?}{=} -3$$
$$-3 = -3 \qquad \text{True}$$

The solution is $-\dfrac{3}{2}$.

Now Try Exercise 15

Note that checks are always made with the *original* equation. In some of the following examples, the check will be omitted to save space. You should check all of your answers.

EXAMPLE 3 Solve the equation $16 = 4x + 6 - 2x$.

Solution   Again we must isolate the variable, x. Since the right side of the equation has two like terms containing the variable, x, we will first combine these like terms.

Step 3
$$16 = 4x + 6 - 2x$$
$$16 = 2x + 6 \qquad \text{Like terms were combined.}$$

Step 4
$$16 - 6 = 2x + 6 - 6 \qquad \text{Subtract 6 from both sides.}$$
$$10 = 2x$$

Step 5
$$\frac{10}{2} = \frac{2x}{2} \qquad \text{Divide both sides by 2.}$$
$$5 = x$$

Now Try Exercise 29

The preceding solution can be condensed as follows.

$$16 = 4x + 6 - 2x$$
$$16 = 2x + 6 \qquad \text{Like terms were combined.}$$
$$10 = 2x \qquad \text{6 was subtracted from both sides.}$$
$$5 = x \qquad \text{Both sides were divided by 2.}$$

EXAMPLE 4 Solve the equation $5x - 2(x + 4) = 3$.

Solution

Step 2
$$5x - 2(x + 4) = 3$$
$$5x - 2x - 8 = 3 \qquad \text{Distributive property was used.}$$

Step 3
$$3x - 8 = 3 \qquad \text{Like terms were combined.}$$

Step 4
$$3x - 8 + 8 = 3 + 8 \qquad \text{Add 8 to both sides.}$$
$$3x = 11$$

Step 5
$$\frac{3x}{3} = \frac{11}{3} \qquad \text{Divide both sides by 3.}$$
$$x = \frac{11}{3}$$

Now Try Exercise 57

The solution to Example 4 can be condensed as follows:

$$5x - 2(x + 4) = 3$$
$$5x - 2x - 8 = 3 \qquad \text{Distributive property was used.}$$
$$3x - 8 = 3 \qquad \text{Like terms were combined.}$$
$$3x = 11 \qquad \text{8 was added to both sides.}$$
$$x = \frac{11}{3} \qquad \text{Both sides were divided by 3.}$$

EXAMPLE 5 Solve the equation $3p - (2p + 5) = 7$.

Solution
$$3p - (2p + 5) = 7$$
$$3p - 2p - 5 = 7 \qquad \text{Distributive property was used.}$$
$$p - 5 = 7 \qquad \text{Like terms were combined.}$$
$$p = 12 \qquad \text{5 was added to both sides.}$$

Now Try Exercise 61

2 Solve Equations Containing Decimal Numbers or Fractions

Example 6 illustrates two methods to solve an equation that contains decimal numbers.

EXAMPLE 6 Solve the equation $x + 1.24 - 0.07x = 4.96$.

Solution We will work this example using two methods. In method 1, we work with decimal numbers throughout the solving process. In method 2, we multiply both sides of the equation by a power of 10 to change the decimal numbers to integers.

Method 1
$$x + 1.24 - 0.07x = 4.96$$

$$0.93x + 1.24 = 4.96 \qquad \text{Like terms were combined;} \\ 1x - 0.07x = 0.93x.$$

$$0.93x + 1.24 \;-\; 1.24 = 4.96 \;-\; 1.24 \qquad \text{Subtract 1.24 from both sides.}$$

$$0.93x = 3.72$$

$$\frac{0.93x}{0.93} = \frac{3.72}{0.93} \qquad \text{Divide both sides by 0.93.}$$

$$x = 4$$

Method 2 We can eliminate the decimal numbers from the equation by multiplying both sides of the equation by 10 if the decimal numbers are given in tenths, by 100 if the decimal numbers are given in hundredths, and so on. In Example 6, since the decimal numbers are in hundredths, you can eliminate the decimals from the equation by multiplying both sides of the equation by 100. This alternate method would give the following.

$$x + 1.24 - 0.07x = 4.96$$

$$100(x + 1.24 - 0.07x) = 100(4.96) \qquad \text{Multiply both sides of equation by 100.}$$

$$100(x) + 100(1.24) - 100(0.07x) = 496 \qquad \text{Distributive property}$$

$$100x + 124 - 7x = 496$$

$$93x + 124 = 496 \qquad \text{Like terms were combined.}$$

$$93x = 372 \qquad \text{124 was subtracted from both sides.}$$

$$x = 4 \qquad \text{Both sides were divided by 93.}$$

Study both methods provided to see which method you prefer.

Now Try Exercise 33

Often, the first step in solving equations containing fractions is to multiply both sides of the equation by the LCD to eliminate the fractions from the equations. Examples 7–9 illustrate this procedure.

EXAMPLE 7 Solve $\frac{1}{5}(x + 1) = 1$.

Solution The LCD of the fraction is 5. We will begin by multiplying both sides of the equation by the LCD. This step will eliminate fractions from the equation.

$$\frac{1}{5}(x + 1) = 1$$

Step 1
$$5\left[\frac{1}{5}(x + 1)\right] = 5 \cdot 1 \qquad \text{Multiply both sides by the LCD, 5.}$$

$$\cancel{5}\left(\frac{1}{\cancel{5}}\right)(x + 1) = 5$$

$$x + 1 = 5$$

Step 4
$$x = 4 \qquad \text{1 was subtracted from both sides.}$$

Step 6   Check

$$\frac{1}{5}(x + 1) = 1$$

$$\frac{1}{5}(4 + 1) \stackrel{?}{=} 1$$

$$\frac{1}{\cancel{5}}(\cancel{5}) \stackrel{?}{=} 1$$

$$1 = 1 \quad \text{True}$$

The solution is 4.

Now Try Exercise 37

Example 7 could also be written as $\dfrac{x + 1}{5} = 1$. To solve this equation, we would begin by multiplying both sides of the equation by the LCD, 5, as follows.

$$\frac{x + 1}{5} = 1$$

$$5\left(\frac{x + 1}{5}\right) = 5 \cdot 1$$

$$x + 1 = 5$$

$$x = 4$$

EXAMPLE 8 Solve the equation $\dfrac{d}{2} + 3d = 14$.

Solution   Multiply both sides of the equation by the LCD, 2. This step will eliminate fractions from the equation.

Step 1 $2\left(\dfrac{d}{2} + 3d\right) = 2 \cdot 14$ Multiply both sides by the LCD, 2.

Step 2 $2\left(\dfrac{d}{2}\right) + 2 \cdot 3d = 2 \cdot 14$ Distributive property

$$d + 6d = 28$$

Step 3 $7d = 28$ Like terms were combined.

Step 5 $d = 4$ Both sides were divided by 7.

Step 6   Check $\dfrac{d}{2} + 3d = 14$

$$\frac{4}{2} + 3(4) \stackrel{?}{=} 14$$

$$2 + 12 \stackrel{?}{=} 14$$

$$14 = 14 \quad \text{True}$$

Now Try Exercise 81

EXAMPLE 9 Solve the equation $\dfrac{1}{5}x - \dfrac{3}{8}x = \dfrac{1}{10}$.

Solution   The LCD of 5, 8, and 10 is 40. Multiply both sides of the equation by 40 to eliminate fractions from the equation.

$$\frac{1}{5}x - \frac{3}{8}x = \frac{1}{10}$$

Step 1 $40\left(\dfrac{1}{5}x - \dfrac{3}{8}x\right) = 40\left(\dfrac{1}{10}\right)$ Multiply both sides by the LCD, 40.

Step 2 $40\left(\dfrac{1}{5}x\right) - 40\left(\dfrac{3}{8}x\right) = 40\left(\dfrac{1}{10}\right)$ Distributive property

$$8x - 15x = 4$$

Step 3		$-7x = 4$	Like terms were combined.

Step 5 $x = -\dfrac{4}{7}$ Both sides were divided by -7.

Step 6   Check $\dfrac{1}{5}x - \dfrac{3}{8}x = \dfrac{1}{10}$

$\dfrac{1}{5}\left(-\dfrac{4}{7}\right) - \dfrac{3}{8}\left(-\dfrac{4}{7}\right) \overset{?}{=} \dfrac{1}{10}$ Substitute $-\dfrac{4}{7}$ for each x.

$-\dfrac{4}{35} + \dfrac{3}{14} \overset{?}{=} \dfrac{1}{10}$ Divided out common factors, then multiplied fractions.

$-\dfrac{8}{70} + \dfrac{15}{70} \overset{?}{=} \dfrac{7}{70}$ Wrote each fraction with the LCD, 70.

$\dfrac{7}{70} = \dfrac{7}{70}$ True

Now Try Exercise 91

Helpful Hint

Some of the most commonly used terms in algebra are "evaluate," "simplify," "solve," and "check." Make sure you understand what each term means and when each term is used.

Evaluate: To *evaluate an expression* means to find its numerical value.

Evaluate $16 \div 2^2 + 36 \div 4$
$= 16 \div 4 + 36 \div 4$
$= 4 + 36 \div 4$
$= 4 + 9$
$= 13$

Evaluate $-x^2 + 3x - 2$ when $x = 4$
$= -4^2 + 3(4) - 2$
$= -16 + 3(4) - 2$
$= -16 + 12 - 2$
$= -4 - 2$
$= -6$

Simplify: To *simplify an expression* means to perform the operations and combine like terms.

Simplify $3(x - 2) - 4(2x + 3)$
$3(x - 2) - 4(2x + 3) = 3x - 6 - 8x - 12$
$= -5x - 18$

Note that when you simplify an expression containing variables you do not generally end up with just a numerical value unless all the variable terms happen to add to zero.

Solve: To *solve an equation* means to find the value or the values of the variable that make the equation a true statement.

Solve $2x + 3(x + 1) = 18$
$2x + 3x + 3 = 18$
$5x + 3 = 18$
$5x = 15$
$x = 3$

Check: To *check the proposed solution to an equation,* substitute the value in the original equation. If this result is true, then the answer checks. For example, to check the solution to the equation just solved, we substitute 3 for x in the original equation.

Check

$$2x + 3(x + 1) = 18$$
$$2(3) + 3(3 + 1) \stackrel{?}{=} 18$$
$$2(3) + 3(4) \stackrel{?}{=} 18$$
$$6 + 12 \stackrel{?}{=} 18$$
$$18 = 18 \quad \text{True}$$

Since we obtained a true statement, the 3 checks.

It is important to realize that expressions may be evaluated or simplified (depending on the type of problem) and equations are solved and then checked.

EXERCISE SET 2.4

Warm-Up Exercises

Fill in the blanks with the appropriate word, phrase, or symbol(s) from the following list.

expression   equation   variable was x
LCD   a power of ten   multiplication property of equality
to isolate the variable

1. The _____ allows us to multiply or divide both sides of an equation by the same nonzero number.

2. The fundamental strategy in solving a linear equation is _____ .

3. To solve an equation involving decimal numbers, you may want to first multiply both sides of the equation by _____ to change the decimal numbers into integers.

4. To solve an equation involving fractions, you may want to first multiply both sides of the equation by the fractions' _____ to change the fractions into integers.

5. Something that might get evaluated or simplified is called an _____ .

6. Something that might get solved is called an _____ .

Practice the Skills

Solve each equation.

7. $5x - 6 = 19$

8. $2t - 4 = 8$

9. $-4w - 9 = 11$

10. $-4x + 6 = 20$

11. $3x + 6 = 12$

12. $6 - 3x = 18$

📌 13. $5x - 2 = 10$

14. $-2t + 9 = 21$

15. $-5k - 9 = -19$

16. $-4x - 7 = -6$

17. $12 - x = 5$

18. $-3x - 3 = -12$

19. $8 + 3x = 19$

20. $-2x + 7 = -10$

21. $16x + 5 = -14$

22. $19 = 25 + 4x$

23. $-4.2 = 3x + 31.8$

24. $-24 + 16x = -24$

25. $7r - 16 = -2$

26. $-2w + 4 = -8$

27. $60 = -5s + 9$

28. $15 = 7x + 1$

29. $14 = 5x + 8 - 3x$

30. $15 = 6x - 3 + 3x$

31. $2.3x - 9.34 = 6.3$

32. $x + 0.05x = 21$

33. $0.91y + 2.25 - 0.01y = 5.85$

34. $0.15 = 0.05x - 1.35 - 0.20x$

35. $28.8 = x + 1.40x$

36. $8.40 = 2.45x - 1.05x$

37. $\dfrac{1}{7}(x + 6) = 4$

38. $\dfrac{m - 6}{5} = 2$

📌 39. $\dfrac{d + 3}{7} = 9$

40. $\dfrac{1}{5}(x + 2) = -3$

41. $\dfrac{1}{3}(t - 7) = -7$

42. $\dfrac{2}{3}(n - 3) = 8$

43. $\dfrac{3}{4}(x - 5) = -12$

44. $\dfrac{1}{4} = \dfrac{z + 1}{4}$

45. $\dfrac{x + 4}{7} = \dfrac{2}{7}$

46. $\dfrac{4x + 5}{6} = \dfrac{7}{2}$

47. $\dfrac{3}{4} = \dfrac{4m - 5}{6}$

48. $\dfrac{5}{6} = \dfrac{5t - 4}{2}$

49. $4(n + 3) = 12$

50. $3(x - 2) = 12$

51. $-2(x - 3) = 26$

52. $5(3 - x) = 15$

53. $-4 = -(x + 7)$

54. $-3(2 - 3x) = 9$

55. $12 = 4(x - 3)$

56. $-2(x + 8) - 5 = 1$

57. $2x - 3(x + 5) = 6$

58. $5(3x + 1) - 12x = -2$

59. $-3r - 4(r + 2) = 11$

60. $9 = -2(a - 3)$

61. $x - 3(2x + 3) = 36$

62. $3y - (y + 5) = 9$

63. $5x + 3x - 4x - 7 = 9$

64. $4(x + 2) = 13$

65. $0.7(x - 3) = 1.4$

66. $21 + (c - 9) = 24$

67. $2.5(4q - 3) = 0.5$

68. $0.1(2.4x + 5) = 1.7$

69. $3 - 2(x + 3) + 2 = 1$

70. $2(3x - 4) - 4x = 12$

71. $1 + (x + 3) + 6x = 6$

72. $5x - 2x + 7x = -81$

73. $4.85 - 6.4x + 1.11 = 25.8$

74. $5.76 - 4.24x - 1.9x = 27.864$

75. $7 = 8 - 5(m + 3)$

76. $4 = \dfrac{3t + 1}{7}$

77. $9 = \dfrac{2s + 9}{5}$

78. $12 = \dfrac{4d - 1}{3}$

79. $x + \dfrac{2}{3} = \dfrac{3}{5}$

80. $n - \dfrac{1}{4} = \dfrac{1}{2}$

81. $\dfrac{r}{3} + 2r = 6$

82. $\dfrac{x}{4} - 6x = 23$

83. $\dfrac{3}{7} = \dfrac{3t}{4} + 1$

84. $\dfrac{5}{8} = \dfrac{5t}{6} + 2$

85. $\dfrac{1}{2}r + \dfrac{1}{5}r = 7$

86. $\dfrac{x}{3} - \dfrac{3x}{4} = \dfrac{1}{12}$

87. $\dfrac{2}{8} + \dfrac{3}{4} = \dfrac{w}{5}$

88. $\dfrac{x}{4} - \dfrac{x}{6} = \dfrac{1}{4}$

89. $\dfrac{1}{2}x + 5 = \dfrac{1}{8}$

90. $\dfrac{4}{5} + n = \dfrac{1}{3}$

91. $\dfrac{4}{5}s - \dfrac{3}{4}s = \dfrac{1}{10}$

92. $\dfrac{1}{3}x - \dfrac{3}{4}x = \dfrac{1}{5}$

93. $\dfrac{4}{9} = \dfrac{1}{3}(n - 7)$

94. $-\dfrac{3}{8} = \dfrac{1}{8} - \dfrac{2x}{7}$

95. $-\dfrac{3}{5} = -\dfrac{1}{6} - \dfrac{3}{4}q$

96. $-\dfrac{3}{5} = -\dfrac{1}{6} - \dfrac{5}{4}m$

Concept/Writing Exercises

97. a) Explain why it is easier to solve the equation $3x + 2 = 11$ by first subtracting 2 from both sides of the equation rather than by first dividing both sides of the equation by 3.

b) Solve the equation.

98. a) Explain why it is easier to solve the equation $5x - 3 = 12$ by first adding 3 to both sides of the equation rather than by first dividing both sides of the equation by 5.

b) Solve the equation.

Challenge Problems

For Exercises 99–101, solve the equation.

99. $3(x - 2) - (x + 5) - 2(3 - 2x) = 18$

100. $-6 = -(x - 5) - 3(5 + 2x) - 4(2x - 4)$

101. $4[3 - 2(x + 4)] - (x + 3) = 13$

102. Solve the equation $\square\odot - \triangledown = @$ for $\odot$.

Group Activity

In Chapter 3, we will discuss procedures for writing application problems as equations. Let's look at an application now.

Birthday Party John Logan purchased 2 large chocolate bars and a birthday card. The birthday card cost $3. The total cost was $9. What was the price of a single chocolate bar?

This problem can be represented by the equation $2x + 3 = 9$, which can be used to solve the problem. Solving the equation we find that x, the price of a single chocolate bar, is $3.

For Exercises 103 and 104, each group member should do parts **a)** *and* **b)**. *Then do part* **c)** *as a group.*

a) *Obtain an equation that can be used to solve the problem.*

b) *Solve the equation and answer the question.*

c) *Compare and check each other's work.*

103. **Stationery** Eduardo Verner purchased three boxes of stationery. He also purchased wrapping paper and thank-you cards. If the wrapping paper and thank-you cards together cost $6, and the total he paid was $42, find the cost of a box of stationery.

104. **Candies** Mahandi Ison purchased three rolls of peppermint candies and the local newspaper. The newspaper cost 50 cents. He paid $2.75 in all. What did a roll of candies cost?

Cumulative Review Exercises

[1.4] **105.** True or false: Every real number is a rational number.

[1.9] **106.** Evaluate $[5(2 - 6) + 3(8 \div 4)^2]^2$.

[2.2] **107.** To solve an equation, what do you need to do to the variable?

[2.3] **108.** To solve the equation $7 = -4x$, would you add 4 to both sides of the equation or divide both sides of the equation by -4? Explain your answer.

Mid-Chapter Test: 2.1–2.4

To find out how well you understand the chapter material to this point, take this brief test. The answers, and the section where the material was initially discussed, are given in the back of the book. Review any questions that you answered incorrectly.

In Exercises 1 and 2, combine like terms.

1. $5x - 9y - 12 + 4y - 7x + 6$

2. $\dfrac{2}{5}x - 8 - \dfrac{3}{4}x + \dfrac{1}{2}$

In Exercises 3 and 4, use the distributive property to remove parentheses.

3. $-4(2a - 3b + 16)$

4. $1.6(2.1x - 3.4y - 5.2)$

5. Simplify $5(t - 3) - 3(t + 7) - 2$.

6. Is $x = 2$ a solution of $3(x - 4) = -2(x + 1)$?

7. Is $p = \dfrac{2}{5}$ a solution of $7p - 3 = 2p - 5$?

In Exercises 8–10, solve each equation and check your solution.

8. $x - 5 = -9$

9. $120 + x = -40$

10. $-16 = 7 + y$

11. When solving the equation $\dfrac{x}{4} = 5$, what would you do to isolate the variable? Explain.

In Exercises 12–15, solve each equation and check your solution.

12. $4 = 12y$

13. $\dfrac{x}{8} = 3$

14. $-\dfrac{x}{5} = -2$

15. $-x = \dfrac{3}{7}$

In Exercises 16–20, solve each equation.

16. $6x - 3 = 12$

17. $-4 = -2w - 7$

18. $\dfrac{3}{8} = \dfrac{4n - 1}{6}$

19. $-5(x + 4) - 7 = 3$

20. $8 - 9(y + 4) + 6 = -2$

2.5 Solving Linear Equations with the Variable on Both Sides of the Equation

1 Solve equations with the variable on both sides of the equals sign.

2 Solve equations containing decimal numbers or fractions.

3 Identify identities and contradictions.

Understanding Algebra

As the equations get more complicated, our ultimate goal remains the same: *to isolate the variable on one side of the equation.*

1 Solve Equations with the Variable on Both Sides of the Equals Sign

The equation $4x + 6 = 2x + 4$ contains the variable, x, on both sides of the equals sign. To solve equations of this type, we rewrite the equation so that all terms containing the variable are on only one side of the equals sign, and all terms not containing the variable are on the other side of the equals sign. The following steps in the procedure are only guidelines to use to solve these types of equations. For example, there may be times when you may choose to use the distributive property, step 2, before multiplying both sides of the equation by the LCD (step 1). We will illustrate this variation in Examples 9 and 10.

> **To Solve Linear Equations with the Variable on Both Sides of the Equals Sign**
>
> 1. **Fractions:** If the equation contains fractions, multiply **both** sides of the equation by the least common denominator (LCD). This will eliminate fractions from the equation.
> 2. **Parentheses:** Use the distributive property to remove parentheses.
> 3. **Like terms:** Combine like terms on each side of the equals sign.
> 4. **Addition property:** Use the addition property to rewrite the equation with all terms containing the variable on one side of the equals sign and all terms not containing the variable on the other side of the equals sign. It may be necessary to use the addition property twice to accomplish this goal.
> 5. **Multiplication property:** Use the multiplication property to isolate the variable.
> 6. **Check:** Check the solution in the original equation.

Remember: *our goal in solving a linear equation is to isolate the variable, that is, to obtain an equation in which the variable is alone on one side of the equation.* For example, consider the equation $3x + 4 = x + 12$. It contains no fractions or parentheses nor are there any like terms on the same side of the equals sign. Therefore, we start with step 4 above and use the addition property twice. Notice in the steps outlined below that we subtract x from both sides and then subtract 4 from both sides:

$$3x + 4 = x + 12$$

$$3x \boxed{-x} + 4 = x \boxed{-x} + 12 \qquad \text{Addition property (subtract } x \text{ from both sides)}$$

$$2x + 4 = 12 \qquad \text{Variable appears only on left side of equation.}$$

Notice that the variable, x, now appears on only one side of the equation. However, $+4$ still appears on the same side.

$$2x + 4 = 12$$

$$2x + 4 \boxed{-4} = 12 \boxed{-4} \qquad \text{Addition property (subtract 4 from both sides)}$$

$$2x = 8 \qquad \text{Term with } x \text{ is now isolated (in the form } ax = b).$$

Finally, to find x, we use the multiplication property:

$$2x = 8$$

$$\frac{\overset{1}{\cancel{2}}x}{\cancel{2}} = \frac{\overset{4}{\cancel{8}}}{\cancel{2}} \qquad \text{Multiplication property (divide both sides by 2)}$$

$$x = 4 \qquad \text{Goal accomplished: } x \text{ is isolated.}$$

The solution to the equation is 4.

EXAMPLE 1 Solve the equation $4x + 6 = 2x + 4$. ——————

Solution   We start by getting all the terms with the variable on one side of the equals sign and all terms without the variable on the other side. The terms with the variable may be collected on either side of the equals sign. We will illustrate two methods of solving this equation.

Method 1   Isolate the variable term on the left.

$$4x + 6 = 2x + 4$$

Step 4 $4x - 2x + 6 = 2x - 2x + 4$ Subtract $2x$ from both sides.

$$2x + 6 = 4$$

Step 4 $2x + 6 - 6 = 4 - 6$ Subtract 6 from both sides.

$$2x = -2$$

Step 5 $\dfrac{2x}{2} = \dfrac{-2}{2}$ Divide both sides by 2.

$$x = -1$$

Method 2   Isolate the variable term on the right.

$$4x + 6 = 2x + 4$$

Step 4 $4x - 4x + 6 = 2x - 4x + 4$ Subtract $4x$ from both sides.

$$6 = -2x + 4$$

Step 4 $6 - 4 = -2x + 4 - 4$ Subtract 4 from both sides.

$$2 = -2x$$

Step 5 $\dfrac{2}{-2} = \dfrac{-2x}{-2}$ Divide both sides by -2.

$$-1 = x$$

The same answer is obtained whether we collect the terms with the variable on the left or right side.

Step 6   Check

$$4x + 6 = 2x + 4$$

$$4(-1) + 6 \stackrel{?}{=} 2(-1) + 4$$

$$-4 + 6 \stackrel{?}{=} -2 + 4$$

$$2 = 2 \qquad \text{True}$$

Since the check is true, the solution is -1.

Now Try Exercise 19

EXAMPLE 2 Solve the equation $2x - 3 - 5x = 13 + 4x - 2$. ——————

Solution   We will choose to collect the terms containing the variable on the right side of the equation in order to create a positive coefficient of x. Since there are like terms *on the same side of the equals sign*, we will begin by combining these like terms.

Step 3 $2x - 3 - 5x = 13 + 4x - 2$

$$-3x - 3 = 4x + 11 \qquad \text{Combined like terms.}$$

Step 4 $-3x + 3x - 3 = 4x + 3x + 11$ Add $3x$ to both sides.

$$-3 = 7x + 11$$

Step 4 $-3 - 11 = 7x + 11 - 11$ Subtract 11 from both sides.

$$-14 = 7x$$

Step 5 $\dfrac{-14}{7} = \dfrac{7x}{7}$ Divide both sides by 7.

$$-2 = x$$

Step 6   Check

$$2x - 3 - 5x = 13 + 4x - 2$$
$$2(-2) - 3 - 5(-2) \stackrel{?}{=} 13 + 4(-2) - 2$$
$$-4 - 3 + 10 \stackrel{?}{=} 13 - 8 - 2$$
$$-7 + 10 \stackrel{?}{=} 5 - 2$$
$$3 = 3 \qquad \text{True}$$

Since the check is true, the solution is -2.

Now Try Exercise 29

The solution to Example 2 could be condensed as follows:

$$2x - 3 - 5x = 13 + 4x - 2$$

$-3x - 3 = 4x + 11$	Combined like terms.
$-3 = 7x + 11$	Added $3x$ to both sides.
$-14 = 7x$	Subtracted 11 from both sides.
$-2 = x$	Divided both sides by 7.

We solved Example 2 by moving the terms containing the variable to the right side of the equation. Now rework the problem by moving the terms containing the variable to the left side of the equation. You should obtain the same answer.

EXAMPLE 3 Solve the equation $2(p + 3) = -3p + 10$.

Solution

$$2(p + 3) = -3p + 10$$

Step 2	$2p + 6 = -3p + 10$	Distributive property was used.
Step 4	$2p + 3p + 6 = -3p + 3p + 10$	Add $3p$ to both sides.
	$5p + 6 = 10$	
Step 4	$5p + 6 - 6 = 10 - 6$	Subtract 6 from both sides.
	$5p = 4$	
Step 5	$\dfrac{5p}{5} = \dfrac{4}{5}$	Divide both sides by 5.
	$p = \dfrac{4}{5}$	

The solution is $\dfrac{4}{5}$.

Now Try Exercise 27

Understanding Algebra

In Example 3, the variable could also have been isolated on the right side by first subtracting $2p$:

$$2p + 6 = -3p + 10$$
$$6 = -5p + 10$$
$$-4 = -5p$$
$$\frac{-4}{-5} = p$$
$$\frac{4}{5} = p$$

The solution to Example 3 could be condensed as follows:

$$2(p + 3) = -3p + 10$$

$2p + 6 = -3p + 10$	Distributive property was used.
$5p + 6 = 10$	Added $3p$ to both sides.
$5p = 4$	Subtracted 6 from both sides.
$p = \dfrac{4}{5}$	Divided both sides by 5.

EXAMPLE 4 Solve the equation $2(x - 5) + 3 = 3x + 9$.

Solution

$$2(x - 5) + 3 = 3x + 9$$

Step 2	$2x - 10 + 3 = 3x + 9$	Distributive property was used.
Step 3	$2x - 7 = 3x + 9$	Combined like terms.
Step 4	$-7 = x + 9$	Subtracted $2x$ from both sides.
Step 4	$-16 = x$	Subtracted 9 from both sides.

The solution is -16.

Now Try Exercise 35

EXAMPLE 5 Solve the equation $7 - 2x + 5x = -2(-3x + 4)$.

Solution
$$7 - 2x + 5x = -2(-3x + 4)$$

Step 2	$7 - 2x + 5x = 6x - 8$	Used the distributive property.
Step 3	$7 + 3x = 6x - 8$	Combined like terms.
Step 4	$7 = 3x - 8$	Subtracted $3x$ from both sides.
Step 4	$15 = 3x$	Added 8 to both sides.
Step 5	$5 = x$	Divided both sides by 3.

The solution is 5.

Now Try Exercise 63

2 Solve Equations Containing Decimal Numbers or Fractions

Now we will solve an equation that contains decimal numbers. We will illustrate two procedures for solving Example 6.

EXAMPLE 6 Solve the equation $5.74x + 5.42 = 2.24x - 9.28$.

Solution

Method 1 Notice that there are no like terms on the same side of the equals sign that can be combined.

$$5.74x + 5.42 = 2.24x - 9.28$$

Step 4 $5.74x - 2.24x + 5.42 = 2.24x - 2.24x - 9.28$ Subtract $2.24x$ from both sides.
$$3.50x + 5.42 = -9.28$$

Step 4 $3.50x + 5.42 - 5.42 = -9.28 - 5.42$ Subtract 5.42 from both sides.
$$3.50x = -14.70$$

Step 5 $\dfrac{3.50x}{3.50} = \dfrac{-14.70}{3.50}$ Divide both sides by 3.50.
$$x = -4.20$$

The solution is -4.20.

Method 2 Since the given equation has numbers given in hundredths, we will multiply both sides of the equation by 100.

$$5.74x + 5.42 = 2.24x - 9.28$$
$$100(5.74x + 5.42) = 100(2.24x - 9.28) \quad \text{Multiply both sides by 100.}$$
$$100(5.74x) + 100(5.42) = 100(2.24x) - 100(9.28) \quad \text{Distributive property}$$
$$574x + 542 = 224x - 928$$

Step 4 $574x + 542 - 542 = 224x - 928 - 542$ Subtract 542 from both sides.
$$574x = 224x - 1470$$

Step 4 $574x - 224x = 224x - 224x - 1470$ Subtract $224x$ from both sides.
$$350x = -1470$$

Step 5 $\dfrac{350x}{350} = \dfrac{-1470}{350}$ Divide both sides by 350.
$$x = -4.20$$

Notice we obtain the same answer using either method. You may use either method to solve equations of this type.

Now Try Exercise 25

Understanding Algebra

To eliminate decimal numbers from an equation, multiply by a power of 10:

If equation contains numbers to . . .	. . . then multiply both sides by
tenths	10
hundredths	100
thousandths	1000

and so on.

Now let's solve some equations that contain fractions.

EXAMPLE 7 Solve the equation $\frac{1}{2}a = \frac{3}{4}a + \frac{1}{5}$.

Solution   The least common denominator is 20. Begin by multiplying both sides of the equation by the LCD.

$$\frac{1}{2}a = \frac{3}{4}a + \frac{1}{5}$$

Step 1 $20\left(\frac{1}{2}a\right) = 20\left(\frac{3}{4}a + \frac{1}{5}\right)$ Multiply both sides by the LCD, 20.

Step 2 $10a = \overset{5}{\cancel{20}}\left(\frac{3}{4}a\right) + \overset{4}{\cancel{20}}\left(\frac{1}{\cancel{5}}\right)$ Distributive property

$$10a = 15a + 4$$

Step 4 $-5a = 4$ Subtracted $15a$ from both sides.

Step 5 $a = -\frac{4}{5}$ Divided both sides by -5.

Step 6   Check

$$\frac{1}{2}a = \frac{3}{4}a + \frac{1}{5}$$

$$\frac{1}{2}\left(-\frac{4}{5}\right) \overset{?}{=} \frac{3}{4}\left(-\frac{4}{5}\right) + \frac{1}{5}$$

$$-\frac{2}{5} \overset{?}{=} -\frac{3}{5} + \frac{1}{5}$$

$$-\frac{2}{5} = -\frac{2}{5}$$ True

The solution is $-\frac{4}{5}$.

Now Try Exercise 43

Now Try Exercise 43

> ## Understanding Algebra
>
> To eliminate fractions from equations, multiply both sides of the equation by the LCD of the fractions in the equation.

> ## Understanding Algebra
>
> It is very helpful to place each side of the equation in parentheses before multiplying both sides by the LCD.

Helpful Hint

The equation in Example 7, $\frac{1}{2}a = \frac{3}{4}a + \frac{1}{5}$, could have been written as $\frac{a}{2} = \frac{3a}{4} + \frac{1}{5}$ because $\frac{1}{2}a$ is the same as $\frac{a}{2}$, and $\frac{3}{4}a$ is the same as $\frac{3a}{4}$. You would solve the equation $\frac{a}{2} = \frac{3a}{4} + \frac{1}{5}$ the same way you solved the equation in Example 7.

EXAMPLE 8 Solve the equation $\frac{x}{4} + 3 = 2(x - 2)$.

Solution   We will begin by multiplying both sides of the equation by the LCD, 4.

$$\frac{x}{4} + 3 = 2(x - 2)$$

$$4\left(\frac{x}{4} + 3\right) = 4[2(x - 2)]$$ Multiply both sides by the LCD, 4.

$$4\left(\frac{x}{4}\right) + 4(3) = 4[2(x - 2)]$$ Used the distributive property (on left).

$$x + 12 = 8(x - 2)$$

$$x + 12 = 8x - 16$$ Used the distributive property (on right).

$$12 = 7x - 16$$ Subtracted x from both sides.

$$28 = 7x$$ Added 16 to both sides.

$$4 = x$$ Divided both sides by 7.

A check will show that 4 is the solution.

Now Try Exercise 61

In Example 8, we began the solution by multiplying both sides of the equation by the LCD. In Example 9, we will solve the same equation, but this time we will begin by using the distributive property.

EXAMPLE 9 Solve the equation in Example 8, $\frac{x}{4} + 3 = 2(x - 2)$, by first using the distributive property.

Solution   Begin by using the distributive property.

$$\frac{x}{4} + 3 = 2(x - 2)$$

$$\frac{x}{4} + 3 = 2x - 4 \qquad \text{Used the distributive property (on right).}$$

$$4\left(\frac{x}{4} + 3\right) = 4(2x - 4) \qquad \text{Multiply both sides by the LCD, 4.}$$

$$4\left(\frac{x}{4}\right) + 4(3) = 4(2x) - 4(4) \qquad \text{Distributive property (on left and right)}$$

$$x + 12 = 8x - 16$$

$$12 = 7x - 16 \qquad x \text{ was subtracted from both sides.}$$

$$28 = 7x \qquad 16 \text{ was added to both sides.}$$

$$4 = x \qquad \text{Both sides were divided by 7.}$$

The solution is 4.

Now Try Exercise 65

Notice that we obtained the same answer in Examples 8 and 9.

EXAMPLE 10 Solve the equation $\frac{1}{2}(2x + 3) = \frac{2}{3}(x - 6) + 4$.

Notice that this equation contains one term on the left side of the equals sign and two terms on the right side of the equals sign.

Solution   We will work this problem by first using the distributive property.

$$\frac{1}{2}(2x + 3) = \frac{2}{3}(x - 6) + 4$$

$$\frac{1}{2}(2x) + \frac{1}{2}(3) = \frac{2}{3}(x) - \frac{2}{3}(\overset{2}{6}) + 4 \qquad \text{Distributive property (on left and right)}$$

$$x + \frac{3}{2} = \frac{2}{3}x - 4 + 4$$

$$x + \frac{3}{2} = \frac{2}{3}x \qquad \text{Combined like terms.}$$

$$6\left(x + \frac{3}{2}\right) = 6\left(\frac{2}{3}x\right) \qquad \text{Multiply both sides by the LCD, 6.}$$

$$6x + 6\left(\frac{3}{2}\right) = 6\left(\frac{2}{3}x\right) \qquad \text{Used the distributive property.}$$

$$6x + \overset{3}{6}\left(\frac{3}{2}\right) = \overset{2}{6}\left(\frac{2}{3}x\right)$$

$$6x + 9 = 4x$$

$$2x + 9 = 0 \qquad \text{Subtracted } 4x \text{ from both sides.}$$

$$2x = -9 \qquad \text{Subtracted 9 from both sides.}$$

$$x = -\frac{9}{2} \qquad \text{Divided both sides by 2.}$$

Check   Substitute $-\dfrac{9}{2}$ for each x in the equation.

$$\frac{1}{2}(2x + 3) = \frac{2}{3}(x - 6) + 4$$

$$\frac{1}{2}\left[2\left(-\frac{9}{2}\right) + 3\right] \stackrel{?}{=} \frac{2}{3}\left(-\frac{9}{2} - 6\right) + 4$$

$$\frac{1}{2}[-9 + 3] \stackrel{?}{=} \frac{2}{3}\left(-\frac{9}{2} - \frac{12}{2}\right) + 4$$

$$\frac{1}{2}[-6] \stackrel{?}{=} \frac{2}{3}\left(-\frac{21}{2}\right) + 4$$

$$-3 \stackrel{?}{=} -7 + 4$$

$$-3 = -3 \qquad\qquad \text{True}$$

The solution is $-\dfrac{9}{2}$.

Now Try Exercise 75

In Example 10, we began by using the distributive property. We could have also begun by multiplying both sides of the equation by the LCD, 6, before using the distributive property. Work Example 10 again now by first multiplying both sides of the equation by the LCD, 6.

Example 10 could have also been written as $\dfrac{2x + 3}{2} = \dfrac{2(x - 6)}{3} + 4$. If you were given the equation in this form, you could begin by using the distributive property on $2(x - 6)$ or you could begin by multiplying both sides of the equation by the LCD, 6. Because this is just another way of writing the equation in Example 10, the answer would be $-\dfrac{9}{2}$.

We will discuss solving equations containing fractions in more detail later in the book.

3 Identify Identities and Contradictions

Thus far all the equations we have solved have had a single value for a solution. Additionally, there are two other types of equations based on their set of solutions. All three are listed below:

> **Types of Equations**
>
> A **conditional equation** is true for a specific value(s) of the variable.
> An **identity** is true for all values of the variable.
> A **contradiction** is not true for any value of the variable.

Understanding Algebra

The solution in Example 11 could have been stopped at "$3x - 5 = 3x - 5$." Since one side is identical to the other side, the equation is true for infinitely many values of x. We say the solution is "*all real numbers.*"

EXAMPLE 11 Solve the equation $5x - 5 - 2x = 3(x - 2) + 1$.

Solution

$$5x - 5 - 2x = 3(x - 2) + 1$$

$$5x - 5 - 2x = 3x - 6 + 1 \qquad \text{Used the distributive property.}$$

$$3x - 5 = 3x - 5 \qquad\qquad \text{Combined like terms.}$$

Since the same expression appears on both sides of the equals sign, the statement is true for infinitely many values of x. If we continue to solve this equation further, we might obtain

$$3x - 5 = 3x - 5$$
$$3x = 3x \qquad \text{Added 5 to both sides.}$$
$$0 = 0 \qquad \text{Subtracted } 3x \text{ from both sides.}$$

The answer is: all real numbers.

NOTE: *When solving an equation that is always true, like the equation in Example 11, write your answer as "all real numbers."*

Now Try Exercise 47

EXAMPLE 12 Solve the equation $-2x + 5 + 3x = 5x - 4x + 7$.

Solution

$$-2x + 5 + 3x = 5x - 4x + 7$$
$$x + 5 = x + 7 \qquad \text{Combined like terms.}$$
$$x - x + 5 = x - x + 7 \qquad \text{Subtract } x \text{ from both sides.}$$
$$5 = 7 \qquad \text{False}$$

The answer is: no solution.

NOTE: *When solving an equation that is never true, like the equation in Example 12, write your answer as "no solution."*

Now Try Exercise 31

Understanding Algebra

When solving an equation, if you obtain an obviously false statement, as in Example 12, the equation has *no solution*. We state the answer formally as "no solution."

Helpful Hint

When solving equations, remember two important things: (1) your goal is to isolate the variable, and (2) whatever you do to one side of the equation you must also do to the other side. That is, you must treat both sides of the equation equally.

EXERCISE SET 2.5

Math XL   MyMathLab
MathXL®   MyMathLab

Warm-Up Exercises

Fill in the blanks with the appropriate word, phrase, or symbol(s) from the following list.

identity	conditional equation	contradiction	True
specific value(s) of the variable	least common denominator	power of 10	False
all values of the variable	no real numbers	isolate the variable	

1. If a linear equation has infinitely many solutions, it is called a(n) _____ .

2. If a linear equation has a specific solution, it is called a(n) _____ .

3. To eliminate fractions from an equation, multiply both sides of the equation by the _____ .

4. If there is no solution to a linear equation, it is called a(n) _____ .

5. A conditional equation is true for _____ .

6. An identity is true for _____ .

7. A contradiction is true for _____ .

8. The ultimate goal in the process of solving linear equations is to _____ .

9. (True or False) The equation $2x + 0 = 0$ is an example of a contradiction. _____

10. To eliminate decimal numbers from an equation, multiply both sides of the equation by a _____ .

Practice the Skills

Solve each equation.

11. $3x = -2x + 10$

12. $y + 4 = 2y - 9$

13. $-4x + 10 = 6x$

14. $3a = 4a + 8$

15. $5x + 3 = 6$

16. $-6x = 2x + 16$

17. $21 - 6p = 3p - 2p$

18. $8 - 3x = 4x + 50$

19. $2x - 8 = 3x - 6$

20. $5x + 7 = 3x + 5$

21. $6 - 2y = 9 - 8y + 6y$

22. $-4 + 2y = 2y - 6 + y$

23. $124.8 - 9.4x = 4.8x + 32.5$

24. $9 - 0.5x = 4.5x + 8.5$

25. $0.62x - 0.65 = 9.75 - 2.63x$

26. $8.71 - 2.44x = 11.02 - 5.74x$

27. $5x + 3 = 2(x + 6)$

28. $x - 14 = 3(x + 2)$

29. $4y - 2 - 8y = 19 + 5y - 3$

30. $3x - 5 + 9x = 2 + 4x + 9$

31. $2(x - 2) = 4x - 6 - 2x$

32. $4r = 10 - 2(r - 4)$

33. $-(w + 2) = -6w + 11$

34. $7(-3m + 5) = 3(10 - 6m)$

35. $-3(2t - 5) + 5 = 3t + 13$

36. $4(x - 3) + 2 = 2x + 12$

37. $\dfrac{a}{5} = \dfrac{a - 3}{2}$

38. $\dfrac{b}{16} = \dfrac{b - 6}{4}$

39. $\dfrac{n}{10} = 9 - \dfrac{n}{5}$

40. $6 - \dfrac{x}{4} = \dfrac{x}{8}$

41. $\dfrac{7}{2} - \dfrac{x}{3} = 2x$

42. $\dfrac{x}{4} - 3 = -2x$

43. $\dfrac{5}{8} + \dfrac{1}{4}a = \dfrac{1}{2}a$

44. $\dfrac{3}{4}x + \dfrac{1}{2} = \dfrac{1}{2}x$

45. $0.1(x + 10) = 0.3x - 4$

46. $5(3.2x - 3) = 2(x - 4)$

47. $2(x + 4) = 4x + 3 - 2x + 5$

48. $3(y - 1) + 9 = 8y + 6 - 5y$

49. $5(3n + 3) = 2(5n - 4) + 6n$

50. $-4(-3z - 5) = -(10z + 8) - 2z$

51. $-(3 - p) = -(2p + 3)$

52. $12 - 2x - 3(x + 2) = 4x + 6 - x$

53. $-(x + 4) + 5 = 4x + 1 - 5x$

54. $18x + 3(4x - 9) = -6x + 45$

55. $35(2x - 1) = 7(x + 4) + 3x$

56. $10(x - 10) + 5 = 5(2x - 20)$

57. $0.4(x + 0.7) = 0.6(x - 4.2)$

58. $0.5(6x - 8) = 1.4(x - 5) - 0.2$

59. $\dfrac{3}{5}x - 2 = x - \dfrac{1}{2}$

60. $\dfrac{3}{5}x + 4 = \dfrac{1}{5}x + 5$

61. $\dfrac{y}{5} + 2 = 3(y - 4)$

62. $2(x - 4) = \dfrac{x}{5} + 10$

63. $12 - 3x + 7x = -2(-5x + 6)$

64. $-2x - 3 - x = -3(-2x + 7)$

65. $3(x - 6) - 4(3x + 1) = x - 22$

66. $-2(-3x + 5) + 6 = 4(x - 2)$

67. $5 + 2x = 6(x + 1) - 5(x - 3)$

68. $4 - (6x + 6) = -(-2x + 10)$

69. $7 - (-y - 5) = 2(y + 3) - 6(y + 3)$

70. $12 - 6x + 3(2x + 3) = 2x + 5$

71. $\dfrac{3}{5}(x - 6) = \dfrac{2}{3}(3x - 5)$

72. $\dfrac{1}{2}(2d + 4) = \dfrac{1}{3}(4d - 4)$

73. $\dfrac{3(2r - 5)}{5} = \dfrac{3r - 6}{3}$

74. $\dfrac{3(x - 4)}{4} = \dfrac{5(2x - 3)}{3}$

75. $\dfrac{2}{7}(5x + 4) = \dfrac{1}{2}(3x - 4) + 1$

76. $\dfrac{5}{12}(x + 2) = \dfrac{2}{3}(2x + 1) + \dfrac{1}{6}$

77. $\dfrac{a - 5}{2} = \dfrac{3a}{4} + \dfrac{a - 25}{6}$

78. $\dfrac{a - 7}{3} = \dfrac{a + 5}{2} - \dfrac{7a - 1}{6}$

Concept/Writing Exercises

79. a) Construct a *conditional equation* containing three terms on the left side of the equals sign and two terms on the right side of the equals sign.

b) Explain how you know your answer to part **a)** is a conditional equation.

c) Solve the equation.

80. a) Construct a *conditional equation* containing two terms on the left side of the equals sign and three terms on the right side of the equals sign.

b) Explain how you know your answer to part **a)** is a conditional equation.

c) Solve the equation.

81. a) Construct an *identity* containing three terms on the left side of the equals sign and two terms on the right side of the equals sign.

b) Explain how you know your answer to part **a)** is an identity.

c) What is the solution to the equation?

82. a) Construct an *identity* containing two terms on the left side of the equals sign and three terms on the right side of the equals sign.

b) Explain how you know your answer to part **a)** is an identity.

c) What is the solution to the equation?

83. a) Construct a *contradiction* containing three terms on the left side of the equals sign and two terms on the right side of the equals sign.

b) Explain how you know your answer to part **a)** is a contradiction.

c) What is the solution to the equation?

84. a) Construct a *contradiction* containing three terms on the left side of the equals sign and four terms on the right side of the equals sign.

b) Explain how you know your answer to part **a)** is a contradiction.

c) What is the solution to the equation?

Challenge Problems

85. Solve the equation $5\ast - 1 = 4\ast + 5\ast$ for $\ast$.

86. Solve the equation $2\triangle - 4 = 3\triangle + 5 - \triangle$ for $\triangle$.

87. Solve the equation $3\odot - 5 = 2\odot - 5 + \odot$ for $\odot$.

88. Solve $-2(x + 3) + 5x = 3(4 - 2x) - (x + 2)$.

89. Solve $4 - [5 - 3(x + 2)] = x - 3$.

Group Activity

Discuss and answer Exercise 90 as a group. In the next chapter, we will be discussing procedures for writing application problems as equations. Let's get some practice now.

90. Chocolate Bars Consider the following word problem. Mary Kay purchased two large chocolate bars. The total cost of the two chocolate bars was equal to the cost of one chocolate bar plus $6. Find the cost of one chocolate bar.

a) Each group member: Represent this problem as an equation with the variable x.

b) Each group member: Solve the equation you determined in part **a)**.

c) As a group, check your equation and your answer to make sure that it makes sense.

Cumulative Review Exercises

[1.5] **91.** Evaluate.

    a) $|4|$ **b)** $|-7|$ **c)** $|0|$

[1.9] **92.** $\dfrac{x^a}{x^b}$

[2.1] **93.** Explain the difference between factors and terms.

94. Simplify $2(x - 3) + 4x - (4 - x)$.

[2.4] **95.** Solve $2(x - 3) + 4x - (4 - x) = 0$.

96. Solve $(x + 4) - (4x - 3) = 16$.

2.6 Formulas

1 Use the simple interest formula and the distance formula.

2 Use geometric formulas.

3 Solve for a variable in a formula.

> **Formula**
>
> A **formula** is an equation commonly used to express a specific relationship mathematically.

For example, the formula for the area of a rectangle is

$$\text{area} = \text{length} \cdot \text{width} \quad \text{or} \quad A = lw$$

To **evaluate a formula,** substitute the appropriate numerical values for the variables and perform the indicated operations.

1 Use the Simple Interest Formula and the Distance Formula

A formula commonly used in banking is the **simple interest formula.**

> **Simple Interest Formula**
>
> $$\text{interest} = \text{principal} \cdot \text{rate} \cdot \text{time or } i = prt$$

Understanding Algebra

Formulas are used in business, science, and many other disciplines. A formula is an equation that states a relationship involving several variables.

This formula is used to determine the simple interest, i, earned on some savings accounts, or the simple interest an individual must pay on certain loans. In the simple interest formula $i = prt$, p is the principal (the amount invested or borrowed), r is the interest rate in decimal form, and t is the amount of time of the investment or loan.

EXAMPLE 1 Auto Loan To buy a car, Mary Beth Orrange borrowed $10,000 from a bank for 3 years. The bank charged 5% simple annual interest for the loan. How much interest will Mary Beth owe the bank?

Solution   Understand and Translate   Since the bank charged simple interest, we use the simple interest formula to solve the problem. We are given that the rate, r, is 5%, or 0.05 in decimal form. The principal, p, is $10,000 and the time, t, is 3 years. We substitute these values in the simple interest formula and solve for the interest, i.

Understanding Algebra

$$i = prt$$

i interest received
p principal: amount invested
r rate: interest rate (as a decimal)
t time: time of investment

Carry Out

$$i = prt$$
$$i = 10{,}000(0.05)(3)$$
$$i = 1500$$

Check   There are various ways to check this problem. First ask yourself "Is the answer realistic?" $1500 is a realistic answer. The interest on $10,000 for 1 year at 5% is $500. Therefore for 3 years, an interest of $1500 is correct.

Answer   Mary Beth will pay $1500 interest. After 3 years, when she repays the loan, she will pay the principal, $10,000, plus the interest, $1500 for a total of $11,500.

Now Try Exercise 83

EXAMPLE 2 Savings Account John Starmack invests $4000 in a savings account that earns simple interest for 2 years. If the interest earned from the account is $500, find the rate.

Solution   Understand and Translate   We use the simple interest formula, $i = prt$. We are given the principal, p, the time, t, and the interest, i. We are asked to find the rate, r. We substitute the given values in the simple interest formula and solve the resulting equation for r.

$$i = prt$$
$$500 = 4000(r)(2)$$

Carry Out

$$500 = 8000r$$
$$\frac{500}{8000} = \frac{8000r}{8000}$$
$$0.0625 = r$$

Check and Answer   The simple interest rate of 0.0625 or 6.25% per year is realistic. If we substitute $p = \$4000$, $r = 0.0625$ and $t = 2$, we obtain the interest, $i = \$500$. Thus, the answer checks. The simple interest rate is 6.25%.

Now Try Exercise 85

Another important formula is the distance formula.

Distance Formula

$$\text{distance} = \text{rate} \cdot \text{time} \quad \text{or} \quad d = r \cdot t$$

EXAMPLE 3 Auto Race At a NASCAR auto race, Dale Earnhardt, Jr., completed the race in 3.2 hours at an average speed of 156.25 miles per hour. Determine the distance of the race.

Solution   Understand and Translate   We are given the rate, 156.25 miles per hour, and the time is 3.2 hours. We are asked to find the distance.

$$\text{distance} = \text{rate} \cdot \text{time}$$

Carry Out

$$= (156.25)(3.2) = 500$$

Answer   Thus, the distance of the race was 500 miles.

Now Try Exercise 89

Understanding Algebra

The analysis of units in a given problem is sometimes called *dimensional analysis*.

Understanding Algebra

distance = rate × time

If you are traveling at a constant rate of 55 mph for 2 hours, you have traveled 55 × 2 = 110 miles.

Let's look at the units in Example 3. The rate is given in miles per hour and the time is given in hours. If we analyze the units (a process called *dimensional analysis*), we see that the answer is given in miles.

$$\text{distance} = \text{rate} \cdot \text{time}$$
$$= \frac{\text{miles}}{\text{hour}} \cdot \text{hour}$$
$$= \text{miles}$$

Now we will discuss geometric formulas that will be used throughout the book.

2 Use Geometric Formulas

The **perimeter,** P, is the sum of the lengths of the sides of a figure. Perimeters are measured in the same common unit as the sides. For example, perimeter may be measured in centimeters, inches, or feet. The **area,** A, is the measure of the amount of surface within the figure's boundaries. Areas are measured in square units. For example, area may be measured in square centimeters, square inches, or square feet. **Table 2.1** gives the formulas for finding the areas and perimeters of triangles and quadrilaterals. **Quadrilateral** is a general name for a four-sided figure.

In **Table 2.1,** the letter h is used to represent the *height* of the figure. In the figure of the trapezoid, the sides b and d are called the *bases* of the trapezoid. In the triangle, the side labeled b is called the *base* of the triangle.

Understanding Algebra

Legend for **Table 2.1**

s = side
w = width
l = length
h = height
b = base
d = trapezoid's
  second base

TABLE 2.1   Formulas for Areas and Perimeters of Quadrilaterals and Triangles*

Figure	Sketch	Area	Perimeter
Square		$A = s^2$	$P = 4s$
Rectangle		$A = lw$	$P = 2l + 2w$
Parallelogram		$A = lh$	$P = 2l + 2w$
Trapezoid		$A = \frac{1}{2}h(b + d)$	$P = a + b + c + d$
Triangle		$A = \frac{1}{2}bh$	$P = a + b + c$

EXAMPLE 4 **Building an Exercise Area** Dr. Alex Taurke, a veterinarian, decides to fence in a large rectangular area in the yard behind his office for exercising dogs that are boarded overnight. The part of the yard to be fenced in will be 40 feet long and 23 feet wide (see **Fig. 2.2**).

a) How much fencing is needed?

b) How large, in square feet, will the fenced-in area be?

Solution

a) Understand To find the amount of fencing required, we need to find the perimeter of the rectangular area to be fenced in. To find the perimeter, P,

*See Appendix C for additional information on geometry and geometric figures.

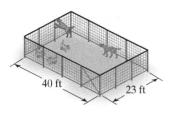

FIGURE 2.2

substitute 40 for the length, l, and 23 for the width, w, in the perimeter formula, $P = 2l + 2w$.

$$P = 2l + 2w$$

Carry Out $\qquad P = 2(40) + 2(23) = 80 + 46 = 126$

Check and Answer   By looking at **Figure 2.2,** we can see that a perimeter of 126 feet is a reasonable answer. Thus, 126 feet of fencing will be needed to fence in the area for the dogs to exercise.

b) To find the fenced-in area, substitute 40 for the length and 23 for the width in the formula for the area of a rectangle. Since we are multiplying an amount measured in feet by a second amount measured in feet, the answer will be in square feet (or ft²).

$$A = lw$$
$$= 40(23) = 920 \text{ square feet (or } 920 \text{ ft}^2)$$

Based upon the data given, an area of 920 ft² is reasonable. The area to be fenced in will be 920 square feet.

Now Try Exercise 91

EXAMPLE 5 Panoramic Photo Heather Hunter enlarges rectangular panoramic photos, like the one shown below. One of her enlarged panoramic photos has a perimeter of 116 inches and a length of 40 inches. Find the width of the photo.

© Allen R. Angel

Solution   Understand and Translate   The perimeter, P, is 116 inches and the length, l, is 40 inches. Substitute these values into the formula for the perimeter of a rectangle and solve for the width, w.

$$P = 2l + 2w$$
$$116 = 2(40) + 2w$$

Carry Out $\qquad\qquad 116 = 80 + 2w$

$\qquad 116 - 80 = 80 - 80 + 2w \qquad$ Subtract 80 from both sides.

$\qquad\qquad\qquad 36 = 2w$

$$\frac{36}{2} = \frac{2w}{2} \qquad\qquad \text{Divide both sides by 2.}$$

$\qquad\qquad\qquad 18 = w$

Check and Answer   By comparing the length and width, you should realize that the dimensions of a length of 40 inches and a width of 18 inches is reasonable. The answer is, the width of the photo is 18 inches.

Now Try Exercise 25

EXAMPLE 6 **Sailboat** A small sailboat has a triangular sail that has an area of 30 square feet and a base of 5 feet (see **Fig. 2.3**). Determine the height of the sail.

Solution Understand and Translate We use the formula for the area of a triangle given in **Table 2.1** on page 134.

5 ft

FIGURE 2.3

$$A = \frac{1}{2}bh$$

$$30 = \frac{1}{2}(5)h$$

Carry Out

$$2 \cdot 30 = 2 \cdot \frac{1}{2}(5)h \quad \text{Multiply both sides by 2.}$$

$$60 = 5h$$

$$\frac{60}{5} = \frac{5h}{5} \quad \text{Divide both sides by 5.}$$

$$12 = h$$

Check and Answer The height of the triangle is 12 feet. By looking at **Figure 2.3**, you may realize that a sail 12 feet tall and 5 feet wide at the base is reasonable. Thus, the height of the sail is 12 feet.

Now Try Exercise 93

Another figure that we see and use daily is the circle. The **circumference**, C, is the length (or perimeter) of the curve that forms a circle. The **radius**, r, is the line segment from the center of the circle to any point on the circle (**Fig. 2.4a**). The **diameter** of a circle is a line segment through the center whose endpoints both lie on the circle (**Fig. 2.4b**). *Note that the length of the diameter is twice the length of the radius.*

The formulas for both the area and the circumference of a circle are given in **Table 2.2**.

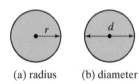

(a) radius   (b) diameter

FIGURE 2.4

TABLE 2.2   Formulas for Circles

Circle	Area	Circumference
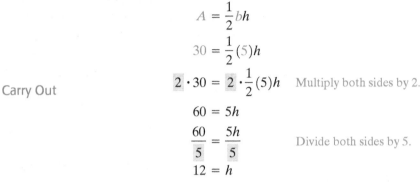	$A = \pi r^2$	$C = 2\pi r$

The value of **pi**, symbolized by the Greek lowercase letter π, is an irrational number that cannot be exactly expressed as a decimal number or a numerical fraction. Pi is *approximately* 3.14. Here it is approximated to 100 digits:

$\pi \approx$ 3.14159 26535 89793 23846 26433 83279 50288 41971 69399 37510 58209 74944 59230 78164 06286 20899 86280 34825 34211 7068...

EXAMPLE 7 **Pizza** A Pizza Hut large pizza has a diameter of 14 inches. Determine the area and circumference of the pizza.

Solution The radius is half the diameter, so $r = \frac{14}{2} = 7$ inches.

$A = \pi r^2$ $C = 2\pi r$

$A = \pi(7)^2$ $C = 2\pi(7)$

$A = \pi(49)$ $C \approx 43.98$ inches

$A \approx 153.94$ square inches

To obtain our answers 153.94 and 43.98, we used the $\boxed{\pi}$ key on a calculator and rounded our final answer to the nearest hundredth. If you do not have a calculator with a $\boxed{\pi}$ key and use 3.14 for π, your answer for the area would be 153.86.

Now Try Exercise 95

Table 2.3 below gives formulas for finding the volume of certain three-dimensional figures. **Volume** is the measure of the space occupied by a figure, and it is measured in cubic units, such as cubic centimeters or cubic feet.

EXAMPLE 8 **Spaceship Earth** The inside of Spaceship Earth at Epcot Center in Disney World, Florida, is a sphere with a diameter of 165 feet (see photo). Determine the volume of Spaceship Earth.

Solution   Understand and Translate   **Table 2.3** gives the formula for the volume of a sphere. The formula involves the radius. Since the diameter is 165 feet, its radius is $\frac{165}{2} = 82.5$ feet.

$$V = \frac{4}{3}\pi r^3$$

Carry Out $V = \frac{4}{3}\pi(82.5)^3 = \frac{4}{3}\pi(561{,}515.625) \approx 2{,}352{,}071.15$

Check and Answer   The volume inside the sphere is very large, so the answer of about 2,352,071.15 cubic feet is reasonable.

Now Try Exercise 103

Spaceship Earth

Understanding Algebra

Legend for **Table 2.3**

w = width

l = length

h = height

r = radius

TABLE 2.3   **Formulas for Volumes of Three-Dimensional Figures**

Figure	Sketch	Volume
Rectangular solid		$V = lwh$
Right circular cylinder		$V = \pi r^2 h$
Right circular cone		$V = \frac{1}{3}\pi r^2 h$
Sphere		$V = \frac{4}{3}\pi r^3$

3 Solve for a Variable in a Formula

Often in this course and in other mathematics and science courses, you will be given an equation or formula solved for one variable and have to solve it for a different variable.

To solve for a variable in a formula, treat each of the quantities, except the one for which you are solving, as if they were constants. Then solve for the desired variable by isolating it on one side of the equation.

EXAMPLE 9 **Distance Formula** Solve the distance formula $d = rt$ for t.

Solution   We must get t all by itself on one side of the equals sign. Since t is multiplied by r, we divide both sides of the equation by r to isolate the t.

$$d = rt$$

$$\frac{d}{r} = \frac{\cancel{r}t}{\cancel{r}} \quad \text{Divide both sides by } r.$$

$$\frac{d}{r} = t$$

Therefore, $t = \dfrac{d}{r}$.

Now Try Exercise 45

EXAMPLE 10 **Perimeter of Rectangle** The formula for the perimeter of a rectangle is $P = 2l + 2w$. Solve this formula for the length, l.

Solution   We must get l all by itself on one side of the equation.

$$P = 2l + 2w$$

$$P - 2w = 2l + 2w - 2w \qquad \text{Subtract } 2w \text{ from both sides.}$$

$$P - 2w = 2l$$

$$\frac{P - 2w}{2} = \frac{2l}{2} \qquad \text{Divide both sides by 2.}$$

$$\frac{P - 2w}{2} = l \quad \left(\text{or} \quad l = \frac{P}{2} - w \right)$$

Now Try Exercise 53

Some formulas contain fractions. When a formula contains a fraction, we can eliminate the fraction by multiplying both sides of the equation by the least common denominator.

EXAMPLE 11 The formula for the area of a triangle is $A = \dfrac{1}{2}bh$. Solve this formula for h.

Solution   We begin by multiplying both sides of the equation by the LCD, 2, to eliminate the fraction.

$$A = \frac{1}{2}bh$$

$$2 \cdot A = \cancel{2} \cdot \frac{1}{\cancel{2}}bh \quad \text{Multiply both sides by 2.}$$

$$2A = bh$$

$$\frac{2A}{b} = \frac{\cancel{b}h}{\cancel{b}} \qquad \text{Divide both sides by } b \text{ to isolate } h.$$

$$\frac{2A}{b} = h$$

Thus, $h = \dfrac{2A}{b}$.

Now Try Exercise 51

Write Equations in $y = mx + b$ Form

When discussing graphing later in this book, we will need to solve many equations for the variable y, and write the equation in the form $y = mx + b$, where m and b represent real numbers. Examples of equations in this form are

$$y = 2x + 4, \ y = -\frac{1}{2}x - 3, \text{ and } y = \frac{4}{5}x + \frac{1}{3}.$$

EXAMPLE 12 Solve the equation $6x + 3y = 12$ for y. Write the answer in $y = mx + b$ form.

Solution   Begin by isolating the term containing the variable y.

$$6x + 3y = 12$$

$$6x - 6x + 3y = 12 - 6x \qquad \text{Subtract } 6x \text{ from both sides.}$$

$$3y = 12 - 6x$$

$$\frac{3y}{3} = \frac{12 - 6x}{3} \qquad \text{Divide both sides by 3.}$$

$$y = \frac{12 - 6x}{3}$$

$$y = \frac{12}{3} - \frac{6x}{3} \qquad \text{Wrote as two fractions.}$$

$$y = 4 - 2x$$

$$y = -2x + 4$$

Now Try Exercise 67

Helpful Hint

Notice that in Example 12, when we obtained $y = \dfrac{12 - 6x}{3}$, we had solved the equation for y since the y was isolated on one side of the equation. When we wrote the answer as $y = -2x + 4$, we wrote the equation in $y = mx + b$ form.

EXAMPLE 13 Solve the equation $y - \dfrac{1}{3} = \dfrac{1}{4}(x - 6)$ for y. Write the answer in $y = mx + b$ form.

Solution   Multiply both sides of the equation by the LCD, 12.

$$y - \frac{1}{3} = \frac{1}{4}(x - 6)$$

$$12\left(y - \frac{1}{3}\right) = 12 \cdot \frac{1}{4}(x - 6) \qquad \text{Multiply both sides by 12.}$$

$$12y - 4 = 3(x - 6) \qquad \text{Distributive property used on left.}$$

$$12y - 4 = 3x - 18 \qquad \text{Distributive property used on right.}$$

$$12y = 3x - 14 \qquad \text{Added 4 to both sides.}$$

$$y = \frac{3x - 14}{12} \qquad \text{Divided both sides by 12.}$$

$$y = \frac{3x}{12} - \frac{14}{12} \qquad \text{Write as two fractions.}$$

$$y = \frac{1}{4}x - \frac{7}{6}$$

Now Try Exercise 79

In Example 13, you may wish to use the distributive property on the right side of the equation before multiplying both sides of the equation by the LCD, 12. Try working the example using this method now to see which procedure you prefer.

EXERCISE SET 2.6

Math XL MathXL®   *MyMathLab* MyMathLab

Warm-Up Exercises

Fill in the blanks with the appropriate word, phrase, or symbol(s) from the following list.

formula	quadrilateral	rate · time
time	evaluating	cubic feet

radius	π	diameter
square inches	decimal	

1. A four-sided figure is called a _____ .

2. Half the diameter is the _____ .

3. An equation used to express a specific relationship mathematically is called a _____ .

4. Interest is found by multiplying the principal times the rate times the _____ .

5. A possible unit of measure for volume is _____ .

6. A possible unit of measure for area is _____ .

7. When the circumference of a circle is divided by its diameter, the result is _____ .

8. Distance = _____ .

9. The process of substituting values and performing indicated operations on a formula is called _____ it.

10. When calculating simple interest, the rate should be expressed as a _____ .

Practice the Skills

Use the formula to find the value of the variable indicated. Round decimal answers to the nearest hundredth.

11. $d = rt$ (distance formula); find d when $r = 60$ and $t = 8$.

12. $P = 4s$ (perimeter of a square); find P when $s = 6$.

13. $A = lw$ (area of a rectangle); find A when $l = 12$ and $w = 8$.

14. $A = s^2$ (area of a square); find A when $s = 9$.

15. $i = prt$ (simple interest formula); find i when $p = 2000$, $r = 0.06$, and $t = 3$.

16. $c = 2.54i$ (to change inches to centimeters); find c when $i = 12$.

17. $P = 2l + 2w$ (perimeter of a rectangle); find P when $l = 8$ and $w = 10$.

18. $f = 1.47m$ (to change speed from mph to ft/sec); find f when $m = 60$.

19. $A = \pi r^2$ (area of a circle); find A when $r = 10$.

20. $A = \dfrac{m + n}{2}$ (mean of two values); find A when $m = 16$ and $n = 56$.

21. $A = \dfrac{a + b + c}{3}$ (mean of three values); find A when $a = 72, b = 81$, and $c = 93$.

22. $p = i^2 r$ (formula for finding electrical power); find r when $p = 2000$ and $i = 4$.

23. $z = \dfrac{x - m}{s}$ (statistics formula for finding the z-score); find z when $x = 100, m = 80$, and $s = 10$.

24. $A = \dfrac{1}{2}bh$ (area of a triangle); find b when $A = 30$ and $h = 10$.

25. $P = 2l + 2w$ (perimeter of a rectangle); find l when $P = 28$ and $w = 6$.

26. $A = P(1 + rt)$ (banking formula to find the amount in an account); find r when $A = 1050, t = 1$, and $P = 1000$.

27. $V = \pi r^2 h$ (volume of a cylinder); find h when $V = 678.24$ and $r = 6$.

28. $V = \dfrac{4}{3}\pi r^3$ (volume of a sphere); find V when $r = 8$.

29. $B = \dfrac{703w}{h^2}$ (for finding body mass index); find w when $B = 24$ and $h = 61$.

30. $S = C + rC$ (for determining selling price when an item is marked up); find S when $C = 160$ and $r = 0.12$ (or 12%).

In Exercises 31–36, use **Tables 2.1, 2.2,** *and* **2.3** *to find the formula for the area or volume of the figure. Then determine either the area or volume.*

31.

32.
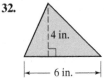

33.
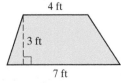

34.
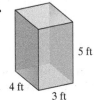

35.

36.
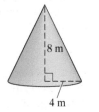

In Exercises 37 and 38, use the formula $C = \dfrac{5}{9}(F - 32)$ to find the Celsius temperature (C) equivalent to the given Fahrenheit temperature (F).

37. $F = 50°$

38. $F = 86°$

In Exercises 39 and 40, use the formula $F = \dfrac{9}{5}C + 32$, to find the Fahrenheit temperature (F) equivalent to the given Celsius temperature (C).

39. $C = 25°$

40. $C = -40°$

In Exercises 41–44, find the missing quantity. Use the ideal gas law, $P = KT/V$, where P is pressure, T is temperature, V is volume, and K is a constant.

41. $T = 20, K = 2, V = 1$

42. $P = 80, T = 100, V = 5$

43. $T = 30, P = 3, K = 0.5$

44. $P = 100, K = 2, V = 6$

In Exercises 45–66, solve for the indicated variable.

45. $A = lw$, for l

46. $P = 4s$, for s

47. $d = rt$, for t

48. $C = \pi d$, for d

49. $i = prt$, for t

50. $V = lwh$, for l

51. $A = \dfrac{1}{2}bh$, for b

52. $E = IR$, for I

53. $P = 2l + 2w$, for w

54. $PV = KT$, for T

55. $3 - 2r = n$, for r

56. $4m + 5n = 25$, for n

57. $y = mx + b$, for b

58. $y = mx + b$, for x

59. $d = a + b + c$, for b

60. $ax + by = c$, for y

61. $ax + by + c = 0$, for y

62. $V = \pi r^2 h$, for h

63. $V = \dfrac{1}{3}\pi r^2 h$, for h

64. $A = \dfrac{m + 2d}{3}$, for d

65. $A = \dfrac{m + d}{2}$, for m

66. $L = \dfrac{c + 2d}{4}$, for d

In Exercises 67–82, solve each equation for y. Write the answer in $y = mx + b$ form. See Examples 12 and 13.

67. $2x + y = 8$

68. $6x + 2y = -12$

69. $-3x + 3y = -18$

70. $-2y + 4x = -8$

71. $4x = 6y - 8$

72. $15 = 3y - x$

73. $5y = -10 + 3x$

74. $-2y = -3x - 18$

75. $-6y = 15 - 3x$

76. $-12 = -2x - 3y$

77. $-10 = -x - 2y$

78. $4x + 3y = 20$

79. $y + 3 = -\dfrac{1}{3}(x - 4)$

80. $y - 3 = \dfrac{2}{3}(x + 4)$

81. $y - \dfrac{1}{5} = 2\left(x + \dfrac{1}{3}\right)$

82. $y + 5 = \dfrac{3}{4}\left(x + \dfrac{1}{2}\right)$

Problem Solving

In Exercises 83–86, use the simple interest formula.

83. Auto Loan Thang Tran decided to borrow $6000 from Citibank to help pay for a car. His loan was for 3 years at a simple interest rate of 8%. How much interest will Thang pay?

84. Simple Interest Loan Holly Broesamle lent her brother $4000 for a period of 2 years. At the end of the 2 years, her brother repaid the $4000 plus $640 interest. What simple interest rate did her brother pay?

85. Savings Account Mary Seitz invested a certain amount of money in a savings account paying 3% simple interest per year. When she withdrew her money at the end of 3 years, she received $450 in interest. How much money did Mary place in the savings account?

86. Savings Account Peter Ostroushko put $6000 in a savings account earning $3\dfrac{1}{2}$% simple interest per year. When he withdrew his money, he received $840 in interest. How long had he left his money in the account?

In Exercises 87–90, use the distance formula.

87. Average Speed On her way from Omaha, Nebraska, to Kansas City, Kansas, Peg Hovde traveled 180 miles in 3 hours. What was her average speed?

88. Walk Lisa Feintech went for a walk where she walked at an average speed of 3.4 miles per hour for 2 hours. How far did she walk?

89. Fastest Car The fastest speed recorded on land was about 763.2 miles per hour by a jet-powered car called ThrustSSC. If, during the speed trial, the car traveled for 0.01 hour, how far had the car traveled?

The ThrustSSC

90. Fastest Plane The fastest aircraft is the Lockheed SR-71 Blackbird. If, during the trial run, the plane covered a distance of 660 miles in 0.3 hours, determine the plane's average speed.

Use the formulas given in **Tables 2.1, 2.2,** *and* **2.3** *to work Exercises 91–104.*

91. DVD Player A portable DVD player has a screen with a length of 8 inches and a width (or height) of 6 inches. Determine the area of the screen.

92. Television A plasma television has a screen with a length of 34.9 inches and a width (or height) of 19.6 inches. Determine the perimeter of the screen.

93. Yield Sign A yield traffic sign is triangular with a base of 36 inches and a height of 31 inches. Find the area of the sign.

94. Fencing Milt McGowen has a rectangular lot that measures 100 feet by 60 feet. If Milt wants to fence in his lot, how much fencing will he need?

95. Swimming Pool A circular above-ground swimming pool has a diameter of 24 feet. Determine the circumference of the pool.

96. Living Room Table A round living room table top has a diameter of 3 feet. Find the area of the table top.

97. Kite Below we show a kite. Determine the area of the kite.

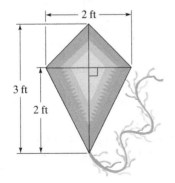

98. Laptop The carrying case for a laptop computer measures 17 inches long by 14 inches wide by 6 inches deep. Determine the volume of the case.

99. Trapezoidal Sign Canter Martin made a sign to display at a baseball game. The sign was in the shape of a trapezoid. Its bases are 4 feet and 3 feet, and its height is 2 feet. Find the area of the sign.

100. Jacuzzi The inside of a circular jacuzzi is 8 feet in diameter. If the water inside the jacuzzi is 3 feet deep, determine, in cubic feet, the volume of water in the jacuzzi.

101. Banyan Tree The largest banyan tree in the continental United States is at the Edison House in Fort Myers, Florida. The circumference of the aerial roots of the tree is 390 feet. Find the *diameter* of the aerial roots to the nearest tenth of a foot.

102. Amphitheater The seats in an amphitheater are inside a trapezoidal area as shown in the figure. The bases of the trapezoidal area are 80 feet and 200 feet, and the height is 100 feet. Find the area of the floor occupied by seats.

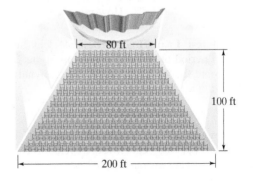

103. Basketball Find the volume of a basketball if its diameter is 9 inches.

104. Oil Drum Roberto Sanchez has an empty oil drum that he uses for storage. The oil drum is 4 feet high and has a diameter of 24 inches. Find the volume of the drum in cubic feet.

105. Body Mass Index A person's body mass index (BMI) is found by multiplying a person's weight, w, in pounds by 703, then dividing this product by the square of the person's height, h, in inches.

    a) Write a formula to find the BMI.

    b) Brandy Belmont is 5 feet 3 inches tall and weighs 135 pounds. Find her BMI.

106. Body Mass Index Refer to Exercise 105. Mario Guzza's weight is 162 pounds, and he is 5 feet 7 inches tall. Find his BMI.

Challenge Problems

107. Cereal Box A cereal box is to be made by folding the cardboard along the dashed lines as shown in the figure on the right.

© Allen Angel\Allen R. Angel

    a) Using the formula

$$\text{volume} = \text{length} \cdot \text{width} \cdot \text{height}$$

    write an equation for the volume of the box.

    b) Find the volume of the box when $x = 7$ cm.

    c) Write an equation for the surface area of the box.

d) Find the surface area when $x = 7$ cm.

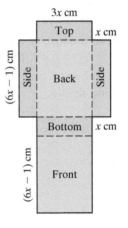

Concept/Writing Exercises

108. When using the distance formula, what happens to the distance if the rate is doubled and the time is halved? Explain.

109. When using the simple interest formula, what happens to the simple interest if both the principal and rate are doubled but the time is halved? Explain.

110. Consider the formula for the area of a square, $A = s^2$. If the length of the side of a square, s, is doubled, what is the change in its area? Explain.

111. Consider the formula for the volume of a cube, $V = s^3$. If the length of the side of a cube, s, is doubled, what is the change in its volume? Explain.

112. Which would have the greater area, a square whose side has a length of s inches, or a circle whose diameter has a length of s inches? Explain, using a sketch.

113. Which would have the greater area, a square whose diagonal has a length of s inches, or a circle whose diameter has a length of s inches? Explain, using a sketch.

Group Activity

114. Square Face on Cube Consider the following photo. The front of the figure is a square with a smaller black square

© Allen R. Angel

painted on the center of the larger square. Suppose the length of one side of the larger square is A, and the length of one side of the smaller (black) square is B. Also the thickness of the block is C.

    a) Group member one: Determine an expression for the surface area of the black square.

    b) Group member two: Determine an expression for the surface area of the larger square (which includes the smaller square).

    c) Group member three: Determine the surface area of the larger square minus the black square (the purple area shown).

    d) As a group, write an expression for the volume of the entire solid block.

    e) As a group, determine the volume of the entire solid block if its length is 1.5 feet and its width is 0.8 feet.

Cumulative Review Exercises

[1.7] **115.** Evaluate $-\dfrac{4}{15} + \dfrac{3}{5}$.

116. Evaluate $-6 + 7 - 4 - 3$.

[1.9] **117.** Evaluate. $[4(12 \div 2^2 - 3)^2]^2$.

[2.4] **118.** Solve the equation $\dfrac{r}{2} + 2r = 20$.

2.7 Ratios and Proportions

1 Understand ratios.

2 Solve proportions using cross-multiplication.

3 Solve applications.

4 Use proportions to change units.

5 Use proportions to solve problems involving similar figures.

1 Understand Ratios

Ratio

A **ratio** is a quotient of two quantities.

Ratios provide a way to compare two numbers or quantities. The ratio of the number a to the number b may be written

$$a \text{ to } b, \quad a : b, \quad \text{or} \quad \frac{a}{b}$$

where a and b are called the **terms of the ratio.** Notice that the symbol : can be used to indicate a ratio.

EXAMPLE 1 **Favorite Movies** Several children in sixth grade were asked to name their favorite movie of 2007. The results are indicated on the graph in **Figure 2.5.**

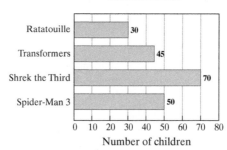

Favorite Movies

FIGURE 2.5   Number of children

a) Find the ratio of the number of children who selected *Shrek the Third* to those who selected *Transformers*. Then write the ratio in lowest terms.

b) Find the ratio of the number of children who selected *Spider-Man 3* to the total number in the survey.

Solution   We will use our five-step problem-solving procedure.

a) Understand and Translate   The ratio we are seeking is

Number who selected *Shrek the Third* : Number who selected *Transformers*

Carry Out   We substitute the appropriate values into the ratio.

This gives

$$70 : 45$$

To write the ratio in *lowest terms,* we simplify by dividing each number in the ratio by 5, the greatest number that divides both terms in the ratio. This gives

$$14 : 9$$

Check and Answer   Our division is correct. The ratio is $14 : 9$.

b) We use the same procedure as in part **a)**. Fifty children selected *Spider-Man 3*. There were $50 + 70 + 45 + 30$ or 195 children surveyed. Thus, the ratio is $50 : 195$, which simplifies to

$$10 : 39$$

Now Try Exercise 33

Understanding Algebra

A *ratio* is another word for a fraction. It can be denoted 3 different ways: $\dfrac{a}{b}$, $a : b$, or with the word "to" as "a to b."

Spider-Man 3

The answer in Example 1, part **a)** could have also been written $\frac{14}{9}$ or 14 to 9. The answer in part **b)** could have also been written $\frac{10}{39}$ or 10 to 39.

EXAMPLE 2 Cholesterol Level There are two types of cholesterol: low-density lipoprotein, (LDL—considered the harmful type of cholesterol) and high-density lipoprotein (HDL—considered the healthful type of cholesterol). Some doctors recommend that the ratio of LDL to HDL be less than or equal to 4 : 1. Mr. Suarez's cholesterol test showed that his LDL was 167 milligrams per deciliter, and his HDL was 40 milligrams per deciliter. Is Mr. Suarez's ratio of LDL to HDL less than or equal to the recommended 4 : 1 ratio?

Solution Understand We need to determine if Mr. Suarez's LDL to HDL ratio is less than or equal to 4 : 1.

Translate Mr. Suarez's LDL to HDL ratio is 167 : 40. To make the second term equal to 1, we divide both terms in the ratio by the second term, 40.

Carry Out
$$\frac{167}{40} : \frac{40}{40}$$
$$\text{or } 4.175 : 1$$

Check and Answer Our division is correct. Therefore, Mr. Suarez's ratio is not less than or equal to the desired 4 : 1 ratio.

Now Try Exercise 87

EXAMPLE 3 Gas–Oil Mixture Some power equipment, such as chainsaws and blowers, use a gas–oil mixture to run the engine. The instructions on a particular chainsaw indicate that 5 gallons of gasoline should be mixed with 40 ounces of special oil to obtain the proper gas–oil mixture. Find the ratio of gasoline to oil in the proper mixture.

Solution Understand To express these quantities in a ratio, both quantities must be in the same units. We can either convert 5 gallons to ounces or 40 ounces to gallons.

Translate Let's change 5 gallons to ounces. Since there are 128 ounces in 1 gallon, 5 gallons of gas equals 5(128) or 640 ounces. The ratio we are seeking is

ounces of gasoline : ounces of oil

Carry Out   640 : 40
                    or 16 : 1   Divide both terms by 40 to simplify.

Check and Answer Our simplification is correct. The correct ratio of gas to oil for this chainsaw is 16 : 1.

Now Try Exercise 23

EXAMPLE 4 Gear Ratio The *gear ratio* of two gears is defined as

$$\text{gear ratio} = \frac{\text{number of teeth on the driving gear}}{\text{number of teeth on the driven gear}}$$

Find the gear ratio of the gears shown in **Figure 2.6.**

Solution Understand and Translate To find the gear ratio we need to substitute the appropriate values.

Carry Out $\text{gear ratio} = \dfrac{\text{number of teeth on driving gear}}{\text{number of teeth on driven gear}} = \dfrac{60}{8} = \dfrac{15}{2}$

Thus, the gear ratio is 15 : 2. Gear ratios are generally given as some quantity to 1. If we divide both terms of the ratio by the second term, we will obtain a ratio of some number to 1. Dividing both 15 and 2 by 2 gives a gear ratio of 7.5 : 1.

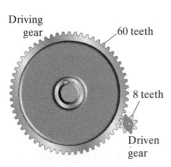

Driving gear   60 teeth
8 teeth
Driven gear

FIGURE 2.6

Check and Answer   The gear ratio is 7.5 : 1. This means that as the driving gear goes around once the driven gear goes around 7.5 times. (A typical first gear ratio on a passenger car may be 3.545 : 1.)

Now Try Exercise 27

2 Solve Proportions Using Cross-Multiplication

> **Proportion**
>
> A **proportion** is a special type of equation. It is a statement of equality between two ratios.

One way of denoting a proportion is $a : b = c : d$, which is read "*a* is to *b* as *c* is to *d*." In this text we write proportions as

$$\frac{a}{b} = \frac{c}{d}$$

> ### Understanding Algebra
>
> When two ratios are set equal, we call it a *proportion*. For example, consider $\frac{3}{12} = \frac{1}{4}$. The numbers 3 and 4 are called the *extremes* and 12 and 1 are called the *means* of the proportion. *The product of the means* $(12 \cdot 1 = 12)$ *always equals the product of the extremes* $(3 \cdot 4 = 12)$.

The *a* and *d* are *referred* to as the **extremes**, and the *b* and *c* are referred to as the **means** of the proportion. In Sections 2.4 and 2.5, we solved equations containing fractions by multiplying both sides of the equation by the LCD to eliminate fractions. For example, for the proportion

$$\frac{x}{3} = \frac{35}{15}$$

$$15 \left(\frac{x}{3} \right) = 15 \left(\frac{35}{15} \right) \qquad \text{Mulyiply both sides by the LCD, 15.}$$

$$5x = 35$$

$$x = 7$$

Another method that can be used to solve proportions is **cross-multiplication**.

> **Cross-Multiplication**
>
> If $\dfrac{a}{b} = \dfrac{c}{d}$, then $ad = bc$.
>
> *The product of the extremes, ad, is equal to the product of the means, bc.*

If any three of the four quantities of a proportion are known, the fourth quantity can easily be found.

EXAMPLE 5 Solve $\dfrac{x}{3} = \dfrac{35}{15}$ for *x* by cross-multiplying.

Solution

$$\frac{x}{3} = \frac{35}{15}$$

$$x \cdot 15 = 3 \cdot 35$$

$$15x = 105$$

$$x = \frac{105}{15} = 7$$

Check

$$\frac{x}{3} = \frac{35}{15}$$

$$\frac{7}{3} \stackrel{?}{=} \frac{35}{15}$$

$$\frac{7}{3} = \frac{7}{3} \qquad \text{True}$$

Now Try Exercise 37

Earlier, we solved the proportion $\dfrac{x}{3} = \dfrac{35}{15}$ by multiplying both sides of the equation by 15. In Example 5, we solved the same proportion using cross-multiplication. Notice we obtained the same solution, 7, in each case.

EXAMPLE 6 Solve $\dfrac{-8}{3} = \dfrac{64}{x}$ for x by cross-multiplying.

Solution

$$\frac{-8}{3} = \frac{64}{x}$$

$$-8 \cdot x = 3 \cdot 64$$

$$-8x = 192$$

$$\frac{-8x}{-8} = \frac{192}{-8}$$

$$x = -24$$

Check

$$\frac{-8}{3} = \frac{64}{x}$$

$$\frac{-8}{3} \overset{?}{=} \frac{64}{-24}$$

$$\frac{-8}{3} \overset{?}{=} \frac{8}{-3}$$

$$\frac{-8}{3} = \frac{-8}{3} \quad \text{True}$$

Now Try Exercise 41

3 Solve Applications

Often, practical problems can be solved using proportions. Below are specific directions for translating application problems into proportions.

To Solve Problems Using Proportions

1. Understand the problem.
2. Translate the problem into mathematical language.
   a) First, represent the unknown quantity by a variable.
   b) Second, set up the proportion by listing the given ratio on one side of the equals sign, and the variable and the other given quantity on the other side of the equals sign. When setting up the proportion, the same respective quantities should occupy the same respective positions on the left and the right. For example, an acceptable proportion might be

$$\text{Given ratio} \left\{ \frac{\text{miles}}{\text{hour}} = \frac{\text{miles}}{\text{hour}} \right.$$

3. Carry out the mathematical calculations necessary to solve the problem.
   a) Once the proportion is correctly written, drop the units and cross-multiply.
   b) Solve the resulting equation and label with the appropriate units.
4. Check the answer obtained in step 3.
5. Make sure you have answered the question.

Understanding Algebra

When solving applied problems involving proportions, it is crucial that each ratio has the same units! For example, if one ratio is given in miles/hour and the second ratio is given in feet/hour, one of the ratio's units must be changed before setting up the proportion.

EXAMPLE 7 **Painting** A gallon of paint will cover a surface area of 575 square feet.

a) How many gallons of paint are needed to cover a house with a surface area of 6525 square feet?

b) If a gallon of paint costs $24.99, what will it cost to paint the house?

Solution

a) *Understand*   The given ratio is 1 gallon per 575 square feet. The unknown quantity is the number of gallons necessary to cover 6525 square feet.

Translate   Let x = number of gallons of paint needed.

$$\text{Given ratio} \left\{ \frac{1 \text{ gallon}}{575 \text{ square feet}} = \frac{x \text{ gallons}}{6525 \text{ square feet}} \right. \begin{array}{l} \longleftarrow \text{Unknown} \\ \longleftarrow \text{Given quantity} \end{array}$$

Note how the amount, in gallons, and the area, in square feet, are given in the same relative positions.

Carry Out

$$\frac{1}{575} = \frac{x}{6525}$$

$$1(6525) = 575x \quad \text{Cross-multiply.}$$

$$6525 = 575x. \quad \text{Solve.}$$

$$\frac{6525}{575} = x$$

$$11.3 \approx x$$

Check   Both ratios in the proportion, $\frac{1}{575}$ and $\frac{11.3}{6525}$, have approximately the same value of 0.00173. Thus, the answer of about 11.3 gallons checks.

Answer   The amount of paint needed to cover an area of 6525 square feet is about 11.3 gallons.

b) Assuming the painter only buys full gallons of paint, he will need to buy 12 gallons in order to paint the house. Since each gallon costs $24.99, the cost to paint the house is found by multiplication.

$$12 \times 24.99 = \$299.88$$

The cost to paint the house is $299.88.

Now Try Exercise 61

EXAMPLE 8 At a charity luncheon, the guests meet and get autographs from members of the New York Yankees. If a particular player signs, on the average, 33 autographs in 4 minutes, how much time must be allowed for him to sign 350 autographs?

Solution   The unknown quantity is the time needed for the player to sign 350 autographs. We are given that, on the average, he signs 33 autographs in 4 minutes. We will use this given ratio in setting up our proportion.

Translate   We will let x represent the time to sign 350 autographs.

$$\text{Given ratio} \left\{ \frac{33 \text{ autographs}}{4 \text{ minutes}} = \frac{350 \text{ autographs}}{x \text{ minutes}} \right.$$

Carry Out

$$\frac{33}{4} = \frac{350}{x}$$

$$33x = 4(350)$$

$$33x = 1400$$

$$x = \frac{1400}{33} \approx 42.4$$

Check and Answer   Both ratios in the proportion, $\frac{33}{4}$ and $\frac{350}{42.4}$, have approximately the same value of 8.25. Thus, about 42.4 minutes would be needed for the player to sign the 350 autographs.

Now Try Exercise 55

EXAMPLE 9 **Drug Dosage** A nurse is to give a patient 250 milligrams of the drug simethicone. The drug is available only in a solution whose concentration is 40 milligrams of simethicone per 0.6 milliliter of solution. How many milliliters of solution should the nurse give the patient?

Solution   Understand and Translate   We can set up the proportion using the medication on hand as the given ratio and the number of milliliters needed to be given as the unknown.

$$\text{Given ratio} \left\{ \frac{40 \text{ milligrams}}{0.6 \text{ milliliter}} = \frac{250 \text{ milligrams}}{x \text{ milliliters}} \right. \begin{array}{l} \longleftarrow \text{Desired} \\ \longleftarrow \text{medication} \\ \longleftarrow \text{Unknown} \end{array}$$

Carry Out

$$\frac{40}{0.6} = \frac{250}{x}$$

$$40x = 0.6(250) \qquad \text{Cross-multiply.}$$

$$40x = 150 \qquad \text{Solve.}$$

$$x = \frac{150}{40} = 3.75$$

Check and Answer   The nurse should administer 3.75 milliliters of the simethicone solution.

Now Try Exercise 69

Avoiding Common Errors

When you are setting up a proportion, it does not matter which unit in the given ratio is in the numerator and which is in the denominator as long as the units in the other ratio are *in the same relative position*. For example,

$$\frac{60 \text{ miles}}{1.5 \text{ hours}} = \frac{x \text{ miles}}{4.2 \text{ hours}} \quad \text{and} \quad \frac{1.5 \text{ hours}}{60 \text{ miles}} = \frac{4.2 \text{ hours}}{x \text{ miles}}$$

will both give the same answer of 168 (try it and see). When setting up the proportion, set it up so that it makes the most sense to you. Notice that when setting up a proportion containing different units, the same units should not be multiplied by themselves during cross-multiplication.

CORRECT	INCORRECT
$\dfrac{\text{miles}}{\text{hour}} = \dfrac{\text{miles}}{\text{hour}}$	$\dfrac{\text{miles}}{\text{hour}} \bowtie \dfrac{\text{hour}}{\text{miles}}$

---

4 Use Proportions to Change Units

Proportions can also be used to convert from one quantity to another. For example, you can use a proportion to convert a measurement in feet to a measurement in meters, or to convert from pounds to kilograms.

EXAMPLE 10 Converting Kilometers to Miles   There are approximately 1.6 kilometers in 1 mile. What is the distance, in miles, of 78 kilometers?

Solution   Understand and Translate   We know that 1 mile $\approx$ 1.6 kilometers. We use this known fact in one ratio of our proportion. In the second ratio, we set the quantities with the same units in the same respective positions. The unknown quantity is the number of miles, which we will call x.

$$\text{Known ratio} \left\{ \frac{1 \text{ mile}}{1.6 \text{ kilometers}} = \frac{x \text{ miles}}{78 \text{ kilometers}} \right.$$

Note that both numerators contain the same units, and both denominators contain the same units.

Carry Out   Now solve for x by cross-multiplying.

$$\frac{1}{1.6} = \frac{x}{78}$$

$$1(78) = 1.6x \quad \text{Cross-multiply.}$$

$$78 = 1.6x \quad \text{Solve.}$$

$$\frac{78}{1.6} = \frac{1.6x}{1.6}$$

$$48.75 = x$$

Check and Answer   Thus, 78 kilometers equals about 48.75 miles.

Now Try Exercise 75

EXAMPLE 11 Exchanging Currency When people travel to a foreign country they often need to exchange currency. Donna Boccio visited Cancun, Mexico. She stopped by a local bank and was told that $1 U.S. could be exchanged for 10.96 pesos.

a) How many pesos would she get if she exchanged $150 U.S.?

b) Later that same day, Donna went to the city market where she purchased a ceramic figurine. The price she negotiated for the figurine was 245 pesos. Using the exchange rate given, determine the cost of the figurine in U.S. dollars.

Solution

a) Understand   We use the fact that $1 U.S. can be exchanged for 10.96 Mexican pesos. We use this known fact for one ratio in our proportion. In the second ratio, we set the quantities with same units in the same respective positions.

Translate   The unknown quantity is the number of pesos, which we shall call x.

$$\text{Given ratio} \begin{cases} \dfrac{\$1 \text{ U.S.}}{10.96 \text{ pesos}} = \dfrac{\$150 \text{ U.S.}}{x \text{ pesos}} \end{cases}$$

Note that both numerators contain U.S. dollars and both denominators contain pesos.

Carry Out

$$\frac{1}{10.96} = \frac{150}{x}$$

$$1x = 10.96(150)$$

$$x = 1644$$

Check and Answer   Thus, $150 U.S. could be exchanged for 1644 Mexican pesos.

b) Understand and Translate   We use the same given ratio that we used in part **a)**. Now we must find the equivalent in U.S. dollars of 245 Mexican pesos. Let's call the equivalent U.S. dollars x.

$$\text{Given ratio} \begin{cases} \dfrac{\$1 \text{ U.S.}}{10.96 \text{ pesos}} = \dfrac{\$x \text{ U.S.}}{245 \text{ pesos}} \end{cases}$$

Carry Out

$$\frac{1}{10.96} = \frac{x}{245}$$

$$1(245) = 10.96x$$

$$245 = 10.96x$$

$$22.35 \approx x$$

Check and Answer   The cost of the figurine in U.S. dollars is $22.35.

Now Try Exercise 85

> **Helpful Hint**
>
> Some of the problems we have just worked using proportions could have been done without using proportions. However, when working problems of this type, students often have difficulty in deciding whether to multiply or divide to obtain the correct answer. By setting up a proportion, you may be better able to understand the problem and have more success in obtaining the correct answer.

5   Use Proportions to Solve Problems Involving Similar Figures

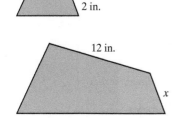

Understanding Algebra

Two figures are called *similar* if they have the same shape but (possibly) different size.

> **Similar Figures**
>
> Two figures are said to be **similar** when their corresponding angles are equal and their corresponding sides are in proportion.

Proportions can be used to solve problems involving similar figures.

EXAMPLE 12   The figures to the left are similar. Find the length of the side indicated by the *x*.

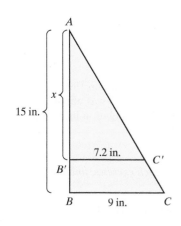

Solution   We set up a proportion of corresponding sides to find the length of side *x*.

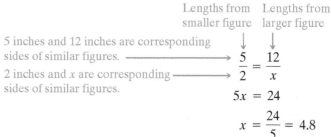

5 inches and 12 inches are corresponding sides of similar figures.

2 inches and *x* are corresponding sides of similar figures.

$$\frac{5}{2} = \frac{12}{x}$$

$$5x = 24$$

$$x = \frac{24}{5} = 4.8$$

Thus, the side indicated by *x* is 4.8 inches in length.

Now Try Exercise 51

Note in Example 12 that the proportion could have also been set up as

$$\frac{5}{12} = \frac{2}{x}$$

because one pair of corresponding sides is in the numerators and another pair is in the denominators.

EXAMPLE 13   Triangles ABC and $AB'C'$ are similar triangles. Find the length of side AB'.

Solution   We set up a proportion of corresponding sides to find the length of side AB'. We will let x represent the length of side AB'.

$$\frac{\text{length of } AB}{\text{length of } BC} = \frac{\text{length of } AB'}{\text{length of } B'C'}$$

Now we insert the proper values and solve for the variable, x.

$$\frac{15}{9} = \frac{x}{7.2}$$

$$(15)(7.2) = 9x$$

$$108 = 9x$$

$$12 = x$$

Thus, the length of side AB' is 12 inches.

Now Try Exercise 53

EXERCISE SET 2.7

Math XL
MathXL®

MyMathLab
MyMathLab

Warm-Up Exercises

Fill in the blanks with the appropriate word, phrase, or symbol(s) from the following list.

ratio	cross-multiplying	similar	$c:d$	$d:c$
units	proportion	means	extremes	

1. A _____ is a statement of equality between two ratios.

2. In the proportion $\dfrac{a}{b} = \dfrac{p}{q}$, a and q are called _____ .

3. In the proportion $\dfrac{a}{b} = \dfrac{p}{q}$, b and p are called _____ .

4. A method for solving proportions is _____ .

5. Two figures that have equal corresponding angles and have their corresponding sides in proportion are called _____ .

6. Another way of expressing the ratio $\dfrac{c}{d}$ is _____ .

7. When solving an applied problem involving proportions, it is crucial that the two ratios have the same _____ .

8. The quotient of two quantities is called a _____ .

In Exercises 9–12, is the proportion set up correctly?

9. $\dfrac{\text{gal}}{\text{min}} = \dfrac{\text{gal}}{\text{min}}$

10. $\dfrac{\text{mi}}{\text{hr}} = \dfrac{\text{mi}}{\text{hr}}$

11. $\dfrac{\text{ft}}{\text{sec}} = \dfrac{\text{sec}}{\text{ft}}$

12. $\dfrac{\text{tax}}{\text{cost}} = \dfrac{\text{cost}}{\text{tax}}$

Practice the Skills

The results of a mathematics examination are 6 A's, 4 B's, 9 C's, 3 D's, and 2 F's. Write the following ratios in lowest terms.

13. A's to C's   6:9 , 2:3

14. F's to total grades   2:24, 1:12

15. D's to A's   3:6, 1:2

16. Grades better than C to total grades

17. Total grades to D's

18. Grades better than C to grades less than C

Determine the following ratios. Write each ratio in lowest terms.

19. 7 gallons to 4 gallons

20. 50 cents to 60 dollars

21. 5 ounces to 15 ounces

22. 18 liters to 24 liters

23. 3 hours to 30 minutes

24. 6 feet to 4 yards

25. 7 dimes to 12 quarters

26. 26 ounces to 4 pounds

In Exercises 27 and 28, find the gear ratio. Write the ratio as some quantity to 1. (See Example 4.)

27. Driving gear, 40 teeth; driven gear, 5 teeth

28. Driving gear, 30 teeth; driven gear, 8 teeth

In Exercises 29–32, **a)** *Determine the indicated ratio, and* **b)** *write the ratio as some quantity to 1.*

29. **American Consumers** Each year the average American consumer drinks approximately 50 gallons of soft drinks compared to 26 gallons of coffee, 23 gallons of milk, and less than 10 gallons of fruit juices. What is the ratio of the number of gallons of soft drinks consumed to the number of gallons of milk consumed?

30. **Mail Letter** In January 2009, the cost to mail a one-ounce letter was 42 cents and the cost to mail a two-ounce letter was 59 cents. What is the ratio of the cost to mail a one-ounce letter to the cost to mail a two-ounce letter?

31. **Minimum Wage** The minimum wage in the United States in 1996 was $4.75 per hour and the minimum wage in 2009 was $7.25 per hour. What is the ratio of the U.S. minimum wage in 2009 to the U.S. minimum wage in 1996?

32. **Population** The United States population in 1990 was about 249 million, and the population in 2008 was about 305 million. What is the ratio of the U.S. population in 2008 to the U.S. population in 1990?

Exercises 33–36 show graphs. For each exercise, find the indicated ratio.

33. **Traveling the Toll Roads** See figure on p. 153.

a) Determine the ratio of the toll rate on the Delaware Turnpike to the toll rate on the Garden State Parkway.

b) Determine the ratio of the toll rate on the NJ Turnpike to the toll rate on PA Route 66.

How Toll Rates Compare

	Cents per mile
Garden State Parkway	2.4
New Jersey Turnpike	5.3
Atlantic City Expressway	5.7
NY Thruway-Berkshire	5.9
PA Turnpike	6.3
NY Thruway (I-87/I-90)	6.7
PA Route 66	7.1
NY Thruway-New England	8.1
Richmond (VA) Downtown	20.0
Pocahontas Parkway, VA	28.4
Delaware Turnpike (I-95)	35.7

Source: Pennsylvania Turnpike Commission, 2008

34. Number of Passports Processed

   a) Estimate the ratio of passports processed in the United States in 1999 to those processed in the United States in 2007.

   b) Estimate the ratio of passports processed in the United States in 2002 to those processed in the United States in 2004.

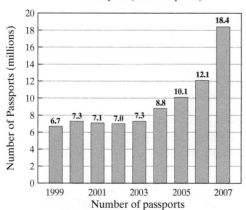

Passports Processed in the U.S.
Fiscal year (Oct.1–Sept. 30)

Number of Passports (millions): 1999: 6.7, 2001: 7.3, 7.1, 7.0, 2003: 7.3, 8.8, 2005: 10.1, 12.1, 2007: 18.4

Number of passports

Source: U.S. State Dept.

35. Favorite Doughnut

   a) Determine the ratio of people whose favorite doughnut is glazed to people whose favorite doughnut is filled.

   b) Determine the ratio of people whose favorite doughnut is frosted to people whose favorite doughnut is plain.

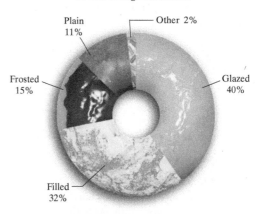

Favorite Doughnut Flavors

Plain 11%, Other 2%, Frosted 15%, Glazed 40%, Filled 32%

Source: The Heller Research Group

36. Commuting to Work

   a) Determine the ratio of workers who drove alone to work to those who carpooled to work.

   b) Determine the ratio of workers who walked to work to those who worked at home.

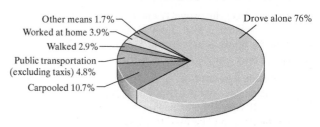

Commuting to Work, 2006

Other means 1.7%, Worked at home 3.9%, Walked 2.9%, Public transportation (excluding taxis) 4.8%, Carpooled 10.7%, Drove alone 76%

Source: www.factfinder.census.gov

Solve each proportion for the variable by cross-multiplying.

37. $\dfrac{x}{3} = \dfrac{20}{5}$ **38.** $\dfrac{x}{8} = \dfrac{24}{48}$ **39.** $\dfrac{5}{3} = \dfrac{75}{a}$ **40.** $\dfrac{x}{3} = \dfrac{90}{30}$

41. $\dfrac{-7}{3} = \dfrac{21}{p}$ **42.** $\dfrac{-12}{13} = \dfrac{36}{x}$ **43.** $\dfrac{15}{45} = \dfrac{x}{-6}$ **44.** $\dfrac{y}{6} = \dfrac{7}{42}$

45. $\dfrac{3}{z} = \dfrac{-1.5}{27}$ **46.** $\dfrac{3}{12} = \dfrac{-1.4}{z}$ **47.** $\dfrac{9}{12} = \dfrac{x}{8}$ **48.** $\dfrac{2}{20} = \dfrac{x}{200}$

The following figures are similar. For each pair, find the length of the side indicated by x.

49.
3 in., 8 in., 12 in., x

50.
2 ft, 1.8 ft, 0.8 ft, x

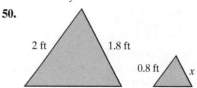

51.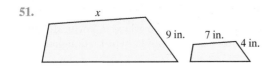

52.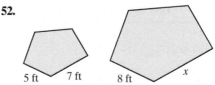

53.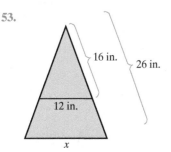

54.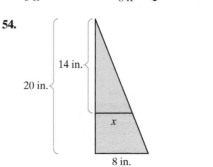

Problem Solving

In Exercises 55–74, write a proportion that can be used to solve the problem. Then solve the equation to obtain the answer.

55. Washing Clothes A bottle of liquid Tide contains 100 fluid ounces. If one wash load requires 4 ounces of the detergent, how many washes can be done with one bottle of Tide?

56. Laying Cable A telephone cable crew is laying cable at a rate of 42 feet an hour. How long will it take them to lay 252 feet of cable?

57. Truck Mileage A 2009 Toyota Tacoma is rated to get 26 miles per gallon. How far can it travel on 15.5 gallons of gas?

58. Purchasing Stock If 2 shares of stock can be purchased for $38.25, how many shares can be purchased for $344.25?

59. Model Train A model train set is in a ratio of 1 : 20. That is, one foot of the model represents 20 feet of the original train. If a caboose is 30 feet long, how long should the model be?

60. Property Tax The property tax in the city of Hendersonville, North Carolina, is $9.475 per $1000 of assessed value. If the Estever's house is assessed at $145,000, how much property tax will they owe?

61. Insecticide Application The instructions on a bottle of liquid insecticide say "use 3 teaspoons of insecticide per gallon of water." If your sprayer has an 8-gallon capacity, how much insecticide should be used to fill the sprayer?

62. Spreading Fertilizer If a 40-pound bag of fertilizer covers 5000 square feet, how many pounds of fertilizer are needed to cover an area of 26,000 square feet?

63. Blue Heron The photograph shows a blue heron. If the blue heron, that measures 3.5 inches in the photo is actually 3.75 feet tall, approximately how long is its beak if it measures 0.4 inch in the photo?

64. Maps On a map, 0.5 inch represents 22 miles. What will be the length on a map that corresponds to a distance of 55 miles?

65. Onion Soup A recipe for 6 servings of French onion soup requires $1\frac{1}{2}$ cups of thinly sliced onions. If the recipe were to be made for 15 servings, how many cups of onions would be needed?

66. John Grisham Novel Karen Estes is currently reading a John Grisham novel. If she reads 72 pages in 1.3 hours, how long will it take her to read the entire 656-page novel?

67. Wall Street Bull Suppose the famous bull near the New York Stock Exchange (see photo below) is a replica of a real bull in a ratio of 2.95 to 1. That is, the metal bull is 2.95 times larger than the regular bull. If the length of the Wall Street bull is 28 feet long, approximately how long is the bull that served as its model?

68. Flood When they returned home from vacation, the Duncans had a foot of water in their basement. They contacted their fire department, which sent equipment to pump out the water. After the pump had been on for 30 minutes, 3 inches of water had been removed. How long, from the time they started pumping, did it take to remove all the water from the basement?

69. Drug Dosage A nurse must administer 220 micrograms of atropine sulfate. The drug is available in solution form. The concentration of the atropine sulfate solution is 400 micrograms per milliliter. How many milliliters should be given?

70. Dosage by Body Surface A doctor asks a nurse to administer 0.7 gram of meprobamate per square meter of body surface. The patient's body surface is 0.6 square meter. How much meprobamate should be given?

71. Reading a Novel Mary read 40 pages of a novel in 30 minutes. If she continues reading at the same rate, how long will it take her to read the entire 760-page book?

72. Swimming Laps Jason Abbott swims 3 laps in 2.3 minutes. Approximately how long will it take him to swim 30 laps if he continues to swim at the same rate?

73. Prader-Willi Syndrome It is estimated that each year in the United States about 1 in every 12,000 (1 : 12,000) people is born with a genetic disorder called Prader-Willi syndrome. If there were approximately 4,315,000 births in the United States in 2007, approximately how may children were born with Prader-Willi syndrome?

74. Scrapbooking Penelope Penna completed 4 scrapbook pages in 20.5 minutes. Approximately how long will it take her to complete 36 scrapbook pages if she continues to complete the scrapbook at the same rate?

In Exercises 75–86, use a proportion to make the conversion. Round your answers to two decimal places.

75. Convert 78 inches to feet.

76. Convert 22,704 feet to miles (5280 feet = 1 mile).

77. Convert 26.1 square feet to square yards (9 square feet = 1 square yard).

78. Convert 146.4 ounces to pounds.

79. Newborn One inch equals 2.54 centimeters. Find the length of a newborn, in inches, if it measures 50.8 centimeters.

80. Distance One mile equals approximately 1.6 kilometers. Find the distance, in kilometers, from San Diego, California, to San Francisco, California—a distance of 520 miles.

San Francisco, California

81. Baseball Todd Helton holds the major league record for most doubles, 59, in a 162-game season. In the first 60 games of a season, how many doubles would a player need to hit to be on schedule to break Helton's record?

82. Topsoil A 40-pound bag of topsoil covers 12 square feet (one inch deep). How many pounds of the topsoil are needed to cover 350 square feet (one inch deep)?

83. Interest on Savings Jim Chao invests a certain amount of money in a savings account. If he earned $110.52 in 180 days, how much interest would he earn in 500 days assuming the interest rate stays the same?

84. Gold If gold is selling for $834 per 480 grains (a troy ounce), what is the cost per grain?

85. Mexican Pesos Suppose that the exchange rate from U.S. dollars to Mexican pesos is $1 per 10.1 pesos. How many pesos would Elizabeth Averbeck receive if she exchanged $200 U.S.?

86. Currency Exchange When John Gauzer visited the United States from Canada, he exchanged $10.56 Canadian for $10 U.S. If he exchanges his remaining $600 Canadian for U.S. dollars, how much more in dollars will he receive?

87. Cholesterol See Example 2. Ken Rauch's LDL is 127 milligrams per deciliter (mg/dL). His HDL is 60 mg/dL. Is Mr. Rauch's ratio of LDL to HDL less than or equal to the 4 : 1 recommended level?

88. Cholesterol

a) Another ratio used by some doctors when measuring cholesterol level is the ratio of total cholesterol to HDL.* Is this ratio increased or decreased if the total cholesterol remains the same but the HDL is increased? Explain.

b) Doctors recommend that the ratio of total cholesterol to HDL be less than or equal to 4.5 : 1. If Mike's total cholesterol is 220 mg/dL and his HDL is 50 mg/dL, is his ratio less than or equal to 4.5 : 1? Explain.

*Total cholesterol includes both LDL and HDL, plus other types of cholesterol.

Concept/Writing Exercises

89. For the proportion $\frac{a}{b} = \frac{c}{d}$, if a increases while b and d stay the same, what must happen to c? Explain.

90. For the proportion $\frac{a}{b} = \frac{c}{d}$, if a and c remain the same while d decreases, what must happen to b? Explain.

Challenge Problems

91. Wear on Tires A new Goodyear tire has a tread of about 0.34 inch. After 5000 miles the tread is about 0.31 inch. If the legal minimum amount of tread for a tire is 0.06 inch, how many more miles will the tires last?

92. Apple Pie The recipe for the filling for an apple pie calls for

12 cups sliced apples $\frac{1}{4}$ teaspoon salt

$\frac{1}{2}$ cup flour $1\frac{1}{2}$ cups sugar

1 teaspoon nutmeg   2 tablespoons butter or margarine

1 teaspoon cinnamon

Determine the amount of each of the other ingredients that should be used if only 8 cups of apples are available.

93. Insulin Insulin comes in 10-cubic-centimeter (cc) vials labeled in the number of units of insulin per cubic centimeter. Thus, a vial labeled U40 means there are 40 units of insulin per cubic centimeter of fluid. If a patient needs 25 units of insulin, how many cubic centimeters of fluid should be drawn up into a syringe from the U40 vial?

Group Activity

Discuss and answer Exercises 94 and 95 as a group.

94. a) Each group member: Find the ratio of your height to your arm span (finger tips to finger tips) when your arms are extended horizontally outward. You will need help from your group in getting these measurements.

b) If a box were to be drawn about your body with your arms extended, would the box be a square or a rectangle? If a rectangle, would the longer length be your arm span or your height measurement? Explain.

c) Compare these results with other members of your group.

d) What one ratio would you use to report the height to arm span for your group as a whole? Explain.

95. A special ratio in mathematics is called the *golden ratio*. Do research in a history of mathematics book or on the Internet, and as a group write a paper that explains what the golden ratio is and why it is important.

Cumulative Review Exercises

[1.10] *Name each illustrated property.*

96. $x + 3 = 3 + x$

97. $3(xy) = (3x)y$

98. $2(x - 3) = 2x - 6$

[2.5] **99.** Solve $3(4x - 3) = 6(2x + 1) - 15$

[2.6] **100.** Solve $y = mx + b$ for m.

2.8 Inequalities in One Variable

1 Solve linear inequalities.

2 Solve linear inequalities that have all real numbers as their solution, or have no solution.

Understanding Algebra

An *inequality* expresses a relationship between two quantities.

Symbol	Read as
<	is less than
>	is greater than
≤	is less than or equal to
≥	is greater than or equal to

1 Solve Linear Inequalities

Inequalities

A mathematical statement containing one or more of the symbols $<$, $>$, $\leq$, or $\geq$ is called an **inequality**. The direction of the symbol is sometimes called the **sense** or **order of the inequality**.

Examples of Inequalities in One Variable

$$x + 3 < 5 \qquad x + 4 \geq 2x - 6 \qquad 4 > -x + 3$$

To solve an inequality, we must isolate the variable on one side of the inequality symbol. To do this, we make use of properties very similar to those used to solve equations. Here are four properties used to solve inequalities.

Properties Used to Solve Inequalities

For real numbers, a, b, and c:

1. If $a > b$, then $a + c > b + c$.
2. If $a > b$, then $a - c > b - c$.
3. If $a > b$ **and** $c > 0$, then $ac > bc$.
4. If $a > b$ **and** $c > 0$, then $\dfrac{a}{c} > \dfrac{b}{c}$.

When any of these four properties is used, *the direction of the inequality symbol does not change.*

EXAMPLE 1 Solve the inequality $x - 5 > -2$, and graph the solution on a number line.

Solution To isolate the variable, x, add 5 to both sides of the inequality.

$$x - 5 > -2$$
$$x - 5 + 5 > -2 + 5 \quad \text{Add 5 to both sides.}$$
$$x > 3$$

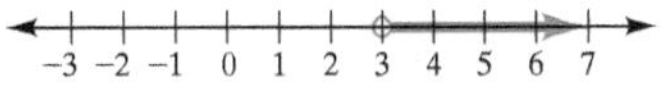

FIGURE 2.7

The solution is all real numbers greater than 3. We can illustrate the solution on a number line by placing an open circle at 3 on a number line and drawing an arrow to the right (**Fig. 2.7**).

The open circle at the 3 indicates that the 3 is *not* part of the solution. The arrow going to the right indicates that all the values greater than 3 are solutions to the inequality.

Now Try Exercise 13

EXAMPLE 2 Solve the inequality $2x + 6 \le -2$, and graph the solution on a number line.

Solution To isolate the variable, subtract 6 from both sides of the inequality.

$$2x + 6 \le -2$$
$$2x + 6 - 6 \le -2 - 6 \quad \text{Subtract 6 from both sides.}$$
$$2x \le -8$$
$$\frac{2x}{2} \le \frac{-8}{2} \quad \text{Divide both sides by 2.}$$
$$x \le -4$$

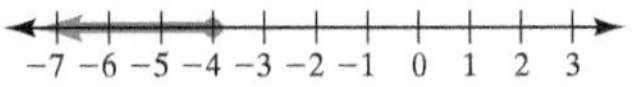

FIGURE 2.8

The solution is all real numbers less than or equal to -4. We can illustrate the solution on a number line by placing a closed, or darkened, circle at -4 and drawing an arrow to the left (**Fig. 2.8**.)

The darkened circle at -4 indicates that -4 *is* a part of the solution. The arrow going to the left indicates that all the values less than -4 are also solutions to the inequality.

Now Try Exercise 21

Notice in properties 3 and 4 that we specified that $c > 0$. What happens when an inequality is multiplied or divided by a negative number? Example 3 will illustrate that *when an inequality is multiplied or divided by a negative number, the direction of the inequality symbol changes.*

Understanding Algebra

When you multiply both sides of an inequality by a negative number, the direction of the inequality changes. Observe:

$$-2 < 6$$

Multiply both sides by -1:

$$2 > -6$$

EXAMPLE 3 ────────

a) Multiply both sides of the inequality $8 > -4$ by -2.

b) Divide both sides of the inequality $8 > -4$ by -2.

Solution

a)

$$8 > -4$$

$$-2(8) < -2(-4) \quad \text{Change the direction of the inequality symbol.}$$

$$-16 < 8$$

b)

$$8 > -4$$

$$\frac{8}{-2} < \frac{-4}{-2} \quad \text{Change the direction of the inequality symbol.}$$

$$-4 < 2$$

Now Try Exercise 9

Now we state two additional properties, used when both sides of an inequality are multiplied or divided by a negative number.

> **Additional Properties Used to Solve Inequalities**
>
> 5. If $a > b$ **and** $c < 0$, then $ac < bc$.
>
> 6. If $a > b$ **and** $c < 0$, then $\dfrac{a}{c} < \dfrac{b}{c}$.

EXAMPLE 4 Solve the inequality $-2x < 8$, and graph the solution on a number line.

Solution   To isolate the variable, we can divide both sides of the inequality by -2. When we do this, however, we must remember to *change the direction* of the inequality symbol.

$$-2x < 8$$

$$\frac{-2x}{-2} > \frac{8}{-2} \quad \begin{array}{l}\text{Divide both sides by } -2\text{, and change the} \\ \text{direction of the inequality symbol.}\end{array}$$

$$x > -4$$

FIGURE 2.9

The solution is all real numbers greater than -4. The solution is graphed on a number line in **Figure 2.9**.

Now Try Exercise 19

EXAMPLE 5 Solve the inequality $4 \geq -5 - x$, and graph the solution on a number line. We will illustrate two methods that can be used to solve this inequality.

Solution

Method 1

$$4 \geq -5 - x$$

$$4 + 5 \geq -5 + 5 - x \quad \text{Add 5 to both sides.}$$

$$9 \geq -x$$

$$-1(9) \leq -1(-x) \quad \begin{array}{l}\text{Multiply both sides by } -1\text{, and change the} \\ \text{direction of the inequality symbol.}\end{array}$$

$$-9 \leq x$$

The inequality $-9 \leq x$ can also be written $x \geq -9$.

Method 2

$$4 \geq -5 - x$$

$$4 + x \geq -5 - x + x \quad \text{Add } x \text{ to both sides.}$$

$$4 + x \geq -5$$

$$4 - 4 + x \geq -5 - 4 \quad \text{Subtract 4 from both sides.}$$

$$x \geq -9$$

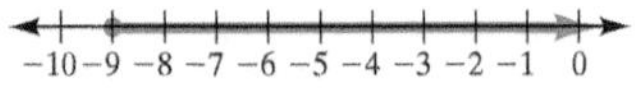

FIGURE 2.10

The solution is graphed on a number line in **Figure 2.10**.

Now Try Exercise 17

Notice in Example 5, Method 1, we wrote $-9 \le x$ as $x \ge -9$. Although the solution $-9 \le x$ is correct, it is customary to write the solution to an inequality with the variable on the left. One reason we write the variable on the left is that it often makes it easier to graph the solution on the number line.

> **Helpful Hint**
>
> $a > x$ means $x < a$ Note that both inequality symbols point to x.
>
> $a < x$ means $x > a$ Note that both inequality symbols point to a.
>
> **Examples**
>
> $-3 > x$ means $x < -3$
>
> $-5 \le x$ means $x \ge -5$

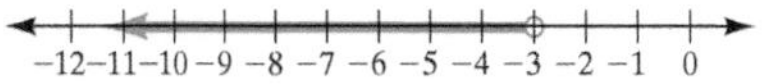

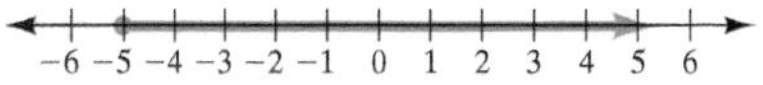

Understanding Algebra

We can rewrite the inequality $3 > x$ as $x < 3$. They mean the same thing — in each case the inequality symbol points to the smaller quantity.

Now let's solve inequalities where the variable appears on both sides of the inequality symbol. We will use the same basic procedure that we used to solve equations. However, we must remember that whenever we multiply or divide both sides of an inequality by a negative number, we must change the direction of the inequality symbol.

EXAMPLE 6 Solve the inequality $-5p + 9 < -2p + 6$, and graph the solution on a number line.

Solution
$$-5p + 9 < -2p + 6$$
$$-5p + 5p + 9 < -2p + 5p + 6 \qquad \text{Add } 5p \text{ to both sides.}$$
$$9 < 3p + 6$$
$$9 - 6 < 3p + 6 - 6 \qquad \text{Subtract 6 from both sides.}$$
$$3 < 3p$$
$$\frac{3}{3} < \frac{3p}{3} \qquad \text{Divide both sides by 3.}$$
$$1 < p$$
$$\text{or} \qquad p > 1$$

FIGURE 2.11

The solution is graphed in **Figure 2.11**.

Now Try Exercise 33

EXAMPLE 7 Solve the inequality $\frac{1}{2}x + 3 \le -\frac{1}{3}x + 7$, and graph the solution on a number line.

Solution   Since the inequality contains fractions, we begin by multiplying both sides of the inequality by the LCD, 6, to eliminate the fractions.

$$\frac{1}{2}x + 3 \le -\frac{1}{3}x + 7$$
$$6\left(\frac{1}{2}x + 3\right) \le 6\left(-\frac{1}{3}x + 7\right) \qquad \text{Multiply both sides by the LCD, 6.}$$
$$3x + 18 \le -2x + 42 \qquad \text{Distributive property}$$
$$5x + 18 \le 42 \qquad 2x \text{ was added to both sides.}$$
$$5x \le 24 \qquad 18 \text{ was subtracted from both sides.}$$
$$x \le \frac{24}{5} \qquad \text{Both sides were divided by 5.}$$

FIGURE 2.12

The solution is graphed in **Figure 2.12**.

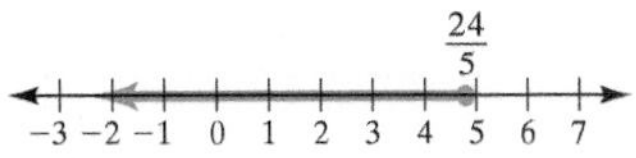

Now Try Exercise 53

2 Solve Linear Inequalities That Have All Real Numbers as Their Solution, or Have No Solution

In Examples 8 and 9, we illustrate two special types of inequalities. Example 8 is an inequality that is true for all real numbers, and Example 9 is an inequality that is never true for any real number.

EXAMPLE 8 Solve the inequality $2(x + 3) \leq 5x - 3x + 8$, and graph the solution on a number line.

Solution

$$2(x + 3) \leq 5x - 3x + 8$$

$$2x + 6 \leq 5x - 3x + 8 \qquad \text{Distributive property was used.}$$

$$2x + 6 \leq 2x + 8 \qquad \text{Like terms were combined.}$$

$$2x - 2x + 6 \leq 2x - 2x + 8 \qquad \text{Subtract } 2x \text{ from both sides.}$$

$$6 \leq 8$$

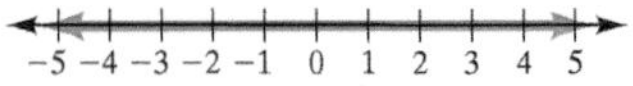

FIGURE 2.13

Since 6 is always less than or equal to 8, the solution is *all real numbers* **(Fig. 2.13)**.

Now Try Exercise 37

EXAMPLE 9 Solve the inequality $4(x + 1) > x + 5 + 3x$, and graph the solution on a number line.

Solution

$$4(x + 1) > x + 5 + 3x$$

$$4x + 4 > x + 5 + 3x \qquad \text{Distributive property was used.}$$

$$4x + 4 > 4x + 5 \qquad \text{Like terms were combined.}$$

$$4x - 4x + 4 > 4x - 4x + 5 \qquad \text{Subtract } 4x \text{ from both sides.}$$

$$4 > 5$$

FIGURE 2.14

Since 4 is never greater than 5, the answer is *no solution* **(Fig. 2.14)**. There is no real number that makes the statement true.

Now Try Exercise 43

EXERCISE SET 2.8

Warm-Up Exercises

Fill in the blanks with the appropriate word, phrase, or symbol(s) from the following list.

$<$	$>$	$a + c \geq b + c$	$a + c \leq b + c$	$6 < -5$
no solution	all real numbers	inequality symbols	$5 > -6$	direction

1. When solving an inequality, if you obtain the result $5 < 8$, the solution must be _____ .

2. If $a \leq b$ and $c < 0$ then what can be said about $a + c$? _____ .

3. When solving an inequality, if you obtain the result $-3 < -4$, the solution must be _____ .

4. If $a < b$ and $c < 0$ then ac _____ bc.

5. If $a < b$ and $c > 0$ then ac _____ bc.

6. Collectively, the symbols $\leq$, $\geq$, $<$, and $>$ are called _____ .

7. An equivalent statement to $-6 < 5$ is _____ .

8. When multiplying or dividing both sides of an inequality by a negative number, the _____ of the inequality changes.

Practice the Skills

9. a) Multiply both sides of $-7 < 3$ by -4.

   b) Divide both sides of $-7 < 3$ by -4.

10. a) Multiply both sides of $12 > -5$ by -3.

   b) Divide both sides of $12 > -5$ by -3.

Solve each inequality, and graph the solution on a number line.

11. $x + 2 > 6$

12. $y + 9 \geq 6$

13. $x - 5 > -1$

14. $x - 3 \geq -9$

15. $-x + 3 < 8$

16. $7 < 3 + w$

17. $8 \leq 2 - r$

18. $6 \leq -3 - x$

19. $-2x < 3$

20. $-12 \geq -3b$

21. $2t + 3 \leq 5$

22. $6n - 12 < -12$

23. $-4x - 3 > 5$

24. $7x - 4 \leq 9$

25. $4 - 6x > -5$

26. $8 < 4 - 2q$

27. $15 > -9x + 50$

28. $3x - 4 < 5$

29. $7 > 2x + 10$

30. $-4x < 2x + 15$

31. $16s + 2 \leq 16s - 9$

32. $-2x - 4 \leq -5x + 12$

33. $x - 4 \leq 3x + 8$

34. $-4n - 6 > 4n - 20$

35. $-x + 4 < -3x + 6$

36. $2(x - 3) < 4x + 10$

37. $6(2m - 4) \geq 2(6m - 12)$

38. $-2(w + 3) \leq 4w + 5$

39. $x + 3 < x + 4$

40. $y + 4 \geq y - 3$

41. $6(3 - x) < 2x + 15$

42. $2(3 - x) + 4x < -6$

43. $4x - 4 < 4(x - 5)$

44. $-2(-5 - x) > 3(x + 2) + 4 - x$

45. $5(2x + 3) \geq 6 + (x + 2) - 2x$

46. $-3(-2x + 12) < -4(x + 2) - 6$

47. $1.2x + 3.1 < 3.5x - 3.8$

48. $-5.3r - 6.7 \geq 2.3 - 6.5r$

49. $1.2(m - 3) \geq 4.6(2 - m) + 1.7$

50. $-4.6(4 - x) < 2.4(x - 3) - 0.2$

51. $\dfrac{x}{2} \geq \dfrac{x}{3} + 5$ $x \geq 30$

52. $\dfrac{x}{7} - 1 \geq \dfrac{x}{8}$

53. $t + \dfrac{1}{6} > \dfrac{2}{3}t$ $t > -\dfrac{1}{2}$

54. $\dfrac{3}{5}r - 9 < \dfrac{3}{8}r$

55. $\dfrac{1}{8}(4 - r) \leq \dfrac{1}{4}$

56. $5 - \dfrac{1}{6}x < \dfrac{3}{2}x$

57. $\dfrac{2}{3}(t + 2) \leq \dfrac{1}{4}(2t - 6)$

58. $\dfrac{3}{4}(n - 4) \geq \dfrac{2}{3}(n - 4)$

Problem Solving

59. Chicago Temperatures The following chart shows the average high and low monthly temperatures in Chicago over a 126-year period. Notice that the months are not listed in order.

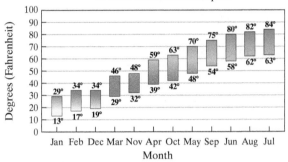

Monthly Average Temperatures
Ranked Coldest to Warmest

O'Hare International Airport

Note: Numbers indicate average monthly highs and lows.

Source: WGN-TV

a) In what months was the average high temperature >65°F?

b) In what months was the average high temperature ≤59°F?

c) In what months was the average low temperature <29°F?

d) In what months was the average low temperature ≥58°F?

60. Hours Worked The following graph indicates the average hours worked per person, per year.

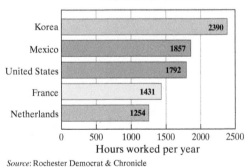

Global Hours Worked

Source: Rochester Democrat & Chronicle

a) In which countries was the number of hours worked ≥1850?

b) In which countries was the number of hours worked ≥1500 but ≤1900?

c) In which countries was the number of hours worked >1300 but ≤1800?

d) In which countries was the number of hours worked ≥1792 and ≤1792?

61. The inequality symbols discussed so far are $<$, $\leq$, $>$, and $\geq$. Can you name an inequality symbol that we have not mentioned in this section?

62. Consider the inequality $-4x + 3 \leq 1$. Explain what is wrong with the following solution.

$$-4x + 3 \leq 1$$
$$-4x + 3 - 3 \leq 1 - 3$$
$$-4x \leq -2$$
$$\frac{-4x}{-4} \leq \frac{-2}{-4}$$
$$x \leq \frac{1}{2}$$

63. Consider the inequality $xy > 6$, where x and y represent real numbers. Explain why we *cannot* do the following step:

$$\frac{xy}{y} > \frac{6}{y} \qquad \text{Divide both sides by } y.$$

Challenge Problems

64. Solve the following inequality.

$$3(2 - x) - 4(2x - 3) \leq 6 + 2x - 4x$$

65. Solve the following inequality.

$$6x - 6 > -4(x + 3) + 5(x + 6) - x$$

Cumulative Review Exercises

[1.9] **66.** Evaluate $-x^2$ for $x = 3$.

67. Evaluate $-x^2$ for $x = -5$.

[2.5] **68.** Solve $4 - 3(2x - 4) = 5 - (x + 3)$.

[2.7] **69. Electric Bill** The Milford Electric Company charges $0.174 per kilowatt-hour of electricity. The Vega's monthly electric bill was $87 for the month of July. How many kilowatt-hours of electricity did the Vega's use in July?

Chapter 2 Summary

IMPORTANT FACTS AND CONCEPTS	EXAMPLES

Section 2.1

The **terms** of an expression are the parts that are added.	$2x^2 - 3xy + 5$ has 3 terms: $2x^2$, $-3xy$, and 5.
The numerical part of a term is called its **numerical coefficient.**	The numerical coefficient of $\dfrac{3x}{4}$ is $\dfrac{3}{4}$.
A **constant** is a term that is a number without a variable.	In $3x^2 + 2x - 7$, the -7 is a constant.

Like terms have the same variables with the same exponents.	$7x$ and x; $6y^2$ and $2y^2$; $3(x + 4)$ and $-8(x + 4)$
To Combine Like Terms	
1. Determine which terms are like terms.	$-3x^2 + 4y - 7x^2 + 6 - y - 9$
2. Add or subtract the coefficients of the like terms.	$= -3x^2 - 7x^2 + 4y - y + 6 - 9$
3. Multiply the number found in step 2 by the common variable(s).	$= -10x^2 + 3y - 3$

Distributive Property	
For any real numbers a, b, and c, $$a(b + c) = ab + ac$$	$-5(3r - 6) = -15r + 30$

To Simplify an Expression	$2(3c - 1) - 5(c + 4) - 6$
1. Use the distributive property to remove any parentheses.	$= 6c - 2 - 5c - 20 - 6$
2. Combine like terms.	$= c - 28$

When two or more expressions are multiplied, each expression is a **factor** of the product.	Since $7 \cdot 8 = 56$, the 7 and the 8 are factors of 56.

Section 2.2

A **linear equation** in one variable is an equation that can be written in the form $$ax + b = c$$ where a, b, and c are real numbers and $a \neq 0$.	$9x - 2 = 16$

The **solution to an equation** is the number or numbers that when substituted for the variable or variables make the equation a true statement.	The solution to $2x + 3 = 9$ is 3.
The solution to an equation may be **checked** by substituting the value that is believed to be the solution for the variable in the original equation.	To check whether -2 is the solution to $-7x + 1 = 15$: $$-7x + 1 = 15$$ $$-7(-2) + 1 \stackrel{?}{=} 15$$ $$14 + 1 \stackrel{?}{=} 15$$ $$15 = 15 \quad \text{True}$$ Thus, -2 is the solution.
Two or more equations with the same solution are called **equivalent equations.**	$-4x = 12$, $2x - 3 = -9$, and $x = -3$ are equivalent equations

Addition Property of Equality	Solve the equation $x - 9 = -2$.
If $a = b$, then $a + c = b + c$ for any real numbers a, b, and c.	$$x - 9 = -2$$ $$x - 9\ +\ 9 = -2\ +\ 9$$ $$x = 7$$

Section 2.3

Two numbers are **reciprocals** of each other when their product is 1.	3 and $\dfrac{1}{3}$ are reciprocals since $3 \cdot \dfrac{1}{3} = 1$.

IMPORTANT FACTS AND CONCEPTS	EXAMPLES

Section 2.3 (cont.)

Multiplication Property of Equality

If $a = b$, then $a \cdot c = b \cdot c$ for any real numbers a, b, and c.

Solve the equation $\frac{3}{7}x = 6$.

$$\frac{3}{7}x = 6$$

$$\frac{7}{3} \cdot \frac{3}{7}x = \frac{7}{3} \cdot 6$$

$$x = 14$$

Section 2.4

To Solve Linear Equations with a Variable on Only One Side of the Equals Sign

1. If the equation contains fractions, multiply *both* sides of the equation by the least common denominator (LCD).

2. Use the distributive property to remove parentheses.

3. Combine like terms on the same side of the equal sign.

4. Use the addition property to obtain an equation with the term containing the variable on one side of the equal sign and a constant on the other side.

5. Use the multiplication property to isolate the variable.

6. Check the solution in the original equation.

Solve the equation $3(x - 5) - 6x = -2$.

$$3(x - 5) - 6x = -2$$
$$3x - 15 - 6x = -2$$
$$-3x - 15 = -2$$
$$-3x - 15 + 15 = -2 + 15$$
$$-3x = 13$$
$$\frac{-3x}{-3} = \frac{13}{-3}$$
$$x = -\frac{13}{3}$$

A check will show that $-\frac{13}{3}$ is the solution.

Section 2.5

To Solve Linear Equations with the Variable on Both Sides of the Equals Sign

1. If the equation contains fractions, multiply *both* sides of the equation by the LCD.

2. Use the distributive property to remove parentheses.

3. Combine like terms on the same side of the equals sign.

4. Use the addition property to rewrite the equation with all terms containing the variable on one side of the equals sign and all terms not containing the variable on the other side of the equals sign.

5. Use the multiplication property to isolate the variable.

6. Check the solution in the original equation.

Solve the equation $9 - 3x - 2(x + 5) = 4x + 7 - x$.

$$9 - 3x - 2(x + 5) = 4x + 7 - x$$
$$9 - 3x - 2x - 10 = 4x + 7 - x$$
$$-5x - 1 = 3x + 7$$
$$-5x + 5x - 1 = 3x + 5x + 7$$
$$-1 = 8x + 7$$
$$-1 - 7 = 8x + 7 - 7$$
$$-8 = 8x$$
$$\frac{-8}{8} = \frac{8x}{8}$$
$$-1 = x$$

A check will show that -1 is the solution.

A **conditional equation** is an equation that has a single value for a solution.

An **identity** is an equation that is true for infinitely many values of the variable.

A **contradiction** is an equation that has no solution.

$3x - 2 = 8$ is a conditional equation since its solution is $\frac{10}{3}$.

$-4(x + 3) = -5x - 12 + x$ is an identity because the equation is true for all real numbers.

$-9x + 7 + 6x = -5x + 1 + 2x$ is a contradiction because the equation is never true and has no solution.

Section 2.6

Simple Interest Formula

$$\text{interest} = \text{principal} \cdot \text{rate} \cdot \text{time} \quad \text{or} \quad i = prt$$

Determine the interest earned on a $5000 investment at 3% simple interest for 2 years.

$$i = prt$$
$$i = 5000(0.03)(2)$$
$$i = \$300$$

IMPORTANT FACTS AND CONCEPTS	EXAMPLES

Section 2.6 (cont.)

Distance Formula

$$\text{distance} = \text{rate} \cdot \text{time} \quad \text{or} \quad d = r \cdot t$$

Timothy John completed a snowmobile race in 2.4 hours at an average speed of 75 miles per hour. Determine the distance of the race.

$$d = rt$$
$$d = (75)(2.4)$$
$$d = 180 \text{ miles}$$

Area is the measure of the amount of surface within the figure's boundaries. Areas are measured in square units.

Perimeter is the sum of the lengths of the sides of a figure. Perimeters are measured in the same common unit as the sides.

Formulas for areas and perimeters of quadrilaterals and triangles can be found in **Table 2.1** on page 134.

Determine the perimeter and area of the following trapezoid.

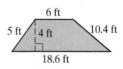

$$P = a + b + c + d$$
$$P = 5 + 6 + 10.4 + 18.6$$
$$P = 40 \text{ ft}$$
$$A = \frac{1}{2}h(b + d)$$
$$A = \frac{1}{2}(4)(6 + 18.6)$$
$$A = 49.2 \text{ ft}^2$$

The **circumference** of a circle is the length (or perimeter) of the curve that forms a circle.

Formulas for the area and circumference of a circle can be found in **Table 2.2** on page 136.

Determine the area and circumference of the following circle.

$$A = \pi r^2$$
$$A = \pi (4)^2$$
$$A = \pi (16)$$
$$A \approx 50.27 \text{ cm}^2$$
$$C = 2\pi r$$
$$C = 2\pi (4)$$
$$C = 8\pi$$
$$C \approx 25.13 \text{ cm}$$

Volume may be considered the space occupied by a figure. Volume is measured is cubic units.

Volume formulas can be found in **Table 2.3** on page 137.

Determine the volume of the following figure.

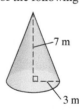

$$V = \frac{1}{3}\pi r^2 h$$
$$V = \frac{1}{3}\pi (3)^2 (7)$$
$$V = \frac{1}{3}\pi (9)(7)$$
$$V = 21\pi$$
$$V \approx 65.97 \text{ m}^3$$

IMPORTANT FACTS AND CONCEPTS	EXAMPLES

Section 2.6 (cont.)

To **solve for a variable in a formula,** treat each of the quantities, except the one for which you are solving, as if they were constants. Then solve for the desired variable by isolating it on one side of the equation.	Solve $V = lwh$, for h. $$V = lwh$$ $$\frac{V}{lw} = \frac{lwh}{lw}$$ $$\frac{V}{lw} = h$$

Section 2.7

A **ratio** is a quotient of two quantities.	3 to 5, 3 : 5, $\dfrac{3}{5}$
A **proportion** is a statement of equality between two ratios. In the proportion $\dfrac{a}{b} = \dfrac{c}{d}$, the a and d are called the **extremes**, and the b and c are called the **means** of the proportion.	$\dfrac{7}{10} = \dfrac{21}{30}$ 7 and 30 are the extremes. 10 and 21 are the means.
Cross-Multiplication If $\dfrac{a}{b} = \dfrac{c}{d}$, then $ad = bc$.	Solve $\dfrac{-9}{2} = \dfrac{126}{x}$ for x by cross-multiplying. $$\frac{-9}{2} = \frac{126}{x}$$ $$-9 \cdot x = 2 \cdot 126$$ $$-9x = 252$$ $$\frac{-9x}{-9} = \frac{252}{-9}$$ $$x = -28$$
To Solve Problems Using Proportions **1.** Understand the problem. **2.** Translate the problem into mathematical language. **3.** Carry out the mathematical calculations necessary to solve the problem. **4.** Check the answer obtained in step 3. **5.** Make sure you have answered the question. See page 147 for more details on proportions.	Melanie Jo can type 40 words per minute. If she types for 20.5 minutes, how many words will she type? $$\frac{40 \text{ words}}{1 \text{ minute}} = \frac{x \text{ words}}{20.5 \text{ minutes}}$$ $$40(20.5) = 1(x)$$ $$820 = x$$ Melanie Jo will type 820 words.
Similar figures are figures whose corresponding angles are equal and whose corresponding sides are in proportion.	These two figures are similar. 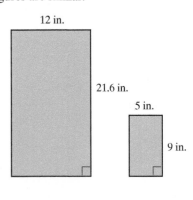

IMPORTANT FACTS AND CONCEPTS	EXAMPLES

Section 2.8

An **inequality** is a mathematical statement containing one or more of the following symbols: $>, <, \geq, \leq$.	$x + 7 \leq 3x - 5$

Properties Used to Solve Inequalities	**1.** If $x - 5 > 3$, then $x - 5 + 5 > 3 + 5$.
For real numbers, a, b, and c:	**2.** If $x + 4 \geq -9$, then $x + 4 - 4 \geq -9 - 4$.
1. If $a > b$, then $a + c > b + c$.	**3.** If $\frac{1}{3}x > 2$, then $\left(\frac{1}{3}x\right)(3) > 2(3)$.
2. If $a > b$, then $a - c > b - c$.	**4.** If $6x > 12$, then $\frac{6x}{6} > \frac{12}{6}$.
3. If $a > b$ **and** $c > 0$, then $ac > bc$.	
4. If $a > b$ **and** $c > 0$, then $\frac{a}{c} > \frac{b}{c}$.	**5.** If $-\frac{1}{4}x > 8$, then $(-4)\left(-\frac{1}{4}x\right) < (-4)8$.
5. If $a > b$ **and** $c < 0$, then $ac < bc$.	**6.** If $-7x \geq 35$, then $\frac{-7x}{-7} \leq \frac{35}{-7}$.
6. If $a > b$ **and** $c < 0$, then $\frac{a}{c} < \frac{b}{c}$.	

Chapter 2 Review Exercises

[2.1] *Use the distributive property to simplify.*

1. $3(x + 8)$ **2.** $5(x - 2)$ **3.** $-2(x + 4)$

4. $-(x + 2)$ **5.** $-(m + 8)$ **6.** $-4(4 - x)$

7. $5(5 - p)$ **8.** $6(4x - 5)$ **9.** $-5(5t - 5)$

10. $4(-x + 3)$ **11.** $\frac{1}{2}(2x + 4)$ **12.** $-\frac{1}{3}(3 + 6y)$

13. $-(x + 2y - z)$ **14.** $-3(2a - 5b + 7)$

[2.1] *Simplify.*

15. $10q - 6q$ **16.** $5 - 3y + 3$ **17.** $1 + 3x + 2x$

18. $-2x - x + 3y$ **19.** $4m + 2n + 4m + 6n$ **20.** $9x + 3y + 2$

21. $6x - 2x + 3y + 6$ **22.** $x + 8x - 9x + 3$ **23.** $-4x^2 - 8x^2 + 3$

24. $-2(3a^2 - 4) + 6a^2 - 8$ **25.** $2x + 3(x + 4) - 5$ **26.** $-4 + 2(3 - 2b) + b$

27. $6 - (-7x + 6) - 7x$ **28.** $2(2x + 5) - 10 - 4$ **29.** $-6(4 - 3x) - 18 + 4x$

30. $4y - 3(x + y) + 6x^2$ **31.** $\frac{1}{4}d + 2 - \frac{3}{5}d + 5$ **32.** $3 - (a - b) + (a - b)$

33. $\frac{5}{6}x - \frac{1}{3}(2x - 6)$ **34.** $\frac{2}{3} - \frac{1}{4}n - \frac{1}{3}(n + 2)$

[2.2–2.5] *Solve.*

35. $-3x = -3$ **36.** $t + 6 = -7$ **37.** $x - 4 = 7$

38. $\frac{x}{3} = -9$ **39.** $5x + 1 = 12$ **40.** $14 = 3 + 2x$

41. $4c + 11 = -21$ **42.** $9 - 2a = 15$ **43.** $-x = -12$

44. $3(x - 2) = 6$ **45.** $-12 = 3(2x - 8)$ **46.** $4(6 + 2x) = 0$

47. $-6n + 2n + 6 = 0$ **48.** $-3 = 3w - (4w + 6)$ **49.** $6 - (2n + 3) - 4n = 6$

50. $4x + 6 - 7x + 9 = 18$ **51.** $5 + 3(x - 1) = 3(x + 1) - 1$ **52.** $8.4r - 6.3 = 6.3 + 2.1r$

53. $19.6 - 21.3t = 80.1 - 9.2t$ **54.** $0.35(c - 5) = 0.45(c + 4)$ **55.** $0.2(x + 6) = -0.3(2x - 1)$

56. $-2.3(x - 8) = 3.7(x + 4)$ **57.** $\frac{p}{3} + 2 = \frac{1}{4}$ **58.** $\frac{d}{6} + \frac{1}{7} = 2$

59. $\frac{3}{5}(r - 6) = 3r$ **60.** $\frac{2}{3}w = \frac{1}{6}(w - 2)$ **61.** $8x - 5 = -4x + 19$

62. $-(w + 2) = 2(3w - 6)$

63. $2x + 6 = 3x + 9 - 3$

64. $-5a + 3 = 2a + 10$

65. $5p - 2 = -2(-3p + 6)$

66. $3x - 12x = 24 - 9x$

67. $4(2x - 3) + 4 = 8x - 8$

68. $4 - c - 2(4 - 3c) = 3(c - 4)$

69. $2(x + 7) = 6x + 9 - 4x$

70. $-5(3 - 4x) = -6 + 20x - 9$

71. $4(x - 3) - (x + 5) = 0$

72. $-2(4 - x) = 6(x + 2) + 3x$

73. $\dfrac{x + 3}{2} = \dfrac{x}{2}$

74. $\dfrac{y}{7} = \dfrac{y - 5}{2}$

75. $\dfrac{1}{5}(3s + 4) = \dfrac{1}{3}(2s - 8)$

76. $\dfrac{2(2t - 4)}{5} = \dfrac{3t + 6}{4} - \dfrac{3}{2}$

77. $\dfrac{2}{5}(2 - x) = \dfrac{1}{6}(-2x + 2)$

78. $\dfrac{x}{4} + \dfrac{x}{6} = \dfrac{1}{2}(x + 3)$

[2.6]   *Use the formula to find the value of the variable indicated.*

79. $y = mx + b$ (slope-intercept form of a line); find m when $y = 7$, $x = 2$, and $b = 1$.

80. $A = \dfrac{1}{2}h(b + d)$ (area of a trapezoid); find A when $h = 12$, $b = 3$, and $d = 5$.

Determine the area or volume of the figure.

81.

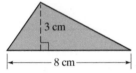

82.

Solve for the indicated variable.

83. $P = 2l + 2w$, for l

84. $y - y_1 = m(x - x_1)$, for m

85. $-x + 3y = 2$, for y

86. Spring Break Yong Wolfer traveled to Florida for spring break at an average speed of 61.7 miles per hour for 5 hours. How for did he travel?

87. Flower Garden Chrishawn Miller has a rectangular flower garden that measures 20 feet by 12 feet. What is the area of Chrishawn's flower garden?

88. Tuna Fish Find the volume of a tuna fish can if its diameter is 4 inches and its height is 2 inches.

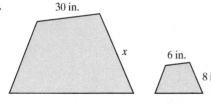

[2.7]   *Determine the following ratios. Write each ratio in lowest terms.*

89. 15 inches to 20 inches

90. 80 ounces to 12 pounds

91. 4 minutes : 40 seconds

Solve each proportion.

92. $\dfrac{x}{4} = \dfrac{8}{16}$

93. $\dfrac{5}{20} = \dfrac{x}{80}$

94. $\dfrac{3}{t} = \dfrac{15}{45}$

95. $\dfrac{20}{45} = \dfrac{15}{q}$

96. $\dfrac{6}{5} = \dfrac{-12}{x}$

97. $\dfrac{b}{6} = \dfrac{8}{-3}$

98. $\dfrac{-7}{9} = \dfrac{-12}{y}$

99. $\dfrac{x}{-15} = \dfrac{30}{-5}$

The following pairs of figures are similar. For each pair, find the length of the side indicated by x.

100.

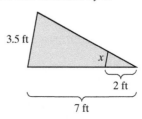

101.

[2.8]   Solve each inequality, and graph the solution on a number line.

102. $3x + 4 \geq 10$

103. $-4a + 10 > 4a - 14$

104. $5 - 3r \leq 2r + 15$

105. $2(x + 4) \leq 2x - 5$

106. $2(x + 3) > 6x - 4x + 4$

107. $x + 6 > 9x + 30$

108. $x - 8 \leq -3x + 11$

109. $-(y + 2) < -2(-2y + 5)$

110. $\dfrac{x}{2} < \dfrac{2}{3}(x + 3)$

111. $\dfrac{3}{10}(t - 2) \leq \dfrac{3}{4}(4 + 2t)$

[2.7]   Set up a proportion and solve each problem.

112. Boat Trip A boat travels 40 miles in 1.8 hours. If it travels at the same rate, how long will it take for it to travel 140 miles?

113. Washing Dishes If Adam Kloza can wash 12 dishes in 3.5 minutes, how many dishes can he wash in 21 minutes?

114. Copy Machine If a copy machine can copy 20 pages per minute, how many pages can be copied in 22 minutes?

115. Map Scale If the scale of a map is 1 inch to 60 miles, what distance on the map represents 380 miles?

116. Model Car Bryce Winston builds a model car to a scale of 1 inch to 1.5 feet. If the completed model is 10.5 inches, what is the size of the actual car?

© Jupiter Unlimited

117. Money Exchange Suppose that one U.S. dollar can be exchanged for 9.165 Mexican pesos, find the value of 1 peso in terms of U.S. dollars.

118. Ketchup If a machine can fill and cap 80 bottles of ketchup in 50 seconds, how many bottles of ketchup can it fill and cap in 2 minutes?

Chapter 2 Practice Test

CHAPTER Test Prep VIDEOS

Chapter Test Prep Videos provide fully worked-out solutions to any of the exercises you want to review. Chapter Test Prep Videos are available via MyMathLab, or on YouTube (search "Angel Elementary Algebra" and click on "Channels").

Use the distributive property to simplify.

1. $-3(4 - 2x)$

2. $-(x + 3y - 4)$

Simplify.

3. $5x - 8x + 4$

4. $4 + 2x - 3x + 6$

5. $-y - x - 4x - 6$

6. $a - 2b + 6a - 6b - 3$

7. $2x^2 + 3 + 2(3x - 2)$

Solve Exercises 8–16.

8. $2.4x - 6.3 = 3.3$

9. $\dfrac{5}{6}(x - 2) = x - 3$

10. $2x - 3(-2x + 4) = -13 + x$

11. $3x - 4 - x = 2(x + 5)$

12. $-3(2x + 3) = -2(3x + 1) - 7$

13. $ax + by + c = 0$, for x

14. $-6x + 5y = -2$, for y

15. $\dfrac{1}{7}(2x - 5) = \dfrac{3}{8}x - \dfrac{5}{7}$

16. $\dfrac{9}{x} = \dfrac{3}{-15}$

17. What do we call an equation that has
   a) exactly one solution,
   b) no solution,
   c) all real numbers as its solution?

Solve Exercises 18–21, and graph the solution on a number line.

18. $2x - 4 < 4x + 10$

19. $3(x + 4) \geq 5x - 12$

20. $4(x + 3) + 2x < 6x - 3$

21. $-(x - 2) - 3x = 4(1 - x) - 2$

22. The following figures are similar. Find the length of side x.

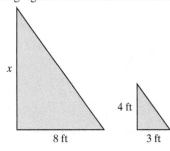

23. Simple Interest Loan Laura Hoye lent her sister $2000 for a period of 1 year. At the end of 1 year, her sister repaid the $2000 plus $80 interest. What simple interest rate did her sister pay?

24. Peanut Butter Pie A peanut butter pie has a diameter of 9 inches. Determine the circumference of the pie.

25. Travel Time While traveling, you notice that you traveled 25 miles in 35 minutes. If your speed does not change, how long will it take you to travel 125 miles?

Cumulative Review Test

Take the following test and check your answers with those given in the back of the book. Review any questions that you answered incorrectly. The section where the material was covered is indicated after the answer.

1. Multiply $\dfrac{52}{15} \cdot \dfrac{10}{13}$

2. Divide $\dfrac{5}{24} \div \dfrac{2}{9}$

3. Insert $<$, $>$, or $=$ in the shaded area to make a true statement: $|-2|$ 1.

4. Evaluate $-5 - (-4) + 12 - 8$.

5. Subtract -6 from -7.

6. Evaluate $20 - 6 \div 3 \cdot 2$.

7. Evaluate $3[6 - (4 - 8^2)] - 30$.

8. Evaluate $-2x^2 - 6x + 8$ when $x = -2$.

9. Name the illustrated property.

$$-5(x - 3y - 4z) = -5x + 15y + 20z$$

Simplify.

10. $8x + 2y + 4x - y$

11. $9 - \dfrac{2}{3}x + 16 + \dfrac{3}{4}x$

Solve.

12. $7t + 3 = -4$

13. $4(x - 2) = 5(x - 1) + 3x + 2$

14. $\dfrac{3}{4}n - \dfrac{1}{5} = \dfrac{2}{3}n$

15. $A = \dfrac{a + b + c}{3}$, for b

16. $\dfrac{40}{30} = \dfrac{3}{x}$

Solve, and graph the solution on a number line.

17. $x - 3 > 7$

18. $2x - 7 \le 3x + 5$

19. Trampoline A circular trampoline has a diameter of 22 feet. Determine the area of the trampoline.

20. Earnings If Samuel earns $10.50 after working for 2 hours mowing a lawn, how much does he earn after 8 hours?

3

Applications of Algebra

3.1 Changing Application Problems into Equations

3.2 Solving Application Problems

Mid-Chapter Test: Sections 3.1–3.2

3.3 Geometric Problems

3.4 Motion, Money, and Mixture Problems

Chapter 3 Summary

Chapter 3 Review Exercises

Chapter 3 Practice Test

Cumulative Review Test

Goals of This Chapter

The emphasis of this chapter is to get you to express real-world problems mathematically and solve them. This process of representing real-life situations mathematically is called *modeling*. For many students, this chapter is the most important chapter in the entire text. The material presented in this chapter will not only help you succeed in this course, but will help you succeed throughout life!

The mixture of chemicals in the laboratory is an important process. In some cases, algebra can be used to determine the amounts of the chemicals needed for a specific process. In Example 6 on page 208 you will see how to determine the mixture proportions for a particular solution.

© Olivier Le Queinec\Shutterstock

3.1 Changing Application Problems into Equations

1. Translate phrases into mathematical expressions.

2. Express the relationship between two related quantities.

3. Write expressions involving multiplication.

4. Translate applications into equations.

1 Translate Phrases into Mathematical Expressions

> **Helpful Hint**
>
> **Study Tip**
>
> It is important that you prepare for this chapter carefully. Make sure you read the book and work the examples carefully. *Attend class every day, and most of all, work all the exercises assigned to you.*
>
> As you read through the examples in the rest of the chapter, think about how they can be expanded to other, similar problems. For example, in Example 1 **a**) we will state that the distance, *d*, increased by 10 miles, can be represented by $d + 10$. You can generalize this to other, similar problems. For example, a weight, *w*, increased by 15 pounds, can be represented as $w + 15$.

One practical advantage of knowing algebra is that you can use it to solve everyday problems by first *translating application problems into mathematical language*. One purpose of this section is to help you take an application problem, also referred to as a *word* or *verbal problem*, and write it as a mathematical equation.

Often the most difficult part of solving an application problem is translating it into an equation. Before you can translate a problem into an equation, you must understand the meaning of certain words and phrases and how they are expressed mathematically. **Table 3.1** is a list of selected words and phrases and the operations they imply. We used the variable *x*. However, any variable could have been used.

TABLE 3.1

Word or Phrase	Operation	Statement	Algebraic Form
Added to	Addition	8 *added to* a number	$x + 8$
More than		6 *more than* a number	$x + 6$
Increased by		A number *increased by* 3	$x + 3$
The sum of		*The sum of* a number and 4	$x + 4$
Subtracted from	Subtraction	6 *subtracted from* a number	$x - 6$
Less than		2 *less than* a number	$x - 2$
Decreased by		A number *decreased by* 5	$x - 5$
The difference between		*The difference between* a number and 9	$x - 9$
Multiplied by	Multiplication	A number *multiplied by* 6	$6x$
The product of		*The product of* 4 and a number	$4x$
Twice a number, 3 times a number, etc.		*Twice a number*	$2x$
Of, when used with a percent or fraction		20% *of* a number	$0.20x$
Divided by	Division	A number *divided by* 8	$\dfrac{x}{8}$
The quotient of		*The quotient of* a number and 6	$\dfrac{x}{6}$

Often a statement contains more than one operation. The following chart provides some examples of this.

Statement	Algebraic Form
Four more than twice a number	$\underbrace{2x}_{\text{Twice a number}} + 4$
Five less than 3 times a number	$\underbrace{3x}_{\text{Three times a number}} - 5$
Three times the sum of a number and 8	$3\underbrace{(x + 8)}_{\text{The sum of a number and 8}}$
Twice the difference between a number and 4	$2\underbrace{(x - 4)}_{\text{The difference between a number and 4}}$

Subtraction is not commutative. That is, $a - b \neq b - a$. Therefore, you must be very careful when writing expressions involving subtraction. Study the following examples.

5 less than 3 times a number

CORRECT	INCORRECT
$3x - 5$	~~$5 - 3x$~~

5 subtracted from 3 times a number

CORRECT	INCORRECT
$3x - 5$	~~$5 - 3x$~~

the difference between $3x$ and 5

CORRECT	INCORRECT
$3x - 5$	~~$5 - 3x$~~

Understanding Algebra

Subtraction is *not* commutative. For example, $6 - 9$ is not equal to $9 - 6$. *Thus, $x - 7$ is different from $7 - x$, so beware!*

Often an algebraic expression can be written in several different ways.

Algebraic Expression	Statements
$2x + 3$	Three more than twice a number The sum of twice a number and 3 Twice a number, increased by 3 Three added to twice a number
$3x - 4$	Four less than 3 times a number Three times a number, decreased by 4 The difference between 3 times a number and 4 Four subtracted from 3 times a number

EXAMPLE 1 Express each statement as an algebraic expression.

a) The distance, d, increased by 10 miles

b) Six times the height, h

c) Eight less than twice the area, a

d) Four pounds more than 5 times the weight, w

Solution

a) $d + 10$ **b)** $6h$ **c)** $2a - 8$ **d)** $5w + 4$

Now Try Exercise 13

2 Express the Relationship between Two Related Quantities

When two numbers are related to each other, we will often represent one number as x and the other number as an expression containing x.

Statement	One Number	Other Number
John is 5 years older than Mary	Let x = Mary's age	Let $x + 5$ = John's age
Mike's age now and Mike's age in 8 years	Let x = Mike's age now	Let $x + 8$ = Mike's age in 8 years
The first number is 6 times the second number	Let x = second number	Let $6x$ = the first number
The first number is 12% less than the second number	Let x = second number	Let $x - 0.12x$ = the first number

Understanding Algebra

It is important to first determine what quantity we are representing with a letter. Then we should express it literally as "Let x = "

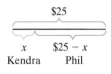

x $\$25 - x$

Kendra   Phil

FIGURE 3.1

Understanding Algebra

In general, if T represents the total to be divided into two parts, then if one part is called x, the other part will be $T - x$. See **Figure 3.2**.

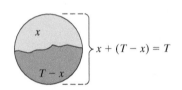

$x + (T - x) = T$

FIGURE 3.2

Now let's consider a problem in which one quantity is divided into two parts. For example, suppose $\$25$ is divided between Kendra and Phil.

If Kendra gets . . .	Then Phil gets . . .
$\$20$	$\$25 - \$20$ or $\$5$
$\$15$	$\$25 - \$15$ or $\$10$
$\$8$	$\$25 - \$8$ or $\$17$
$\$2$	$\$25 - \$2$ or $\$23$

In general, if we let $x =$ the amount Kendra gets, then $25 - x =$ is the amount Phil gets. Note that the sum of x and $25 - x$ is 25. (See **Figure 3.1**.)

EXAMPLE 2 For each part, determine what to let $x =$.

a) Mary weighs 15 pounds more than Sue. $x + 15$ $x =$ Sue's weight

b) The length of a rectangle is 4 inches more than twice its width. $2w + 4 = L$

c) Joe earns $\$56.20$ less than Larry. $x - 56.20$ $x =$ Larry

d) The theater sold 525 tickets. Some were adults' tickets and some were children's tickets. $525 - x$ (Adult) $525 - y$ (children)

Solution In general, when writing expressions to represent word problems, if a quantity A is expressed in terms of a quantity B, then we let $x =$ quantity B.

a) Since Mary's weight is expressed in terms of Sue's weight, we let $x =$ Sue's weight.

b) Since the length of a rectangle is expressed in terms of its width, we let $x =$ width of the rectangle.

c) Since the amount Joe earns is expressed in terms of what Larry earns, we let $x =$ amount Larry makes.

d) Here, since neither quantity of adults' tickets nor children's tickets is expressed in terms of the other's quantity, we can let $x =$ number of adults' tickets sold or let $x =$ number of children's tickets sold. If we let $x =$ number of adults' tickets sold, then $525 - x$ will equal the number of children's tickets sold. If we let $x =$ number of children's tickets sold, then $525 - x$ will equal the number of adults' tickets sold.

Now Try Exercise 37

EXAMPLE 3 For each relationship, select a variable to represent one quantity and state what that variable represents. Then express the second quantity in terms of the variable selected.

a) The Dukes scored 12 points more than the Tigers. $x + 12$ $x =$ Tigers

b) An adult robin is 4.3 times the weight of a baby robin.

c) Bill and Mary share $\$75$. $75 - g$ $g =$ Mary

d) Kim has 7 more than 5 times the amount Sylvia has. $7x + 5$ $x =$ Sylvia

e) The length of a rectangle is 3 feet less than 4 times its width. $4w - 3$

Solution To express the relationships, we must first decide which quantity we will let the variable represent. To give you practice with variables other than x, we will select different letters to represent the variable.

a) Since the number of points scored by the Dukes is expressed in terms of the number of points scored by the Tigers, we will select the variable t.

Let $t =$ number of points scored by the Tigers.

Then $t + 12 =$ number of points scored by the Dukes.

b) The weight of an adult robin is given in terms of the weight of a baby robin.

Let w = weight of a baby robin.

Then $4.3w$ = weight of an adult robin.

c) We are not told how much of the $75 each person receives. In this case we can let the variable represent the amount either person receives. We will let a represent the amount Bill receives.

Let a = amount Bill receives.

Then $75 - a$ = amount Mary receives.

d) The amount Kim has is given in terms of the amount Sylvia has.

Let s = amount Sylvia has.

Then $5s + 7$ = amount Kim has.

e) The length of the rectangle is given in terms of the width of the rectangle.

Let w = width of the rectangle.

Then $4w - 3$ = length of the rectangle.

Now Try Exercise 47

3 Write Expressions Involving Multiplication

Consider the statement "the cost of 3 items at $5 each." The cost would be 3 times $5 and we could express the cost as $3 \cdot 5$ or $3(5)$. Now consider the statement "the cost of x items at $5 each." The cost would be x times $5 and we could express the cost as $x \cdot 5$ or $x(5)$. It is customary to write this product as $5x$. Thus, the cost of x items at $5 each is represented as $5x$.

Finally, consider the statement "the cost of x items at y dollars each." We write the cost of x items at y dollars as **xy**.

EXAMPLE 4 Write each statement as an algebraic expression.

a) The cost of purchasing x pens at $2 each $2x$

b) A 5% commission on x dollars in sales $0.05x$

c) The dollar amount earned in h hours if a person earns $6.50 per hour $6.50h$

d) The number of cents in q quarters $25q$

e) The number of ounces in x pounds $16x$

Solution

a) We can reason like this:

1 pen would cost	1(2) dollars	= $2
2 pens would cost	2(2) dollars	= $4
3 pens would cost	3(2) dollars	= $6
$\vdots$	$\vdots$	$\vdots$
x pens would cost	$x(2)$ dollars	or **$2x$** dollars

Thus the cost would be $2x$ dollars.

b) A 5% commission on $1 sales would be 0.05(1), on $2 sales 0.05(2), on $3 sales 0.05(3), on $4 sales 0.05(4), and so on. Therefore, the commission on sales of x dollars would be $0.05(x)$ or $0.05x$.

Note: If you need a review on changing a percent to a decimal number, review Appendix A.

c) In one hour the person would earn 1($6.50). In two hours the person would earn 2($6.50), and in h hours the person would earn $h($6.50) or $6.50h$.

d) We know that each quarter is worth 25 cents. Thus, one quarter is 1(25) cents. Two quarters is 2(25) cents, and so on. Therefore, q quarters is $q(25)$ cents or $25q$ cents.

e) Each pound is equal to 16 ounces. Using the same reasoning as in part **d)**, we see that x pounds is $16x$ ounces.

Now Try Exercise 71

EXAMPLE 5 Truck Rental Maria Mears rented a truck for 1 day. She paid a daily fee of $88 and a mileage fee of 75 cents per mile. Write an expression that represents her total cost when she drives x miles.

Solution   Maria's total cost consists of two parts, the daily fee and the mileage fee. Notice the daily fee is given in terms of dollars, and the mileage fee is given in cents. When writing an expression to represent the total cost, we want the units to be the same. Therefore, we will use a mileage fee of $0.75 per mile, which is equal to 75 cents per mile.

Let x = number of miles driven.

Then $0.75x$ = cost of driving x miles.

$$\overbrace{\underset{88\quad+\quad0.75x}{\text{daily fee + mileage fee}}}^{\text{total cost}}$$

Thus, the expression that represents Maria's total cost is $88 + 0.75x$.

Now Try Exercise 75

© John A. Rizzo/Getty Images, Inc.-Photodisc/Royalty Free

EXAMPLE 6 Write a Sum or Difference In a bus the number of males was 3 more than twice the number of females. Write an expression for

a) the sum of the number of males and females

b) the difference between the number of males and females

c) the difference between the number of females and males

Solution   Since the number of males is expressed in terms of the number of females, we let the variable represent the number of females. We will choose x to represent the variable.

Let x = number of females.

Then $2x + 3$ = number of males.

a) The expression for the sum of the number of males and females is

$$\underset{(2x+3)}{\underbrace{\text{number of males}}}\quad+\quad\underset{x}{\underbrace{\text{number of females}}}$$

b) The expression for the difference between the number of males and females is

$$\underset{(2x+3)}{\underbrace{\text{number of males}}}\quad-\quad\underset{x}{\underbrace{\text{number of females}}}$$

c) The expression for the difference between the number of females and males is

$$\underset{x}{\underbrace{\text{number of females}}}\quad-\quad\underset{(2x+3)}{\underbrace{\text{number of males}}}$$

Notice that parentheses are needed around the $2x + 3$ since both terms $2x$ and 3 are being subtracted.

Now Try Exercise 87

> **Helpful Hint**
>
> ### Using Parentheses When Writing Expressions
>
> **Sum:** When writing the sum of two quantities, parentheses may be used to help in the under-standing of the problem, but they are not necessary.
>
> | Examples | Answers |
> |---|---|
> | Find the sum of x and $2x - 3$. | $x + (2x - 3)$ or $x + 2x - 3$ |
> | Find the sum of $3c - 4$ and $c + 5$. | $(3c - 4) + (c + 5)$ or $3c - 4 + c + 5$ |
>
> **Difference:** When writing the difference of two quantities, when only *a single term* is being subtracted, parentheses may be used in the understanding of the problem, but they are not necessary.
>
> | Examples | Answers |
> |---|---|
> | Subtract r from $3r - 2$. | $(3r - 2) - r$ or $3r - 2 - r$ |
> | Find the difference between $2s + 6$ and s. | $(2s + 6) - s$ or $2s + 6 - s$ |
>
> When writing the difference of two quantities, *when two or more terms are being sub-tracted, parentheses* **must** *be placed around all the terms being subtracted*, since all the terms are being subtracted and not just the first term.
>
> | Examples | Answers |
> |---|---|
> | Subtract $x + 2$ from $3x$. | $3x - (x + 2)$ |
> | Subtract $3t - 4$ from $5t$. | $5t - (3t - 4)$ |
> | Subtract $r - 5$ from $2r + 3$. | $(2r + 3) - (r - 5)$ or $2r + 3 - (r - 5)$ |
> | Find the difference between 6 and $m + 3$. | $6 - (m + 3)$ |
> | Find the difference between $4n - 9$ and $2n - 3$. | $(4n - 9) - (2n - 3)$ or $4n - 9 - (2n - 3)$ |

Expressions Involving Percent

Example 7 involves percent. Whenever we perform a calculation involving percent, we change the percent to a decimal number or a fraction first.

When shopping we may see a "25% off" sign. We assume that this means 25% off of the *original cost*, even though this is not stated. If we let c represent the original cost, then 25% of the original cost would be represented as $0.25c$. Twenty-five percent off the original cost means the original cost, c, decreased by 25% of the original cost. Twenty five percent off the original cost would be represented as $c - 0.25c$.

$$25\% \text{ off the original cost}$$

$$c - 0.25c$$

Original cost —— decreased by —— 25% of the original cost

Now let's work an example involving percent.

EXAMPLE 7 Write each statement as an algebraic expression.

a) The cost of a pair of boots, c, increased by 6% $c + 0.06c$

b) The population in the town of Brooksville, p, decreased by 12% $p - 0.12p$

Solution

a) The question asks for the cost increased by 6%. We assume that this means the cost increased by 6% of the original cost. Therefore, the answer is $c + 0.06c$.

b) Using the same reasoning as in part **a)**, the answer is $p - 0.12p$.

Now Try Exercise 79

Understanding Algebra

If the sales tax rate is 6%, the *tax* on an item costing x dollars is $0.06x$.

The *total amount*, which is the cost of the item plus the tax on the item, is represented as $x + 0.06x$, which can also be written as $1.06x$.

Avoiding Common Errors

In Example 7 **a)** we asked you to represent a cost, c, increased by 6%. Note, the answer is $c + 0.06c$. Often, students write the answer to this question as $c + 0.06$. It is important to realize that a percent of a quantity must always be a percent multiplied by some number or letter. Some phrases involving the word percent and the correct and incorrect interpretations follow.

PHRASE	CORRECT	INCORRECT
A $7\frac{1}{2}$ % sales tax on c dollars	$0.075c$	~~0.075~~
The cost, c, increased by a $7\frac{1}{2}$ % sales tax	$c + 0.075c$	~~$c + 0.075$~~
The cost, c, reduced by 25%	$c - 0.25c$	~~$c - 0.25$~~

---

4 Translate Applications into Equations

When writing application problems as equations, the word *is* often means *is equal to* and is represented by an equals sign. Some examples of statements written as equations follow.

Statement	Equation
Six times a number *is* 42.	$6x = 42$
Five more than twice a number *is* 4.	$2x + 5 = 4$
A number decreased by 4 *is* 3 more than twice the number.	$x - 4 = 2x + 3$
The sum of a number and the number increased by 4 *is* 60.	$x + (x + 4) = 60$
Twice the difference of a number and 3 *is* the sum of the number and 20.	$2(x - 3) = x + 20$
A number increased by 15% *is* 120.	$x + 0.15x = 120$
Six less than three times a number *is* one-fourth the number.	$3x - 6 = \frac{1}{4}x$

Now let's work some examples where we write equations.

EXAMPLE 8 Translate Words into Equations Write each problem as an equation.

a) A New York City subway car has 36 seats. The number of seats in s subway cars *is* 180.

b) The number of cents in d dimes *is* 120.

c) The cost of x gallons of gasoline at $4.20 per gallon *is* $35.20.

Solution

a) 1 subway car has 36 seats, 2 subway cars have 72 seats, and s subway cars have $36s$ seats. Since there are 180 seats, the equation is $36s = 180$.

b) The number of cents in d dimes is $d(10)$ or $10d$. Since the number of cents in d dimes *is* 120, the equation is $10d = 120$.

c) Using similar reasoning as in parts **a)** and **b)**, the equation is $4.20x = 35.20$.

Now Try Exercise 109

> **Helpful Hint**
>
> In a written expression certain other words may be used in place of *is* to represent the equals sign. Some of these are *will be, was, yields,* and *gives.* For example,
>
>   "When 4 is added to a number, the sum *will be* 20" can be expressed as $x + 4 = 20$.
>
>   "Six subtracted from a number *was* $\frac{1}{2}$ the number" can be expressed as $x - 6 = \frac{1}{2}x$.
>
>   "A rental car cost \$75 per day. The cost for renting the car for x days *was* \$150" can be expressed as $75x = 150$.

EXAMPLE 9   **Translate Words into an Equation**   Write the problem as an equation.

One number is 4 less than twice the other. Their sum is 14.

Solution

$$\text{Let } x = \text{one number.}$$
$$\text{Then } 2x - 4 = \text{second number.}$$

Now we write the equation using the information given.

$$\text{first number} + \text{second number} = 14$$
$$x + (2x - 4) = 14$$

Now Try Exercise 99

> **Understanding Algebra**
>
> If x is an integer, then $x + 1$ represents the *next* **consecutive integer.**
>
>   If y is an even integer, then $y + 2$ represents the *next* **consecutive even integer**.
>
>   If z is an odd integer, then $z + 2$ represents the *next* **consecutive odd integer**.

In Example 10 we will use the term *consecutive even integers.*

EXAMPLE 10   **Consecutive Even Integers**   Write the problem as an equation.

For two consecutive even integers, the sum of the smaller and 3 times the larger is 22.

Solution   First, we express the two consecutive even integers in terms of the variable.

$$\text{Let } x = \text{smaller consecutive even integer.}$$
$$\text{Then } x + 2 = \text{larger consecutive even integer.}$$

Now we write the equation using the information given.

$$\text{smaller} + 3 \text{ times the larger} = 22$$
$$x + 3(x + 2) = 22$$

Now Try Exercise 107

EXAMPLE 11   **Translate Words into an Equation**   Write the problem as an equation.

One train travels 3 miles more than twice the distance another train travels. The total distance traveled by both trains is 800 miles.

Solution   First express the distance traveled by each train in terms of the variable.

$$\text{Let } x = \text{distance traveled by one train.}$$
$$\text{Then } 2x + 3 = \text{distance traveled by second train.}$$

Now write the equation using the information given.

$$\text{distance of train 1} + \text{distance of train 2} = \text{total distance}$$
$$x + (2x + 3) = 800$$

Now Try Exercise 121

EXAMPLE 12 **Translate Words into an Equation** Write the problem as an equation.

Lori Soushon is 4 years older than 3 times the age of her son Ron. The difference in Lori's age and Ron's age is 26 years.

Solution   Since Lori's age is given in terms of Ron's age, we will let the variable represent Ron's age.

$$\text{Let } x = \text{Ron's age.}$$
$$\text{Then } 3x + 4 = \text{Lori's age.}$$

We are told that the difference in Lori's age and Ron's age is 26 years. The word *difference* indicates subtraction. Since Lori is older than Ron, we must subtract Ron's age from Lori's age to get a positive number.

$$\text{Lori's age} - \text{Ron's age} = 26$$
$$(3x + 4) - x = 26$$

NowTry Exercise 117

Example 13 will involve percent.

EXAMPLE 13 **Translate Words into an Equation.** Write the problem as an equation.

The 2009 property tax for Danielle's house was 3.9% greater than her property tax in 2008. Her property tax in 2009 was $4008.

Solution   In this example, we will choose to use the variable *t*, for tax. Since the 2009 property tax is based upon the 2008 property tax, we will let the variable represent the 2008 property tax.

$$\text{Let } t = 2008 \text{ property tax.}$$
$$\text{Then } t + \underbrace{0.039t}_{} = 2009 \text{ property tax.}$$

this represents the 3.9% increase

Since Danielle's 2009 property tax *was* $4008, the equation we write is $t + 0.039t = 4008$.

NowTry Exercise 123

Helpful Hint

It is important that you understand this section and work all your assigned homework problems. You will use the material learned in this section in the next three sections and throughout the book.

EXERCISE SET 3.1   Math⋅XL   MyMathLab
MathXL®   MyMathLab

Warm-Up Exercises

Fill in the blanks with the appropriate word, phrase, or symbol(s) from the following list.

$2c + 7$	$2c - 7$	$c + 0.07$	$c + 7$	$c + 2$	$c + 0.07c$
$7 - c$	$c - 0.07c$	equals	$0.07c$	$c - 7$	$c + 3$

1. If *c* represents the cost of an item, then the 7% tax on that item is represented by _____ .

2. Consider the statement "Barry is seven years older than Chuck." If *c* represents Chuck's age, then _____ is the expression that represents Barry's age.

3. A seven-foot board is cut into two pieces. If the length of one piece is represented by *c*, then _____ represents the length of the other piece.

4. If *c* represents an odd number, the next consecutive odd number is represented by _____ .

5. If c represents the dollar cost of an item, and then the cost is increased by 7¢, the new cost is represented by _____ .

6. If c represents the cost of an item, and then the cost is decreased by 7%, the new cost is represented by _____ .

7. Simone is 7 years older than twice Carla's age. If c represents Carla's age, _____ represents Simone's age.

8. A first number is 7 less than two times a second number. If c represents the second number, then the first number is represented by _____ .

9. When translating a problem, the word "is" gets translated to an _____ symbol.

10. If c represents the cost of an item and if the sales tax is 7%, then the amount you need to pay for the item is represented by _____ .

Practice the Skills

In Exercises 11–30, express the statement as an algebraic expression. See Example 1.

11. The height, h, increased by 4 inches

12. The weight, w, increased by 20 pounds

13. The age, a, decreased by 5 years

14. The time, t, decreased by 3 hours

15. Five times the height, h

16. Seven times the length, l

17. Twice the distance, d

18. Three times the rate, r

19. One-half the age, a

20. One-third the weight, w

21. Five subtracted from r

22. Nine subtracted from p

23. m subtracted from 12

24. n subtracted from 4

25. Eight pounds more than twice the weight, w

26. Six inches more than 3 times the height, h

27. Four years less than 5 times the age, a

28. One mile more than $\frac{1}{2}$ the distance, d

29. One-third the weight, w, decreased by 9 pounds

30. One-fifth the height, h, increased by 2 feet

In Exercises 31–44, determine what x =. See Example 2.

31. Paul is 4 inches taller than Sonya.

32. The length of a rectangle is 5 inches greater than its width.

33. The length of Tortuga Beach is 60 feet shorter than the length of Jones Beach.

© Allen R. Angel

34. Wilma ran 4 miles per hour faster than Natasha.

35. The United States won 3 times the number of medals that Finland won.

36. The distance to Georgia is $\frac{1}{2}$ the distance to Tennessee.

37. The Cadillac costs $200 more than twice the cost of the Chevy.

38. Noah received 25 more votes than 3 times the number of votes that Tawnya received.

39. June's grade was 2 points less than twice Teri's grade.

40. Alberto's salary was $2000 greater than 4 times Nick's salary.

41. $60 is divided between Kristen and Yvonne.

42. Drawka has 25 marbles. They are either red or blue marbles.

43. Together Don and Angela weigh 270 pounds.

44. Together Oliver and Dalane have 1053 clients.

In Exercises 45–56, select a variable to represent one quantity and state what that variable represents. Express the second quantity in terms of the variable selected. See Example 3. Note that the variable you select may be different than the variable used in the answers in the back of the book.

45. The table costs 5 times as much as the chair.

46. Joan's house is 810 square feet larger than Alfredo's house.

47. The area of the living room is 20 square feet greater than twice the area of the kitchen.

48. The amount in Darla's savings account is $250 less than 4 times the amount in Carmen's savings account.

49. The length of the rectangle is 2 inches less than 6 times the width.

50. A total of $600 is to be divided between Evita and Brian.

51. A total of 20 medals were won by Sweden and Brazil.

52. A movie theatre sold a total of 220 more adults' tickets than children's tickets.

53. Mike's age is 2 years more than $\frac{1}{2}$ George's age.

54. The book *Golden Angels* sold 4 copies less than 5 times the amount the book *Flycatcher* sold.

55. Jan and Edward used two different treadmills for exercise. The total distance walked between them was 6.4 miles.

56. On a 540-mile trip Cheng and Elsie shared the driving.

In Exercises 57–84, write the indicated expression. See Examples 3–7.

57. Age Dan Graber is n years old now. Write an expression that represents his age in 8 years.

58. Speed-Reading John Debruzzi used to read p words per minute. After taking a speed-reading course, his speed increased by 60 words per minute. Write an expression that represents his new reading speed.

59. Motorcycle Melissa Blum is selling her motorcycle. She was asking x dollars for the motorcycle but has cut the price in half. Write an expression that represents the new price.

© Lawrence Gilligan

© Allen R. Angel

See Exericse 65.

60. Age Cathy Bennett's son is one-third as old as Cathy, c. Write an expression for her son's age.

61. Age Gayle Krzemien's age is one less than twice Mary Lou Baker's age, a. Write an expression for Gayle's age.

62. Calories The calories in a serving of mixed nuts is 280 calories less than twice the number of calories in a serving of cashew nuts, c. Write an expression for the number of calories in a serving of mixed nuts.

63. Temperature The average daily temperature in Jacksonville, Florida, in July is 30° less than twice its average daily temperature in January, t. Write an expression for the average daily temperature in July.

64. Population In 2008, the population of China was 100 million more than 1.1 times the population of India, p. Write an expression for the population of China in millions.

65. Weight Anika Angel weighed p pounds at birth. At age 6 months her weight was 2.3 pounds less than twice her birth weight. Write an expression for Anika's weight at age 6 months.

66. Population Increase The city of Clarkville has a population of 4000. If the population increases by 300 people per year, write an expression that represents the population after n years.

67. Profits Monica and Julia share in the profits of a toy store. If the total profit is $80,000 and m is the amount Monica receives, write an expression for the amount Julia receives.

68. Charity Event A total of 83 men and women attended a charity event. If the number of men who attended is m, write an expression for the number of women who attended.

69. Home Runs Hank Aaron had 673 less than twice the number of home runs Babe Ruth had, r. Write an expression for the number of home runs Hank Aaron had.

© Allen R. Angel

70. In 2007, the country with the highest average life expectancy was Andorra and the country with the lowest average life expectancy was Swaziland. The average life expectancy in Andorra was 21.1 years greater than twice that in Swaziland, *s*. Write an expression for the average life expectancy in Andorra. (*Source:* CIA World Factbook).

71. Money Carolyn Curley found that she had *x* dimes in her handbag. Write an expression that represents this quantity of money in cents.

72. Weight Jason Mahar's weight is *w* pounds. Write an expression that represents his weight in ounces.

73. Money Susan Grady has *d* dollars in her purse. Write an expression that represents this quantity of money in cents.

74. Soil A total of six hundred pounds of soil is put onto two trucks. If *a* pounds of soil is placed onto one truck, write an expression for the amount of soil placed onto the other truck.

75. Truck Rental Bob Melina rented a truck for a trip. He paid a daily fee of $45 and a mileage fee of 40 cents a mile. Write an expression that represents his total cost when he travels *x* miles in one day.

76. Soil Delivery Mary Vachon had topsoil delivered to her house. The total cost included a delivery charge of $48 plus $60 per cubic yard of soil. Write an expression for the total cost if Mary has *x* cubic yards of soil delivered.

77. Sales Increase Barry Cogan is a sales representative for a medical supply company. His 2010 sales increased by 20% over his 2009 sales, *s*. Write an expression for his 2010 sales.

78. Salary Increase Charles Idion, an engineer, had a salary increase of 15% over last year's salary, *s*. Write an expression for this year's salary.

79. Electricity Use Jean Olson's electricity use in 2009 decreased by 12% from her 2008 electricity use, *e*. Write an expression for her 2009 electricity use.

80. Shirt Sale At a 25% off everything sale, Bill Winchief purchased a new shirt. If *c* represents the original cost, write an expression for the sale price of the shirt.

81. Car Cost The cost of a new car purchased in Collier County included a 7% sales tax. If *c* represents the cost of the car before tax, write an expression for the total cost, including the sales tax.

82. The number of rolls of film sold in 2009 was 74.5% fewer than the number of rolls sold in 1999. Write an expression for the number of rolls sold in 2009 if *r* represents the number of rolls sold in 1999. (*Source:* Photo Marketing Association)

83. In 2007, the state with the greatest median age was Maine and the state with the lowest was Utah. The median age in Utah was 30.7% less than that of Maine. If *m* represents the median age in Maine, write an expression for the median age in Utah. (*Source:* U.S. Census Bureau)

84. Growth in North Las Vegas North Las Vegas, Nevada, according to the U.S. Census Bureau, had the greatest population growth from 2005 to 2006 of any major city in the United States. Its population in 2006 was 11.9% greater than its population in 2005. If *p* represents North Las Vegas's population in 2005, write an expression for its 2006 population.

North Las Vegas

In Exercises 85–98, write the indicated expression. You will need to select the variable to use. Note that the variable you use may be different than the variable used in the answer section. See Example 6.

85. Weight Jennifer's weight is 15 pounds more than Frieda's weight. Write an expression for the sum of their weights.

86. Length The Chestnut-mandibled toucan is 3 inches longer than the keel-billed toucan (shown). Write an expression for the sum of their lengths.

87. Height Armando is taller than his son Luis. Armando is 1 inch less than twice Luis's height. Write an expression for the *difference* in Armando's and Luis's height.

88. Profits A company's profits in 2009 were $100 less than the company's profits in 2010. Write an expression for the *difference* in the 2010 and 2009 profits.

89. Numbers A first number is 40 less than 3 times a second number. If the second number is represented by *x*, write an expression for the first number subtracted from the second number.

90. Numbers A first number is 16 less than twice a second number. If the second number is represented by *n*, write an expression for the first number subtracted from the second number.

91. Weight Jill's four-year-old child weighs 3 pounds less than twice the weight of her two-year-old child. Write an expression for the sum of their weights.

92. Assessed Value The assessed value of Glen Sandifer's house is $200 more than twice that of Olga Thompson's house. Write an expression for the sum of the assessed values.

93. Land Area The largest state in area is Alaska and the smallest is Rhode Island. The area of Alaska is 462 square miles more than 479 times the area of Rhode Island. Write an expression for the sum of the areas of the two states.

94. Black Bear The number of black bear sightings in 2009 in Ocala National Forest was 6 less than twice the number of sightings in 2005. Write an expression for the number of 2005 sightings subtracted from the number of 2009 sightings.

95. Stocks The price of Apple Computer stock is 39.4% greater than the cost of Research in Motion stock. Write an expression for the sum of the prices of Research in Motion and Apple Computer stocks.

96. Car Cost The cost of a 2009 Chevrolet Corvette LT-1 coupe increased by 2.1% over the cost of a 2008 model. Write an expression for the sum of the costs of a 2008 and a 2009 Corvette.

97. Bank Assets The 2008 assets of Fifth Third Bancorp were 11.2% higher than their 2007 assets. Write an expression for the 2008 assets subtracted from the 2007 assets.

98. Spam The number of pieces of spam (or junk mail) that Laura Hoye received in 2009 was 12% less than the number she received in 2008. Write an expression for the difference between the number of pieces of spam she received in 2008 and 2009.

In Exercises 99–130, write an equation to represent the problem. See Examples 8–13.

99. Two Numbers One number is 4 times another. The sum of the two numbers is 20.

100. Age Marie is 6 years older than Denise. The sum of their ages is 48.

101. Consecutive Integers The sum of two consecutive integers is 41.

102. Even Integers The product of two consecutive even integers is 74.

103. Numbers Twice a number, decreased by 8 is 12.

104. Consecutive Integers For two consecutive integers, the sum of the smaller and twice the larger is 29.

105. Numbers One-fifth of the sum of a number and 10 is 150.

106. Numbers One-third of the sum of a number and 12 is 5.

107. Even Integers For two consecutive even integers, the sum of the smaller and twice the larger is 22.

108. Odd Integers For two consecutive odd integers, the sum of 3 times the smaller and the larger is 14.

109. Earnings John Jones earns $12.50 per hour. If he works h hours his earnings will be $150.

110. Employees The T. W. Wilson company plans to increase its number of employees by 20 per year. The increase in the number of employees in t years will be 120.

111. Top Soil Abe Mantell purchased x bags of topsoil at a cost of $2.99 a bag. The total he paid was $17.94.

112. Plants Mark Ernsthausen purchased p plants at a nursery for $5.99 each. The total he paid was $65.89.

113. Quarters The number of cents in q quarters is 175.

114. Seconds The number of seconds in m minutes is 480.

115. Age Darta Aguilar is 1 year older than twice Julie Chesser's age. The sum of their ages is 52.

116. Horses Marc Campbell owns more horses than Selina Jones owns. The number of horses that Marc owns is 3 less than five times the number that Selina owns. The difference in the number of horses owned by Marc and Selina is 5.

117. Baseball Cards Jakob Meyer owns 300 more than twice the number of baseball cards that Saul Gonzales owns. The difference in the number of cards that Jakob and Saul own is 420.

118. Jogging David Ostrow jogs 5 times as far as Jennifer Freer. The total distance traveled by both people is 8 miles.

🢐 **119. Amtrak** An Amtrak train travels 4 miles less than twice the distance traveled by a Southern Pacific train. The total distance traveled by both trains is 890 miles.

120. Wagon Ride On a wagon ride the number of girls was 6 less than twice the number of boys. The total number of boys and girls on the wagon was 18.

© Allen R. Angel

121. Distance Walked Donna Douglas walked 2 miles less than 3 times as far as Malik Oamar walked. Together they walked a total of 12.6 miles.

122. Distance Lilia Orlova rollerbladed 4 miles less than twice the distance she ran. The total distance she traveled was 15 miles.

123. Viper The cost of a new Dodge Viper increased by 0.2% over last year's model. The new price is $86,460.

124. Income Dan Tadeo's 2009 income was 4.6% greater than his 2008 income. His income in 2009 was $56,900.

125. Population The population of the town of Tom's Valley decreased by 1.9%. The population after the decrease was 12,087.

126. DVD Player At the Better Buy Warehouse, Anne Long purchased a DVD player that was reduced by 10% for $208.

127. New Car Carlotta Diaz bought a new car. The cost of the car plus a 7% sales tax was $32,600.

128. Sport Coat David Gillespie purchased a sport coat at a 25% off sale. He paid $195 for the sport coat.

129. Cost of Meal Beth Rechsteiner ate at a steakhouse. The cost of the meal plus a 15% tip was $42.50.

130. Railroad In a narrow gauge railway, the distance between the tracks is about 64% of the distance between the tracks in a standard gauge railroad. The difference in the distances between the tracks in the two types of railroads is about 1.67 feet.

© Allen R. Angel

Challenge Problem

131. Time

a) Write an algebraic expression for the number of seconds in d days, h hours, m minutes, and s seconds.

b) Use the expression found in part **a)** to determine the number of seconds in 4 days, 6 hours, 15 minutes, and 25 seconds.

Group Activity

Exercises 132 and 133 will help prepare you for the next section, where we set up and solve application problems. Discuss and work each exercise as a group. For each exercise, write down the quantity you are being asked to find and represent this quantity with a variable. Then write an equation containing your variable that can be used to solve the problem. Do not solve the equation.

132. Water Usage An average bath uses 30 gallons of water and an average shower uses 6 gallons of water per minute. How long a shower would result in the same water usage as a bath?

133. Salary Plans An employee has a choice of two salary plans. Plan A provides a weekly salary of $200 plus a 5% commission on the employee's sales. Plan B provides a weekly salary of $100 plus an 8% commission on the employee's sales. What must be the weekly sales for the two plans to give the same weekly salary?

Cumulative Review Exercises

[1.9] **134.** Evaluate $3[(4 - 16) \div 2] + 5^2 - 3$.

[2.6] **135.** $P = 2l + 2w$; find l when $P = 40$ and $w = 5$.

136. Solve $3x - 2y = 6$ for y.

[2.7] **137.** Solve the proportion $\dfrac{3.6}{x} = \dfrac{10}{7}$.

[2.8] **138.** Solve the inequality $2x - 4 > 3$ and graph the solution on a number line.

3.2 Solving Application Problems

1 Use the problem-solving procedure.

2 Set up and solve number application problems.

3 Set up and solve application problems involving money.

4 Set up and solve applications concerning percent.

1 Use the Problem-Solving Procedure

The general problem-solving procedure given in Section 1.2 can be used to solve all types of verbal problems. Below, we present the **five-step problem-solving procedure** again so you can easily refer to it. We have included some additional information under steps 1 and 2, since in this section we are going to emphasize translating application problems into equations.

Problem-Solving Procedure for Solving Applications

1. **Understand the problem.** Identify the quantity or quantities you are being asked to find.
2. **Translate the problem into mathematical language (express the problem as an equation).**
   a) Choose a variable to represent one quantity, *and write down exactly what it represents*. Represent any other quantity to be found in terms of this variable.
   b) Using the information from step a), write an equation that represents the application.
3. **Carry out the mathematical calculations (solve the equation).**
4. **Check the answer (using the *original* application).**
5. **Answer the question asked.**

Sometimes we will combine two steps in the problem-solving procedure when it helps to clarify the explanation. We may not show the check of a problem to save space. Even if we do not show a check, you should check the problem yourself and make sure your answer is reasonable and makes sense.

2 Set Up and Solve Number Application Problems

The examples presented here involve information and data but do not contain percents.

EXAMPLE 1 **An Unknown Number** Two subtracted from 4 times a number is 10. Find the number.

Solution   Understand   To solve this problem, we need to express the statement given as an equation. We are asked to find the unknown number.

Translate   Let x = the unknown number. Now write the equation.

$$\underbrace{\text{2 subtracted from 4 times a number}}_{4x - 2} \overset{\text{is}}{\underset{=}{\downarrow}} \overset{10}{\underset{10}{\downarrow}}$$

Carry Out
$$4x = 12$$
$$x = 3$$

Check   Substitute 3 for the number in the original problem, two subtracted from 4 times a number is 10.

$$4(3) - 2 \overset{?}{=} 10$$
$$10 = 10 \quad \text{True}$$

Answer   Since the solution checks, the unknown number is 3.

Now Try Exercise 7

EXAMPLE 2 Number Problem The sum of two numbers is 26. Find the two numbers if the larger number is 2 less than three times the smaller number.

Solution Understand We are given that "the larger number is 2 less than three times the smaller number." Notice that the larger number is expressed in terms of the smaller number. Therefore, we will let the variable represent the smaller number.

Translate

$$\text{Let } x = \text{smaller number.}$$
$$\text{Then } 3x - 2 = \text{larger number.}$$

The sum of the two numbers is 26. Therefore, we write the equation

$$\text{smaller number} + \text{larger number} = 26$$
$$x + (3x - 2) = 26$$

Carry Out Now we solve the equation.

$$4x - 2 = 26$$
$$4x = 28$$
$$x = 7$$

The smaller number is 7. Now we find the larger number.

$$\text{larger number} = 3x - 2$$
$$= 3(7) - 2 \qquad \text{Substitute 7 for } x.$$
$$= 19$$

The larger number is 19.

Check The sum of the two numbers is 26.

$$7 + 19 \stackrel{?}{=} 26$$
$$26 = 26 \qquad \text{True}$$

Answer The two numbers are 7 and 19.

Now Try Exercise 13

Helpful Hint

When reading a word problem, ask yourself, "How many answers are required?" In Example 2, the question asked for the two numbers. The answer is 7 and 19. It is important that you read the question and identify what you are being asked to find. If the question had asked "Find the *smaller* of the two numbers if the larger number is 2 less than three times the smaller number," then the answer would have been only the 7. If the question had asked to find the *larger* of the two numbers, then the answer would have been only 19. *Make sure you answer the question asked in the problem.*

EXAMPLE 3 2008 Summer Olympics In the 2008 Olympics in Beijing, China, the United States won the most medals and China won the second greatest number of medals. The United States won 90 less than twice the number of medals won by China. If the difference between the number of medals won by the United States and China was 10, determine the number of medals won by the United States.

Solution Understand The word *difference* in the problem indicates that this problem will involve subtraction. We are asked to find the number of medals won by the United States. Since the number of medals won by the United States is given in terms of the number of medals won by China, we will let the variable represent medals won by China. We will use the variable c.

Translate

$$\text{Let } c = \text{medals won by China.}$$
$$\text{Then } 2c - 90 = \text{medals won by the United States.}$$

© Pete Niesen\Shutterstock

Since we are dealing with positive amounts, we must subtract the smaller quantity from the larger. Since the difference in medals between the United States and China is 10, we write the following equation.

$$\underbrace{\text{number of medals won by U.S.}}_{2c - 90} - \underbrace{\text{number of medals won by China}}_{c} = 10$$

Carry Out
$$2c - 90 - c = 10$$
$$c - 90 = 10$$
$$c = 100$$

Check and Answer   Remember c represents the number of medals won by China. We are asked to find the number of medals won by the United States, which we have represented as $2c - 90$. Now, we substitute the known value of 100 for c in the expression $2c - 90$: $2(100) - 90 = 110$. *The answer is that the United States won 110 medals.* Notice that the difference in the number of medals won by the United States and China is $110 - 100 = 10$, so the answer checks.

Now Try Exercise 27

EXAMPLE 4 Bicycles The Chain Wheel Drive Bicycle Company presently manufactures 800 bicycles a month. Each month after this month the company plans to increase production by 150 bicycles a month until its monthly production reaches 1700 bicycles. How long will it take the company to reach its production goal?

Solution   Understand   We are asked to find the *number of months* that it will take for the company's production to reach 1700 bicycles a month. Next month its production will increase by 150 bicycles. In two months, its production will increase by 2(150) over the present month's production. In n months, its production will increase by $n(150)$ or $150n$. We will use this information when we write the equation to solve the problem.

Translate
Let n = number of months.

Then $150n$ = increase in production over n months.

$$(\text{present production}) + \left(\begin{array}{c}\text{increased production} \\ \text{over } n \text{ months}\end{array}\right) = \text{future production}$$

$$800 + 150n = 1700$$

Carry Out
$$150n = 900$$
$$n = \frac{900}{150}$$
$$n = 6 \text{ months}$$

Check and Answer   As a check, let's list the number of bicycles produced this month and for the next 6 months.

Presently	Next month	Month 2	Month 3	Month 4	Month 5	Month 6
↓	↓	↓	↓	↓	↓	↓
800	950	1100	1250	1400	1550	1700

Thus, in 6 months the company will produce 1700 bicycles per month.

Now Try Exercise 23

3 Set Up and Solve Application Problems Involving Money

When setting up an equation that involves money, you must make sure that all the monetary units entered into the equation are the same, either all dollars or all cents. When pieces of information are given in both dollars and cents, we generally convert the amount given in cents to an equivalent amount of dollars. For example, when renting a truck the cost may be $50 a day plus 90 cents a mile. When writing the equation, we would write the 90 cents a mile as $0.90 a mile. The cost of traveling x miles at 90 cents a mile would be written $0.90x$.

EXAMPLE 5 Grub Problem Part of Kim Martello's lawn was destroyed by grubs. She decided to purchase new sod to lay down. The cost of the sod is 45 cents per square foot plus a delivery charge of $59. If the total cost of delivery plus the sod was $284, how many square feet of sod was delivered?

Solution   Understand   The total cost consists of two parts, a cost of 45 cents per square foot of sod, plus a delivery charge of $59. We need to determine the number of square feet of sod that will result in a total cost of $284.

Translate

$$\text{Let } x = \text{number of square feet of sod.}$$
$$\text{Then } 0.45x = \text{cost of } x \text{ square feet of sod.}$$

$$\text{sod cost } + \text{ delivery cost } = \text{ total cost}$$

$$0.45x + 59 = 284 \qquad \text{Subtract 59 from both sides.}$$

Carry Out

$$0.45x = 225$$

$$\frac{0.45x}{0.45} = \frac{225}{0.45}$$

$$x = 500$$

Check   The cost of 500 square feet of sod at 45 cents a square foot is $500(0.45) = \$225$. Adding the $225 to the delivery cost of $59 gives $284, so the answer checks.

Answer   Five hundred square feet of sod was delivered.

Now Try Exercise 35

EXAMPLE 6 Photo Printer Elsie Newman is going to purchase a photo printer to print pictures from her digital camera. She is considering a Hewlett-Packard (HP) printer and a Lexmark printer. The HP printer costs $419 and the cost for the ink and paper is 14 cents per photo printed. The Lexmark printer costs $299 and the cost for the ink and paper is 18 cents per photo. How many photos would need to be printed for the total cost of the printers, ink, and paper to be the same?

Solution   Understand   The HP printer has a greater initial cost ($419 versus $299); however, its cost per photo printed is less (14 cents versus 18 cents). We are asked to find the number of photos printed so that the total cost of the two printers will be the same.

Translate

$$\text{Let } n = \text{number of photos.}$$
$$\text{Then } 0.14n = \text{cost for printing } n \text{ photos with the HP printer}$$
$$\text{and } 0.18n = \text{cost for printing } n \text{ photos with the Lexmark printer.}$$

$$\text{total cost of HP printer} = \text{total cost of Lexmark printer}$$

$$\left(\begin{array}{c}\text{initial}\\\text{cost}\end{array}\right) + \left(\begin{array}{c}\text{cost}\\\text{for } n \text{ photos}\end{array}\right) = \left(\begin{array}{c}\text{initial}\\\text{cost}\end{array}\right) + \left(\begin{array}{c}\text{cost}\\\text{for } n \text{ photos}\end{array}\right)$$

$$419 + 0.14n = 299 + 0.18n$$

Carry Out

$$120 + 0.14n = 0.18n \qquad \text{299 was subtracted from both sides.}$$

$$120 = 0.04n \qquad \text{0.14}n \text{ was subtracted from both sides.}$$

$$\frac{120}{0.04} = \frac{0.04n}{0.04}$$

$$3000 = n$$

Check and Answer   The total cost would be the same when 3000 photos were printed. We will leave the check of this answer for you.

Now Try Exercise 39

Understanding Algebra

Recall, the word *percent* means *per hundred*. So, 30% of 80 is $0.30 \times 80 = 24$.

In application problems involving percent, we are always taking percents *of* quantities. Remember, "of" means multiply.

4 Set Up and Solve Applications Concerning Percent

Now we'll look at some application problems that involve percent. Remember that a percent is always a percent of something. Thus if the cost of an item, c, is increased by 8%, we would represent the new cost as $c + 0.08c$, and not $c + 0.08$. See the Avoiding Common Errors box on page 178.

EXAMPLE 7 **Water Bike Rental** At a beachfront hotel, the cost for a water bike rental is $30 per half hour, which includes a $7\frac{1}{2}$% sales tax. Find the cost of the rental before tax.

Solution Understand We are asked to find the cost of the water bike rental before tax. The cost of the rental before tax plus the tax on the water bike must equal $30.

Translate   Let x = cost of the rental before tax.
                    Then $0.075x$ = tax on the rental.

(cost of the water bike rental before tax) + (tax on the rental) = 30

$$x + 0.075x = 30$$

Carry Out $$1.075x = 30$$

$$x = \frac{30}{1.075}$$

$$x \approx 27.91$$

Check and Answer A check will show that if the cost of the rental is $27.91, the cost of the rental including a $7\frac{1}{2}$% tax is about $30.

Now Try Exercise 47

EXAMPLE 8 **Caloric Intake** If the caloric intake for men in the United States increased 10% from 1971 to 2009 and reached 2695 calories in 2009, determine the average caloric intake for men in 1971.

Solution Understand We represent the 2009 caloric intake in terms of the unknown 1971 caloric intake. We use c to represent the 1971 caloric intake and the 2009 caloric intake can be expressed in terms of c.

Translate   Let c = the 1971 caloric intake.
                    Then $c + 0.10c$ = the 2009 caloric intake.

Since the 2009 caloric intake is 2695 calories, we set up the following equation.

$$\underbrace{2009 \text{ caloric intake}}_{c + 0.10c} \quad \text{is} \quad 2695$$

$$c + 0.10c = 2695$$

Carry Out $$1.10c = 2695$$

$$c = \frac{2695}{1.10}$$

$$c = 2450$$

Check and Answer Since c represents the 1971 caloric intake, and it is less than the 2009 caloric intake, our answer is reasonable. The 1971 caloric intake for men was 2450 calories.

Now Try Exercise 49

EXAMPLE 9 **Salary Plans** Jeanne Pirie has accepted a position selling medical supplies and equipment. During her first year, she is given a choice of salary plans. Plan 1 is a $450 weekly base salary plus a 3% commission of weekly sales. Plan 2 is a straight 10% commission of weekly sales. What weekly amount of sales, in dollars, would result in Jeanne receiving the same salary from both plans?

Solution   Understand   We are asked to find the *amount of sales*, in dollars, that will result in the same total salary from both plans. To solve this problem, we write expressions to represent the salary from each of the plans and set the salaries equal to one another.

Translate

Let x = amount of sales in dollars.

Then $0.03x$ = commission from plan 1 sales

and $0.10x$ = commission from plan 2 sales.

salary from plan 1 = salary from plan 2

base salary + 3% commission = 10% commission

$$450 + 0.03x = 0.10x$$

Carry Out

$$450 = 0.07x$$

or $$0.07x = 450$$

$$\frac{0.07x}{0.07} = \frac{450}{0.07}$$

$$x \approx 6428.57$$

Check   We will leave it up to you to show that sales of $6428.57 result in Jeanne receiving the same weekly salary from both plans.

Answer   Jeanne's weekly salary will be the same from both plans if she sells $6428.57 worth of medical supplies and equipment.

Now Try Exercise 59

Helpful Hint

Here are some suggestions if you find you are having some difficulty with application problems.

1. Instructor—Make an appointment to see your instructor. Make sure you have read the material in the book and attempted all the homework problems. Go with specific questions for your instructor.

2. Tutoring—If your college learning center offers free tutoring, you may wish to take advantage of tutoring.

3. Study Group—Form a study group with classmates. Exchange phone numbers and e-mail addresses. You may be able to help one another.

4. Student's Solutions Manual—If you get stuck on an exercise you may want to use the Student's Solutions Manual to help you understand a problem. Do not use the Solutions Manual in place of working the exercises. In general, the Solutions Manual should be used only to check your work.

5. MyMathLab—MyMathLab provides exercises correlated to the text. In addition, online tools such as video lectures, animations, and a multimedia textbook are available to help you understand the material.

6. Math XL®—MathXL is a powerful online homework, tutorial, and assessment system correlated specifically to this text. You can take chapter tests in MathXL and receive a personalized study plan based on your test results. The study plan links directly to tutorial exercises for the objectives you need to study or retest.

7. Pearson Tutor Center—Once the program has been initiated by your instructor, you can get individual tutoring by phone, fax, or e-mail.

It is important that you keep trying! Remember, the more you practice, the better you will become at solving application problems.

EXERCISE SET 3.2

MathXL®   MyMathLab

Warm-Up Exercises

Fill in the blanks with the appropriate word, phrase, or symbol(s) from the following list.

$2x + (2x + 2) = 20$ $x + (x + 2) = 20$ $x + (2x) = 20$

$x + (2x + 2) = 20$ $(2x + 10) - x = 20$ $x + (10x - 2) = 20$

$(2x + 2) - x = 20$

1. The statement "a number (x) plus two more than twice that number is 20" can be represented by the equation _____ .

2. The statement "a number (x) plus twice that number is 20" can be represented by the equation _____ .

3. The statement "the sum of two consecutive odd numbers is 20" can be represented by the equation _____ .

4. The statement "the sum of two numbers is 20 and the larger number is 2 less than ten times the smaller number (x)" can be represented by the equation _____ .

5. The statement "the difference of two numbers is 20 and the larger number is 2 more than twice the smaller number (x)" can be represented by the equation _____ .

6. The statement "the difference of two numbers is 20 and the larger number is 10 more than twice the smaller number (x)" can be represented by the equation _____ .

Practice the Skills/Problem Solving

Exercises 7–32 involve finding a number or numbers. Review Examples 1–4, then set up an equation that can be used to solve the problem. Solve the equation and **answer the question asked.**

7. **Unknown Number** Three subtracted from 4 times a number is 17. Find the number.

8. **Unknown Number** Five subtracted from 6 times a number is 13. Find the number.

9. **Consecutive Integers** The sum of two consecutive integers is 87. Find the numbers.

10. **Consecutive Integers** The sum of two consecutive integers is 113. Find the numbers.

11. **Odd Integers** The sum of two consecutive odd integers is 96. Find the numbers.

12. **Even Integers** The sum of two consecutive even integers is 146. Find the numbers.

13. **Sum of Numbers** One number is 3 more than twice a second number. Their sum is 27. Find the numbers.

14. **Sum of Numbers** One number is 5 less than 3 times a second number. Their sum is 43. Find the numbers.

15. **Difference of Numbers** The larger of two numbers is 4 less than five times the smaller. When the smaller number is subtracted from the larger, the difference is 4. Find the two numbers.

16. **Sum of Numbers** One number is 2 less than 3 times a second number. Their sum is 26. Find the numbers.

17. **Difference of Numbers** The larger of two integers is 8 less than twice the smaller. When the smaller number is subtracted from the larger, the difference is 17. Find the two numbers.

18. **Facing Pages** The sum of the two facing page numbers in an open book is 145. What are the page numbers?

19. **Grandma's Gifts** Grandma gave some baseball cards to Richey and some to Erin. She gave 3 times the amount to Erin as she did to Richey. If the total amount she gave to both of them was 260 cards, how many cards did she give to Richey?

20. **Ski Shop** The Alpine Valley Ski Shop sold 6 times as many downhill skis as cross-country skis. Determine the number of pairs of cross-country skis sold if the difference in the number of pairs of downhill and cross-country skis sold is 1800.

21. **Animal Art** Joseph Murray built a horse for display at a baseball stadium. It took him 1.4 hours more than twice the number of hours to attach the baseball gloves to the horse than to build the horse. If the total time it took him to build the horse and attach the gloves was 32.6 hours, how long did it take to attach the gloves?

The author, Allen R. Angel, is shown in this photo.

22. **Candle Shop** A candle shop makes 60 candles per week. It plans to increase the number of candles it makes by 8 per week until it reaches a production of 132 candles per week. How many weeks will it take for the shop to reach its production schedule?

23. **Collecting Frogs** Mary Shapiro collects ceramic and stuffed frogs. She presently has 422 frogs. She wishes to add 6 a week to her collection until her collection reaches a total of 500 frogs. How long will it take Mary's frog collection to reach 500 frogs?

24. **Population** The town of Dover currently has a population of 6500. If its population is increasing at a rate of 1200 people per year, how long will it take for the population to reach 20,600?

25. **Circuit Boards** The FGN Company produces circuit boards. It now has 4600 employees nationwide. It wishes to reduce

the number of employees by 250 per year through retirements, until its total employment is 2200. How long will this take?

26. Computers The CTN Corporation has a supply of 3600 computers. It wishes to ship 120 computers each week until its supply drops to 2000. How long will this take?

27. Tornados According to The Weather Channel, the greatest number of tornados in the United States occurs in June and the fewest number occurs in December. The average number of tornados in June is 16 less than 11 times the average number of tornados in December. If the difference between the average number of tornados in June and December is 204, determine the average number of tornados in December and June.

28. Watching TV According to the Kaiser Family Foundation, in the United States, the amount of time per day spent by 8–18-year-olds watching television is 16 minutes more than 5 times the number of minutes they spend reading. If the total amount of time per day reading and watching television is 274 minutes, determine the number of minutes spent watching television.

29. Housekeepers The average hourly wage paid to hotel housekeepers in New York City is $1.46 more than twice the average wage paid to hotel housekeepers in New Orleans. Determine the average hourly wage paid to housekeepers in New York City if the difference in their average hourly wages is $8.10.

30. Albums According to *Billboard Magazine*, the top-selling album of all time is Michael Jackson's *Thriller* and the second biggest selling album was AC/DC's *Back in Black*. The sum of the sales of those two titles is 150 million albums. *Thriller* sold 24 million albums more than twice that of *Back in Black*. Determine the sales of both albums.

31. Pork Production Costs According to *Pig International*, a 2008 study showed that pork production was most expensive in Japan. In Japan, the cost of producing a kilogram of pork was 14 cents less than 3 times what it cost to produce a kilogram of pork in the United States. If the sum of the Japan cost and the U.S. cost was $2.94, determine the cost for each country.

32. Oil Consumption According to the U.S. Energy Information Administration, oil and liquid fuel consumption was projected to be 4.8% higher in 2015 than in 2008. If the sum of consumption for these two years is 209.6 quadrillion Btu, determine the projected consumption for 2015.

Exercises 33–46 involve money. Read Examples 5–6, then set up an equation that can be used to solve the problem. Solve the equation and answer the question asked.

33. Gasoline Luvia Rivera has only $48 to purchase gasoline. If gasoline costs $3.84 per gallon, determine how many gallons of gasoline Luvia can purchase.

34. Truck Rental Carol Battle rents a truck for one day and pays $50 per day plus 30 cents a mile. How far can Carol drive in one day if she has only $92?

35. Copy Machine Yamil Bernz purchased a copy machine for $2100 and a one-year maintenance protection plan that costs 2 cents per copy made. If he spends a total of $2462 in a year, which includes the cost of the machine and the copies made, determine the number of copies he made.

36. Gym Membership At Goldies Gym there is a one-time membership fee of $300 plus dues of $40 per month. If Carlos Manieri has spent a total of $700 for Goldies Gym, how long has he been a member?

37. Television Miles Potier's Time Warner cable bill costs $72.68 per month plus $3.95 for each On Demand movie he watches that month. If his cable bill for December was $96.38, determine the number of On Demand movies he watched in December.

38. Hardwood Floors Ruth Zasada is having hardwood floors installed in her living room. The cost for the material is $2840 plus an installation charge of $1.90 per square foot. If the total cost for the material plus installation is $5120, determine the area of her living room.

39. Truck Rental Howard Sporn is considering two companies from which to rent a truck. American Truck Rental charges $20 per day and 25 cents a mile. SavMor Truck Rental charges $35 a day and 15 cents a mile. How far would Howard need to drive in one day for the both companies to have the same total cost?

40. Washing Machines Scott Montgomery is considering two washing machines, a Kenmore® and a Neptune®. The Neptune costs $454 while the Kenmore costs $362. The energy guides indicate that the Kenmore will cost an estimated $84 per year to operate and the Neptune will cost an estimated $38 per year to operate. How long will it be before the total cost is the same for both washing machines?

41. Salaries Brooke Mills is being recruited by a number of high-tech companies. Data Technology Corporation has offered her an annual salary of $40,000 per year plus a $2400 increase per year. Nuteck has offered her an annual salary of $49,600 per year plus an $800 increase per year. In how many years will the salaries from the companies be the same?

42. Racquet Club The Coastline Racquet Club has two payment plans for its members. Plan 1 has a monthly fee of $20 plus $8 per hour for court time. Plan 2 has no monthly fee, but court time is $16.25 per hour. If court time is rented in 1-hour intervals, how many hours would you have to play per month so that plan 1 becomes a better buy?

43. Printers Hector Hanna will purchase one of two laser printers, a Hewlett-Packard (HP) or a Lexmark®. The HP costs $499 and the Lexmark costs $419. Suppose, because of the price of the ink cartridges, the cost of printing a page on the HP is $0.06 per page and the cost of printing a page on the Lexmark is $0.08 per page. How many pages would need to be printed for the two printers to have the same total cost?

44. Satellite or Cable Sean Stewart is deciding whether to select a satellite receiver or cable for his television programming. The satellite receiver costs $298.90 and the monthly charge is $68.70. With cable there is no initial cost to purchase equipment, but the monthly charge for comparable channels is $74.80. After how many months will the total cost of the two systems be equal?

45. Newsletter Neil Simpson had a professional organization newsletter printed and sent out to all the members. The total cost included a $600 printing cost plus a 39 cents mailing cost for each envelope. If the total cost was $1380, determine how many newsletters were mailed.

46. Patio Resurfacing Elizabeth Chu is having her patio resurfaced using concrete pavers. She is considering two companies for the job. A & E Pavers charges $1500 for the pavers plus $40 per hour for labor to install the pavers. The Jerilyn Fairman Company charges $1800 for the pavers plus $25 per hour to install the pavers. How many hours of labor would result in the same total cost with both companies?

*Exercises 47–68 involve percents. Read Examples 7–9, then set up an equation that can be used to solve the problem. Solve the equation and **answer the question asked.***

47. Airfare The airfare for a flight from Amarillo, Texas, to New Orleans cost $295.34, which includes a 7% sales tax. What is the cost of the flight before tax? *Source:* expedia.com

48. New Car Yoliette Fournier purchased a new car. The cost of the car, including a 7.5% sales tax was $24,600. What was the cost of the car before tax?

49. Salary Increase Zhen Tong just received a job offer that will pay him 30% more than his present job does. If the salary at his new job will be $30,200, determine his present salary.

50. New Headquarters Tarrach and Associates plans on increasing the size of its headquarters by 20%. If its new headquarters is to be 14,200 square feet, determine the size of its present headquarters.

51. Auto Exports According to the Federal Reserve Bank of Chicago, in 2007 exports of new light vehicles increased 41% over 1996 in the United States. If in 2007 about 1.7 million light vehicles were exported, determine the number of vehicles exported in 1996.

52. Retirement Income Ray and Mary Burnham have decided to retire. They estimate their annual income after retirement will be reduced by 15% from their pre-retirement income. If they estimate their retirement income to be $42,000, determine their pre-retirement income.

53. Autographs A tennis star was hired to sign autographs at a convention. She was paid $3000 plus 3% of all admission fees collected at the door. The total amount she received for the day was $3750. Find the total amount collected at the door.

54. Sale At a 1-day 20% off sale, Jane Demsky purchased a hat for $25.99. What is the regular price of the hat?

55. Wage Cut A manufacturing plant is running at a deficit. To avoid layoffs, the workers agree on a temporary wage cut of 2%. If the average salary in the plant after the wage cut is $38,600, what was the average salary before the wage cut?

56. Teachers During the 2006 contract negotiations, the city school board approved a 5% pay increase for its teachers effective in 2007. If Dana Frick, a first-grade teacher, projects his 2007 annual salary to be $46,400, what was his 2006 salary?

57. Earnings and Education The U.S. Census Bureau reported that in 2005, graduates with an associate's degree earned an average of 24.6% less than graduates with a bachelor's degree. If, in 2005, the average graduate with an associate's degree earned $37,600, determine the average salary of a graduate with a bachelor's degree.

58. Sales Volume Mona Fabricant receives a weekly salary of $350. She also receives a 6% commission on the total sales she makes. What must her sales be in a week, if she is to make a total of $710?

59. Salary Plans Vince McAdams, a salesman, is given a choice of two salary plans. Plan 1 is a weekly salary of $600 plus 2% commission of sales. Plan 2 is a straight commission of 10% of sales. How much in sales must Vince make in a week for both plans to result in the same salary?

60. Area The Johnson Performing Arts Center has increased in size. The area of the new building is 42% larger than the area of the original building. If the area of the new building is 56,000 square feet, determine the area of the original building.

61. Book The number of pages in the third edition of a book was 4% less than the number of pages in the second edition. If the number of pages in the third edition is 480, determine the number of pages in the second edition.

62. Financial Planning Belen Poltorade, a financial planner, is offering her customers two financial plans for managing their assets. With plan 1 she charges a planning fee of $1000 plus 1% of the assets she will manage for the customers. With plan 2 she charges a planning fee of $500 plus 2% of the assets she will manage. How much in customer assets would result in both plans having the same total fees?

63. Salary Plans Becky Schwartz, a saleswoman, is offered two salary plans. Plan 1 is $400 per week salary plus a 2% commission of sales. Plan 2 is a $250 per week salary plus a 16% commission of sales. How much would Becky need to make in sales for the salary to be the same from both plans?

64. Art Show Bill Rush wants to rent a building for a week to show his artwork and has been offered two rental plans. Plan 1 is a rental fee of $500 plus 3% of the dollar sales he makes.

Plan 2 is $100 plus 15% of the dollar sales he makes. What dollar sales would result in both plans having the same total cost?

© Keith Levit\Shutterstock

65. Eating Out After Linda Kodama is seated in a restaurant, she realizes that she has only $30. From this $30 she must pay a 7% tax and she wishes to leave a 15% tip on the price of the meal before tax. What is the maximum price for a meal that she can afford to pay?

66. Membership Fees The Holiday Health Club has reduced its annual membership fee by 10%. In addition, if you sign up on a Monday, the Club will take an additional $20 off the already reduced price. If Jorge Sanchez purchases a year's membership on a Monday and pays $250, what is the regular membership fee?

© Andresr\Shutterstock

67. Estate Phil Dodge left an estate valued at $140,000. In his will, he specified that his wife will get 25% more of his estate than his daughter. How much will his wife receive?

68. Charitable Giving Charles Ford made a $200,000 cash contribution to two charities, the American Red Cross and the United Way. The amount received by the American Red Cross was 30% greater than the amount received by the United Way. How much did the United Way receive?

69. Oil Use According to the International Energy Agency, the demand for oil in North America is far greater than in any other region. In 2007, North America used an average of 5.1 million gallons of oil per day less than twice that used by Europe, the second greatest user. The total used by both regions in one day was 40.8 million gallons. Determine the number of gallons of oil used in one day in Europe in 2007.

70. Refer to Exercise 69. Determine the number of gallons of oil used in one day in North America in 2007.

Concept/Writing Exercises

71. Outline the five-step problem-solving procedure we use.

72. Explain the concept of *percent increase* to a friend. If you made $8 per hour last month and got a 15% increase, what is your new hourly wage?

Challenge Problems

73. Average Value To find the *average* of a set of values, you find the sum of the values and divide the sum by the number of values.

a) If Paul Lavenski's first three test grades are 74, 88, and 76, write an equation that can be used to find the grade that Paul must get on his fourth exam to have an 80 average.

b) Solve the equation from part **a)** and determine the grade Paul must receive.

74. Driver Education A driver education course costs $45 but saves those under age twenty-five 10% of their annual insurance premiums until they reach age twenty-five. Scott Day has just turned 18, and his insurance costs $600 per year.

a) How long will it take for the amount saved from insurance to equal the price of the course?

b) Including the cost of the course, when Scott turns 25, how much will he have saved?

© Gene Chutka/iStockPhoto

Cumulative Review Exercises

[1.9]   **75.** Evaluate $4[(4 - 6) \div 2] + 3^2 - 1$.

[1.10]   **76.** Name the following property: $3x + 4 = 4 + 3x$.

[2.6]   **77.** Solve the formula $A = \dfrac{1}{2}bh$ for h.

[2.7]   **78.** Solve the proportion $\dfrac{4.5}{6} = \dfrac{9}{x}$.

Mid-Chapter Test: 3.1–3.2

To find out how well you understand the chapter material to this point, take this brief test. The answers and the section where the material was initially discussed are given in the back of the book. Review any questions you answered incorrectly.

In Exercises 1–6, express each statement as an algebraic expression.

1. Six times the weight, w

2. Five inches more than 3 times the height, h

3. Represent the cost, c, increased by 20%, as a mathematical expression.

4. Dennis Donahue rents a truck for $60 per day plus 95 cents per mile, m. Write an expression for the total cost of the rental for one day.

5. Write an expression for the number of cents in n half-dollars.

6. Twenty-five dollars is divided between Amy Keyser and Sherry Norris. If Amy gets x dollars, how much will Sherry get?

7. Explain why the cost, c, of an item at a 25% off sale is not $c - 25$. Write the correct algebraic expression for the cost of an item at a 25% off sale.

8. In the statement, determine what $x =$.

   A Gaudy Leaf Frog is 2 centimeters longer than 3 times the length of a Poison Dart Frog (see photos).

© Allen R. Angel

Gaudy Leaf Frog

© Allen R. Angel

Poison Dart Frog

9. Select a variable to represent one quantity and state what that variable represents. Express the second quantity in terms of the variable selected.

   The distance Mary traveled is 6 miles more than 4 times the distance Pedro traveled.

10. The value of a car in 2005 was 18% less than its value in 2006. Write an expression for the difference in the value of the car from 2006 to 2005.

In Exercises 11 and 12, write the problem as an equation. Do not solve.

11. The population of Cedar Oaks increased by 12%. The population after the increase was 38,619.

12. For two consecutive odd integers, the sum of the smaller and 3 times the larger is 26.

In Exercises 13–20, write an equation that can be used to solve the problem. Solve the equation and answer the question asked.

13. Consecutive Integers The sum of two consecutive integers is 93. Find the numbers.

14. Numbers The larger of two integers is one less than 3 times the smaller. When the smaller number is subtracted from the larger, the difference is 7. Find the numbers.

15. Candy A candy manufacturer presently produces 240 boxes of candy a day and wants to increase production by 20 boxes per day until it produces 600 boxes of candy per day. How many days will it take for production to reach 600 boxes per day?

© Jupiter Unlimited

See Exercise 16.

16. Tennis Kristina Schmid is considering joining one of two tennis clubs. At Dale's Tennis Club the monthly fee is $90, and court time is $4 per hour. At Abel's Tennis Club the monthly fee is $30, but court time is $8 per hour. How many hours in a month would Kristina need to play for the total cost to be the same with both clubs?

17. Television The cost of a television plus a 7% sales tax is $749. Find the cost of the television before tax.

18. Clients Anita and Betty together have a total of 600 clients. If Anita has 12 more than twice the number of clients Betty has, determine the number of clients each person has.

19. Truck Rental A truck cost $36 a day plus 18 cents a mile to rent. If the total cost for a one-day rental is $45.36, how many miles were driven?

20. Salary Plans A salesman is offered two salary plans. Plan 1 is $200 per week plus 8% commission of the dollar sales he makes. Plan 2 is $300 per week plus 6% of the dollar sales he makes. How much in sales must the salesman make in a week for the two plans to have the same total salary?

3.3 Geometric Problems

1 Solve geometric problems.

1 Solve Geometric Problems

This section serves two purposes. One is to reinforce the geometric formulas introduced in Section 2.6. The second is to reinforce procedures for setting up and solving verbal problems discussed in Sections 3.1 and 3.2.

EXAMPLE 1 **Sandbox** Christine O'Connor is planning to build a sandbox for her daughter. She has 30 feet of lumber with which to build the perimeter. What should be the dimensions of the rectangular sandbox if the length is to be 3 feet longer than the width (**Fig. 3.3**)?

Solution Understand We are asked to find the dimensions of the sandbox that Christine plans to build. The perimeter of the sandbox will be 30 feet. Since the length is given in terms of the width, we will let w represent the width. Then we can express the length in terms of w. To solve this problem, we use the formula for the perimeter of a rectangle, $P = 2l + 2w$, where $P = 30$ feet.

Translate

Let w = width of the sandbox.

Then $w + 3$ = length of the sandbox.

$$P = 2l + 2w$$

Carry Out

$$30 = 2(w + 3) + 2w$$
$$30 = 2w + 6 + 2w$$
$$30 = 4w + 6$$
$$24 = 4w$$
$$6 = w$$

Understanding Algebra

Recall some useful geometry formulas:

Rectangle   Area: $A = l \cdot w$
             Perimeter: $P = 2l + 2w$

Triangle   Area: $A = \frac{1}{2}b \cdot h$

            Sum of the measures
            of the interior
            angles = 180°

Quadrilateral Sum of the measures
            of the interior
            angles = 360°

Circle   Area $= \pi r^2$
            Circumference $= 2\pi r$

w
$l = w + 3$

FIGURE 3.3

The width is 6 feet. Since the length is 3 feet longer than the width, the length is $6 + 3 = 9$ feet.

Check   We will check the solution by substituting the appropriate values in the perimeter formula.

$$P = 2l + 2w$$
$$30 \stackrel{?}{=} 2(9) + 2(6)$$
$$30 = 30 \qquad \text{True}$$

Answer   The width of the sandbox will be 6 feet and the length will be 9 feet.

Now Try Exercise 23

A triangle that contains two sides of equal length is called an **isosceles triangle**. In isosceles triangles, the angles opposite the two sides of equal length have equal measures.

EXAMPLE 2 Corner Lot Mr. and Mrs. Harmon Katz have a corner lot that is in the shape of an isosceles triangle. Two angles of their triangular lot are the same and the third angle is 30° greater than the other two. Find the measure of all three angles (see **Fig. 3.4**).

Solution   Understand   To solve this problem, you must know that the sum of the angles of any triangle measures 180°. We are asked to find the measure of each of the three angles, where the two smaller angles have the same measure. We will let *x* represent the measure of the smaller angles, and then we will express the larger angle in terms of *x*.

Translate   Let x = the measure of each smaller angle.

Then $x + 30$ = the measure of the larger angle.

sum of the 3 angles = 180

Carry Out $x + x + (x + 30) = 180$

$3x + 30 = 180$

$3x = 150$

$x = \dfrac{150}{3} = 50$

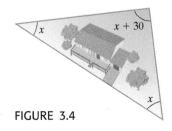

FIGURE 3.4

The two smaller angles are each 50°. The larger angle is $x + 30°$ or $50° + 30° = 80°$.

Check and Answer   Since $50° + 50° + 80° = 180°$, the answer checks. The two smaller angles are each 50° and the larger angle is 80°.

Now Try Exercise 11

Recall from Section 2.6 that a quadrilateral is a four-sided figure. Quadrilaterals include squares, rectangles, parallelograms, and trapezoids. The sum of the measures of the angles of any quadrilateral is 360°.

EXAMPLE 3 Water Trough Sarah Fuqua owns horses and uses a water trough whose ends are trapezoids. The measure of the two bottom angles of the trapezoid are the same, and the measure of the two top angles are the same. The bottom angles measure 15° less than twice the measure of the top angles. Find the measure of each angle.

Solution   Understand   To help visualize the problem, we draw a picture of the trapezoid, as in **Figure 3.5**. We use the fact that the sum of the measures of the four angles of a quadrilateral is 360°.

FIGURE 3.5

Translate   Let x = the measure of each of the two smaller angles.

Then $2x - 15$ = the measure of each of the two larger angles.

$$\left(\begin{array}{c}\text{measure of the}\\\text{two smaller angles}\end{array}\right) + \left(\begin{array}{c}\text{measure of the}\\\text{two larger angles}\end{array}\right) = 360$$

$$x + x + (2x - 15) + (2x - 15) = 360$$

Carry Out

$$x + x + 2x - 15 + 2x - 15 = 360$$
$$6x - 30 = 360$$
$$6x = 390$$
$$x = 65$$

Each smaller angle is 65°. Each larger angle is $2x - 15 = 2(65) - 15 = 115°$.

Check and Answer   Since $65° + 65° + 115° + 115° = 360°$, the answer checks. Each smaller angle is 65° and each larger angle is 115°.

Now Try Exercise 27

EXAMPLE 4 **Fenced-In Area** Ronald Yates recently started an ostrich farm. He is separating the ostriches by fencing in three equal rectangular areas, as shown in **Figure 3.6**. The length of the fenced-in area, l, is to be 30 feet greater than the width and the total amount of fencing available is 660 feet. Find the length and width of the fenced-in area.

Solution   Understand   The fencing consists of four pieces of fence of length w, and two pieces of fence of length l.

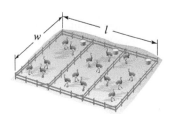

FIGURE 3.6

Translate   Let w = width of fenced-in area.

Then $w + 30$ = length of fenced-in area.

$$\left(\begin{array}{c}\text{4 pieces of fence}\\\text{of length } w\end{array}\right) + \left(\begin{array}{c}\text{2 pieces of fence}\\\text{of length } w + 30\end{array}\right) = 660$$

Carry Out

$$4w + 2(w + 30) = 660$$
$$4w + 2w + 60 = 660$$
$$6w + 60 = 660$$
$$6w = 600$$
$$w = 100$$

Since the width is 100 feet, the length is $w + 30$ or $100 + 30$ or 130 feet.

Check and Answer   Since $4(100) + 2(130) = 660$, the answer checks. The width of the fenced-in area is 100 feet and the length is 130 feet.

Now Try Exercise 37

EXERCISE SET 3.3

Warm-Up Exercises

Fill in the blanks with the appropriate word, phrase, or symbol(s) from the following list.

| 360° | 180° | 90° | $2l + 12$ | 12 | equilateral |
| 10 | quadrilateral | $l \cdot w$ | 45° | isosceles | |

1. In a rectangle, the length is 1 inch more than twice the width and the perimeter is 62 inches. Then the width is _____ inches.

2. The area of a rectangle is 120 square inches. If the length is 10 inches, then the width is _____ inches.

3. The sum of the measures of the interior angles of a quadrilateral is _____.

4. The sum of the measures of the angles of a triangle is _____.

5. A triangle with two equal sides is called _____.

6. A triangle with three equal sides is called _____.

7. The area of a rectangle of length l and width w is _____.

8. A four-sided figure is called a _____.

9. If one angle of an isosceles triangle is 90°, then each other angle must measure _____ .

10. The perimeter of a rectangle of length *l* and width 6 is _____ .

Practice the Skills/Problem Solving

*Solve the following geometric problems.**

11. Isosceles Triangle In an isosceles triangle, one angle is 42° greater than the other two equal angles. Find the measure of all three angles. See Example 2.

12. Triangular Building This building in New York City, referred to as the Flatiron Building, has a perimeter in the shape of an isosceles triangle. If the shortest side of the triangle is 50 feet shorter than the two longer sides, and the perimeter is 196 feet, determine the length of the three sides of the triangle.

© Allen R. Angel

13. A Special Triangle An **equilateral triangle** is a triangle that has three sides of the same length. The perimeter of an equilateral triangle is 34.5 inches. Find the length of each side.

14. Equilateral Triangle The perimeter of an equilateral triangle is 48.6 centimeters. Find the length of each side. See Exercise 13.

15. Complementary Angles Two angles are **complementary angles** if the sum of their measures is 90°. Angle *A* and angle *B* are complementary angles, and angle *A* is 21° more than twice angle *B*. Find the measures of angle *A* and angle *B*.

Complementary Angles

16. Complementary Angles Angles *A* and *B* are complementary angles, and angle *B* is 14° less than angle *A*. Find the measures of angle *A* and angle *B*. See Exercise 15.

17. Supplementary Angles Two angles are **supplementary angles** if the sum of their measures is 180°. Angle *A* and angle *B* are supplementary angles, and angle *B* is 8° less than three times angle *A*. Find the measures of angle *A* and angle *B*.

Supplementary Angles

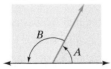

18. Supplementary Angles Angles *A* and *B* are supplementary angles and angle *A* is 2° more than 4 times angle *B*. Find the measures of angle *A* and angle *B*. See Exercise 17.

19. Vertical Angles When two lines intersect, the opposite angles are called **vertical angles**. Vertical angles have equal measures. Determine the measures of the vertical angles indicated in the following figure.

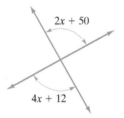

2x + 50

4x + 12

20. Vertical Angles A pair of vertical angles is indicated in the following figure. Determine the measure of the vertical angles indicated. See Exercise 19.

5x + 12   4x + 22

21. Unknown Angles One angle of a triangle is 10° greater than the smallest angle, and the third angle is 30° less than twice the smallest angle. Find the measures of the three angles.

22. Unknown Angles One angle of a triangle is 20° larger than the smallest angle, and the third angle is 6 times as large as the smallest angle. Find the measures of the three angles.

23. Dimensions of Rectangle The length of a rectangle is 6 feet more than its width. What are the dimensions of the rectangle if the perimeter is 44 feet?

24. Dimensions of Rectangle The perimeter of a rectangle is 120 feet. Find the length and width of the rectangle if the length is twice the width.

25. Tennis Court The length of a regulation tennis court is 6 feet greater than twice its width. The perimeter of the court is 228 feet. Find the length and width of the court.

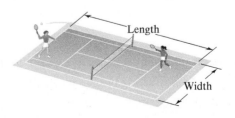

Length

Width

26. **Patio** Rikki Blair is building a rectangular patio. The perimeter of the patio is to be 96 feet. Determine the dimensions of the patio if the length is to be 6 feet less than twice the width.

27. **Parallelogram** In a parallelogram the opposite angles have the same measures. Each of the two larger angles in a parallelogram is 20° less than 3 times the smaller angles. Find the measure of each angle.

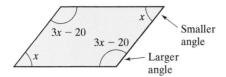

28. **Parallelogram** The two smaller angles of a parallelogram have equal measures, and the two larger angles each measure 27° less than twice each smaller angle. Find the measure of each angle.

29. **Rhombus** A rhombus is a parallelogram with four equal sides. Each of the two larger angles of a rhombus is 5 times as large as the two smaller angles. Find the measure of each of the four angles.

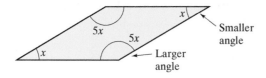

30. **Rhombus** Each of the two larger angles of a rhombus are 20° less than four times the two smaller angles. Find the measure of each of the four angles.

31. **Quadrilateral** The measure of one angle of a quadrilateral is 10° greater than the smallest angle; the third angle is 14° greater than twice the smallest angle; and the fourth angle is 21° greater than the smallest angle. Find the measures of the four angles of the quadrilateral.

32. **Quadrilateral** The measure of one angle of a quadrilateral is twice the smallest angle; the third angle is 20° greater than the smallest angle; and the fourth angle is 20° less than twice the smallest angle. Find the measures of the four angles of the quadrilateral.

33. **Building a Bookcase** A bookcase is to have four shelves, including the top, as shown. The height of the bookcase is to be 3 feet more than the width. Find the width and height of the bookcase if only 30 feet of lumber is available.

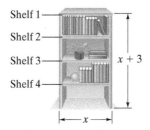

34. **Bookcase** A bookcase is to have four shelves as shown. The height of the bookcase is to be 2 feet more than the width, and only 20 feet of lumber is available. What should be the width and height of the bookcase?

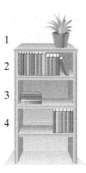

35. **American Flag** The dimensions of the American flag appear in the figure below. The perimeter of this particular flag is 580 inches.

a) Determine its length and width.

b) What is the width of each of the stripes?

c) The (left-to-right) width of the blue rectangle is always 76% of the vertical height of the flag. How many inches is that blue width?

d) The vertical height of the blue rectangle is always 53.85% of the vertical height of the flag. How many inches is the blue height?

e) What is the area of this flag?

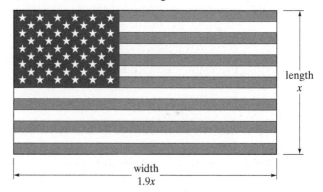

Source: www.usflag.org

36. **Storage Shelves** Carlotta Perez plans to build storage shelves as shown. She has only 45 feet of lumber for the entire unit and wishes the width to be 3 times the height. Find the width and height of the unit.

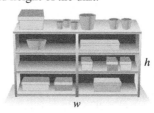

37. **Fenced-In Area** A rectangular area is to be fenced in along a straight river bank as illustrated. The length of the fenced-in area is to be 5 feet greater than the width, and the total amount of fencing to be used is 71 feet. Find the width and length of the fenced-in area.

38. Gardening Trina Zimmerman is placing a border around and within a garden where she intends to plant flowers (see the figure). She has 60 feet of bordering, and the length of the garden is to be 2 feet greater than the width. Find the length and width of the garden. The red shows the location of all the bordering in the figure.

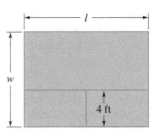

Challenge Problems

39. One way to express the area of the figure on the right is $(a + b)(c + d)$. Can you determine another expression, using the area of the four rectangles, to represent the area of the figure?

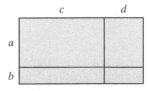

Group Activity

Discuss and answer Exercise 40 as a group.

40. Consider the four pieces shown. Two are squares and two are rectangles.

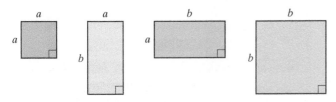

a) Individually, rearrange and place the four pieces together to form one square.

b) The area of the square you constructed is $(a + b)^2$. Write another expression for the area of the square by adding the four individual areas.

c) Compare your answers. If each member of the group did not get the same answers to parts **a)** and **b)**, work together to determine the correct answer.

d) Answer the following question as a group. If b is twice the length of a, and the perimeter of the square you created is 54 inches, find the length of a and b.

e) Use the values of a and b found in part **d)** to find the area of the square you created.

f) Use the values of a and b found in part **d)** to find the areas of the four individual pieces that make up the large square.

g) Does the sum of the areas of the four pieces found in part **f)** equal the area of the large square found in part **e)**? Is this what you expected? Explain.

Cumulative Review Exercises

Insert either $>$, $<$, or $=$ in each shaded area to make the statement true.

[1.5]   **41.** $-|-6|$ ▨ $|-4|$

   42. $|-3|$ ▨ $-|3|$

[1.7]   **43.** Evaluate $-8 - (-2) + (-4)$.

[2.1]   **44.** Simplify $-7y + x - 3(x - 2) + 2y$.

[2.6]   **45.** Solve $6x + 3y = 9$ for y.

3.4 Motion, Money, and Mixture Problems

1 Solve motion problems involving two rates.

2 Solve money problems.

3 Solve mixture problems.

We now discuss three additional types of applications: motion, money, and mixture problems. These problems are grouped in the same section because, as you will learn shortly, you use the same general multiplication procedure to solve them. We begin by discussing motion problems.

1 Solve Motion Problems Involving Two Rates

A **motion problem** is one in which an object is moving at a specific rate for a specific period of time. Examples of motion problems include a car traveling at a constant speed or a person walking at a constant speed or a boat being rowed at a constant speed. In this section, we will discuss motion problems that involve *two rates*, such as two trains traveling at different speeds. We will use the distance formula, distance = rate × time, and construct tables like the following one to organize the information. The formula at the top of the table shows how the distance in the last column is calculated.

	Rate ×	Time =	Distance
Item	Rate	Time	Distance
Item 1			distance 1
Item 2			distance 2

Examples 1 and 2 illustrate the procedure used.

Understanding Algebra

Motion problems involve *rates*. Units of rates include miles per hour (mph), feet per second (ft/s) and meters per second (m/s).

The formula we use in motion problems is:

distance = rate × time

or $d = r \cdot t$.

EXAMPLE 1 **Camping Trip** Maryanne and Paul Justinger and their son Danny are on a canoe trip on the Erie Canal. Danny is in one canoe and Paul and Maryanne are in a second canoe. Both canoes start at the same time from the same point and travel in the same direction. The parents paddle their canoe at 2 miles per hour and their son paddles his canoe at 4 miles per hour. In how many hours will the two canoes be 5 miles apart?

Solution Understand and Translate We are asked to find the time it takes for the canoes to become separated by 5 miles. We construct a table to aid us in setting up the problem.

Let t = time when canoes are 5 miles apart.

Draw a sketch to help visualize the problem (**Fig. 3.7**). When the two canoes are 5 miles apart, each has traveled for the same number of hours, t.

Canoe	Rate	Time	Distance
Parents	2	t	$2t$
Son	4	t	$4t$

Since the canoes are traveling in the same direction, the distance between them is found by subtracting the distance traveled by the slower canoe from the distance traveled by the faster canoe.

$$\left(\begin{array}{c}\text{distance traveled}\\\text{by faster canoe}\end{array}\right) - \left(\begin{array}{c}\text{distance traveled}\\\text{by slower canoe}\end{array}\right) = 5 \text{ miles}$$

$$4t \qquad - \qquad 2t \qquad = 5$$

Carry Out

$$2t = 5$$

$$t = 2.5$$

Answer After 2.5 hours the two canoes will be 5 miles apart.

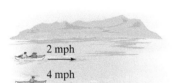

(a) Beginning of trip

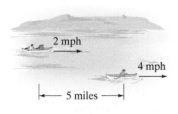

(b) After t hours

FIGURE 3.7

Now Try Exercise 7

EXAMPLE 2 **Paving Roads** Two highway paving crews are 20 miles apart working toward each other. One crew paves 0.4 mile of road per day more than the other crew, and the two crews meet after 10 days. Find the rate at which each crew paves the road.

Solution   Understand and Translate   We are asked to find the two rates. We are told that both crews work for 10 days.

$$\text{Let } r = \text{rate of slower crew.}$$
$$\text{Then } r + 0.4 = \text{rate of faster crew.}$$

We make a sketch (**Fig. 3.8**) and set up a table of values.

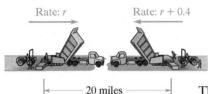

Rate: *r*   Rate: *r* + 0.4

|← 20 miles →|
covered in 10 days

FIGURE 3.8

Crew	Rate	Time	Distance
Slower	r	10	$10r$
Faster	$r + 0.4$	10	$10(r + 0.4)$

The total distance covered by both crews is 20 miles. Since the crews are moving in opposite directions, the distance between them is found by adding the two distances.

$$\left(\begin{array}{c}\text{distance covered}\\ \text{by slower crew}\end{array}\right) + \left(\begin{array}{c}\text{distance covered}\\ \text{by faster crew}\end{array}\right) = 20 \text{ miles}$$

$$10r \quad + \quad 10(r + 0.4) \quad = 20$$

Carry Out

$$10r + 10r + 4 = 20$$
$$20r + 4 = 20$$
$$20r = 16$$
$$\frac{20r}{20} = \frac{16}{20}$$
$$r = 0.8$$

Answer   The slower crew paves 0.8 mile of road per day and the faster crew paves $r + 0.4$ or $0.8 + 0.4 = 1.2$ miles of road per day.

Now Try Exercise 23

Understanding Algebra

Notice that in Example 2, the rate, r, is measured in *miles* (of road) *per day.*

Helpful Hint

When working with two different moving items, if the items are moving in the same direction, the solution will involve subtracting the smaller distance from the larger distance as in Example 1. If the items are moving in opposite directions, the solution will involve adding the distances together as in Example 2.

Understanding Algebra

Reminder:

interest = principal × rate × time

2 Solve Money Problems

One type of money problem involves simple interest. When working with simple interest problems involving two amounts, we can use a table like the one below.

Understanding Algebra

In money problems, *"rate"* applies to rate of interest and is expressed as a decimal.
   In context, it is easily distinguished from *rate* used in motion problems.

	Principal	×	Rate	×	Time	=	Interest
Account	Principal		Rate		Time		Interest
Account 1							interest 1
Account 2							interest 2

EXAMPLE 3 **Investments** Carmine DeSanto has $15,000 to invest. He is considering two investments. One is a loan he can make to another party that pays him 8% simple interest for a year. A second investment is a 1-year certificate of deposit that pays 5%. Carmine decides that he wants to place some money in each investment, and he wants to earn a total of $1125 interest in 1 year from the two investments. How much money should Carmine put in each investment?

Solution   Understand and Translate

Let x = amount to be invested at 5%.

Then $15{,}000 - x$ = amount to be invested at 8%.

We use the simple interest formula, interest = principal · rate · time, to solve this problem.

Account	Principal	Rate	Time	Interest
CD	x	0.05	1	$0.05x$
Loan	$15{,}000 - x$	0.08	1	$0.08(15{,}000 - x)$

Since the sum of the interest from the two investments is $1125, we write the equation

$$\left(\begin{array}{c}\text{interest from}\\ \text{5\% CD}\end{array}\right) + \left(\begin{array}{c}\text{interest from}\\ \text{8\% investment}\end{array}\right) = \text{total interest}$$

$$0.05x + 0.08(15{,}000 - x) = 1125$$

Carry Out

$$0.05x + 0.08(15{,}000) - 0.08(x) = 1125$$
$$0.05x + 1200 - 0.08x = 1125$$
$$-0.03x + 1200 = 1125$$
$$-0.03x = -75$$
$$x = \frac{-75}{-0.03} = 2500$$

Check and Answer   Thus, $2500 should be invested at 5% interest. The amount to be invested at 8% is

$$15{,}000 - x = 15{,}000 - 2500 = 12{,}500$$

The total amount invested is $2500 + $12,500 = $15,000, which checks with the information given.

Now Try Exercise 33

In Example 3, we let x represent the amount invested at 5%. If we had let x represent the amount invested at 8%, the answer would not have changed. Rework Example 3 now, letting x represent the amount invested at 8%.

In other types of problems involving two amounts of money, we generally set up similar tables, as illustrated in the next example.

EXAMPLE 4   Rocking Chairs Johnson's Patio Furniture Store sells two types of rocking chairs. The single-person rocking chair sells for $130 each and the two-person rocking chair sells for $240 each. On a given day 10 rocking chairs were sold for a total of $1740. Determine the number of single-person and the number of two-person rocking chairs that were sold.

Solution   Understand and Translate   We are asked to find the number of each type of rocking chair sold.

Let x = number of single–person rocking chairs sold.

Then $10 - x$ = number of two–person rocking chairs sold.

The income received from the sale of the single-person rocking chairs is found by multiplying the number of single-person rocking chairs sold by the cost of a single-person rocking chair. The income received from the sale of the two-person rocking chairs is found by multiplying the number of two-person rocking chairs sold by the cost of a two-person rocking chair.

$\begin{pmatrix} \text{Number of} \\ \text{Rocking chairs} \end{pmatrix} \times \begin{pmatrix} \text{Cost of} \\ \text{Rocking chairs} \end{pmatrix} = \begin{pmatrix} \text{Income from} \\ \text{Rocking chairs} \end{pmatrix}$			
Rocking Chair	Number of Rocking Chairs	Cost	Income from Rocking Chairs
Single	x	130	$130x$
Double	$10 - x$	240	$240(10 - x)$

$$\begin{pmatrix} \text{income from} \\ \text{single-person} \\ \text{rocking chairs} \end{pmatrix} + \begin{pmatrix} \text{income from} \\ \text{two-person} \\ \text{rocking chairs} \end{pmatrix} = \text{total income}$$

$$130x \quad + \quad 240(10 - x) = 1740$$

Carry Out

$$130x \quad + \quad 2400 - 240x = 1740$$
$$-110x + 2400 = 1740$$
$$-110x = -660$$
$$x = \frac{-660}{-110} = 6$$

Check and Answer   Six single-person rocking chairs and $10 - 6$ or 4 two-person rocking chairs were sold.

Check

$$\text{income from 6 single-person rocking chairs} = \underline{780}$$
$$\text{income from 4 two-person rocking chairs} = \underline{960}$$
$$\text{total} = 1740 \quad \text{True}$$

Now Try Exercise 43

3 Solve Mixture Problems

Any problem in which two or more quantities are combined to produce a single quantity or a single quantity is separated into two or more quantities may be considered a **mixture problem**.

Mixture problems in this section will generally be one of two types. In one type, we will mix two solids, as illustrated in **Figure 3.9a**, and be concerned about the value or cost of the mixture. In the second type, we will mix two liquids or solutions, as illustrated in **Figure 3.9b**, and be concerned about the content or strength of the mixture.

Type 1
Mixing solids together

Type 2
Mixing liquids, or solutions, together

(a) Concerned about the value or the cost of the mixture

(b) Concerned about the content or the strength of the mixture

FIGURE 3.9

As we did with motion problems involving two rates and with money problems, we will use a table to help analyze mixture problems.

When we construct a table for mixture problems, our table will generally have three rows. One row will be for each of the two individual items being mixed, and the third row will be for the mixture of the two items.

If we know the total weight of two items is 10 pounds and one item weighs x pounds, then the second item weighs $(10 - x)$ pounds.
   Reason:

item 1 + item 2 = total
  x + $(10 - x)$ = 10

Type 1—Mixing Solids

When working with mixture problems involving solids, we generally use the fact that the value (or cost) of one part of the mixture plus the value (or cost) of the second part of the mixture is equal to the total value (or total cost) of the mixture.

When we are combining two solid items and are interested in the *value* of the mixture, the following table, or a variation of it, is often used.

	Quantity	× Price (per unit)	= Value of Item
Item	Quantity	Price	Value of Item
Item 1			value of item 1
Item 2			value of item 2
Mixture			value of mixture

When we use this table, we generally use the following formula to solve the problem.

value of item 1 + value of item 2 = value of mixture

Now let's look at a mixture problem where we discuss the value or cost of the mixture.

EXAMPLE 5 Grass Seed Scott's Family grass seed sells for $2.65 per pound, and Scott's Spot Filler grass seed sells for $2.30 per pound. How many pounds of each should be mixed to get a 10-pound mixture that sells for $2.40 per pound?

Solution   Understand and Translate   We are asked to find the number of pounds of each type of grass seed.

Let x = number of pounds of Family grass seed.

Then $10 - x$ = number of pounds of Spot Filler grass seed.

We make a sketch of the situation (**Fig. 3.10**), then construct a table.

FIGURE 3.10

The cost or value of the seeds is found by multiplying the number of pounds by the price per pound.

Type of Seed	Number of Pounds	Cost per Pound	Cost of Seed
Family	x	2.65	$2.65x$
Spot Filler	$10 - x$	2.30	$2.30(10 - x)$
Mixture	10	2.40	$2.40(10)$

$$\left(\begin{array}{c}\text{cost of}\\\text{Family Seed}\end{array}\right) + \left(\begin{array}{c}\text{cost of Spot}\\\text{Filler Seed}\end{array}\right) = \text{cost of mixture}$$

$$2.65x \quad + \quad 2.30(10 - x) \quad = 2.40(10)$$

Carry Out
$$2.65x \quad + \quad 23.0 - 2.30x \quad = 24.0$$
$$0.35x + 23.0 = 24.0$$
$$0.35x = 1.00$$
$$x \approx 2.86$$

Answer   Thus, about 2.86 pounds of the Family grass seed must be mixed with $10 - x$ or $10 - 2.86 = 7.14$ pounds of the Spot Filler grass seeds to make a mixture that sells for $2.40 a pound.

Now Try Exercise 47

Type 2—Mixing Solutions

We generally solve mixture problems involving solutions by using the fact that the amount of one part of the mixture plus the amount of the second part of the mixture is equal to the total amount of the mixture.

When working with solutions, we use the following formula: *amount of substance in the solution = quantity of solution × strength of solution (in percent written as a decimal).* When we are mixing two quantities and are interested in the *composition* of the mixture, we generally use the following table or a variation of the table.

	Quantity ×	Strength =	Amount of Substance
Solution	Quantity	Strength	Amount of Substance
Solution 1			amount of substance in solution 1
Solution 2			amount of substance in solution 2
Mixture			amount of substance in mixture

When using this table, we generally use the following formula to solve the problem.

$$\left(\begin{array}{c}\text{amount of substance}\\\text{in solution 1}\end{array}\right) + \left(\begin{array}{c}\text{amount of substance}\\\text{in solution 2}\end{array}\right) = \left(\begin{array}{c}\text{amount of substance}\\\text{in mixture}\end{array}\right)$$

Let us now look at an example of a mixture problem where two solutions are combined.

EXAMPLE 6 Mixing Acid Solutions Mr. Dave Lumsford needs a 10% acetic acid solution for a chemistry experiment. After checking the store room, he finds that there are only 5% and 20% acetic acid solutions available. Mr. Lumsford decides to make the 10% solution by combining the 5% and 20% solutions. How many liters of the 5% solution must he add to 8 liters of the 20% solution to get a solution that is 10% acetic acid?

Solution   Understand and Translate   We are asked to find the number of liters of the 5% acetic acid solution to mix with 8 liters of the 20% acetic acid solution.

Let x = number of liters of 5% acetic acid solution.

Let's draw a sketch of the problem (**Fig. 3.11**).

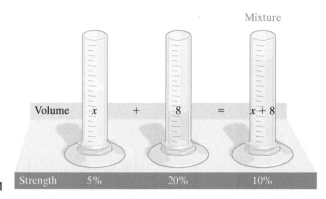

FIGURE 3.11

The amount of acid in a given solution is found by multiplying the number of liters by the percent strength.

Solution	Liters	Strength	Amount of Acetic Acid
5%	x	0.05	$0.05x$
20%	8	0.20	$0.20(8)$
Mixture	$x + 8$	0.10	$0.10(x + 8)$

$$\begin{pmatrix} \text{amount of acid} \\ \text{in 5\% solution} \end{pmatrix} + \begin{pmatrix} \text{amount of acid} \\ \text{in 20\% solution} \end{pmatrix} = \begin{pmatrix} \text{amount of acid} \\ \text{in 10\% mixture} \end{pmatrix}$$

$$0.05x + 0.20(8) = 0.10(x + 8)$$

Carry Out

$$0.05x + 1.6 = 0.10x + 0.8$$
$$0.05x + 0.8 = 0.10x$$
$$0.8 = 0.05x$$
$$\frac{0.8}{0.05} = x$$
$$16 = x$$

Answer   Sixteen liters of 5% acetic acid solution must be added to the 8 liters of 20% acetic acid solution to get a 10% acetic acid solution. The total number of liters that will be obtained is $16 + 8$ or 24.

Now Try Exercise 55

EXAMPLE 7 Nicole Pappas, a medical researcher, has 40% and 5% solutions of phenobarbital. How much of each solution must she mix to get 0.6 liter of a 20% phenobarbital solution?

Solution   Understand and Translate   We are asked to find how much of the 40% and 5% phenobarbital solutions must be mixed to get 0.6 liter of a 20% solution. We can choose to let x be the amount of either the 40% or the 5% solution. We will choose as follows:

Let x = number of liters of the 40% solution.

Then $0.6 - x$ = number of liters of the 5% solution.

Remember from Section 3.1 that if a total of 0.6 liter is divided in two, if one part is x, the other part is $0.6 - x$.

Let's draw a sketch of the problem (**Fig. 3.12**).

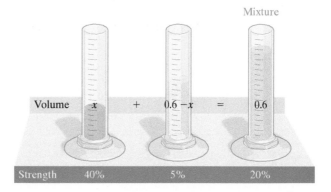

FIGURE 3.12

The amount of phenobarbital in a given solution is found by multiplying the number of liters by the percent strength.

Solution	Liters	Strength	Amount of Phenobarbital
40%	x	0.40	$0.40x$
5%	$0.6 - x$	0.05	$0.05(0.6 - x)$
Mixture	0.6	0.20	$0.6(0.20)$

$$\begin{pmatrix} \text{amount of phenobarbital} \\ \text{in 40\% solution} \end{pmatrix} + \begin{pmatrix} \text{amount of phenobarbital} \\ \text{in 5\% solution} \end{pmatrix} = \begin{pmatrix} \text{amount of phenobarbital} \\ \text{in mixture} \end{pmatrix}$$

$$0.40x + 0.05(0.6 - x) = (0.6)(0.20)$$

Carry Out

$$0.40x + 0.03 - 0.05x = 0.12$$
$$0.35x + 0.03 = 0.12$$
$$0.35x = 0.09$$
$$x \approx 0.26$$

Answer   Since the answer was less than 0.6 liter, the answer is reasonable. About 0.26 liter of the 40% solution must be mixed with about $0.6 - x = 0.60 - 0.26 = 0.34$ liter of the 5% solution to get 0.6 liter of the 20% mixture.

Now Try Exercise 63

In Example 7, we chose to let $x =$ number of liters of the 40% solution. We could have selected to let $x =$ number of liters of the 5% solution. Then $0.6 - x$ would be the number of liters of the 40% solution. Had you worked the problem out like this, you would have found that x was approximately 0.34 liter. Try reworking Example 7 now letting $x =$ number of liters of the 5% solution.

EXAMPLE 8 An orange punch contains 4% orange juice. If 5 ounces of water is added to 8 ounces of the punch, determine the percent of orange juice in the mixture.

Solution   Understand and Translate   We are asked to find the percent of orange juice in the mixture.

Let $x =$ percent of orange juice in the mixture.

We will again set up a table.

Solution	Ounces	Percent of Juice	Amount of Juice
Punch	8	0.04	8(0.04)
Water	5	0.00	5(0.00)
Mixture	13	x	$13x$

$$\left(\begin{array}{c} \text{amount of juice} \\ \text{in punch} \end{array} \right) + \left(\begin{array}{c} \text{amount of juice} \\ \text{in water} \end{array} \right) = \left(\begin{array}{c} \text{amount of juice} \\ \text{in mixture} \end{array} \right)$$
$$8(0.04) \qquad + \qquad 5(0.00) \qquad = 13x$$

Carry Out
$$0.32 + 0.00 = 13x$$
$$0.32 = 13x$$
$$0.025 \approx x$$

Answer   Therefore, the percent of juice in the mixture is about 2.5%.

Now Try Exercise 59

EXERCISE SET 3.4   Math XL   MyMathLab
MathXL®   MyMathLab

Warm-Up Exercises

Fill in the blanks with the appropriate word, phrase, or symbol(s) from the following list.

$d = r \cdot t$	adding	subtracting	multiplying
$i = p \cdot r \cdot t$	$8 - x$	the percent	

1. Solving a motion problem when the two items are traveling in the same direction usually involves _____ the distances.

2. In a mixture problem, if there is a total of 8 liters and the amount of one unknown is x, then the amount of the other unknown is _____ .

3. A formula important in the solution of motion problems is _____ .

4. Solving a money problem may include using the formula _____ .

5. Solving a motion problem when the two items are traveling in different directions usually involves _____ the distances.

6. To find the amount of alcohol in an 8-liter solution, we multiply the quantity of solution times _____ of alcohol in the solution.

Practice the Skills/Problem Solving

In Exercises 7–66, set up an equation that can be used to solve each problem. Solve the equation, and answer the question.

In Exercises 7–32, solve the motion problem. See Examples 1 and 2.

7. **Ferries** Two high-speed ferries leave at the same time from Ft. Myers, Florida, going to Key West, Florida. The first ferry, the *BigCat*, travels at 34 miles per hour. The second ferry, the *Atlantic Cat*, travels at 28 miles per hour. In how many hours will the two ferries be 6 miles apart?

8. **Trains** Two trains in New York City start at the same station going in the same direction on sets of parallel tracks. The local train stops often and averages 18.4 miles per hour. The express train stops less frequently and averages 30.2 miles per hour. In how many hours will the two trains be 5.9 miles apart?

9. **Horseback Riding** Two friends, Jodi Cotton and Abe Mantell, go horseback riding on the same trail in the same direction. Jodi's horse travels at 8 miles per hour while Abe's horse travels at a slower pace. After 2 hours they are 4 miles apart. Find the speed at which Abe's horse is traveling.

10. **Camel Riding** In the Outback in Australia, Betty Sue Adams and Carl Minieri go camel riding in the same direction along the same path. Betty Sue's camel travels at 6 miles per hour while Carl's camel travels at a slower pace. After 3 hours they are 2.4 miles apart. Find the speed of Carl's camel.

11. **Airplanes** A Jet Blue airplane leaves Chicago for New York at the same time a Southwest airplane leaves New York for Chicago. The distance from Chicago to New York is 821 miles. If the Jet Blue plane travels at 560 miles per hour and the Southwest plane travels at 580 miles per hour, how long into their flights will the two planes pass each other?

12. **Walking** Barb Dansky and Sandy Spears are at opposite ends of a shopping mall 4780.4 feet apart walking toward each other. If Barb walks 1.5 feet per second and Sandy walks 2.2 feet per second, how long will it be before they meet?

13. **Walkie-Talkies** Willie and Shanna Johnston have walkie-talkies that have a range of 16.8 miles. Willie and Shanna start at the same point and walk in opposite directions. If Willie walks 3 miles per hour and Shanna walks 4 miles per hour, how long will it take before they are out of range?

14. **Blue Angels** At a Navy Blue Angel air show two F/A-18 Hornet jets travel toward each other, both at a speed of 1000 miles per hour. After they pass each other, if they were to keep flying at the same speed in opposite directions, how long would it take for them to be 500 miles apart?

15. **Product Testing** The Goodyear Tire Company is testing new tires by placing them on a machine that can simulate the tires riding on a road. First, the machine runs the tires for 7.2 hours at 60 miles per hour. Then the tires are run for 6.8 hours at a different speed. After this 14-hour period, the machine indicates that the tires have traveled the equivalent of 908 miles. Find the second speed to which the machine was set.

16. **Ski Lifts** To get to the top of Whistler Mountain, people must use two different ski lifts. The first lift travels 4 miles per hour for 0.2 hours. The second lift travels for 0.3 hours to reach the top of the mountain. If the total distance traveled up the mountain is 1.2 miles, find the average speed of the second ski lift.

17. **Earthquakes** Earthquakes generate circular *p*-waves and *s*-waves, which travel outward (see the figure). Suppose the *p*-waves have a velocity of 3.6 miles per second and the *s*-waves have a velocity of 1.8 miles per second. How long after the earthquake will *p*-waves and *s*-waves be 80 miles apart?

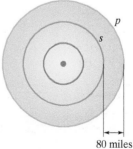

18. Navigating O'Hare Airport Sadie Bragg and Jose Cruz are in Chicago's O'Hare airport walking between terminals. Sadie walks on the moving walkway (like a flat escalator moving along the floor). Her speed (relative to the ground) is 220 feet per minute. Jose starts walking at the same time and walks alongside the walkway at a speed of 100 feet per minute. How long have they been walking when Sadie is 600 feet ahead of Jose?

19. Disabled Boat Two Coast Guard cutters are 225 miles apart traveling toward each other, one from the east and the other from the west, searching for a disabled boat. The eastbound cutter travels 5 miles per hour faster than the westbound cutter. If the two cutters pass each other after 3 hours, find the average speed of each cutter.

20. Snowplowing Two snowplowing crews are clearing snow from a 2.56-mile runway at an airport. Crew A starts at one end of the runway and crew B starts at the other end. They start cleaning at the same time and they work toward each other. Crew A clears the runway at a speed of 0.4 miles per hour faster than crew B. If they meet 0.5 hours after they start, find the average speed of each snowplow.

21. Round Trip Samia Metwali walks for a time at 4 miles per hour, then slows down and walks at 3.2 miles per hour. The total distance she walked was 6 miles. If she walked for 0.5 hour more at 3.2 miles per hour than she did at 4 miles per hour, determine the time Samia walked at 4 miles per hour.

22. Visit to Grandchild Chuck Neumann drove from his house in Auburn Hills, Michigan, to visit his grandchild in Pasadena, Texas, a distance of 1343 miles. Part of the way he drove at 60 miles per hour and part of the way he drove at 70 miles per hour. If he drove for 0.5 hour more at 60 miles per hour than he did at 70 miles per hour, determine the time Chuck drove at 60 miles per hour.

23. Paving Road Two crews are laying blacktop on a road. They start at the same time at opposite ends of a 12-mile road and work toward one another. One crew lays blacktop at an average rate of 0.75 mile a day faster than the other crew. If the two crews meet after 3.2 days, find the rate of each crew.

24. Beach Clean-Up On Earth Day, two groups of people clean a 7-mile stretch of Myrtle Beach. Auturo's group and Jane's group start at the same time at opposite ends of the beach and walk toward each other. Auturo's group is traveling at a rate of 0.5 mile per hour faster than Jane's group, and they meet in 2 hours. Find the speed of each group.

25. Sailing Two sailboats are 9.8 miles apart and sailing toward each other. The larger boat, the *Pythagoras*, sails 4 miles per hour faster than the smaller boat, the *Apollo*. The two boats pass each other after 0.7 hour. Find the speed of each boat.

© EyeWire Collection\Getty Images-Photodisc-Royalty Free

26. Exercising Dien and Phuong Vu belong to a health club and exercise together regularly. They start running on two treadmills at the same time. Dien's machine is set for 6 miles per hour and Phuong's machine is set for 4 miles per hour. When they finish, they compare the distances and find that together they have run a total of 11 miles. How long had they run?

27. Traffic Jam Betty Truitt drives for a number of hours at 70 miles per hour. When traffic slows, she drives at 50 miles per hour. She travels at 50 miles per hour for 0.5 hour longer than she traveled at 70 miles per hour. Betty drives farther at 50 mph than she does at 70 mph. The difference in the distance traveled at 50 mph and 70 mph is 5 miles. Determine how long Betty traveled at 50 miles per hour.

© Ke Wang/Shutterstock

28. Salt Mine The ore at a mine must travel on two different conveyer belts to be loaded onto a train. The second conveyer belt travels at a rate of 0.6 foot per second faster than the first conveyer belt. The ore travels 180 seconds on the first belt and 160 seconds on the second belt. If the total distance traveled by the ore is 1116 feet, determine the speed of the second belt.

29. Ironman Triathlon A triathlon consists of three parts: swimming, cycling, and running. Participants in the Ironman Triathlon in Canada must swim, cycle, and run certain distances. The 2008 women's winner was Australia's Belinda Granger. She swam at an average of 2.64 miles per hour for 0.91 hours then cycled at an average of 22.96 miles per hour for 4.88 hours. Finally, she ran at an average of 7.62 miles per hour for 3.44 hours.

a) Estimate the distance that Belinda swam.

b) Estimate the distance that Belinda cycled.

c) Estimate the distance that Belinda ran.

d) Estimate the total distance covered during the triathlon.

e) Find the winning time of the triathlon.

30. Ironman Triathlon Refer to Exercise 29, about the Ironman Triathlon. The 2008 men's winner of the Ironman was Bryan Rhodes of New Zealand. He swam at an average speed of 2.93 miles per hour for 0.82 hour, then cycled at an average speed of 23.85 miles per hour for 4.70 hours, then ran at an average speed of 8.94 miles per hour for 2.93 hours. Answer the questions in Exercise 29 **a)–e)** using Bryan's data.

31. Bicycling Dom Palmo leaves his house at noon and rides his bicycle south at a uniform rate. His wife, Sue, leaves at the same time heading due north. Dom's rate is 10 kilometers per hour faster than Sue's rate. At 5 PM they are 160 kilometers apart. Find the rate of travel for each cyclist.

32. Auto Travel Two cars are 45 miles apart traveling toward one another. One is traveling at 70 mph and the other at 65 mph. How long will it take them to meet?

In Exercises 33–46, solve the money problem. See Examples 3 and 4.

33. Simple Interest Paul and Donna Petrie invested $12,000, part at 5% simple interest and the rest at 7% simple interest for a period of 1 year. How much did they invest at each rate if their total annual interest from both investments was $800? (Use interest = principal·rate·time.)

34. Simple Interest Jerry Correa invested $7000, part at 8% simple interest and the rest at 5% simple interest for a period of 1 year. If he received a total annual interest of $476 from both investments, how much did he invest at each rate?

35. Simple Interest Aleksandra Tomich invested $6000, part at 6% simple interest and part at 4% simple interest for a period of 1 year. How much did she invest at each rate if each account earned the same interest?

36. Simple Interest Susan Foreman invested $12,500, part at 7% simple interest and part at 6% simple interest for a period of 1 year. How much was invested at each rate if each account earned the same interest?

37. Simple Interest Míng Wang invested $10,000, part at 4% and part at 5% simple interest for a period of 1 year. How much was invested in each account if the interest earned in the 5% account was $320 greater than the interest earned in the 4% account?

38. Simple Interest Sharon Sledge invested $20,000, part at 5% and part at 7% simple interest for a period of 1 year. How much was invested in each account if the interest earned in the 7% account was $440 greater than the interest earned in the 5% account?

39. Rate Increase Patricia Burgess knows that at some point during the calendar year her basic monthly telephone rate increased from $17.10 to $18.40. If she paid a total of $207.80 for basic telephone service for the calendar year, in what month did the rate increase take effect?

40. Cable TV Violet Kokola knows that her subscription rate for the basic tier of cable television increased from $18.20 to $19.50 at some point during the calendar year. She paid a total of $230.10 for the year to the cable company. Determine the month of the rate increase.

41. Wages Mihály Sarett holds two part-time jobs. One job, at Home Depot, pays $6.50 an hour and the second job, at a veterinary clinic, pays $7.00 per hour. Last week Mihály worked a total of 18 hours and earned $122.00. How many hours did Mihály work at each job?

42. Rock and Roll Hall of Fame At the Rock and Roll Hall of Fame in Cleveland, Ohio, adult admission is $22 and child admission is $13. During one day, a total of 1551 adult and child admissions were collected and $27,543 in admission fees was collected. How many child admissions were collected?

Rock and Roll Hall of Fame

43. Baseball Hall of Fame At the Baseball Hall of Fame in Cooperstown, New York, adult admission is $16.50 and child admission is $6.00. During one day a total of 2100 adult and child admissions were collected and $25,200 in admission fees was collected. How many adult admissions were collected?

Baseball Hall of Fame

44. Ticket Sales At a movie theater an evening show cost $7.50 and a matinee cost $4.75. On one day there was one matinee and one evening showing. On that day a total of 310 tickets were sold, which resulted in ticket sales of $2022.50. How many people went to the matinee and how many went to the evening show?

45. Stock Purchase Suppose Nike stock is selling at $78 a share and Kellogg stock is selling at $33 a share. Mike Moussa has a maximum of $10,000 to invest. He wishes to purchase five times as many shares of Kellogg as of Nike. Only whole shares of stock can be purchased.
a) How many shares of each will he purchase?
b) How much money will be left over?

46. Stock Purchase Suppose Wal-Mart stock is selling at $59 a share and Mattel stock is selling at $28 a share. Amy Waller has a maximum of $6000 to invest. She wishes to purchase four times as many shares of Wal-Mart as of Mattel. Only whole shares of stock can be purchased.
a) How many shares of each will she purchase?
b) How much money will be left over?

In Exercises 47–66, solve the mixture problem. See Examples 5–8.

47. Nut Shop Jean Valjean owns a nut shop where walnuts cost $6.80 per pound and almonds cost $6.40 per pound. Jean gets an order that specifically requests a 30-pound mixture of walnuts and almonds that will cost $6.65 per pound. How many pounds of each type of nut should Jean mix to get the desired mixture?

48. Grass Seed Scott's® Family grass seed sells for $2.45 per pound and Scott's Spot Filler grass seed sells for $2.10 per pound. How many pounds of each should be mixed to get a 10-pound mixture that sells for $2.20 per pound?

49. Topsoil Strained topsoil sells for $160 per cubic yard and unstrained topsoil sells for $120 per cubic yard. How many cubic yards of each should be mixed to make 8 cubic yards of a mixture that sells for $150 per cubic yard?

50. Bird Food At Agway Gardens, bird food is sold in bulk. In one barrel are sunflower seeds that sell for $1.80 per pound.

In a second barrel is cracked corn that sells for $1.40 per pound. If a mixture is made by taking 2.5 pounds of the sunflower seeds and 1 pound of the cracked corn, what should the mixture cost per pound?

© Margaret M. Stewart\Shutterstock

51. Bulk Candies A grocery store sells certain candies in bulk. The Good and Plenty cost $2.49 per pound and Sweet Treats cost $2.89 per pound. If Jane Strange takes 3 scoops of Good and Plenty and mixes it with 5 scoops of Sweet Treats, how much per pound should the mixture sell for? Assume each scoop contained the same weight of candy.

© Tiggy Gallery\Shutterstock

52. Coffee House Ruth Cordeff runs a coffee house where chocolate almond coffee beans sell for $7.00 per pound and hazelnut coffee beans sell for $6.10 per pound. A customer asks Ruth to make a 6-pound mixture using the two kinds of beans. How many pounds of each should be used if the mixture is to cost $6.40 per pound?

53. Beef Wellington To make beef Wellington, Chef Ramon uses a marinade that is a blend of two red wines. He mixes 5 liters of a wine that is 12% alcohol by volume with 2 liters of a wine that is 9% alcohol by volume. Determine the alcohol content of the mixture.

54. Pharmacy Susan Staples, a pharmacist, has a 60% solution of sodium iodite. She also has a 25% solution of the same drug. She gets a prescription calling for a 40% solution of the drug. How much of each solution should she mix to make 0.5 liter of the 40% solution?

55. Sulfuric Acid In chemistry class, Todd Corbin has 1 liter of a 20% sulfuric acid solution. How much of a 12% sulfuric acid solution must he mix with the 1 liter of 20% solution to make a 15% sulfuric acid solution?

56. Paint Nick Cooper has two cans of white paint, one with a 2% yellow pigment and the other with a 5% yellow pigment. Nick wants to mix the two paints to get paint with a 4% yellow pigment. How much of the 5% yellow pigment paint should be mixed with 0.4 gallon of the 2% yellow pigment paint to get the desired paint?

57. Mouthwash The label on the Listerine® Cool Mint Antiseptic mouthwash says that it is 21.6% alcohol by volume. The label on the Scope Original Mint mouthwash says that it is 15.0% alcohol by volume. If Hans mixes 6 ounces of the Listerine with 4 ounces of the Scope, what is the percent alcohol content of the mixture?

58. Clorox Clorox® bleach is 5.25% sodium hypochlorite. The instructions on the Clorox bottle say to add 1 cup of Clorox to 4 cups (a quart) of water. Find the percent of sodium hypochlorite in the mixture.

59. Orange Juice Mary Ann Terwilliger has made 6 quarts of an orange juice punch for a party. The punch contains 12% orange juice. She feels that she may need more punch, but she has no more orange juice so she adds $\frac{1}{2}$ quart of water to the punch. Find the percent of orange juice in the new mixture.

60. Insecticide The active ingredient in one type of Ortho® insect spray is 50% malathion. The instructions on the bottle say to add 1 fluid ounce to a gallon (128 fluid ounces) of water. What percent of malathion will be in the mixture?

© Alistair Scott\Shutterstock

61. Hawaiian Punch The label on a 12-ounce can of frozen concentrate Hawaiian Punch® indicates that when the can of concentrate is mixed with 3 cans (36 ounces) of cold water, the resulting mixture is 10% juice. Find the percent of pure juice in the concentrate.

62. Salt Concentration Suppose the dolphins at Sea World must be kept in salt water with an 0.8% salt content. After a week of warm weather, the salt content has increased to 0.9% due to water evaporation. How much water with 0% salt content must be added to 50,000 gallons of the 0.9% salt water to lower the salt concentration to 0.8%?

63. Bleach Clorox® bleach is 5.25% sodium hypochlorite and swimming pool shock treatment is 10.5% sodium hypochlorite. How much of each item must be mixed to get 6 cups of a mixture that is 7.2% sodium hypochlorite?

64. Antifreeze Prestone® antifreeze contains 12% ethylene glycose, and Zerex® antifreeze contains 9% ethylene glycose. How much of each type antifreeze should be mixed to get 10 quarts of a mixture that is 10% ethylene glycose?

65. Alcohol Solution How many pints of a 12% isotrophic alcohol solution should Jenny Crawford mix with 15 pints of a 5% isotrophic alcohol solution to get a mixture that is 8% isotrophic alcohol?

66. Plant Food Miracle-Gro® All Purpose liquid plant food has 12% nitrogen. Miracle-Gro Quick Start liquid plant food has 4% nitrogen. If 2 cups of the All Purpose plant food are mixed with 3 cups of the Quick Start plant food, determine the percent of nitrogen in the mixture.

Challenge Problems

67. Fat Albert The home base of the Navy's Blue Angels is in Pensacola, Florida. The Angels spend winters in El Centro, California. Assume they fly at about 900 miles per hour when they fly from Pensacola to El Centro in their F/A-18 Hornets. On every trip, their C-130 transport (affectionately called Fat Albert) leaves before them, carrying supplies and support personnel. The C-130 generally travels at about 370 miles per hour. On a trip from Pensacola to El Centro, how long before the Hornets leave should Fat Albert leave if it is to arrive 3 hours before the Hornets? The flying distance between Pensacola and El Centro is 1720 miles.

Group Activity

Discuss and answer Exercises 68 and 69 as a group.

68. Race Horse According to the *Guinness Book of World Records,* the fastest race horse speed recorded was by a horse called Big Racket on February 5, 1945, in Mexico City, Mexico. Big Racket ran a $\frac{3}{4}$-mile race in 62.41 seconds. Find Big Racket's speed in miles per hour. Round your answer to the nearest hundredth.

69. Garage Door Opener An automatic garage door opener is designed to begin to open when a car is 100 feet from the garage. At what rate will the garage door have to open if it is to raise 6 feet by the time a car traveling at 4 miles per hour reaches it? (1 mile per hour ≈ 1.47 feet per second.)

Cumulative Review Exercises

[1.3] **70. a)** Divide $2\frac{3}{4} \div 1\frac{5}{8}$.

   b) Add $2\frac{3}{4} + 1\frac{5}{8}$.

[2.5] **71.** Solve the equation $6(x - 3) = 4x - 18 + 2x$.

[2.7] **72.** Solve the proportion $\frac{6}{x} = \frac{72}{9}$.

[2.8] **73.** Solve the inequality $3x - 4 \le -4x + 3(x - 1)$.

Chapter 3 Summary

IMPORTANT FACTS AND CONCEPTS	EXAMPLES
Section 3.1	
a subtracted from b means $b - a$.	3 subtracted from $5x$ is $5x - 3$.
The difference between a and b means $a - b$.	The difference between 3 and $5x$ is $3 - 5x$.
If T represents the total amount to be divided in two parts, and if x represents one of the parts, then $T - x$ represents the other part.	If \$800 is divided between Jay and Rose and if Rose gets x dollars, then Jay gets $800 - x$ dollars.
A percent is always a percent of some number.	An 8% sales tax on r dollars is $0.08r$. The cost of an item c increased by 5% is $c + 0.05c$.
When writing equations, the words *is, was, will be, yields, gives,* often mean =.	"Two less than 5 times a number *is* the number increased by 3" can be expressed as $5x - 2 = x + 3$.
Consecutive integers, such as 23 and 24, differ by 1 unit. **Consecutive even integers**, such as 24 and 26, differ by 2 units. **Consecutive odd integers**, such as 23 and 25, differ by 2 units.	x and $x + 1$ represent consecutive integers. x and $x + 2$ represent consecutive even integers. x and $x + 2$ represent consecutive odd integers.
Section 3.2	
Problem-Solving Procedure	Three subtracted from 4 times a number is 17. Find the number.
1. Understand the problem.	**Solution: Understand** We need to express the information given as an equation. We are asked to find the unknown number.
2. Translate the problem into mathematical language.	**Translate** Let $x =$ the unknown number, then we can write the equation
3. Carry out the mathematical calculation.	$$4x - 3 = 17$$
4. Check the answer.	**Carry out** $\qquad 4x = 20$
5. Answer the question asked.	$$x = 5$$
(See page 186 for more detailed information.)	**Check** Substitute 5 for the unknown number $$4(5) - 3 = 17$$ $$17 = 17 \quad \text{True}$$ **Answer** The unknown number is 5.
If you are having difficulty with this section, seek help.	See Helpful Hint on page 191 for possible sources for help.

IMPORTANT FACTS AND CONCEPTS	EXAMPLES

Section 3.3

An **isosceles triangle** has two sides of the same length. The angles opposite the sides of equal length have equal measures.

Two angles of an isosceles triangle are each 30° greater than the smallest angle. Find the measures of the three angles.

Solution: Let x = the smallest angle.

Then $x + 30$ = the measure of each larger angle.

$$x + (x + 30) + (x + 30) = 180$$
$$3x + 60 = 180$$
$$3x = 120$$
$$x = 40$$

The smallest angle is 40°, and the two larger angles are $40° + 30°$ or 70°. Note that $40° + 70° + 70° = 180°$, so the answer checks.

Section 3.4

A **motion problem** can involve two rates.

Peter and Paul go walking. They start at the same point at the same time and walk in the same direction. Peter walks at 4 mph and Paul walks at 3.5 mph. In how many hours will they be 1 mile apart?

Solution: Let t = time when they are 1 mile apart.

$$4t - 3.5t = 1$$
$$0.5t = 1$$
$$t = 2$$

In 2 hours they will be 1 mile apart.

A **money problem** can involve two rates of interest or two different costs.

John sold 12 paintings in one day. Some sold at $80 and the others sold at $125. If he collected a total of $1275, how many of each type did he sell?

Solution: Let x = number of $80 paintings.

Then $12 - x$ = number of $125 paintings.

$$80x + 125(12 - x) = 1275$$
$$80x + 1500 - 125x = 1275$$
$$-45x + 1500 = 1275$$
$$-45x = -225$$
$$x = 5$$

Five $80 paintings and $12 - 5$ or 7 $125 paintings were sold.

A **mixture problem** may involve mixing different strengths or different types of solutions, or mixing solid items, such as nuts.

How many liters of an 8% acetic acid solution must be mixed with 6 liters of a 15% acetic acid solution to get a 10% acetic acid solution?

Solution: Let x = number of liters of the 8% solution.

$$0.08x + 0.15(6) = 0.10(x + 6)$$
$$0.08x + 0.9 = 0.10x + 0.6$$
$$0.9 = 0.02x + 0.6$$
$$0.3 = 0.02x$$
$$15 = x$$

Fifteen liters of the 8% solution must be mixed with the 6 liters of the 15% solution.

Chapter 3 Review Exercises

[3.1]

1. **Age** Charles's age is 7 more than 3 times Norman's age, n. Write an expression for Charles's age.

2. **Gasoline** The cost of a gallon of gasoline in California is 1.2 times the cost of a gallon of gasoline in Georgia, g. Write an expression for the cost of a gallon of gasoline in California.

3. **Dress** Write an expression for the cost of a dress, d, reduced by 25%.

4. **Pounds** Write an expression for the number of ounces in y pounds.

5. **Money** Two hundred dollars is divided between Jishing Wang and Norma Agras. If Jishing gets x dollars, write an expression for the amount Norma gets.

6. **Age** Mario is 6 years older than seven times Dino's age. Select a variable to represent one quantity and state what the variable represents. Express the second quantity in terms of the variable selected.

7. Robberies The number of robberies in 2009 was 12% less than the number of robberies in 2008. Write an expression for the difference in the number of robberies between 2008 and 2009.

8. Numbers The smaller of two numbers is 24 less than 3 times the larger. When the smaller is subtracted from the larger, the difference is 8. Write an equation to represent this information. Do not solve the equation.

[3.2] *In Exercises 9–18, set up an equation that can be used to solve the problem. Solve the equation and answer the question.*

9. Numbers One number is 8 more than the other. Find the two numbers if their sum is 74.

10. Consecutive Integers The sum of two consecutive integers is 237. Find the two integers.

11. Numbers The larger of two integers is 3 more than 5 times the smaller integer. Find the two numbers if the smaller subtracted from the larger is 31.

12. New Car Shaana recently purchased a new car. What was the cost of the car before tax if the total cost including a 7% tax was $23,260?

13. Bagels A bakery currently ships 520 bagels per month to various outlets. They wish to increase the shipment of bagels by 20 per month until reaching a shipment level of 900 bagels. How long will this take?

14. Salary Comparison Irene Doo, a salesperson, receives a salary of $600 per week plus a 3% commission on all sales she makes. Her company is planning on changing her salary to $500 per week, plus an 8% commission on all sales she makes. What weekly dollar sales would she have to make for the total salaries from each plan to be the same?

15. Sale Price During a going-out-of-business sale, all prices were reduced by 20%. If, during the sale Kathy Golladay purchased an HDTV stand for $495, what was the original price of the HDTV stand?

[3.3] *Solve each problem.*

19. Unknown Angles One angle of a triangle measures 10° greater than the smallest angle, and the third angle measures 10° less than twice the smallest angle. Find the measures of the three angles.

20. Unknown Angles One angle of a trapezoid measures 10° greater than the smallest angle; a third angle measures five times the smallest angle; and the fourth angle measures 20° greater than four times the smallest angle. Find the measure of the four angles.

21. Garden Steve Rodi has a rectangular garden whose length is 4 feet longer than its width. The perimeter of the garden is 70 feet. Find the width and length of the garden.

22. Designing a House The figure on the right shows plans for a rectangular basement of a house. The dots represents poles in the ground and the lines represent string that has been attached to the poles. The length of the basement is to be 30 feet greater than the width. If a total of 310 feet of string was used to mark off the rooms, find the width and length of the basement.

[3.4] *Solve each problem.*

25. Jogging Two joggers follow the same route. Harold Lowe jogs at 8 kilometers per hour and Susan Karney Fackert at 6 kilometers per hour. If they leave at the same time, how long will it take for them to be 4 kilometers apart?

26. Trains Leaving Two trains going in opposite directions leave from the same station on parallel tracks. One train travels at 50 miles per hour and the other at 60 miles per

See Exercise 15.

16. Landscaping Two Brothers Nursery charges $400 for a tree and $45 per hour to plant the tree. ABC Nursery charges $200 for the same size tree and $65 per hour to plant the tree. How many hours for planting would result in the total price for both landscapers being the same?

17. House Price According to the National Association of Realtors, the median sale price for single-family homes increased 11.7% from June 2003 to January 2005. If the median price was $191,000 in 2005, find the median price in 2003.

18. Tax Refund According to the Internal Revenue Service, the average refund in 2007 was $3 less than 4 times the 1980 average refund. If the average refund in 2007 was $2733, find the average refund in 1980.

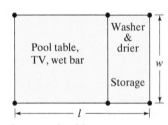

See Exercise 22.

23. Rhombus The two larger angles of a rhombus are each 3 times the measure of the two smaller angles. Find the measure of each angle.

24. Bookcase Wade Ellis is building a bookcase with 4 shelves. The length of the bookcase is to be twice the height, as illustrated. If only 20 feet of lumber is available, what should be the length and height of the bookcase?

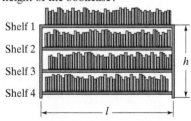

hour. How long will it take for the trains to be 440 miles apart?

27. Pittsburgh Incline The Duquesne Incline in Pittsburgh, Pennsylvania, is shown on the next page. The two cars start at the same time at opposite ends of the incline and travel toward each other at the same speed. The length of the incline is 400 feet and the time it takes for the cars to be at the halfway point is about 22.73 seconds. Determine, in feet per second, the speed the cars travel.

28. Savings Accounts Martha Goshaw wishes to place part of $12,000 into a savings account earning 8% simple interest and part into a savings account earning $7\frac{1}{4}$% simple interest. How much should she invest in each if she wishes to earn $900 in interest for the year?

[3.2–3.4]. *Solve each problem.*

33. Numbers The sum of two consecutive odd integers is 208. Find the two integers.

34. Television What is the cost of a television before tax if the total cost, including a 6% tax, is $477?

35. Medical Supplies Mr. Chang sells medical supplies. He receives a weekly salary of $300 plus a 5% commission on the sales he makes. If Mr. Chang earned $900 last week, what were his sales in dollars?

36. Triangle One angle of a triangle is 8° greater than the smallest angle. The third angle is 4° greater than twice the smallest angle. Find the measure of the three angles of the triangle.

37. Increase Staff The Darchelle Leggett Company plans to increase its number of employees by 25 per year. If the company now has 427 employees, how long will it take before they have 627 employees?

38. Parallelogram The two larger angles of a parallelogram each measure 40° greater than the two smaller angles. Find the measure of the four angles.

39. Copy Centers Copy King charges a monthly fee of $20 plus 4 cents per copy. King Kopie charges a monthly fee of $25 plus 3 cents a copy. How many copies made in a month would result in both companies charging the same amount?

40. Swimming Rita Gonzales and Jim Ham are going swimming in Putnam Lake. They start swimming in the same direction at the same time. Rita swims at 1 mph and Jim swims at a slower pace. After 0.5 hour they are 0.2 mile apart. Find the speed that Jim is swimming.

29. Savings Accounts Aimee Tait invests $4000 into two savings accounts. One account pays 3% simple interest and the other account pays 3.5% simple interest. If the interest earned in the account paying 3.5% simple interest is $94.50 more than the interest earned in the 3% account, how much was invested in each account?

30. Holiday Punch Marcie Waderman is having a holiday party at her house. She made 2 gallons of a punch solution that contains 2% alcohol. How much pure punch must Marcie add to the punch to reduce the alcohol level to 1.5%?

31. Wind Chimes Alan Carmell makes and then sells wind chimes. He makes two types, a smaller one that sells for $8 and a larger one that sells for $20. At an arts and crafts show he sells a total of 30 units, and his total receipts were $492. How many of each type of chime did he sell?

32. Acid Solution Bruce Kennan, a chemist, wishes to make 2 liters of an 8% acid solution by mixing a 10% acid solution and a 5% acid solution. How many liters of each should he use?

41. Butcher A butcher combined ground beef that cost $3.50 per pound with ground beef that cost $4.10 per pound. How many pounds of each were used to make 80 pounds of a mixture that sells for $3.65 per pound?

42. Speed Traveled Two brothers who are 230 miles apart start driving toward each other at the same time. The younger brother travels 5 miles per hour faster than the older brother, and the brothers meet after 2 hours. Find the speed traveled by each brother.

43. Acid Solution How many liters of a 30% acid solution must be mixed with 2 liters of a 12% acid solution to obtain a 15% acid solution?

44. Fencing Kathy Tomaino is partitioning a rectangular yard using fencing, as shown below. If the length is 1.5 times the width and if only 96 feet of fencing is available, find the length and width of the partitioned area.

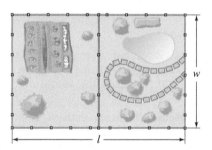

45. Acid Solution Six liters of a 3% sulfuric acid solution is mixed with an 8% sulfuric acid solution. If the mixture is a 4% sulfuric acid solution, determine how many liters of the 8% sulfuric acid solution were used in the mixture.

Chapter 3 Practice Test

Chapter Test Prep Videos provide fully worked-out solutions to any of the exercises you want to review. Chapter Test Prep Videos are available via **MyMathLab** *, or on* **You Tube** *(search "Angel Elementary Algebra" and click on "Channels").*

1. **Money** Five hundred dollars was divided between Boris and Monique. If Monique received n dollars, write an expression for the amount Boris received.

2. **Restaurants** The money Sally Sestini earned was $6000 more than twice what William Rowley earned. Write an expression for what Sally earned.

3. Write an expression for the number of seconds in t minutes.

4. **Season Tickets** The cost of a season ticket for the Dallas Cowboys football games increased by 6% from the previous year's cost, c. Write an expression for the cost of a season ticket for this year.

© Ken Duren\Shutterstock

In Exercises 5–9, select a variable to represent one quantity and state what it represents. Express the second quantity in terms of the variable selected.

5. **Tic Tacs** The number of packages of peppermint flavored Tic Tacs® sold was 105 packages less than 7 times the number of packages of orange flavored Tic Tacs sold.

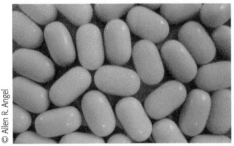
© Allen R. Angel

6. **Men and Women** At a play there were 600 men and women.

7. **Numbers** The larger of two numbers is 1 less than twice the smaller number. Write an expression for the smaller number subtracted from the larger number

8. **Liquid Tide** The number of fluid ounces in a large bottle of Tide® is 18 fluid ounces more than the amount in a smaller bottle. Write an expression for the sum of the amounts in a small and large bottle.

9. **Nuts** The cost of a can of Planters® Deluxe Nuts is 84% greater than the cost of a can of Planters Peanuts. Write an expression for the difference in cost between the Deluxe Nuts and the Peanuts.

In Exercises 10–25, set up an equation that can be used to solve the problem. Solve the problem and answer the question asked.

10. **Integers** The sum of two integers is 158. Find the two integers if the larger is 10 less than twice the smaller.

11. **Consecutive Odd Integers** For two consecutive odd integers, the sum of the smaller and 4 times the larger is 33. Find the integers.

12. **Numbers** One number is 12 less than 5 times the other. Find the two numbers if their sum is 42.

13. **Lawn Furniture** Dona Bishop purchased a set of lawn furniture. The cost of the furniture, including a 6% tax, was $2650. Find the cost of the furniture before tax.

14. **Eating Out** Mark Sullivan has only $40. He wishes to leave a 15% tip. Find the price of the most expensive meal that he can order.

15. **Business Venture** Julie Burgmeier receives twice the profit in a business venture than Peter Ancona does. If the profit for the year was $120,000, how much will each receive?

16. **Snowplowing** William Echols is going to hire a snow plowing service. Elizabeth Suco charges an annual fee of $80, plus $5 each time she plows. Jon Wilkins charges an annual fee of $50, plus $10 each time he plows. How many times would the snow need to be plowed for the cost of both plans to be the same?

17. **Laser Printers** A Delta laser printer cost $499. The cost of printing each page of text is 1 cent. A TexMar laser printer cost $350. The cost of printing each page is 3 cents. How many pages would need to be printed for the total cost of both printers to be the same?

18. **Triangle** A triangle has a perimeter of 75 inches. Find the three sides if one side is 15 inches larger than the smallest side, and the third side is twice the smallest side.

19. **Flag** Paul Murphy's flag has a perimeter of 28 feet. Find the dimensions of the flag if the length is 4 feet less than twice its width.

20. **Trapezoid** The two larger angles of a trapezoid measure 3° more than twice the two smaller angles. Determine the four angles of the trapezoid.

21. **Laying Cable** Ellis and Harlene Matza are digging a shallow 67.2-foot-long trench to lay electrical cable to a new outdoor light fixture they just installed. They start digging at the same time at opposite ends of where the trench is to go, and dig toward each other. Ellis digs at a rate of 0.2 foot per minute faster than Harlene, and they meet after 84 minutes. Find the speed at which each digs.

22. **Running** Alice and Bonnie start running at the same time from the same point and run in the same direction. Alice runs at 8 mph while Bonnie runs at a slower pace. After 2 hours they are 4 miles apart. Determine the speed at which Bonnie is running.

23. **Bulk Candy** A candy shop sells candy in bulk. In one bin is Jelly Belly candy, which sells for $2.20 per pound, and in a second bin is Kits, which sells for $2.75 per pound. How much of each type should be mixed to obtain a 3-pound mixture that sells for $2.40 per pound?

24. Salt Solution How many liters of 20% salt solution must be added to 60 liters of 40% salt solution to get a solution that is 35% salt?

25. Acid Solution A chemist wishes to make 3 liters of a 6% acid solution by mixing an 8% acid solution and a 5% acid solution. How many liters of each should she mix?

Cumulative Review Test

Take the following test and check your answers with those given in the back of the book. Review any questions that you answered incorrectly. The section where the material was covered is indicated after the answer.

1. Social Security The following circle graph shows what the typical retiree receives in social security, as a percent of their total income.

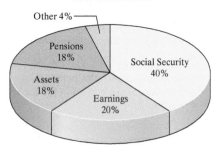

Where Social Security Recipients Get Their Income

Source: Newsweek

If Emily receives $40,000 per year, and her income is typical of all social security recipients, how much is she receiving in social security?

2. Olympic Gold Medals The following graph illustrates the number of gold medals awarded in the 2008 Beijing Olympics for the top 5 countries.

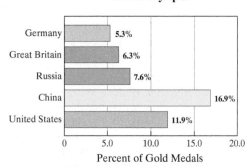

Percent of Gold Medals Awarded in 2008 Olympics

Source: results.beijing2008.cn

a) What is the percentage difference between the number of gold medals awarded to China and Germany?

b) If 302 gold medals were awarded in the 2008 Olympics, how many were awarded to the United States?

3. Carbon Dioxide Levels David Warner, an environmentalist, was checking the level of carbon dioxide in the air. On five readings, he got the results indicated in the table above on the right.

Test	Carbon Dioxide (parts per million)
1	5
2	6
3	8
4	12
5	5

a) Find the mean level of carbon dioxide detected.

b) Find the median level of carbon dioxide detected.

4. Evaluate $\dfrac{5}{12} \div \dfrac{3}{4}$.

5. How much larger is $\dfrac{2}{3}$ inch than $\dfrac{1}{8}$ inch?

6. a) List the set of natural numbers.

b) List the set of whole numbers.

c) What is a rational number?

7. a) Evaluate $|-4|$.

b) Which is greater, $|-5|$ or $|-3|$? Explain.

8. Evaluate $2 - 6^2 \div 2 \cdot 2$.

9. Simplify $4(2x - 3) - 2(3x + 5) - 6$.

In Exercises 10–12, solve the equation.

10. $5x - 6 = x + 14$

11. $6r = 2(r + 3) - (r + 5)$

12. $2(x + 5) = 3(2x - 4) - 4x$

13. If $A = \pi r^2$, find A when $r = 6$.

14. Consider the equation $4x + 8y = 16$.

a) Solve the equation for y and write the equation in $y = mx + b$ form.

b) Find y when $x = -4$.

15. Solve the formula $P = 2l + 2w$ for w.

16. Gas Needed If Lisa Shough's car can travel 50 miles on 2 gallons of gasoline, how many gallons of gas will it need to travel 225 miles?

17. Solve the inequality $3x - 4 \le -1$ and graph the solution on a number line.

18. Calling Plan Lori Sypher is considering two cellular telephone plans. Plan A has a monthly charge of $19.95 plus 35 cents per minute. Plan B has a monthly charge of $29.95 plus 10 cents per minute. How long would Lori need to talk in a month for the two plans to have the same total cost?

19. Sum of Numbers The sum of two numbers is 29. Find the two numbers if the larger is 11 greater than twice the smaller.

20. Quadrilateral One angle of a quadrilateral measures 5° larger than the smallest angle; the third angle measures 50° larger than the smallest angle; and the fourth angle measures 25° greater than 4 times the smallest angle. Find the measure of each angle of the quadrilateral.

Exponents and Polynomials

4.1   Exponents

4.2   Negative Exponents

4.3   Scientific Notation

      Mid-Chapter Test: Sections 4.1–4.3

4.4   Addition and Subtraction of Polynomials

4.5   Multiplication of Polynomials

4.6   Division of Polynomials

      Chapter 4 Summary

      Chapter 4 Review Exercises

      Chapter 4 Practice Test

      Cumulative Review Test

Goals of This Chapter

The major emphasis of this chapter is to teach you how to work with exponents, polynomials, and scientific notation. You must understand the rules of exponents presented in the first two sections in order to be successful with the remaining material in the chapter.

You will use the rules learned in this chapter throughout the book, especially in Chapter 5, when factoring is introduced.

Many areas of science and technology deal with very small and very large numbers. A *googol* is a very large number, 1 followed by 100 zeros. The word googol was first coined by mathematician Edward Kasner (suggested by his 9-year old nephew). Kasner also proclaimed that the number of grains of sand on the beach at Coney Island was less than a googol. In Exercise 94 on page 250, we will examine the scientific notation that allows us to deal more readily with large numbers like a googol in this chapter.

© Bryan Busovicki\Shutterstock

4.1 Exponents

1   Review exponents.

2   Learn the rules of exponents.

3   Simplify an expression before using the expanded power rule.

Understanding Algebra

For now, think of exponents as repeated multiplication. For example, x^3 means $x \cdot x \cdot x$ so x is used as a factor 3 times. In x^3, the x is called the *base* and the 3 is called the *exponent*.

1 Review Exponents

Recall from Section 1.9, in the expression x^n, x is called the **base** and n is called the **exponent**. x^n is read "x to the nth power" or "x raised to the power n."

$$x^2 = \underbrace{x \cdot x}_{\text{2 factors of } x}$$

$$x^4 = \underbrace{x \cdot x \cdot x \cdot x}_{\text{4 factors of } x}$$

$$x^m = \underbrace{x \cdot x \cdot x \cdot \,\cdots\, \cdot x}_{m \text{ factors of } x}$$

EXAMPLE 1   Write *xxxxyyy* using exponents.

Solution

$$\underbrace{xxxx}_{\substack{\text{4 factors} \\ \text{of } x}} \quad \underbrace{yyy}_{\substack{\text{3 factors} \\ \text{of } y}} = x^4 y^3$$

Now Try Exercise 9

Remember:

$$\left. \begin{array}{l} x = 1x \\ x^2 y = 1x^2 y \end{array} \right\}$$

When a term containing a variable is given without a numerical coefficient, the numerical coefficient is assumed to be 1.

$$\left. \begin{array}{l} x = x^1, \\ xy = x^1 y^1, \\ x^2 y = x^2 y^1, \\ 2xy^2 = 2x^1 y^2 \end{array} \right\}$$

When a variable or numerical value is given without an exponent, the exponent of that variable or numerical value is assumed to be 1.

2 Learn the Rules of Exponents

EXAMPLE 2   Multiply $x^4 \cdot x^3$.

Solution

$$\overbrace{x \cdot x \cdot x \cdot x}^{x^4} \cdot \overbrace{x \cdot x \cdot x}^{x^3} = x^7$$

Now Try Exercise 11

Example 2 illustrates the **product rule for exponents**.

Understanding Algebra

When multiplying expressions with the same base, we add the exponents:

$$y^2 \cdot y^4 = y^6$$

Product Rule for Exponents

$$x^m \cdot x^n = x^{m+n}$$

When multiplying expressions with the same base, we keep the base and **add** the exponents.

In Example 2, we showed that $x^4 \cdot x^3 = x^7$. This problem could also be done using the product rule: $x^4 \cdot x^3 = x^{4+3} = x^7$.

EXAMPLE 3 Multiply each expression using the product rule.

a) $3^2 \cdot 3$ **b)** $2^4 \cdot 2^2$ **c)** $x \cdot x^4$ **d)** $x^3 \cdot x^6$ **e)** $y^4 \cdot y^7$

Solution

a) $3^2 \cdot 3 = 3^2 \cdot 3^1 = 3^{2+1} = 3^3$ or 27   **b)** $2^4 \cdot 2^2 = 2^{4+2} = 2^6$ or 64

c) $x \cdot x^4 = x^1 \cdot x^4 = x^{1+4} = x^5$ **d)** $x^3 \cdot x^6 = x^{3+6} = x^9$

e) $y^4 \cdot y^7 = y^{4+7} = y^{11}$

Now Try Exercise 19

Understanding Algebra

Throughout this section, whenever we are working with an expression with a variable in the denominator, we will assume that the denominator does not equal zero. When we are introducing rules of exponents, we will remind you of this. For example, in the Quotient Rule, we will write $x \neq 0$.

Avoiding Common Errors

Note in Example 3 **a)** that $3^2 \cdot 3^1$ is 3^3 and not 9^3. *When multiplying powers of the same base, do not multiply the bases.*

CORRECT	INCORRECT
$3^2 \cdot 3^1 = 3^3$	$3^2 \cdot 3^1 = 9^3$

Note also in Example 3 **b)** that $2^4 \cdot 2^2$ is 2^6 and not 2^8. *When multiplying powers of the same base, do not multiply the exponents.*

CORRECT	INCORRECT
$2^4 \cdot 2^2 = 2^6$	$2^4 \cdot 2^2 = 2^8$

Example 4 will help you understand the **quotient rule for exponents**.

EXAMPLE 4 Divide $x^5 \div x^3$.

Solution

$$\frac{x^5}{x^3} = \frac{\overset{1}{\cancel{x}} \cdot \overset{1}{\cancel{x}} \cdot \overset{1}{\cancel{x}} \cdot x \cdot x}{\underset{1}{\cancel{x}} \cdot \underset{1}{\cancel{x}} \cdot \underset{1}{\cancel{x}}} = \frac{1x^2}{1} = x^2$$

Now Try Exercise 23

When dividing expressions with the same base, keep the base and *subtract* the exponent in the denominator from the exponent in the numerator.

Understanding Algebra

When dividing expressions with the same base, we subtract the exponents:

$$t^7 \div t^4 = \frac{t^7}{t^4} = t^3, t \neq 0$$

Quotient Rule for Exponents

$$\frac{x^m}{x^n} = x^{m-n}, \qquad x \neq 0$$

When dividing expressions with the same base, we keep the base and *subtract* the exponent in the denominator from the exponent in the numerator.

In Example 4, we showed that $\frac{x^5}{x^3} = x^2$. This problem could also be done using the quotient rule: $\frac{x^5}{x^3} = x^{5-3} = x^2$.

EXAMPLE 5 Divide each expression using the quotient rule.

a) $\frac{3^5}{3^2}$ **b)** $\frac{z^8}{z^2}$ **c)** $\frac{x^{12}}{x^5}$ **d)** $\frac{y^{10}}{y^8}$ **e)** $\frac{6^4}{6}$

Solution

a) $\frac{3^5}{3^2} = 3^{5-2} = 3^3$ or 27   **b)** $\frac{z^8}{z^2} = \frac{z^8}{z^2} = z^{8-2} = z^6$ **c)** $\frac{x^{12}}{x^5} = x^{12-5} = x^7$

d) $\frac{y^{10}}{y^8} = y^{10-8} = y^2$ **e)** $\frac{6^4}{6} = \frac{6^4}{6^1} = 6^{4-1} = 6^3$ or 216

Now Try Exercise 25

> **Avoiding Common Errors**
>
> Note in Example 5 **a)** that $\dfrac{3^5}{3^2}$ is 3^3 and not 1^3. *When dividing powers of the same base, do not divide out the bases.*
>
> CORRECT   INCORRECT
>
> $\dfrac{3^3}{3^1} = 3^2 \text{ or } 9$ $\dfrac{3^3}{3^1} \neq 1^2$
>
> Also note in Example 5 **b)** that $\dfrac{z^8}{z^2} = z^6$ and not z^4. *When dividing powers of the same base, do not divide the exponents.*

The answer to Example 5 **c)**, $\dfrac{x^{12}}{x^5}$, is x^7. We obtained this answer using the quotient rule. This answer could also be obtained by dividing out the common factors in both the numerator and denominator as follows.

$$\frac{x^{12}}{x^5} = \frac{(\cancel{x} \cdot \cancel{x} \cdot \cancel{x} \cdot \cancel{x} \cdot \cancel{x}) \cdot x \cdot x \cdot x \cdot x \cdot x \cdot x \cdot x}{(\cancel{x} \cdot \cancel{x} \cdot \cancel{x} \cdot \cancel{x} \cdot \cancel{x})} = x^7$$

We divided out the product of five x's, which is x^5. We can indicate this process in shortened form as follows.

$$\frac{x^{12}}{x^5} = \frac{\overset{1}{\cancel{x^5}} \cdot x^7}{\underset{1}{\cancel{x^5}}} = x^7$$

To simplify an expression like $\dfrac{x^5}{x^{12}}$, where the exponent in the denominator is greater than the exponent in the numerator, we divide out common factors (in this case, the common factor is x^5).

Note: Numerator and denominator must have the same base $\longrightarrow$ $\dfrac{x^5}{x^{12}} = \dfrac{\overset{1}{\cancel{x^5}}}{\underset{1}{\cancel{x^5}} \cdot x^7} = \dfrac{1}{x^7}$

We will now simplify some expressions by dividing out common factors.

EXAMPLE 6 Simplify each expression by dividing out a common factor in both the numerator and denominator.

a) $\dfrac{x^9}{x^{12}}$ **b)** $\dfrac{y^4}{y^9}$

Solution

a) Since the numerator is x^9, we write the denominator with a factor of x^9. Since $x^9 \cdot x^3 = x^{12}$, we rewrite x^{12} as $x^9 \cdot x^3$.

$$\frac{x^9}{x^{12}} = \frac{\overset{1}{\cancel{x^9}}}{\underset{1}{\cancel{x^9}} \cdot x^3} = \frac{1}{x^3}$$

b) $\dfrac{y^4}{y^9} = \dfrac{\overset{1}{\cancel{y^4}}}{\underset{1}{\cancel{y^4}} \cdot y^5} = \dfrac{1}{y^5}$

Understanding Algebra

To divide expressions with the same base when the denominator's exponent is greater than the numerator's, divide out the common factors:

$$t^4 \div t^7 = \frac{t^4}{t^7} = \frac{\overset{1}{\cancel{t^4}}}{\cancel{t^4}\, t^3} = \frac{1}{t^3}, \ t \neq 0$$

Now Try Exercise 27

In the next section, we will show another way to simplify expressions like $\dfrac{x^9}{x^{12}}$ by using the negative exponent rule.

Example 7 leads us to our next rule, the **zero exponent rule**.

EXAMPLE 7   Divide $\dfrac{x^3}{x^3}$.

Solution   By the quotient rule,

$$\frac{x^3}{x^3} = x^{3-3} = x^0$$

However,

$$\frac{x^3}{x^3} = \frac{1x^3}{1x^3} = \frac{1 \cdot \cancel{x} \cdot \cancel{x} \cdot \cancel{x}}{1 \cdot \cancel{x} \cdot \cancel{x} \cdot \cancel{x}} = \frac{1}{1} = 1$$

Since $\dfrac{x^3}{x^3} = x^0$ and $\dfrac{x^3}{x^3} = 1$, then x^0 must equal 1.

Now Try Exercise 29

Zero Exponent Rule

$$x^0 = 1, \qquad x \neq 0$$

Any real number, except 0, raised to the zero power equals 1. Note that 0^0 is undefined.

EXAMPLE 8   Simplify each expression. Assume $x \neq 0$. and $z \neq 0$.

   a) 3^0 **b)** x^0 **c)** $3x^0$ **d)** $(3x)^0$ **e)** $4x^2y^3z^0$

Solution

a) $3^0 = 1$

b) $x^0 = 1$

c) $3x^0 = 3(x^0)$ Remember, the exponent refers only to the immediately
     $\quad\;\; = 3 \cdot 1 = 3$ preceding symbol unless parentheses are used.

d) $(3x)^0 = 1$

e) $4x^2y^3z^0 = 4x^2y^3 \cdot 1 = 4x^2y^3$

Now Try Exercise 37

Avoiding Common Errors

An expression raised to the zero power is not equal to 0; it is equal to 1.

CORRECT	INCORRECT
$x^0 = 1$	$\cancel{x^0 = 0}$
$5^0 = 1$	$\cancel{5^0 = 0}$

The **power rule** will be explained with the aid of Example 9.

EXAMPLE 9   Simplify $(x^3)^2$.

Solution

$$(x^3)^2 = \underbrace{x^3 \cdot x^3}_{2 \text{ factors of } x^3} = x^{3+3} = x^6$$

Now Try Exercise 45

Power Rule for Exponents

$$(x^m)^n = x^{m \cdot n}$$

When raising an exponential expression to a power, keep the base and *multiply* the exponents.

EXAMPLE 10   Simplify each expression.

a) $(x^3)^5$ **b)** $(3^4)^2$ **c)** $(y^5)^7$

Solution

a) $(x^3)^5 = x^{3 \cdot 5} = x^{15}$ **b)** $(3^4)^2 = 3^{4 \cdot 2} = 3^8$ **c)** $(y^5)^7 = y^{5 \cdot 7} = y^{35}$

Now Try Exercise 51

Helpful Hint

Students often confuse the product and power rules. Note the difference carefully.

Product Rule	Power Rule
$x^m \cdot x^n = x^{m+n}$	$(x^m)^n = x^{m \cdot n}$
$2^3 \cdot 2^5 = 2^{3+5} = 2^8$	$(2^3)^5 = 2^{3 \cdot 5} = 2^{15}$

The power rule can be extended to include powers of products and powers of quotients. Consider $(4x^2)^3$, the product $4x^2$ raised to the power 3:

$$(4x^2)^3 = 4x^2 \cdot 4x^2 \cdot 4x^2$$
$$= (4 \cdot 4 \cdot 4)(x^2 \cdot x^2 \cdot x^2)$$
$$= 4^3(x^2)^3 \qquad \text{Observe both 4 and } x^2 \text{ are raised to the power 3.}$$
$$= 64x^6$$

This leads us to the **power of a product rule:***

Power of a Product Rule

$$(xy)^n = x^n y^n$$

When a product is raised to a power, each factor in the product is raised to that power.

EXAMPLE 11   Simplify each expression.

a) $(a^2 b^3)^4$ **b)** $\left(-\dfrac{2}{3}x^6 y\right)^3$

Solution

a) $(a^2 b^3)^4 = (a^2)^4 \cdot (b^3)^4$ Raise each factor to the power 4.
$$= a^8 b^{12}$$

b) $\left(-\dfrac{2}{3}x^6 y\right)^3 = \left(-\dfrac{2}{3}\right)^3 \cdot (x^6)^3 \cdot (y)^3$ Raise each factor to the power 3.
$$= -\frac{8}{27}x^{18} y^3 \qquad \text{Because } \left(-\frac{2}{3}\right)^3 = \left(-\frac{2}{3}\right) \cdot \left(-\frac{2}{3}\right) \cdot \left(-\frac{2}{3}\right)$$

Now Try Exercise 59

---

*When we write exponential expressions, it is always understood that the values of variables we use in definitions are always restricted to avoid 0^0. Thus, when we write $(xy)^n$, for example, n cannot be zero when either x or y is zero.

Just like we extended the power rule to a product, we can apply similar reasoning to extend the power rule to a quotient. Consider $\left(\dfrac{5}{x^3}\right)^2$, the quotient $\dfrac{5}{x^3}$ raised to the power 2:

$$\left(\frac{5}{x^3}\right)^2 = \frac{5}{x^3} \cdot \frac{5}{x^3}$$

$$= \frac{5 \cdot 5}{x^3 \cdot x^3}$$

$$= \frac{5^2}{(x^3)^2} \qquad \text{Observe both the numerator and de-}$$
$$\phantom{= \frac{5^2}{(x^3)^2}} \qquad \text{nominator are raised to the power 2.}$$

$$= \frac{25}{x^6}$$

This leads us to the **power of a quotient rule:**

Power of a Quotient Rule

$$\left(\frac{x}{y}\right)^n = \frac{x^n}{y^n}, \qquad y \neq 0$$

When a quotient is raised to a power, both the numerator and the denominator are raised to that power.

EXAMPLE 12 Simplify each expression.

a) $\left(\dfrac{p^2}{q^3}\right)^4$ **b)** $\left(-\dfrac{x^2}{z^3}\right)^5$

Solution

a) $\left(\dfrac{p^2}{q^3}\right)^4 = \dfrac{(p^2)^4}{(q^3)^4}$ 　　　　Raise numerator and denominator to the power 4.

$$= \frac{p^8}{q^{12}}$$

b) $\left(-\dfrac{x^2}{z^3}\right)^5 = \left(\dfrac{-x^2}{z^3}\right)^5$

$$= \frac{(-x^2)^5}{(z^3)^5} \qquad \text{Raise numerator and denominator to the power 5.}$$

$$= \frac{-x^{10}}{z^{15}} \text{ or } -\frac{x^{10}}{z^{15}} \qquad \text{Either answer is acceptable.}$$

Now Try Exercise 85

We now combine the previous two rules, the power rule for products and the power rule for quotients, into the **expanded power rule**.

Expanded Power Rule for Exponents

$$\left(\frac{ax}{by}\right)^m = \frac{a^m x^m}{b^m y^m}, \quad b \neq 0, y \neq 0$$

Every factor within parentheses is raised to the power outside the parentheses when the expression is simplified.

EXAMPLE 13 Simplify $\left(\dfrac{2r^2s}{t^4}\right)^3$.

Solution

$$\left(\frac{2r^2s}{t^4}\right)^3 = \frac{2^3(r^2)^3 s^3}{(t^4)^3} \qquad \text{Expanded power rule; each factor is raised to the power 3.}$$

$$= \frac{8r^6 s^3}{t^{12}}$$

Now Try Exercise 87

3 Simplify an Expression Before Using the Expanded Power Rule

Whenever we have an expression raised to a power, it helps to simplify the expression in parentheses before using the expanded power rule.

EXAMPLE 14 Simplify $\left(\dfrac{9x^3 y^2}{3xy^2}\right)^3$.

Solution   We first simplify the expression within parentheses by dividing out common factors.

$$\left(\frac{9x^3 y^2}{3xy^2}\right)^3 = \left(\frac{9}{3} \cdot \frac{x^3}{x} \cdot \frac{y^2}{y^2}\right)^3 = (3x^2)^3$$

Now we use the expanded power rule to simplify further.

$$(3x^2)^3 = 3^3 (x^2)^3 = 27x^6$$

Thus, $\left(\dfrac{9x^3 y^2}{3xy^2}\right)^3 = 27x^6$.

Now Try Exercise 93

Helpful Hint

Study Tip

Be very careful when writing exponents. Since exponents are generally smaller than regular text, take your time and write them clearly, and position them properly. If exponents are not written clearly it is very easy to confuse exponents such as 2 and 3, or 1 and 4, or 0 and 6. If you write down or carry an exponent from step to step incorrectly, you will obtain an incorrect answer.

EXAMPLE 15 Simplify $\left(\dfrac{25x^4 y^3}{5x^2 y^7}\right)^4$.

Solution   Begin by simplifying the expression within parentheses.

$$\left(\frac{25x^4 y^3}{5x^2 y^7}\right)^4 = \left(\frac{25}{5} \cdot \frac{x^4}{x^2} \cdot \frac{y^3}{y^7}\right)^4 = \left(\frac{5x^2}{y^4}\right)^4$$

Now use the expanded power rule to simplify further.

$$\left(\frac{5x^2}{y^4}\right)^4 = \frac{5^4 (x^2)^4}{(y^4)^4} = \frac{625x^8}{y^{16}}$$

Thus, $\left(\dfrac{25x^4 y^3}{5x^2 y^7}\right)^4 = \dfrac{625x^8}{y^{16}}$.

Now Try Exercise 95

Avoiding Common Errors

Students sometimes make errors in simplifying expressions containing exponents. One of the most common errors follows.

CORRECT

$$\frac{4}{2x} = \frac{\overset{2}{\cancel{4}}}{\underset{1}{\cancel{2}}x} = \frac{2}{x}$$

$$\frac{x}{xy} = \frac{\overset{1}{\cancel{x}}}{\cancel{x}y} = \frac{1}{y}$$

$$\frac{5x^3y^2}{y^2} = \frac{5x^3\,\overset{1}{\cancel{y^2}}}{\underset{1}{\cancel{y^2}}1} = 5x^3$$

INCORRECT

$$\frac{4}{x+2} = \frac{\overset{2}{\cancel{4}}}{x+\underset{1}{\cancel{2}}} = \frac{2}{x+1}$$

$$\frac{x}{x+y} = \frac{\overset{1}{\cancel{x}}}{\underset{1}{\cancel{x}}+y} = \frac{1}{1+y}$$

$$\frac{5x^3+y^2}{y^2} = \frac{5x^3+\overset{1}{\cancel{y^2}}}{\underset{1}{\cancel{y^2}}} = 5x^3+1$$

The simplifications on the right side are not correct because only common *factors* can be divided out (remember, factors are multiplied together). In the first denominator on the right, $x + 2$, the x and 2 are terms, not factors, since they are being added. Similarly, in the second denominator, $x + y$, the x and the y are terms, not factors, since they are being added. Also, in the numerator $5x^3 + y^2$, the $5x^3$ and y^2 are terms, not factors. No common factors can be divided out in the fractions on the right.

EXAMPLE 16 Simplify $(2a^5b^3)^5 (3a^2b)$.

Solution First simplify $(2a^5b^3)^5$ by using the expanded power rule.

$$(2a^5b^3)^5 = 2^5a^{5\cdot5}b^{3\cdot5} = 32a^{25}b^{15}$$

Now use the product rule to simplify further.

$$(2a^5b^3)^5 (3a^2b) = (32a^{25}b^{15})(3a^2b^1)$$

$$= 32 \cdot 3 \cdot a^{25} \cdot a^2 \cdot b^{15} \cdot b^1$$

$$= 96a^{25+2}b^{15+1}$$

$$= 96a^{27}b^{16}$$

Thus, $(2a^5b^3)^5 (3a^2b) = 96a^{27}b^{16}$.

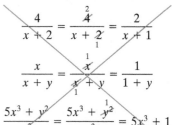

Now Try Exercise 125

Summary of the Rules of Exponents Presented in This Section

1. **Product Rule** $x^m \cdot x^n = x^{m+n}$

2. **Quotient Rule** $\dfrac{x^m}{x^n} = x^{m-n}, \quad x \neq 0$

3. **Zero Exponent Rule** $x^0 = 1, \quad x \neq 0$

4. **Power Rule** $(x^m)^n = x^{m\cdot n}$

5. **Power of a Product Rule** $(xy)^n = x^ny^n$

6. **Power of a Quotient Rule** $\left(\dfrac{x}{y}\right)^n = \dfrac{x^n}{y^n}, \quad y \neq 0$

7. **Expanded Power Rule** $\left(\dfrac{ax}{by}\right)^m = \dfrac{a^mx^m}{b^my^m}, \quad b \neq 0, \quad y \neq 0$

EXERCISE SET 4.1

Math XL MathXL®   *MyMathLab* MyMathLab

Warm-Up Exercises

Fill in the blanks with the appropriate word, phrase, or symbol(s) from the following list.

1	product rule for exponents	power rule for exponents	addition rule for exponents
exponent	base	quotient rule for exponents	Expanded power rule for exponents
0	$p^3q^4r^5$	$\dfrac{p^3r^5}{q^4}$	

1. The only value of x for which x^0 is not equal to 1 is _____ .

2. $(x^2)^8 = x^{16}$ illustrates the _____ .

3. In the expression t^p, t is called the _____ .

4. In the expression t^p, p is called the _____ .

5. $\left(\dfrac{3x^2}{2y^3}\right)^2 = \dfrac{9x^4}{4y^6}$ illustrates the _____ .

6. If there is no exponent written for a variable, it is assumed to be the number _____ .

7. $x^2 \cdot x^8 = x^{10}$ illustrates the _____ .

8. $\dfrac{x^8}{x^3} = x^5$, $x \neq 0$ illustrates the _____ .

9. When $pppqqqqrrrr$ is rewritten using exponents, it is _____ .

10. When $\dfrac{pppprrrr}{qqqq}$ is rewritten using exponents, it is _____ .

Practice the Skills

Multiply.

11. $x^6 \cdot x^4$ **12.** $x^6 \cdot x$ **13.** $-z^4 \cdot z$ **14.** $t^7 \cdot t^2$

15. $y^3 \cdot y^2$ **16.** $4^2 \cdot 4^3$ **17.** $3^2 \cdot 3^3$ **18.** $-x^3 \cdot x^4$

19. $z^3 \cdot z^5$ **20.** $2^4 \cdot 2^2$

Divide.

21. $\dfrac{6^2}{6}$ **22.** $\dfrac{x^4}{x^3}$ **23.** $\dfrac{x^{10}}{x^3}$ **24.** $\dfrac{y^9}{y}$

25. $\dfrac{3^6}{3^2}$ **26.** $\dfrac{4^5}{4^3}$ **27.** $\dfrac{y^4}{y^6}$ **28.** $\dfrac{a^7}{a^9}$

29. $\dfrac{c^4}{c^4}$ **30.** $\dfrac{5^4}{5^4}$ **31.** $\dfrac{q^3}{q^9}$ **32.** $\dfrac{x^9}{x^{13}}$

Simplify.

33. x^0 **34.** 5^0 **35.** $3x^0$ **36.** $-7x^0$

37. $4(5d)^0$ **38.** $-2(8t)^0$ **39.** $-9(-4y)^0$ **40.** $-(-x)^0$

41. $6x^3y^2z^0$ **42.** $-5xy^2z^0$ **43.** $-8r(st)^0$ **44.** $-3(a^2b^5c^3)^0$

Simplify.

45. $(x^4)^2$ **46.** $(a^5)^3$ **47.** $(x^5)^5$ **48.** $(y^5)^2$

49. $(x^3)^1$ **50.** $(x^6)^{20}$ **51.** $(x^4)^3$ **52.** $(x^5)^4$

53. $(n^6)^3$ **54.** $(1.3x)^2$ **55.** $(-2w^2)^3$ **56.** $(-3x)^2$

57. $(-3t^3)^3$ **58.** $(-xy)^4$ **59.** $(4x^3y^2)^3$ **60.** $(3a^2b^4)^3$

Simplify.

61. $\left(\dfrac{x}{3}\right)^2$ **62.** $\left(\dfrac{-2}{x}\right)^3$ **63.** $\left(\dfrac{y}{x}\right)^4$ **64.** $\left(\dfrac{2}{y}\right)^4$

65. $\left(\dfrac{-6}{x}\right)^3$ **66.** $\left(\dfrac{4m}{n}\right)^3$ **67.** $\left(\dfrac{2x}{y}\right)^3$ **68.** $\left(\dfrac{3s}{t^2}\right)^2$

69. $\left(\dfrac{4p}{5}\right)^2$ **70.** $\left(\dfrac{2y^3}{x}\right)^4$ **71.** $\left(\dfrac{3x^4}{y}\right)^3$ **72.** $\left(\dfrac{-4x^2}{5}\right)^2$

Simplify.

73. $\dfrac{a^8b}{ab^4}$ **74.** $\dfrac{x^3y^5}{x^7y}$ **75.** $\dfrac{5x^{12}y^2}{10xy^9}$ **76.** $\dfrac{10x^3y^8}{2xy^{10}}$

77. $\dfrac{30y^5z^3}{5yz^6}$ **78.** $\dfrac{3ab}{27a^3b^4}$ **79.** $\dfrac{35x^4y^9}{15x^9y^{12}}$ **80.** $\dfrac{6m^3n^9}{9m^7n^{12}}$

81. $-\dfrac{36xy^7z}{12x^4y^5z}$ **82.** $\dfrac{4x^4y^7z^3}{32x^5y^4z^9}$ **☞ 83.** $-\dfrac{6x^2y^7z}{3x^5y^9z^6}$ **84.** $-\dfrac{25x^4y^{10}}{30x^3y^7z}$

Simplify.

85. $\left(\dfrac{10x^4}{5x^6}\right)^3$ **86.** $\left(\dfrac{4x^4}{8x^8}\right)^3$ **87.** $\left(\dfrac{6y^6}{2y^3}\right)^3$ **88.** $\left(\dfrac{4xy^5}{y}\right)^3$

89. $\left(\dfrac{6a^2b^4}{3a^7b^9}\right)^0$ **90.** $\left(\dfrac{16y^6}{24y^{10}}\right)^3$ **91.** $\left(\dfrac{x^4y^3}{x^2y^5}\right)^2$ **92.** $\left(\dfrac{2x^7y^2}{4xy}\right)^3$

☞ 93. $\left(\dfrac{9y^2z^7}{18y^9z}\right)^4$ **94.** $\left(\dfrac{y^7z^5}{y^8z^4}\right)^{10}$ **95.** $\left(\dfrac{25s^4t}{5s^6t^4}\right)^3$ **96.** $\left(\dfrac{-64xy^6}{32xy^9}\right)^4$

Simplify.

97. $(3xy^4)^2$ **98.** $(4ab^3)^3$ **99.** $(5ab^3)(b)$ **100.** $(6xy^5)(3x^2y^4)$

101. $(-2xy)(3xy)$ **102.** $(-3x^4y^2)(5x^2y)$ **103.** $(5x^2y)(3xy^5)$ **104.** $(-5xy)(-2xy^6)$

105. $(-3p^2q)^2(-p^2q)$ **106.** $(2c^3d^2)^2(3cd)^0$ **107.** $(7r^3s^2)^2(9r^3s^4)^0$ **108.** $(3x^2)^4(2xy^5)$

Simplify.

109. $(-x)^2$ **110.** $(2xy^4)^3$ **111.** $\left(\dfrac{x^5y^5}{xy^5}\right)^3$ **112.** $(2x^2y^5)(3x^5y^4)^3$

113. $(2.5x^3)^2$ **114.** $(-3a^2b^3c^4)^3$ **115.** $\dfrac{x^9y^3}{x^2y^7}$ **116.** $(xy^4)(xy^4)^3$

117. $\left(-\dfrac{m^4}{n^3}\right)^3$ **118.** $\left(-\dfrac{12x}{16x^7y^2}\right)^2$ **119.** $(-6x^3y^2)^3$ **120.** $(3x^6y)^2(4xy^8)^0$

121. $(-2x^4y^2z)^3$ **122.** $\left(\dfrac{z}{4}\right)^3$ **123.** $(9r^4s^5)^3$ **124.** $(5x^4z^{10})^2(2x^2z^8)$

125. $(4x^2y)(3xy^2)^3$ **126.** $\dfrac{x^2y^6}{x^4y}$ **127.** $(1.3x^2y^4)^2$ **128.** $\left(\dfrac{-3x^3}{4}\right)^3$

☞ 129. $(x^7y^5)(xy^2)^4$ **130.** $(4c^3d^2)(2c^5d^3)^2$ **131.** $\left(\dfrac{-x^4z^7}{x^2z^5}\right)^4$ **132.** $(x^4y^6)^3(3x^2y^5)$

Study the Avoiding Common Errors box on page 229. Simplify the following expressions by dividing out common factors. If the expression cannot be simplified by dividing out common factors, so state.

133. $\dfrac{a+b}{b}$ **134.** $\dfrac{xy}{x}$ **135.** $\dfrac{y^2+3}{y}$ **136.** $\dfrac{a+9}{3}$

137. $\dfrac{6yz^4}{yz^2}$ **138.** $\dfrac{x}{x+1}$ **139.** $\dfrac{a^2+b^2}{a^2}$ **140.** $\dfrac{x^4}{x^2y}$

Problem Solving

141. What is the value of a^3b if $a = 2$ and $b = 5$?

142. What is the value of xy^2 if $x = -3$ and $y = -4$?

143. What is the value of $(xy)^0$ if $x = -5$ and $y = 3$?

144. What is the value of $(xy)^0$ if $x = 2$ and $y = 4$?

145. Consider the expression $(-9x^4y^6)^8$. When the expanded power rule is used to simplify the expression, will the *sign* of

the simplified expression be positive or negative? Explain how you determined your answer.

146. Consider the expression $(-x^5y^7)^9$. When the expanded power rule is used to simplify the expression, will the *sign* of the simplified expression be positive or negative? Explain how you determined your answer.

Write an expression for the total area of the figure or figures shown.

147.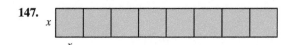

148.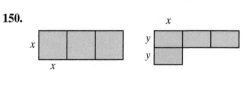

149.

b

a $\boxed{a}$

a

b

b

150.

Concept/Writing Exercises

151. Explain the difference between the product rule and the power rule for exponents.

152. Explain the zero exponent rule. What restrictions are there on the base?

Challenge Problems

Simplify.

153. $(3yz^2)^2 \left(\dfrac{2y^3z^5}{10y^6z^4} \right)^0 (4y^2z^3)^3$

154. $\left(\dfrac{3x^4y^5}{6x^6y^8} \right)^3 \left(\dfrac{9x^7y^8}{3x^3y^5} \right)^2$

Group Activity

Discuss and answer Exercise 155 as a group, according to the instructions.

155. In the next section we will be working with negative exponents. To prepare for that work, use the expression $\dfrac{3^2}{3^3}$ to work parts **a)** through **c)**. Work parts **a)** through **d)** individually, then part **e)** as a group.

   a) Divide out common factors in the numerator and denominator and determine the value of the expression.

   b) Use the quotient rule on the given expression and write down your results.

   c) Write a statement of equality using the results of part **a)** and **b)** above.

   d) Repeat parts **a)** through **c)** for the expression $\dfrac{2^3}{2^4}$.

   e) As a group, compare your answers to parts **a)** through **d)**, then write an exponential expression for $\dfrac{1}{x^m}$.

Cumulative Review Exercises

[1.9] **156.** Evaluate $3^4 \div 3^3 - (5 - 8) + 7$.

[2.1] **157.** Simplify $-4(x - 3) + 5x - 2$.

[2.5] **158.** Solve the equation
$2(x + 4) - 3 = 5x + 4 - 3x + 1$.

[2.6] **159. a)** Use the formula $P = 2l + 2w$ to find the length of the sides of the rectangle shown if the perimeter of the rectangle is 26 inches.

   b) Solve the formula $P = 2l + 2w$ for w.

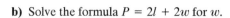

$x + 5$

x

4.2 Negative Exponents

1 Understand the negative exponent rule.

2 Simplify expressions containing negative exponents.

1 Understand the Negative Exponent Rule

One additional rule that involves exponents is the negative exponent rule.

EXAMPLE 1 Simplify $\dfrac{x^3}{x^5}$ by **a)** using the quotient rule and **b)** dividing out common factors.

Solution

a) By the quotient rule,

$$\frac{x^3}{x^5} = x^{3-5} = x^{-2}$$

b) By dividing out common factors,

$$\frac{x^3}{x^5} = \frac{\cancel{x} \cdot \cancel{x} \cdot \cancel{x}}{\cancel{x} \cdot \cancel{x} \cdot \cancel{x} \cdot x \cdot x} = \frac{1}{x^2}$$

Now Try Exercise 35

In Example 1, we see that $\dfrac{x^3}{x^5}$ is equal to both x^{-2} and $\dfrac{1}{x^2}$. Therefore, x^{-2} must equal $\dfrac{1}{x^2}$. That is, $x^{-2} = \dfrac{1}{x^2}$. This is an example of the **negative exponent rule**.

Negative Exponent Rule

$$x^{-m} = \frac{1}{x^m}, \qquad x \neq 0$$

When a variable or number is raised to a negative exponent, the expression may be rewritten as 1 divided by the variable or number raised to that positive exponent.

Examples

$$x^{-6} = \frac{1}{x^6} \qquad 4^{-2} = \frac{1}{4^2} = \frac{1}{16}$$

$$y^{-7} = \frac{1}{y^7} \qquad 5^{-3} = \frac{1}{5^3} = \frac{1}{125}$$

Understanding Algebra

Negative exponents have nothing to do with the sign of a quantity—they simply indicate "reciprocal":

$$(6)^{-2} = (6^2)^{-1} = \frac{1}{6^2} = \frac{1}{36}$$

Avoiding Common Errors

Students sometimes believe that a negative exponent automatically makes the value of the expression negative. This is not true.

EXPRESSION	CORRECT	INCORRECT	ALSO INCORRECT
3^{-2}	$\dfrac{1}{3^2} = \dfrac{1}{9}$	$\cancel{-3^2}$	$\cancel{-\dfrac{1}{3^2}}$
x^{-3}	$\dfrac{1}{x^3}$	$\cancel{-x^3}$	$\cancel{-\dfrac{1}{x^3}}$

To help you see that the negative exponent rule makes sense, consider the following sequence of exponential expressions and their corresponding values.

$$2^3 = 8, \quad 2^2 = 4, \quad 2^1 = 2, \quad 2^0 = 1, \quad 2^{-1} = \frac{1}{2^1} \text{ or } \frac{1}{2}, \quad 2^{-2} = \frac{1}{2^2} \text{ or } \frac{1}{4}, \quad 2^{-3} = \frac{1}{2^3} \text{ or } \frac{1}{8}$$

Note that each time the exponent decreases by 1, the value of the expression is halved. For example, when we go from 2^3 to 2^2, the value of the expression goes from 8 to 4. If we continue decreasing the exponents beyond $2^0 = 1$, the next exponent in the pattern is -1. If we take half of 1 we get $\dfrac{1}{2}$. This pattern illustrates that $x^{-m} = \dfrac{1}{x^m}$.

2 Simplify Expressions Containing Negative Exponents

Generally, *when you are asked to simplify an exponential expression your final answer should contain no negative exponents.* You may simplify exponential expressions using the negative exponent rule and the rules of exponents as shown in the next examples.

EXAMPLE 2 Use the negative exponent rule to write each expression with a positive exponent. Simplify the expressions further when possible.

a) y^{-5} **b)** x^{-4} **c)** 2^{-3} **d)** 6^{-1} **e)** -5^{-3} **f)** $(-5)^{-3}$

Solution

a) $y^{-5} = \dfrac{1}{y^5}$ **b)** $x^{-4} = \dfrac{1}{x^4}$

c) $2^{-3} = \dfrac{1}{2^3} = \dfrac{1}{8}$ **d)** $6^{-1} = \dfrac{1}{6}$

e) $-5^{-3} = -\dfrac{1}{5^3} = -\dfrac{1}{125}$ **f)** $(-5)^{-3} = \dfrac{1}{(-5)^3} = \dfrac{1}{-125} = -\dfrac{1}{125}$

Now Try Exercise 11

EXAMPLE 3 Use the negative exponent rule to write each expression with a positive exponent.

a) $\dfrac{1}{x^{-2}}$ **b)** $\dfrac{1}{4^{-1}}$

Solution   First use the negative exponent rule on the denominator. Then simplify further.

a) $\dfrac{1}{x^{-2}} = \dfrac{1}{\dfrac{1}{x^2}} = 1 \div \dfrac{1}{x^2} = \dfrac{1}{1} \cdot \dfrac{x^2}{1} = x^2$ **b)** $\dfrac{1}{4^{-1}} = \dfrac{1}{\dfrac{1}{4}} = 1 \div \dfrac{1}{4} = \dfrac{1}{1} \cdot \dfrac{4}{1} = 4$

Now Try Exercise 15

Understanding Algebra

Negative exponent in denominator:

$$\dfrac{3}{x^{-4}} = 3 \div x^{-4} = 3 \div \dfrac{1}{x^4}$$

$$= 3 \cdot \dfrac{x^4}{1} = 3x^4$$

(Recall: dividing by a quantity is the same as multiplying by its reciprocal.)

Helpful Hint

From Examples 2 and 3, we can see that when a factor is moved from the denominator to the numerator or from the numerator to the denominator, the sign of the *exponent* changes.

$$x^{-4} = \dfrac{1}{x^4} \qquad\qquad \dfrac{1}{x^{-4}} = x^4$$

$$3^{-5} = \dfrac{1}{3^5} \qquad\qquad \dfrac{1}{3^{-5}} = 3^5$$

Now let's look at additional examples that combine two or more of the rules presented so far.

EXAMPLE 4 Simplify.   **a)** $(z^{-5})^4$ **b)** $(4^2)^{-3}$

Solution

a) $(z^{-5})^4 = z^{(-5)(4)}$ Power rule

$\qquad = z^{-20}$

$\qquad = \dfrac{1}{z^{20}}$ Negative exponent rule

b) $(4^2)^{-3} = 4^{(2)(-3)}$ Power rule

$\qquad = 4^{-6}$

$\qquad = \dfrac{1}{4^6}$ Negative exponent rule

Now Try Exercise 25

EXAMPLE 5 Simplify.   **a)** $x^3 \cdot x^{-5}$ **b)** $3^{-4} \cdot 3^{-7}$

Solution

a) $x^3 \cdot x^{-5} = x^{3+(-5)}$ Product rule

$\qquad = x^{-2}$

$\qquad = \dfrac{1}{x^2}$ Negative exponent rule

b) $3^{-4} \cdot 3^{-7} = 3^{-4+(-7)}$ Product rule

$\qquad = 3^{-11}$

$\qquad = \dfrac{1}{3^{11}}$ Negative exponent rule

Now Try Exercise 51

Avoiding Common Errors

What is the sum of $3^2 + 3^{-2}$? Look carefully at the correct solution.

CORRECT	INCORRECT
$3^2 + 3^{-2} = 9 + \dfrac{1}{9}$	$\cancel{3^2 + 3^{-2} = 0}$
$\qquad = 9\dfrac{1}{9}$	$\cancel{3^2 + 3^{-2} = 3^0 = 1}$

Note that $3^2 \cdot 3^{-2} = 3^{2+(-2)} = 3^0 = 1$.

EXAMPLE 6 Simplify.   **a)** $\dfrac{b^{-5}}{b^{13}}$ **b)** $\dfrac{6^{-8}}{6^{-5}}$

Solution

a) $\dfrac{b^{-5}}{b^{13}} = b^{-5-13}$ Quotient rule

$\qquad = b^{-18}$

$\qquad = \dfrac{1}{b^{18}}$ Negative exponent rule

b) $\dfrac{6^{-8}}{6^{-5}} = 6^{-8-(-5)}$ Quotient rule

$\qquad = 6^{-8+5}$

$\qquad = 6^{-3}$

$\qquad = \dfrac{1}{6^3}$ or $\dfrac{1}{216}$ Negative exponent rule

Now Try Exercise 81

Read the following Helpful Hint carefully.

> **Helpful Hint**
>
> An alternative way to simplify a fraction involving a variable with a negative exponent in the numerator is to move the variable with the negative exponent from the numerator to the denominator and change the sign of the exponent:
>
> $$\frac{x^{-4}}{x^5} = \frac{1}{x^5 \cdot x^4} = \frac{1}{x^{5+4}} = \frac{1}{x^9}$$
>
> Similarly, if we have a fraction involving a variable with a negative exponent in the denominator we can move the variable with the negative exponent from the denominator to the numerator and change the sign of the exponent:
>
> $$\frac{y^3}{y^{-7}} = y^3 \cdot y^7 = y^{3+7} = y^{10}$$
>
> Now consider a division problem where a number or variable has a negative exponent in both its numerator and its denominator, such as in Example 6 **b)**. Another way to simplify such an expression is to move the variable with the more negative exponent from the numerator to the denominator, or from the denominator to the numerator, and change the sign of the exponent from negative to positive. For example,
>
> $$\frac{x^{-8}}{x^{-3}} = \frac{1}{x^8 \cdot x^{-3}} = \frac{1}{x^{8-3}} = \frac{1}{x^5} \qquad \text{Note that } -8 < -3.$$
>
> $$\frac{y^{-4}}{y^{-7}} = y^7 \cdot y^{-4} = y^{7-4} = y^3 \qquad \text{Note that } -7 < -4.$$

EXAMPLE 7   Simplify.

a) $7x^4 (6x^{-9})$ **b)** $\dfrac{16r^3 s^{-3}}{8rs^2}$ **c)** $\dfrac{2x^2 y^5}{8x^7 y^{-3}}$

Solution

a) $7x^4 (6x^{-9}) = 7 \cdot 6 \cdot x^4 \cdot x^{-9} = 42x^{-5} = \dfrac{42}{x^5}$

b) $\dfrac{16r^3 s^{-3}}{8rs^2} = \dfrac{16}{8} \cdot \dfrac{r^3}{r} \cdot \dfrac{s^{-3}}{s^2}$

$\qquad = 2 \cdot r^2 \cdot \dfrac{1}{s^5} = \dfrac{2r^2}{s^5}$ s^{-3} was rewritten in the denominator as s^3

c) $\dfrac{2x^2 y^5}{8x^7 y^{-3}} = \dfrac{2}{8} \cdot \dfrac{x^2}{x^7} \cdot \dfrac{y^5}{y^{-3}}$

$\qquad = \dfrac{1}{4} \cdot \dfrac{1}{x^5} \cdot y^8 = \dfrac{y^8}{4x^5}$ y^{-3} was rewritten in the numerator as y^3

Now Try Exercise 121

EXAMPLE 8   Simplify.

a) $(5x^{-3})^{-2}$ **b)** $(-5x^{-3})^{-2}$ **c)** $(-5x^{-3})^{-3}$

Solution   Begin by using the expanded power rule.

a) $(5x^{-3})^{-2} = 5^{-2} x^{(-3)(-2)}$

$\qquad = 5^{-2} x^6$

$\qquad = \dfrac{1}{5^2} x^6$

$\qquad = \dfrac{x^6}{25}$

b) $(-5x^{-3})^{-2} = (-5)^{-2}x^{(-3)(-2)}$

$$= \frac{1}{(-5)^2}x^6$$

$$= \frac{x^6}{25}$$

c) $(-5x^{-3})^{-3} = (-5)^{-3}x^{(-3)(-3)}$

$$= \frac{1}{(-5)^3}x^9$$

$$= \frac{1}{-125}x^9$$

$$= -\frac{x^9}{125}$$

Now Try Exercise 105

Avoiding Common Errors

Can you explain why the simplification on the right is incorrect?

CORRECT	INCORRECT
$\dfrac{x^3 y^{-2}}{w} = \dfrac{x^3}{wy^2}$	$\dfrac{x^3 + y^{-2}}{w} \ne \dfrac{x^3}{w + y^2}$

The simplification on the right is incorrect because in the numerator $x^3 + y^{-2}$, the y^{-2} *is not a factor*, it is a term.

EXAMPLE 9 Simplify $\left(\dfrac{2}{3}\right)^{-2}$.

Solution By the expanded power rule, we may write

$$\left(\frac{2}{3}\right)^{-2} = \frac{2^{-2}}{3^{-2}} = \frac{\dfrac{1}{2^2}}{\dfrac{1}{3^2}} = \frac{1}{2^2} \cdot \frac{3^2}{1} = \frac{3^2}{2^2} = \frac{9}{4}$$

Now Try Exercise 95

If we examine the results of Example 9, we see that

$$\left(\frac{2}{3}\right)^{-2} = \frac{3^2}{2^2} = \left(\frac{3}{2}\right)^2.$$

This example illustrates that $\left(\dfrac{a}{b}\right)^{-m} = \left(\dfrac{b}{a}\right)^m$ when $a \ne 0$ and $b \ne 0$. Thus, for example, $\left(\dfrac{3}{4}\right)^{-5} = \left(\dfrac{4}{3}\right)^5$ and $\left(\dfrac{5}{9}\right)^{-3} = \left(\dfrac{9}{5}\right)^3$. We can summarize this information as follows.

A Fraction Raised to a Negative Exponent Rule

For a fraction of the form $\dfrac{a}{b}$, $a \ne 0$ and $b \ne 0$, $\left(\dfrac{a}{b}\right)^{-m} = \left(\dfrac{b}{a}\right)^m$.

EXAMPLE 10 Simplify. **a)** $\left(\dfrac{4}{5}\right)^{-3}$ **b)** $\left(\dfrac{x^5}{y^7}\right)^{-4}$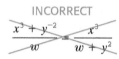

Solution We use the above rule to simplify.

a) $\left(\dfrac{4}{5}\right)^{-3} = \left(\dfrac{5}{4}\right)^3 = \dfrac{5^3}{4^3} = \dfrac{125}{64}$ **b)** $\left(\dfrac{x^5}{y^7}\right)^{-4} = \left(\dfrac{y^7}{x^5}\right)^4 = \dfrac{y^{7\cdot4}}{x^{5\cdot4}} = \dfrac{y^{28}}{x^{20}}$

Now Try Exercise 97

EXAMPLE 11 Simplify.   **a)** $\left(\dfrac{x^2y^{-3}}{z^4}\right)^{-5}$ **b)** $\left(\dfrac{2x^{-3}y^2z}{x^2}\right)^2$

Solution

a) We will work part **a)** using two different methods. In method 1, we begin by using the expanded power rule. In method 2, we use a fraction raised to a negative exponent rule before we use the expanded power rule. You may use either method.

Method 1

$$\left(\frac{x^2y^{-3}}{z^4}\right)^{-5} = \frac{x^{2(-5)}y^{(-3)(-5)}}{z^{4(-5)}} \qquad \text{Expanded power rule}$$

$$= \frac{x^{-10}y^{15}}{z^{-20}} \qquad \text{Multiplied exponents}$$

$$= \frac{y^{15}z^{20}}{x^{10}} \qquad \text{Negative exponent rule}$$

Method 2

$$\left(\frac{x^2y^{-3}}{z^4}\right)^{-5} = \left(\frac{z^4}{x^2y^{-3}}\right)^5 \qquad \left(\frac{a}{b}\right)^{-m} = \left(\frac{b}{a}\right)^m$$

$$= \left(\frac{y^3z^4}{x^2}\right)^5 \qquad \begin{array}{l}\text{Simplified expression within} \\ \text{parentheses}\end{array}$$

$$= \frac{y^{3\cdot5}z^{4\cdot5}}{x^{2\cdot5}} \qquad \text{Expanded power rule}$$

$$= \frac{y^{15}z^{20}}{x^{10}} \qquad \text{Multiplied exponents}$$

b) First simplify the expression within parentheses, then square the results. To simplify, we note that $\dfrac{x^{-3}}{x^2}$ becomes $\dfrac{1}{x^5}$.

$$\left(\frac{2x^{-3}y^2z}{x^2}\right)^2 = \left(\frac{2y^2z}{x^5}\right)^2 = \frac{2^2y^{2\cdot2}z^{1\cdot2}}{x^{5\cdot2}} = \frac{4y^4z^2}{x^{10}}$$

Now Try Exercise 125

Understanding Algebra

Remember: a negative exponent indicates "reciprocal."

$$\left(\frac{2x^2}{3y^4}\right)^{-3} = \left(\frac{3y^4}{2x^2}\right)^3 = \frac{27y^{12}}{8x^6}$$

Summary of Rules of Exponents

1. Product Rule	$x^m \cdot x^n = x^{m+n}$
2. Quotient Rule	$\dfrac{x^m}{x^n} = x^{m-n}, \qquad x \neq 0$
3. Zero Exponent Rule	$x^0 = 1, \qquad x \neq 0$
4. Power Rule	$(x^m)^n = x^{m\cdot n}$
5. Power of a Product Rule	$(xy)^n = x^ny^n$
6. Power of a Quotient Rule	$\left(\dfrac{x}{y}\right)^n = \dfrac{x^n}{y^n}, \qquad y \neq 0$
7. Expanded Power Rule	$\left(\dfrac{ax}{by}\right)^m = \dfrac{a^mx^m}{b^my^m}, \qquad b \neq 0, y \neq 0$
8. Negative Exponent Rule	$x^{-m} = \dfrac{1}{x^m}, \qquad x \neq 0$
9. Fraction Raised to a Negative Exponent Rule	$\left(\dfrac{a}{b}\right)^{-m} = \left(\dfrac{b}{a}\right)^m, \qquad a \neq 0, b \neq 0$

EXERCISE SET 4.2

Math XL · MathXL® · *MyMathLab* · MyMathLab

Warm-Up Exercises

Fill in the blanks with the appropriate word, phrase, or symbol(s) from the following list.

$4x^4$ x^2 -2^4 $\dfrac{1}{x^2}$

$(-2)^4$ 2^{-4} 1 x^4

0 $\dfrac{1}{x^4}$ $\dfrac{1}{4x^4}$ $-2x$

1. The simplified from of x^{-2} is _____ .

2. The simplified form of $(x^{-2})^{-1}$ is _____ .

3. Which is the largest: -2^4, $(-2)^4$, or 2^{-4}? _____

4. Which number is negative: -2^4, $(-2)^4$, or 2^{-4}? _____

5. The simplified form of $\dfrac{x^2}{x^{-2}}$ is _____ .

6. The expression x^{-2} is undefined if x has the value _____ .

7. The simplified form of $\dfrac{x^{-2}}{x^2}$ is _____ .

8. The simplified form of $\left(\dfrac{2x^2y^{-4}}{y^{-4}}\right)^{-2}$ is _____ .

9. The simplified form of $\left(\dfrac{x^{-2}y^{-4}}{2y^{-4}}\right)^{-2}$ is _____ .

10. Which of the following is in simplified form: $-2x$, x^{-2}, or $\left(\dfrac{1}{x}\right)^{-2}$? _____

Practice the Skills

Simplify.

11. x^{-6} **12.** y^{-5} **13.** 5^{-1} **14.** 7^{-2}

15. $\dfrac{1}{t^{-3}}$ **16.** $\dfrac{1}{b^{-4}}$ **17.** $\dfrac{1}{a^{-1}}$ **18.** $\dfrac{1}{y^{-4}}$

19. $\dfrac{1}{6^{-2}}$ **20.** $\dfrac{1}{4^{-3}}$ **21.** $(x^{-2})^{10}$ **22.** $(m^{-5})^{-2}$

23. $(y^{-5})^4$ **24.** $(a^5)^{-4}$ **25.** $(x^4)^{-2}$ **26.** $(x^{-9})^{-2}$

27. $(3^{-2})^{-1}$ **28.** $(2^{-3})^2$ **29.** $y^4 \cdot y^{-2}$ **30.** $x^{-3} \cdot x^1$

31. $x^7 \cdot x^{-5}$ **32.** $d^{-3} \cdot d^{-4}$ **33.** $3^{-2} \cdot 3^4$ **34.** $6^{-3} \cdot 6^6$

35. $\dfrac{r^5}{r^6}$ **36.** $\dfrac{x^2}{x^{-1}}$ **37.** $\dfrac{p^0}{p^{-3}}$ **38.** $\dfrac{x^{-2}}{x^5}$

39. $\dfrac{x^{-7}}{x^{-3}}$ **40.** $\dfrac{z^{-11}}{z^{-12}}$ **41.** $\dfrac{3^2}{3^{-1}}$ **42.** $\dfrac{4^2}{4^{-1}}$

43. 5^{-3} **44.** x^{-7} **45.** $\dfrac{1}{z^{-9}}$ **46.** $\dfrac{1}{3^{-3}}$

47. $(p^{-4})^{-6}$ **48.** $(x^{-3})^{-4}$ **49.** $(y^{-2})^{-3}$ **50.** $z^9 \cdot z^{-12}$

51. $x^3 \cdot x^{-7}$ **52.** $x^{-3} \cdot x^{-5}$ **53.** $x^{-8} \cdot x^{-7}$ **54.** $8^{-3} \cdot 8^3$

55. -4^{-2} **56.** $(-4)^{-2}$ **57.** $-(-4)^{-2}$ **58.** -2^{-3}

59. $(-2)^{-3}$ **60.** $-(-2)^{-3}$ **61.** $(-6)^{-2}$ **62.** -6^{-2}

63. $\dfrac{x^{-5}}{x^5}$ **64.** $\dfrac{y^6}{y^{-8}}$ **65.** $\dfrac{n^{-5}}{n^{-7}}$ **66.** $\dfrac{3^{-4}}{3}$

67. $\dfrac{9^{-3}}{9^{-3}}$ **68.** $(7q^5r^2)^0$ **69.** $(2^{-1} + 3^{-1})^0$ **70.** $(3^{-1} + 4^2)^0$

71. $\dfrac{2}{2^{-5}}$ **72.** $(z^{-5})^{-9}$ **73.** $(x^{-4})^{-2}$ **74.** $(x^{-7})^0$

75. $(x^0)^{-2}$

76. $(12^{-1})^{-2}$

77. $2^{-3} \cdot 2$

78. $7^5 \cdot 7^{-3}$

79. $7^{-5} \cdot 7^3$

80. $\dfrac{z^{-3}}{z^{-7}}$

81. $\dfrac{x^{-1}}{x^{-4}}$

82. $\dfrac{r^6}{r}$

83. $(4^2)^{-1}$

84. $(2^{-2})^{-2}$

85. $\dfrac{5}{5^{-2}}$

86. $\dfrac{x^6}{x^7}$

87. $\dfrac{3^{-4}}{3^{-2}}$

88. $x^{-10} \cdot x^8$

89. $\dfrac{8^{-1}}{8^{-1}}$

90. $2x^{-1}y$

91. $(-6x^2)^{-2}$

92. $(-3z^3)^{-2}$

93. $3x^{-2}y^2$

94. $-5x^4y^{-2}$

95. $\left(\dfrac{1}{2}\right)^{-2}$

96. $\left(\dfrac{3}{5}\right)^{-2}$

97. $\left(\dfrac{5}{4}\right)^{-3}$

98. $\left(\dfrac{3}{5}\right)^{-3}$

99. $\left(\dfrac{c^4}{d^2}\right)^{-2}$

100. $\left(\dfrac{x^2}{y}\right)^{-2}$

101. $-\left(\dfrac{r^4}{s}\right)^{-4}$

102. $-\left(\dfrac{m^3}{n^4}\right)^{-5}$

103. $-7a^{-3}b^{-4}$

104. $(3x^2y^3)^{-2}$

105. $(4x^5y^{-3})^{-3}$

106. $2w(3w^{-5})$

107. $(3z^{-4})(6z^{-5})$

108. $2x^5(3x^{-6})$

109. $4x^4(-2x^{-4})$

110. $(9x^5)(-3x^{-7})$

111. $(4x^2y)(3x^3y^{-1})$

112. $(7a^{-6}b^{-1})(a^9b^0)$

113. $(-5y^2)(4y^{-3}z^5)$

114. $(-3y^{-2})(5x^{-1}y^3)$

115. $\dfrac{24d^{12}}{3d^8}$

116. $\dfrac{8z^{-4}}{32z^{-2}}$

117. $\dfrac{36x^{-4}}{9x^{-2}}$

118. $\dfrac{18m^{-3}n^0}{6m^5n^9}$

119. $\dfrac{3x^4y^{-2}}{6y^3}$

120. $\dfrac{16x^{-7}y^{-2}}{4x^5y^2}$

121. $\dfrac{32x^4y^{-2}}{4x^{-2}y^0}$

122. $\dfrac{21x^{-3}z^2}{7xz^{-3}}$

123. $\left(\dfrac{5x^4y^{-7}}{z^3}\right)^{-2}$

124. $\left(\dfrac{b^4c^{-2}}{2d^{-3}}\right)^{-1}$

125. $\left(\dfrac{2r^{-5}s^9}{t^{12}}\right)^{-4}$

126. $\left(\dfrac{5m^{-1}n^{-3}}{p^2}\right)^{-3}$

127. $\left(\dfrac{x^3y^{-4}z}{y^{-2}}\right)^{-6}$

128. $\left(\dfrac{3p^{-1}q^{-2}r^3}{p^2}\right)^3$

129. $\left(\dfrac{p^6q^{-3}}{4p^8}\right)^2$

130. $\left(\dfrac{x^{12}y^5}{y^{-3}z}\right)^{-4}$

Problem Solving

131. a) Does $p^{-1}q^{-1} = \dfrac{1}{pq}$?

    b) Does $p^{-1} + q^{-1} = \dfrac{1}{p+q}$?

132. a) Does $\dfrac{x^{-1}y^2}{z} = \dfrac{y^2}{xz}$?

    b) Does $\dfrac{x^{-1}+y^2}{z} = \dfrac{y^2}{x+z}$?

Evaluate.

133. $4^2 + 4^{-2}$

134. $8^2 + 8^{-2}$

135. $5^3 + 5^{-3}$

136. $6^{-3} + 6^3$

Evaluate.

137. $5^0 - 3^{-1}$

138. $4^{-1} - 3^{-1}$

139. $2^{-3} - 2^3 \cdot 2^{-3}$

140. $2 \cdot 4^{-1} + 4 \cdot 3^{-1}$

141. $2 \cdot 4^{-1} - 4 \cdot 3^{-1}$

142. $2 \cdot 4^{-1} - 3^{-1}$

143. $3 \cdot 5^0 - 5 \cdot 3^{-2}$

144. $10^2 + 10^{-2}$

Determine the number that when placed in the shaded area makes the statement true.

145. $3^{\blacksquare} = \dfrac{1}{9}$

146. $\dfrac{1}{2^{\blacksquare}} = 64$

147. $\dfrac{1}{6^{\blacksquare}} = 216$

148. $4^{\blacksquare} = \dfrac{1}{256}$

Concept/Writing Exercises

149. Explain the difference between the product rule and the power rule. Give an example of each.

150. a) For what value of x is $x^0 \neq 1$?

    b) Write *pppqqqqrrrrr* using exponents.

Challenge Problems

In Exercises 151–153, determine the number (or numbers) that when placed in the shaded area (or areas) make the statement true.

151. $(x^{\blacksquare}y^3)^{-2} = \dfrac{x^4}{y^6}$

152. $(x^4y^{-3})^{\blacksquare} = \dfrac{y^9}{x^{12}}$

153. $(\blacksquare x^{\blacksquare}y^{-2})^3 = \dfrac{8}{x^9y^6}$

154. For any nonzero real number a, if $a^{-1} = x$, describe the following in terms of x.

a) $-a^{-1}$ **b)** $\dfrac{1}{a^{-1}}$

155. Consider $(3^{-1} + 2^{-1})^0$. We know this is equal to 1 by the zero exponent rule. Determine the error in the following calculation. Explain your answer.

$$(3^{-1} + 2^{-1})^0 = (3^{-1})^0 + (2^{-1})^0$$
$$= 3^{-1(0)} + 2^{-1(0)}$$
$$= 3^0 + 2^0$$
$$= 1 + 1 = 2$$

Group Activity

Discuss and answer Exercise 156 as a group.

156. Often problems involving exponents can be done in more than one way. Consider

$$\left(\frac{3x^2y^3}{x}\right)^{-2}$$

a) Group member 1: Simplify this expression by first simplifying the expression within parentheses.

b) Group member 2: Simplify this expression by first using the expanded power rule.

c) Group member 3: Simplify this expression by first using the negative exponent rule.

d) Compare your answers. If you did not all get the same answers, determine why.

e) As a group, decide which method—**a), b),** or **c)**—was the easiest way to simplify this expression.

Cumulative Review Exercises

[2.7] **157.** **Racing** If a race car travels 104 miles in 52 minutes, how far will it travel in 93 minutes (assuming all conditions stay the same)?

[3.2] **158.** **Even Integers** The sum of two consecutive even integers is 190. Find the numbers.

[3.3] **159.** **Shed** Michael Beattie is building a rectangular shed. The perimeter of the shed is to be 56 feet. Determine the dimensions of the shed if the length is to be 8 feet less than twice the width.

[3.4] **160.** **Simple Interest** Mia Kattee invested $9000, part at 3% and part at 4% simple interest for a period of one year. How much was invested in each account if the interest earned in the 3% account was $32 greater than the interest earned in the 4% account?

4.3 Scientific Notation

1. Convert numbers to and from scientific notation.

2. Recognize numbers in scientific notation with a coefficient of 1.

3. Do calculations using scientific notation.

1   Convert Numbers to and from Scientific Notation

Because it is difficult to work with and compute with really large or really small numbers, we often express such numbers using exponents. For example, the projected world population in 2050 of 8,909,000,000 people could be written as 8.909×10^9. An influenza virus with diameter 0.0000001 meter could be written as 1.0×10^{-7} meter. Numbers such as 8.909×10^9 and 1.0×10^{-7} are in a form called *scientific notation*.

> **Understanding Algebra**
>
> A number is in scientific notation if it is written in the form
>
> $$a \times 10^b$$
>
> where $1 \le a < 10$ and b is an integer.

> **Scientific Notation**
>
> A number written in **scientific notation** is written as a number greater than or equal to 1 and less than 10 ($1 \le a < 10$) multiplied by some power of 10. The exponent on the 10 must be an integer.

Examples of Numbers in Scientific Notation

$$1.2 \times 10^6$$
$$3.762 \times 10^3$$
$$8.07 \times 10^{-2}$$
$$1.0 \times 10^{-5}$$

This is how we change the number 68,400 to scientific notation.

$$68,400 = 6.84 \times 10,000$$ to go from 68,400 to 6.84 the decimal point was moved 4 places to the left

$$= 6.84 \times 10^4$$ Note that $10,000 = 10 \cdot 10 \cdot 10 \cdot 10 = 10^4$.

Therefore, $68,400 = 6.84 \times 10^4$. Note that the exponent on the 10, the 4, is the same as the number of places the decimal point was moved to the left.

Following are general steps to write a number in scientific notation.

> **To Write a Number in Scientific Notation**
>
> 1. Move the decimal point in the original number to the right of the first nonzero digit. This will give a number greater than or equal to 1 and less than 10.
> 2. Count the number of places you moved the decimal point to obtain the number in step 1. If the original number was 10 or greater, the count is considered positive. If the original number was less than 1, the count is considered negative.
> 3. Multiply the number obtained in step 1 by 10 raised to the count (power) found in step 2.

EXAMPLE 1 Write the following numbers in scientific notation. ──

a) 18,500   **b)** 0.0000416   **c)** 3,721,000   **d)** 0.0093

Solution

a) The original number is greater than 10; therefore, the exponent is positive. The decimal point in 18,500 belongs after the last zero.

$$18,500. = 1.85 \times 10^4$$
$$\underset{\text{4 places}}{\curvearrowleft}$$

b) The original number is less than 1; therefore, the exponent is negative.

$$0.0000416 = 4.16 \times 10^{-5}$$

5 places

c) $3,721,000 = 3.721 \times 10^6$

6 places

d) $0.0093 = 9.3 \times 10^{-3}$

3 places

Now Try Exercise 13

When we write a number in scientific notation, we are allowed to leave our answer with a negative exponent, as in parts **b)** and **d)** of Example 1.

Now we explain how to write a number in scientific notation as a number without exponents, or in decimal form.

To Convert a Number from Scientific Notation to Decimal Form

1. Observe the exponent of the power of 10.
2. **a)** If the exponent is positive, move the decimal point in the number (greater than or equal to 1 and less than 10) to the right the same number of places as the exponent. It may be necessary to add zeros to the number. This will result in a number greater than or equal to 10.

   b) If the exponent is 0, do not move the decimal point. Drop the factor 10^0 since it equals 1. This will result in a number greater than or equal to 1 but less than 10.

   c) If the exponent is negative, move the decimal point in the number to the left the same number of places as the exponent. It may be necessary to add zeros to the number. This will result in a number less than 1.

EXAMPLE 2 Write each number without exponents.

a) 2.9×10^4 **b)** 6.28×10^{-3} **c)** 7.95×10^8

Solution

a) Move the decimal point four places to the right (because the exponent, 4, is positive).

$$2.9 \times 10^4 = 2.9 \times 10{,}000 = 29{,}000$$

b) Move the decimal point three places to the left (because the exponent, −3, is negative)

$$6.28 \times 10^{-3} = 0.00628$$

c) Move the decimal point eight places to the right.

$$7.95 \times 10^8 = 795{,}000{,}000$$

Now Try Exercise 29

2 Recognize Numbers in Scientific Notation with a Coefficient of 1

The metric system is used throughout most of the world as the main system of measurement. Prefixes indicate a power of 10 and are always used with some type of base unit. For example, a *millimeter* is $\frac{1}{1000}$ meter. A *megagram* is 1,000,000 grams, and so on. The following table illustrates the meaning of some prefixes.*

Prefix	Meaning	Symbol	Meaning as a Decimal Number
nano	10^{-9}	n	$\frac{1}{1,000,000,000}$ or 0.000000001
micro	10^{-6}	μ	$\frac{1}{1,000,000}$ or 0.000001
milli	10^{-3}	m	$\frac{1}{1000}$ or 0.001
base unit**	10^{0}		1
kilo	10^{3}	k	1000
mega	10^{6}	M	1,000,000
giga	10^{9}	G	1,000,000,000

** The base unit is not a prefix. We included this row to include 10^0 in the chart.

Note that if no numerical coefficient is indicated, it is assumed to be 1. Thus, 10^{-3} means 1.0×10^{-3} and 10^9 means 1.0×10^9. The table below shows the translation of "an 80 gigabyte hard drive", "a 50 micrometer measurement", and "a 325 milligram prescription".

Written Value	Meaning	Scientific Notation	In Decimal Form
80 gigabytes 80 GB	80×10^9 bytes	8.0×10^{10}	80,000,000,000 bytes
50 micrometers 50 μm	50×10^{-6} meters	5.0×10^{-5}	0.00005 meter
325 milligrams 325 mg	325×10^{-3} grams	3.25×10^{-1}	0.325 gram

In **Figure 4.1**, we see that the frequency of FM radio and VHF TV is about 10^8 hertz (10^8 Hz). Thus, the frequency of FM radio is $10^8 = 1.0 \times 10^8 = 100,000,000$ hertz. This number, one hundred million hertz, can also be expressed as 100×10^6 or 100 megahertz, 100 MHz.

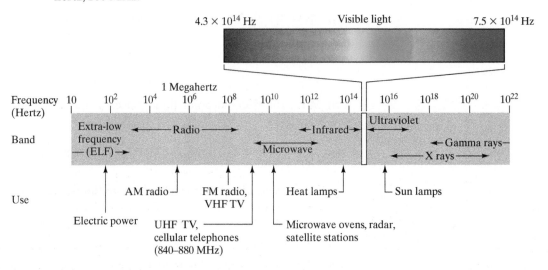

FIGURE 4.1

*There are other prefixes not listed. For example, centi is 10^{-2} or 0.01 times the base unit.

EXAMPLE 3

a) Write 52 kilograms without the metric prefix "kilo" and then express the answer in scientific notation.

b) Write 183 nanoseconds without the metric prefix "nano" and then express the answer in scientific notation.

Solution

a) 52 kilograms (52 kg) = 52×10^3 grams = 52,000 grams = 5.2×10^4 grams

b) 183 nanoseconds (183 ns) = 183×10^{-9} seconds = 0.000000183 second = 1.83×10^{-7} second

Now Try Exercise 45

3 Do Calculations Using Scientific Notation

We can use the rules of exponents presented in Sections 4.1 and 4.2 when working with numbers written in scientific notation.

EXAMPLE 4 Multiply $(4.2 \times 10^6)(2.0 \times 10^{-4})$. Write the answer in decimal form.

Solution   By the commutative and associative properties of multiplication we can rearrange the expression as follows.

$$(4.2 \times 10^6)(2.0 \times 10^{-4}) = (4.2 \times 2.0)(10^6 \times 10^{-4})$$

$$= 8.4 \times 10^{6+(-4)} \qquad \text{Product rule was used.}$$

$$= 8.4 \times 10^2 \qquad \text{Scientific notation}$$

$$= 840 \qquad \text{Decimal form}$$

Now Try Exercise 55

EXAMPLE 5 Divide $\dfrac{3.2 \times 10^{-6}}{5.0 \times 10^{-3}}$. Write the answer in scientific notation.

Solution $$\frac{3.2 \times 10^{-6}}{5.0 \times 10^{-3}} = \left(\frac{3.2}{5.0}\right)\left(\frac{10^{-6}}{10^{-3}}\right)$$

$$= 0.64 \times 10^{-6-(-3)} \qquad \text{Quotient rule was used.}$$

$$= 0.64 \times 10^{-6+3}$$

$$= 0.64 \times 10^{-3}$$

$$= 6.4 \times 10^{-4} \qquad \text{Scientific notation}$$

The answer to Example 5 in decimal form would be 0.00064.

Now Try Exercise 59

EXAMPLE 6 **Biggest Trees** The largest known tree (by volume) is a sequoia, called *General Sherman,* and has an estimated weight of 1.20×10^7 pounds. The largest coast redwood tree, called *Lost Monarch,* has an estimated weight of 1.11×10^6 pounds.

a) How much greater is the weight of the sequoia than the weight of the redwood?

b) How many times greater is the weight of the sequoia than the weight of the redwood?

© Pierdelune\Shutterstock

GENERAL SHERMAN

Solution

a) Understand   We need to subtract 1.11×10^6 from 1.20×10^7. To add or subtract numbers in scientific notation, we generally make the exponents on the 10's the same. This will allow us to add or subtract the numerical values preceding the base while maintaining the common base and exponent on the base.

Translate   We can write 1.20×10^7 as 12.00×10^6. Now we subtract as follows.

Carry Out

$$\begin{array}{r} 12.00 \times 10^6 \\ -1.11 \times 10^6 \\ \hline 10.89 \times 10^6 \quad \text{or } 1.089 \times 10^7 \end{array}$$

Notice that we did not subtract the 10^6's. Think of them as the unit "millions". In other words, 12.00 million minus 1.11 million is 10.89 million.

Check   We can check by writing the numbers out in decimal form:

$$\begin{array}{r} 12{,}000{,}000 \\ -1{,}110{,}000 \\ \hline 10{,}890{,}000 \quad \text{or } 1.089 \times 10^7 \end{array}$$

Answer   The largest sequoia is 1.089×10^7 pounds heavier than the largest coast redwood.

b) Understand   In part **b)** we are asked to find the *number of times* greater the weight of the sequoia is than the weight of the redwood. To find the number of times greater, we perform division.

Translate   Divide the estimated weight of the sequoia by the estimated weight of the redwood.

Carry Out

$$\frac{1.20 \times 10^7}{1.11 \times 10^6} = \frac{1.20}{1.11} \times \frac{10^7}{10^6}$$

$$\approx 1.08 \times 10^{7-6} \quad \text{Quotient rule was used.}$$

$$\approx 1.08 \times 10$$

$$\approx 10.8$$

Check   We can check by writing the numbers out in decimal form:

$$\frac{12{,}000{,}000}{1{,}110{,}000} \approx 10.8$$

Answer   The largest sequoia is 10.8 times heavier than the largest coast redwood.

Now Try Exercise 75

EXAMPLE 7   **Fastest Computer**   As of June 2008, the fastest computer in the world was the IBM "Roadrunner" located at the Los Alamos National Laboratory in New Mexico. It can perform 1.026×10^{15} operations per second, which equates to it taking 0.000000000000000975 second to do one calculation. How long would it take this computer to perform 700 billion (700,000,000,000) calculations? *Source:* www.top500.org

Solution

Understand   The computer could perform 1 calculation in 1(0.000000000000000975) second, 2 calculations in 2(0.000000000000000975) second, 3 calculations in 3(0.000000000000000975) second, and 700 billion calculations in 700,000,000,000 (0.000000000000000975) second.

Translate   The number 0.000000000000000975 written in scientific notation is 9.75×10^{-16}. To compute 700,000,000,000(0.000000000000000975), we convert each calculation to scientific notation:

The IBM Roadrunner computer

Carry Out $700{,}000{,}000{,}000(0.00000000000000975) = (7.0 \times 10^{11})(9.75 \times 10^{-16})$
$$= (7.0 \times 9.75)(10^{11} \times 10^{-16})$$
$$= 68.25 \times 10^{-5}$$
$$= 6.825 \times 10^{-4}$$
$$= 0.0006825$$

Answer   The IBM Roadrunner would take about 0.0006825 of a second to perform 700 billion calculations.

Now Try Exercise 79

EXERCISE SET 4.3

Math XL   MathXL®   MyMathLab   MyMathLab

Warm-Up Exercises

Fill in the blanks with the appropriate word, phrase, or symbol(s) from the following list.

5.12×10^{-4}	5.12×10^{-5}	integer
5.12×10^{5}	5.12×10^{-6}	10
$1 \le a < 10$	11	-11

1. The number 0.0000512 expressed in scientific notation is _____ .

2. If the positive number $a \times 10^{b}$ is written in scientific notation, then a must be _____ .

3. If the positive number $a \times 10^{b}$ is greater than 10, then b must be an _____ .

4. When 51.2×10^{-5} is written in scientific notation, it is _____ .

5. When 0.512×10^{-5} is written in scientific notation, it is _____ .

6. The number 512,000 expressed in scientific notation is _____ .

7. When 6.00×10^{4} is multiplied by 5.00×10^{6} and put into scientific notation, the power of 10 will be _____ .

8. When 2.00×10^{-4} is multiplied by 5.20×10^{-8} and put into scientific notation, the power of 10 will be _____ .

Practice the Skills

Express each number in scientific notation.

9. 20,000
10. 1270
11. 450
12. 0.0125

13. 350,000
14. 3,610,000
15. 7950
16. 0.000089

17. 0.053
18. 19,000
19. 0.000726
20. 0.00000186

21. 5,260,000,000
22. 0.0075
23. 0.00000914
24. 74,100

25. 220,300
26. 0.08
27. 0.005104
28. 416,000

Express each number in decimal form (without exponents).

29. 4.3×10^{4}
30. 1.63×10^{-4}
31. 9.32×10^{-6}
32. 6.15×10^{5}

33. 2.13×10^{-5}
34. 7.26×10^{-6}
35. 6.25×10^{5}
36. 4.6×10^{1}

37. 9.0×10^{6}
38. 6.475×10^{1}
39. 5.35×10^{2}
40. 3.14×10^{-2}

41. 7.73×10^{-7}
42. 6.201×10^{-4}
43. 1.0×10^{4}
44. 7.13×10^{-4}

In Exercises 45–52, write the quantity without metric prefixes and then write the quantity in scientific notation. See Example 3.

45. 8 micrometers
46. 29 micrograms
47. 125 gigawatts
48. 8.7 nanoseconds

49. 15.3 kilometers
50. 80.2 megahertz
51. 48.2 millimeters
52. 3.12 milligrams

Perform each indicated operation and express each number in decimal form (without exponents).

53. $(3.0 \times 10^{2})(3.0 \times 10^{5})$
54. $(2.0 \times 10^{-3})(3.0 \times 10^{2})$
55. $(2.7 \times 10^{-6})(9.0 \times 10^{4})$

56. $(1.3 \times 10^{-8})(1.74 \times 10^6)$ **57.** $(1.6 \times 10^{-2})(4.0 \times 10^{-3})$ **58.** $(4.0 \times 10^5)(1.2 \times 10^{-4})$

59. $\dfrac{3.9 \times 10^{-5}}{3.0 \times 10^{-2}}$ **60.** $\dfrac{6.0 \times 10^{-3}}{3.0 \times 10^1}$ **61.** $\dfrac{7.5 \times 10^6}{3.0 \times 10^3}$

62. $\dfrac{1.4 \times 10^7}{4.0 \times 10^8}$ **63.** $\dfrac{2.0 \times 10^4}{8.0 \times 10^{-2}}$ **64.** $\dfrac{1.6 \times 10^4}{8.0 \times 10^{-3}}$

Perform each indicated operation by first converting each number to scientific notation. Write the answer in scientific notation.

65. $(700{,}000)(8{,}000{,}000)$ **66.** $(0.003)(0.00015)$ **67.** $(0.0004)(320)$

68. $(67{,}000)(200{,}000)$ **69.** $\dfrac{5{,}600{,}000}{8000}$ **70.** $\dfrac{0.00004}{200}$

71. $\dfrac{0.00035}{0.000002}$ **72.** $\dfrac{150{,}000}{0.0005}$

73. List the following numbers from smallest to largest: $7.3 \times 10^2, 3.3 \times 10^{-4}, 1.75 \times 10^6, 5.3$.

74. List the following numbers from smallest to largest: $4.8 \times 10^5, 3.2 \times 10^{-1}, 4.6, 8.3 \times 10^{-4}$.

Problem Solving

In Exercises 75–92, write the answer in decimal form (without exponents) unless asked to do otherwise.

75. Population In 2008, the U.S. population was about 3.05×10^8 people and the world population was about 6.72×10^9 people.

  a) How many people lived outside the United States in 2008?

  b) How many times greater is the world population than the U.S. population?

76. Diapers Laid end to end the 18 billion disposable diapers thrown away in the United States each year would reach the moon and back seven times (seven round trips).

  a) Write 18 billion in scientific notation.

  b) If the distance from earth to the moon is 2.38×10^5 miles, what is the length of all these diapers placed end to end? Write your answer in scientific notation and as a number without exponents.

77. Niagara Falls A treaty between the United States and Canada requires that during the tourist season a minimum of 100,000 cubic feet of water per second flows over Niagara Falls (another 130,000 to 160,000 cubic feet/sec is diverted for power generation). Find the minimum volume of water that will flow over the falls in a 24-hour period during the tourist season.

© Canada Bureau of Travel

78. PGA Tour The top five money leaders from the 2007 PGA Tour are listed above and to the right.

Golfer	Winnings
Tiger Woods	$10,867,052
Phil Mickelson	$5,819,988
Vijay Singh	$4,728,376
Steve Stricker	$4,663,077
K. J. Choi	$4,587,859

Source: www.pgatour.com

  a) Write, in scientific notation, Tiger Woods's and Vijay Singh's approximate money total.

  b) Determine, in scientific notation, the average daily amount that Tiger Woods earned on the PGA tour in 2007.

79. Computer Speed If a computer can do a calculation in 0.000002 second, how long, in seconds, would it take the computer to do 8 trillion (8,000,000,000,000) calculations? Write your answer in scientific notation.

80. Fortune Cookies Steven Yang, who runs M & Y Trading Company, a San Francisco Company, prints about 90% of all the 1.02×10^9 fortunes in fortune cookies in America in any given year.

  a) How many fortunes does Yang print in a year?

  b) How many fortunes does Yang print in a day?

81. Movies The gross ticket sales of the top five movies in the United States as of August 28, 2008, are listed below.

Movie	Year Released	Approximate U.S. Gross Ticket Sales
1. *Titanic*	1997	$601,000,000
2. *The Dark Knight*	2008	$518,000,000
3. *Star Wars Ep. IV: A New Hope*	1977	$461,000,000
4. *Shrek 2*	2004	$437,000,000
5. *E.T.*	1982	$435,000,000

Source: http://www.imdb.com/boxoffice/

a) How much greater was the gross ticket sales of *Titanic* than *E.T.*? Write your answer in scientific notation.

b) How many times greater was the gross ticket sales of *Titanic* than *E.T.*?

82. Melanoma The number of new cases of melanoma has increased from 5.5×10^4 in 2003 to about 6.25×10^4 in 2008.

a) How much greater was the number of cases of melanoma in 2008 than in 2003?

b) How many times greater was the number of cases of melanoma in 2008 than in 2003?

Source: National Cancer Institute

83. World's Richest The worth of Warren Buffett (the world's richest person in 2007) was $\$6.2 \times 10^{10}$. The worth of Charles Ergen (the world's eighty-seventh richest person in 2007) was $\$9.5 \times 10^9$.

Source: www.forbes.com

a) How much greater was the worth of Warren Buffett than the worth of Charles Ergen in 2007?

b) How many times greater was the worth of Warren Buffett than the worth of Charles Ergen in 2007?

84. Light from the Sun The sun is 9.3×10^7 miles from Earth. Light travels at a speed of 1.86×10^5 miles per second. How long, in both seconds and in minutes, does it take light from the sun to reach Earth?

85. Astronomy The mass of Earth, Earth's moon, and the planet Jupiter are listed below.

Earth: 5,794,000,000,000,000,000,000,000 metric tons

Moon: 73,400,000,000,000,000,000 metric tons

Jupiter: 1,899,000,000,000,000,000,000,000,000 metric tons

a) Write the mass of Earth, the moon, and Jupiter in scientific notation.

b) How many times greater is the mass of Earth than the mass of the moon?

c) How many times greater is the mass of Jupiter than the mass of Earth?

86. Missing Persons Of the nearly 47,600 active adult missing-person FBI cases, about 53% were men. Determine, in scientific notation, the approximate number of active adult missing-person FBI cases that were men. *Source: Rochester Democrat & Chronicle*

87. Camera Products and Services The circle graph below shows the percentage of revenue from digital products and services and from traditional products and services during the first quarter of 2008 for Kodak. The company's total revenue for the first quarter of 2008 was $2,093,000,000. How much revenue was from digital products and services? Write your answer in scientific notation.

Kodak First Quarter 2008 Revenues

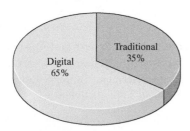

Source: www.bnet.com

88. Chesapeake Bay Oysters The following bar graph shows the approximate oyster population in the Chesapeake Bay.

Chesapeake Bay Oyster Population

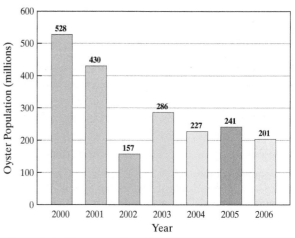

Source: Maryland Department of Natural Resources

a) Give, in scientific notation, the approximate population of oysters in 2000.

b) Give, in scientific notation, the approximate population of oysters in 2006.

c) Determine, in scientific notation, the approximate difference between the population of oysters in 2006 and in 2000.

89. Population Projection The following bar graph shows the population projections for certain states for the year 2025.

Projection of Total Population: 2025

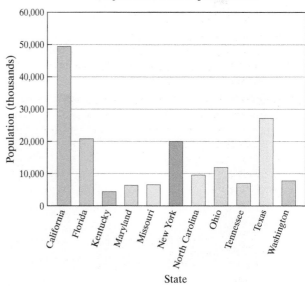

Source: www.census.gov

a) Write, in scientific notation, the approximate projected population of New York in 2025.

b) Determine, in scientific notation, the approximate sum of the projected populations of the two most populated states in 2025.

c) Determine, in scientific notation, the approximate difference between the projected population of the two most populated states in 2025.

90. **The Spice Girls** The Spice Girls hold the Guinness World Record as having the highest ever annual earnings by a girl band. The four group members had a total income of $49,000,000 in 1998. If each member of the band received an equal amount, determine, in scientific notation, the amount earned by each group member in 1998.

91. **Structure of Matter** An article in *Scientific American* states that physicists have created a *standard model* that describes the structure of matter down to 10^{-18} meters. If this number is written without exponents, how many zeroes would there be to the right of the decimal point?

92. **A Large Number** Avogadro's number, named after the nineteenth-century Italian chemist Amedeo Avogadro, is roughly 6.02×10^{23}. It represents the number of atoms in 12 grams of pure carbon.

   a) If this number were written out in decimal form, how many digits would it contain?

   b) What is the number of atoms in 1 gram of pure carbon? Write your answer in scientific notation.

Concept/Writing Exercises

93. Describe the form of a number given in scientific notation.

94. A **googol** is the number 1 followed by 100 zeros and is the largest number many calculators can handle. From what we learned in this section, a googol can be written as 10^{100} or, in scientific notation, as 1.0×10^{100}. What is a googol raised to the fifth power in scientific notation?

95. See Exercise 94.

   a) Estimate the number of seconds that have occurred since January 1, 1900. Is that number more or less than a googol?

   b) The total number of ways of filling in a nine-by-nine *Sudoku* grid is approximately 6.67×10^{21}. How many times greater is a googol than this?

96. The five planets closest to the sun are, in order, Mercury, Venus, Earth, Mars, and Jupiter. Their average distances from the sun are given below:

Planet	Average Distance to the Sun in Miles
Mercury	35,983,610
Venus	67,232,360
Earth	92,957,100
Mars	141,635,300
Jupiter	484,632,000

   In scientific notation, give the ratio of Jupiter's average distance to the sun to Mercury's average distance to the sun.

Challenge Problems

97. **The Movie Contact** In the movie *Contact*, Jodie Foster plays an astronomer who makes the statement "There are 400 billion stars out there just in our universe alone. If only one out of a million of those had planets, and if just one out of a million of those had life, and if just one out of a million of those had intelligent life, there would be literally millions of civilizations out there." Do you believe this statement is correct? Explain your answer.

© NOAO/NSF

98. How many times smaller is 1 nanosecond than one millisecond?

99. How many times, either greater or smaller, is 10^{-12} meters than 10^{-18} meters?

100. **Light Year** Light travels at a speed of 1.86×10^5 miles per second. A **light year** is the distance light travels in one year. Determine the number of miles in a light year.

Group Activity

Discuss and answer Exercise 101 as a group.

101. **A Million versus a Billion** Do you have any idea of the difference in size between a million (1,000,000), a billion (1,000,000,000), and a trillion (1,000,000,000,000)?

   a) Write a million, a billion, and a trillion in scientific notation.

   b) Group member 1: Determine how long it would take to spend a million dollars if you spent $1000 a day.

   c) Group member 2: Repeat part **b)** for a billion dollars.

   d) Group member 3: Repeat part **b)** for a trillion dollars.

   e) As a group, determine how many times greater a billion dollars is than a million dollars.

Cumulative Review Exercises

[1.9] **102.** Evaluate $4x^2 + 3x + \dfrac{x}{2}$ when $x = 0$.

[2.3] **103. a)** If $-x = -\dfrac{3}{2}$, what is the value of x?

  b) If $5x = 0$, what is the value of x?

[2.5] **104.** Solve the equation $2x - 3(x - 2) = x + 2$.

[4.1] **105.** Simplify $\left(\dfrac{-2x^5y^7}{8x^8y^3}\right)^3$.

Mid-Chapter Test: 4.1–4.3

To find out how well you understand the chapter material to this point, take this brief test. The answers, and the section where the material was initially discussed, are given in the back of the book. Review any questions that you answered incorrectly.

Simplify.

1. $y^{11} \cdot y^{20}$

2. $\dfrac{x^{13}}{x^{10}}$

3. $(-3x^5y^7)(-2xy^6)$

4. $\dfrac{6a^{12}b^8}{9a^7b^2}$

5. $(-4x^2y^4)^3$

6. $\left(\dfrac{-5s^4t^6}{10s^6t^3}\right)^2$

7. $(7x^9y^5)(-3xy^4)^2$

8. $\dfrac{p^{-3}}{p^5}$

9. $x^{-4} \cdot x^{-6}$

10. $(3^{-1} + 5^2)^0$

11. $\left(\dfrac{3}{7}\right)^{-2}$

12. $(8x^{-2}y^5)(4x^3y^{-6})$

13. $\dfrac{6m^{-4}n^{-7}}{2m^0n^{-1}}$

14. $\left(\dfrac{2x^{-3}y^{-4}}{x^3yz^{-2}}\right)^{-2}$

15. a) Describe how to write a number 10 or greater in scientific notation.

  b) Describe how to write a number less than 1 in scientific notation.

16. Express 6,540,000,000 in scientific notation.

17. Express 3.27×10^{-5} in decimal form (without exponents).

18. Write 18.9 kilometers without metric prefixes.

19. Multiply $(3.4 \times 10^{-6})(7.0 \times 10^3)$ and express the answer in decimal form (without exponents).

20. Divide $\dfrac{0.00006}{200}$ by first converting to scientific notation.

  Write the answer in scientific notation.

4.4 Addition and Subtraction of Polynomials

1. Identify polynomials.
2. Add polynomials.
3. Subtract polynomials.
4. Subtract polynomials in columns.

1 Identify Polynomials

A polynomial in x is an expression that is the sum of a finite number of terms of the form ax^n, for any real number a and any *whole number n*.

Examples of Polynomials	Not Polynomials	
$8x$	$4x^{1/2}$	(Fractional exponent)
$\dfrac{1}{3}x - 4$	$3x^2 + 4x^{-1} + 5$	(Negative exponent)
$x^2 - 2x + 1$	$4 + \dfrac{1}{x}$	$\left(\dfrac{1}{x} = x^{-1}, \text{negative exponent}\right)$

A polynomial is written in **descending order** when the exponents on the variable decrease from left to right.

Example of Polynomial in Descending Order

$$2x^4 + 4x^2 - 6x + 3$$

The constant term 3 is last because it can be written as $3x^0$. Remember that $x^0 = 1$.

A polynomial can be in more than one variable. For example, $3xy + 2$ is a polynomial in two variables, x and y.

Understanding Algebra

The polynomial $3x^3 - 5x^2 + x + 4$ is written in *descending order of x*. We usually write polynomials in descending order of the variables.

A polynomial with one term is called a **monomial**. A **binomial** is a two-termed polynomial. A **trinomial** is a three-termed polynomial. Polynomials containing more than three terms usually are not given special names.

Type of Polynomial	Number of Terms	Examples
Monomial	One	$8,\ 4x,\ -6x^2$
Binomial	Two	$x + 5,\ x^2 - 6,\ 4y^2 - 5y$
Trinomial	Three	$x^2 - 2x + 3,\ 3z^2 - 6z + 7$

Degree

The **degree of a term in one variable** is the exponent on the variable in that term. The degree of $2x^3$ is 3.

The **degree of a term in two or more variables** is the sum of the exponents on the variables. The degree of $4x^2y^3$ is 5.

The **degree of a polynomial** is the same as that of its highest-degree term.

Term	Degree of Term	
$4x^2$	2	
$2x^2y^5$	7	$(2 + 5 = 7)$
$-23a^3b^4c$	8	$(3 + 4 + 1 = 8)$
$-5x$	1	$(-5x$ is $-5x^1)$
3	0	$(3$ is $3x^0)$

Polynomial	Degree of Polynomial	
$8x^3 + 2x^2 - 3x + 4$	3	$(8x^3$ is highest-degree term.$)$
$x^2 - 4$	2	$(x^2$ is highest-degree term.$)$
$6x - 5$	1	$(6x$ or $6x^1$ is highest-degree term.$)$
4	0	$(4$ or $4x^0$ is highest-degree term.$)$
$x^2y^4 + 2x + 3$	6	$(x^2 y^4$ is highest-degree term.$)$

2 Add Polynomials

In Section 2.1, we stated that like terms are terms having the same variables and the same exponents. That is, like terms may differ only in their numerical coefficients.

Examples of Like Terms

$$3,\ -5$$
$$2x,\ x$$
$$-2x^2,\ 4x^2$$
$$3y^2,\ 5y^2$$
$$3xy^2,\ 5xy^2$$

To Add Polynomials

To add polynomials, combine the like terms of the polynomials.

EXAMPLE 1   Add $(4x^2 + 6x + 3) + (2x^2 + 5x - 1)$.

Solution   Remember that $(4x^2 + 6x + 3) = 1(4x^2 + 6x + 3)$ and $(2x^2 + 5x - 1) = 1(2x^2 + 5x - 1)$.

$$(4x^2 + 6x + 3) + (2x^2 + 5x - 1)$$
$$= 1(4x^2 + 6x + 3) + 1(2x^2 + 5x - 1)$$
$$= \quad 4x^2 + 6x + 3 \ + \ \ 2x^2 + 5x - 1 \qquad \text{Used the distributive property to remove parentheses.}$$
$$= \underline{4x^2 + 2x^2} \ \underline{+ 6x + 5x} \ \underline{+ 3 \ - 1} \qquad \text{Rearranged terms.}$$
$$= \quad 6x^2 \quad + \quad 11x \quad + \quad 2 \qquad \text{Combined like terms.}$$

Now Try Exercise 67

EXAMPLE 2   Add $(5a^2 + 3a + b) + (a^2 - 7a + 3)$.

Solution
$$(5a^2 + 3a + b) + (a^2 - 7a + 3)$$
$$= 5a^2 + 3a + b + a^2 - 7a + 3 \qquad \text{Removed parentheses.}$$
$$= \underline{5a^2 + a^2} \ \underline{+ 3a - 7a} \ + b + 3 \qquad \text{Rearranged terms.}$$
$$= \quad 6a^2 \quad - \quad 4a \quad + b + 3 \qquad \text{Combined like terms.}$$

Now Try Exercise 75

EXAMPLE 3   Add $(3x^2y - 4xy + y) + (x^2y + 2xy + 3y)$.

Solution
$$(3x^2y - 4xy + y) + (x^2y + 2xy + 3y)$$
$$= 3x^2y - 4xy + y + x^2y + 2xy + 3y \qquad \text{Removed parentheses.}$$
$$= \underline{3x^2y + x^2y} \ \underline{- 4xy + 2xy} \ \underline{+ y + 3y} \qquad \text{Rearranged terms.}$$
$$= \quad 4x^2y \quad - \quad 2xy \quad + \quad 4y \qquad \text{Combined like terms.}$$

Now Try Exercise 77

Usually, when we add polynomials, we will do so horizontally as in Examples 1 through 3. Sometimes, it is easier to add polynomials in columns.

> **To Add Polynomials in Columns**
>
> **1.** Arrange polynomials in descending order, one under the other with like terms in the same columns.
> **2.** Add the terms in each column.

EXAMPLE 4   Add $5x^2 - 9x - 3$ and $-3x^2 - 4x + 6$ using columns.

Solution
$$\begin{array}{r} 5x^2 - 9x - 3 \\ -3x^2 - 4x + 6 \\ \hline 2x^2 - 13x + 3 \end{array}$$

Now Try Exercise 83

EXAMPLE 5   Add $5w^3 + 2w - 4$ and $2w^2 - 6w - 3$ using columns.

Solution   Since the polynomial $5w^3 + 2w - 4$ does not have a w^2 term, we will add the term $0w^2$ to the polynomial. This procedure helps in aligning like terms.

$$\begin{array}{r} 5w^3 + 0w^2 + 2w - 4 \\ 2w^2 - 6w - 3 \\ \hline 5w^3 + 2w^2 - 4w - 7 \end{array}$$

Now Try Exercise 85

3 Subtract Polynomials

To Subtract Polynomials

1. Use the distributive property to remove parentheses. This will have the effect of changing the sign of *every* term within the parentheses of the polynomial being subtracted.
2. Combine like terms.

EXAMPLE 6 Subtract $(3x^2 - 2x + 5) - (x^2 - 3x + 4)$.

Solution $(3x^2 - 2x + 5)$ means $1(3x^2 - 2x + 5)$ and $(x^2 - 3x + 4)$ means $1(x^2 - 3x + 4)$. We use this information in the solution, as shown below.

$$(3x^2 - 2x + 5) - (x^2 - 3x + 4) = 1(3x^2 - 2x + 5) - 1(x^2 - 3x + 4)$$

$$= 3x^2 - 2x + 5 - x^2 + 3x - 4 \qquad \text{Removed parentheses.}$$

$$= \underline{3x^2 - x^2} \ \underline{- 2x + 3x} \ \underline{+ 5 - 4} \qquad \text{Rearranged terms.}$$

$$= \qquad 2x^2 \quad + \quad x \qquad + \ 1 \qquad \text{Combined like terms.}$$

Now Try Exercise 97

EXAMPLE 7 Subtract $(-3x^2 - 5x + 3)$ from $(x^3 + 2x + 6)$.

Solution $$(x^3 + 2x + 6) - (-3x^2 - 5x + 3)$$

$$= x^3 + 2x + 6 + 3x^2 + 5x - 3 \qquad \text{Removed parentheses.}$$

$$= x^3 + 3x^2 \ \underline{+ 2x + 5x} \ \underline{+ 6 - 3} \qquad \text{Rearranged terms.}$$

$$= x^3 + 3x^2 + \quad 7x \qquad + \ 3 \qquad \text{Combined like terms.}$$

Now Try Exercise 107

Understanding Algebra

Remember, when a negative sign precedes parentheses, the sign of each term within parentheses is changed:

$$-(-3x^2 - 5x + 3)$$

becomes

$$+3x^2 + 5x - 3$$

Avoiding Common Errors

One of the most common mistakes occurs when subtracting polynomials. When subtracting one polynomial from another, *the sign of each term in the polynomial being subtracted must be changed, not just the sign of the first term.*

CORRECT	INCORRECT
$6x^2 - 4x + 3 - (2x^2 - 3x + 4)$	$6x^2 - 4x + 3 - (2x^2 - 3x + 4)$
$= 6x^2 - 4x + 3 \ - \ 2x^2 \ + \ 3x \ - \ 4$	$= 6x^2 - 4x + 3 - 2x^2 - 3x + 4$
$= 4x^2 - x - 1$	$= 4x^2 - 7x + 7$
	Do not make this mistake!

4 Subtract Polynomials in Columns

To Subtract Polynomials in Columns

1. Write *the polynomial being subtracted* below the polynomial from which it is being subtracted. List like terms in the same column.
2. *Change the sign of each term* in the polynomial being subtracted. (This step can be done mentally, if you like.)
3. Add the terms in each column.

EXAMPLE 8 Subtract $(2x^2 - 4x + 6)$ from $(4x^2 + 5x + 8)$ using columns.

Solution   Align like terms in columns (step 1).

$$
\begin{array}{r}
4x^2 + 5x + 8 \\
-(2x^2 - 4x + 6)
\end{array}
$$
Align like terms.

Change *all* signs in the second row (step 2); then add (step 3).

$$
\begin{array}{r}
4x^2 + 5x + 8 \\
-\,2x^2 + 4x - 6 \\
\hline
2x^2 + 9x + 2
\end{array}
$$
Changed all signs.
Added terms.

Now Try Exercise 113

EXAMPLE 9 Subtract $(2x^2 - 6)$ from $(-3x^3 + 4x - 3)$ using columns.

Solution   To help align like terms, write each expression in descending order. If any power of x is missing, write that term with a numerical coefficient of 0.

$$-3x^3 + 4x - 3 = -3x^3 + 0x^2 + 4x - 3$$
$$2x^2 - 6 = 2x^2 + 0x - 6$$

Align like terms.

$$
\begin{array}{r}
-3x^3 + 0x^2 + 4x - 3 \\
-(2x^2 + 0x - 6)
\end{array}
$$

Change all signs in the second row; then add the terms in each column.

$$
\begin{array}{r}
-3x^3 + 0x^2 + 4x - 3 \\
-\,2x^2 - 0x + 6 \\
\hline
-3x^3 - 2x^2 + 4x + 3
\end{array}
$$

Now Try Exercise 115

NOTE: You may find that you can change the signs mentally and can therefore align and change the signs in one step.

EXERCISE SET 4.4

 Math XL MathXL®   *MyMathLab* MyMathLab

Warm-Up Exercises

Fill in the blanks with the appropriate word, phrase, or symbol(s) from the following list.

$3x - 4$	3	2	1
5	6	$-5x^3 + 3x + 4$	$3x + 4$
7	True	False	

1. When $3x - 5x^3 + 4$ is written in descending order, it is _____ .

2. $(4x^3 + 10x - 1) - (4x^3 + 7x + 3) =$ _____ .

3. $(2x^3 - 8x + 1) + (-2x^3 + 11x + 3) =$ _____ .

4. A trinomial is a polynomial with _____ term(s).

5. A monomial is a polynomial with _____ term(s).

6. A binomial is a polynomial with _____ term(s).

7. The degree of the term $6x^2y^3$ is _____ .

8. The degree of the polynomial $x^6 - 8x^7 + 4$ is _____ .

9. (True or False) The expression $\frac{1}{2}y^3 - 7y + 8$ is a polynomial in y. _____

10. (True or False) The expression $\frac{1}{2y^3} - 7y + 8$ is a polynomial in y. _____

Practice the Skills

Indicate the degree of each term.

11. x^3

12. $6x^2$

13. $-2x$

14. $-56t^9$

15. $7s^4$

16. $4s^7$

17. x^5

18. z^{11}

19. $-3b^8$

20. $5a^4$

21. x^2y

22. a^4b^3

23. $3r^2s^8$

24. $6m^5n^8$

25. $-8x^3y^5z$

26. $-12p^4q^7r$

Indicate which expressions are polynomials. If the polynomial has a specific name—monomial, binomial, or trinomial—give that name.

27. $2x^2 - 6x + 7$

28. $x^2 + 3$

29. -6

30. $4x^{-2}$

31. $9a^4 - 5$

32. $7x + 8$

33. $8x^9$

34. $3x^{1/2} + 2x$

35. $a^{-1} + 4$

36. $x^3 - 8x^2 + 8$

37. $6n^3 - 5n^2 + 4n - 3$

38. $10x^2$

39. $4 - 2b^2 - 5b$

40. $5p^{-3}$

41. $\frac{2}{3}x^2 - \frac{1}{x}$

42. $0.6r^4 - \frac{1}{2}r^3 - 0.4r^2 - \frac{1}{3}$

Express each polynomial in descending order. If the polynomial is already in descending order, so state. Give the degree of each polynomial.

43. 18

44. $4 + 5x$

45. $-4 + x^2 - 2x$

46. $6x - 5$

47. $x + 3x^2 - 8$

48. $4 - 3p^3$

49. $-a - 3$

50. $2x^2 + 5x - 8$

51. $6w^2 - 5w + 9$

52. 15

53. $-4 + x - 3x^2 + 4x^3$

54. $1 - x^3 + 3x$

55. $5x + 3x^2 - 6 - 2x^4$

56. $-3r - 5r^2 + 2r^4 - 6$

Add.

57. $(9x - 2) + (4x - 7)$

58. $(5x - 6) + (2x - 3)$

59. $(-3x + 8) + (2x + 3)$

60. $(-7x - 9) + (-2x + 9)$

61. $(t + 7) + (-3t - 8)$

62. $(4x - 3) + (3x - 3)$

63. $(x^2 + 2.6x - 3) + (4x + 3.8)$

64. $(-4p^2 - 3p - 2) + (-p^2 - 4)$

65. $(4m - 3) + (5m^2 - 4m + 7)$

66. $(-x^2 - 2x - 4) + (4x^2 + 3)$

67. $(2x^2 - 3x + 5) + (-x^2 + 6x - 8)$

68. $(x^2 - 6x + 7) + (-x^2 + 3x + 5)$

69. $(-x^2 - 4x + 8) + \left(5x - 2x^2 + \frac{1}{2}\right)$

70. $(8x^2 + 3x - 5) + \left(x^2 + \frac{1}{2}x + 2\right)$

71. $(5.2n^2 - 6n + 1.7) + (3n^2 + 1.2n - 2.3)$

72. $(8x^2 + 4) + (-2.6x^2 - 5x - 2.3)$

73. $(-7x^3 - 3x^2 + 4) + (4x + 5x^3 - 7)$

74. $(6x^3 - 4x^2 - 7) + (3x^2 + 3x - 3)$

75. $(8x^2 + 2x - y) + (3x^2 - 9x + 5)$

76. $(-7a^2 + 3a - b) + (4a^2 - 2a - 8)$

77. $(2x^2y + 2x - 3) + (3x^2y - 5x + 5)$

78. $(x^2y + x - y) + (2x^2y + 2x - 6y + 3)$

Add using columns.

79. Add $8x - 7$ and $3x + 4$.

80. Add $-x + 5$ and $-4x - 5$.

81. Add $4y^2 - 2y + 4$ and $3y^2 + 1$.

82. Add $6m^2 - 2m + 1$ and $-10m^2 + 8$.

83. Add $-x^2 - 3x + 3$ and $5x^2 + 5x - 7$.

84. Add $-2s^2 - s + 5$ and $3s^2 - 6s$.

85. Add $2x^3 + 3x^2 + 6x - 9$ and $7 - 4x^2$.

86. Add $-3x^3 + 3x + 9$ and $2x^2 - 4$.

87. Add $4n^3 - 5n^2 + n - 6$ and $-n^3 - 6n^2 - 2n + 8$.

88. Add $7x^3 + 5x - 6$ and $3x^3 - 4x^2 - x + 8$.

Subtract.

89. $(4x - 4) - (2x + 2)$

90. $(6x - 5) - (2x - 3)$

91. $(-2x - 3) - (-5x - 7)$

92. $(10x - 3) - (-2x + 7)$

93. $(-r + 5) - (2r + 5)$

94. $(4x + 8) - (3x + 9)$

95. $(-y^2 + 4y - 5.2) - (5y^2 + 2.1y + 7.5)$

96. $(9x^2 + 7x - 5) - (3x^2 + 3.5)$

97. $(5x^2 - x - 1) - (-3x^2 - 2x - 5)$

98. $(-a^2 + 3a + 12) - (-4a^2 - 3)$

99. $(-4.1n^2 - 3n) - (2.3n^2 - 9n + 7.6)$

100. $(7x - 0.6) - (-2x^2 + 4x - 8)$

101. $(8x^3 - 2x^2 - 4x + 5) - (5x^2 + 8)$

102. $\left(9x^3 - \frac{1}{5}\right) - (x^2 + 5x)$

103. $(2x^3 - 4x^2 + 5x - 7) - \left(3x + \frac{3}{5}x^2 - 5\right)$

104. $(-3x^2 + 4x - 7) - \left(x^3 + 4x^2 - \frac{3}{4}x\right)$

105. Subtract $(7x + 4)$ from $(8x + 2)$.

106. Subtract $(-4x + 7)$ from $(-3x - 9)$.

107. Subtract $(5x - 6)$ from $(2x^2 - 4x + 8)$.

108. Subtract $(3x^2 - 5x - 3)$ from $(-x^2 + 3x + 10)$.

109. Subtract $(-2c^2 + 7c - 7)$ from $(-5c^3 - 6c^2 + 7)$.

110. Subtract $(4x^3 - 6x^2)$ from $(3x^3 + 5x^2 + 9x - 7)$.

Subtract using columns.

111. Subtract $(3x - 3)$ from $(6x + 5)$.

112. Subtract $(6x + 8)$ from $(2x - 5)$.

113. Subtract $(2a^2 + 3a - 9)$ from $(5a^2 - 13a + 19)$.

114. Subtract $(4x^2 - 7x + 3)$ from $(8x^2 + 5x - 9)$.

115. Subtract $(6x^2 - 1)$ from $(7x^2 - 3x - 4)$.

116. Subtract $(5n^3 + 7n - 9)$ from $(2n^3 - 6n + 3)$.

117. Subtract $(5x^2 + 4)$ from $(x^2 + 4)$.

118. Subtract $(-5m^2 + 6m)$ from $(m - 6)$.

119. Subtract $(x^2 + 6x - 7)$ from $(4x^3 - 6x^2 + 7x - 9)$.

120. Subtract $(2x^3 + 4x^2 - 9x)$ from $(-5x^3 + 4x - 12)$.

Problem Solving

121. Make up your own addition problem where the sum of two binomials is $-5x - 1$.

122. Make up your own addition problem where the sum of two trinomials is $3x^3 - 2x - 4$.

123. Make up your own subtraction problem where the difference of two trinomials is $7x - 3$.

124. Make up your own subtraction problem where the difference of two trinomials is $-x^2 + 4x - 5$.

125. When two binomials are added, will the sum always, sometimes, or never be a binomial? Explain your answer and give examples to support your answer.

126. When one binomial is subtracted from another, will the difference always, sometimes, or never be a binomial? Explain your answer and give examples to support your answer.

127. When two trinomials are added, will the sum always, sometimes, or never be a trinomial? Explain your answer and give examples to support your answer.

128. When one trinomial is subtracted from another, will the difference always, sometimes, or never be a trinomial? Explain your answer and give examples to support your answer.

129. Write a fourth-degree trinomial in the variable x that has neither a second-degree term nor a constant term.

130. Write a sixth-degree trinomial in the variable x that has no fifth-, fourth-, first-, or zero-degree terms.

Write a polynomial that represents the area of each figure shown.

131.

132.

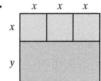

133.

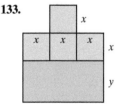

134.

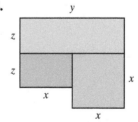

Concept/Writing Exercises

135. Is it possible to have a fourth-degree trinomial in x that has no third-, second-, or zero-degree terms and contains no like terms? Explain.

136. Is it possible to have a fifth-degree trinomial in x that has no fourth-, third-, second-, or first-degree terms and contains no like terms? Explain.

Challenge Problems

Simplify.

137. $(3x^2 - 6x + 3) - (2x^2 - x - 6) - (x^2 + 7x - 9)$

138. $3x^2y - 6xy - 2xy + 9xy^2 - 5xy + 3x$

139. $4(x^2 + 2x - 3) - 6(2 - 4x - x^2) - 2x(x + 2)$

Group Activity

Discuss and answer Exercise 140 as a group.

140. Make up a trinomial, a binomial, and a different trinomial such that (first trinomial) + (binomial) − (second trinomial) = 0.

Cumulative Review Exercises

[1.5] **141.** Insert either $>$, $<$, or $=$ in the shaded area to make the statement true: $|-9|$ ▢ $|-6|$.

[1.6–1.8] *Indicate whether each statement is true or false.*

142. The product of two negative numbers is always a positive number.

143. The sum of two negative numbers is always a negative number.

144. The difference of two negative numbers is always a negative number.

145. The quotient of two negative numbers is always a negative number.

[4.2] **146.** Simplify $\left(\dfrac{b^3 c^{-4}}{2b^{-1}} \right)^{-2}$.

4.5 Multiplication of Polynomials

1 Multiply a monomial by a monomial.

2 Multiply a polynomial by a monomial.

3 Multiply binomials using the distributive property.

4 Multiply binomials using the FOIL method.

5 Multiply binomials using formulas for special products.

6 Multiply any two polynomials.

1 Multiply a Monomial by a Monomial

To multiply two monomials, multiply their coefficients and use the product rule of exponents to determine the exponents on the variables.

EXAMPLE 1 Multiply.

a) $(7x^3)(6x^5)$ **b)** $(4b^2)(-9b^7)$

Solution

a) $(7x^3)(6x^5) = 7 \cdot 6 \cdot x^3 \cdot x^5 = 42x^{3+5} = 42x^8$

b) $(4b^2)(-9b^7) = (4)(-9) \cdot b^2 \cdot b^7 = -36b^{2+7} = -36b^9$

Now Try Exercise 15

EXAMPLE 2 Multiply $(5x^2 y)(8x^5 y^4)$.

Solution   Remember that when a variable is given without an exponent we assume that the exponent on the variable is 1.

$$(5x^2 y)(8x^5 y^4) = 40x^{2+5} y^{1+4} = 40x^7 y^5$$

Now Try Exercise 19

EXAMPLE 3 Multiply.

a) $6xy^2 z^5 (-3x^4 y^7 z)$ **b)** $(-4x^4 z^9)(-3xy^7 z^3)$

Solution

a) $6xy^2 z^5 (-3x^4 y^7 z) = -18x^5 y^9 z^6$

b) $(-4x^4 z^9)(-3xy^7 z^3) = 12x^5 y^7 z^{12}$

Now Try Exercise 21

2 Multiply a Polynomial by a Monomial

To multiply a polynomial by a monomial, we use the distributive property presented earlier.

$$a(b + c) = ab + ac$$

The distributive property can be expanded to

$$a(b + c + d + \cdots + n) = ab + ac + ad + \cdots + an$$

EXAMPLE 4   Multiply $3x(2x^2 + 4)$. ——————

Solution $$3x(2x^2 + 4) = (3x)(2x^2) + (3x)(4)$$
$$= 6x^3 + 12x$$

Now Try Exercise 29

Understanding Algebra

When multiplying a monomial by a polynomial, the monomial is multiplied by each term of the polynomial:

$$3x^2\,(2x^3 - 5x + 7)$$

$$3x^2(2x^3) + 3x^2(-5x) + 3x^2(7)$$

$$6x^5 - 15x^3 + 21x^2$$

EXAMPLE 5   Multiply $-3n(4n^2 - 2n - 1)$. ——————

Solution $$-3n(4n^2 - 2n - 1) = (-3n)(4n^2) + (-3n)(-2n) + (-3n)(-1)$$
$$= -12n^3 + 6n^2 + 3n$$

Now Try Exercise 33

EXAMPLE 6   Multiply $5x^2\,(4x^3 - 2x + 7)$. ——————

Solution $$5x^2\,(4x^3 - 2x + 7) = (5x^2)(4x^3) + (5x^2)(-2x) + (5x^2)(7)$$
$$= 20x^5 - 10x^3 + 35x^2$$

Now Try Exercise 37

EXAMPLE 7   Multiply $2x(3x^2y - 6xy + 5)$. ——————

Solution $$2x(3x^2y - 6xy + 5) = (2x)(3x^2y) + (2x)(-6xy) + (2x)(5)$$
$$= 6x^3y - 12x^2y + 10x$$

Now Try Exercise 39

In Example 8, we perform a multiplication where the monomial is placed to the right of the polynomial. Each term of the polynomial is multiplied by the monomial, as illustrated in the example.

EXAMPLE 8   Multiply $(3x^3 - 2xy + 3)4x$. ——————

Solution $$(3x^3 - 2xy + 3)4x = (3x^3)(4x) + (-2xy)(4x) + (3)(4x)$$
$$= 12x^4 - 8x^2y + 12x$$

Now Try Exercise 41

The problem in Example 8 could be written as $4x(3x^3 - 2xy + 3)$ by the commutative property of multiplication, and then simplified as in Examples 4 through 7.

3 Multiply Binomials Using the Distributive Property

Now we will discuss multiplying a binomial by a binomial. Before we explain how to do this, consider the multiplication problem $43 \cdot 12$.

$$
\begin{array}{r}
43 \\
\underline{12} \\
2(4) \longrightarrow \quad 86 \\
1(4) \longrightarrow \quad \underline{43} \\
516
\end{array}
$$

43 ←—— Multiplicand
12 ←—— Multiplier
86 ←—— 2(3)
43 ←—— 1(3)
516 ←—— Product

Note how the 2 multiplies both the 3 and the 4, and the 1 also multiplies both the 3 and the 4. That is, every digit in the multiplier multiplies every digit in the multiplicand. We can also illustrate the multiplication process as follows.

$$(43)(12) = (40 + 3)\ (10 + 2)$$
$$= (40 + 3)\ (10) + (40 + 3)\ (2)$$
$$= (40)\ (10) + (3)\ (10) + (40)\ (2) + (3)\ (2)$$
$$= \quad 400 \quad + \quad 30 \quad + \quad 80 \quad + \quad 6$$
$$= 516$$

Whenever any two polynomials are multiplied, the same process must be followed. That is, *every term in one polynomial must multiply every term in the other polynomial.*

Consider multiplying $(a + b)(c + d)$. Treating $(a + b)$ as a single term and using the distributive property, we get

$$(a + b)\ (c + d) = (a + b)\ c + (a + b)\ d$$

Using the distributive property a second time gives

$$= ac + bc + ad + bd$$

Notice how each term of the first polynomial was multiplied by each term of the second polynomial, and all the products were added to obtain the answer.

EXAMPLE 9 Multiply $(3x + 2)(x - 5)$.

Solution $(3x + 2)\ (x - 5) = (3x + 2)\ x + (3x + 2)\ (-5)$
$$= 3x(x) + 2(x) + 3x(-5) + 2(-5)$$
$$= 3x^2\ + 2x - 15x - 10$$
$$= 3x^2\ - 13x - 10$$

Now Try Exercise 43

Note that after performing the multiplication, like terms must be combined.

EXAMPLE 10 Multiply $(x - 4)(y + 3)$.

Solution $(x - 4)\ (y + 3) = (x - 4)\ y + (x - 4)\ 3$
$$= xy - 4y + 3x - 12$$

Now Try Exercise 65

4 Multiply Binomials Using the FOIL Method

A commonly used method to multiply two binomials is the **FOIL method**. This procedure also results in each term of one binomial being multiplied by each term in the other binomial. The FOIL method is not actually a different method used to multiply binomials but rather an acronym to help students remember to correctly apply the distributive property.

The FOIL Method

Consider $(a + b)(c + d)$.

F stands for **first**—multiply the first terms of each binomial together:

$$\overset{F}{(a + b)(c + d)} \qquad \text{product } ac$$

O stands for **outer**—multiply the two outer terms together:

$$\overset{O}{(a + b)(c + d)} \qquad \text{product } ad$$

I stands for **inner**—multiply the two inner terms together:

$$\overset{I}{(a + b)(c + d)} \qquad \text{product } bc$$

L stands for **last**—multiply the last terms together:

$$\overset{L}{(a + b)(c + d)} \qquad \text{product } bd$$

The product of the two binomials is the sum of these four products.

$$(a + b)(c + d) = ac + ad + bc + bd$$

EXAMPLE 11 Using the FOIL method, multiply $(2x - 3)(x + 4)$.

Solution

$$(2x - 3)(x + 4)$$

$$\begin{array}{cccc} F & O & I & L \end{array}$$
$$= (2x)(x) + (2x)(4) + (-3)(x) + (-3)(4)$$
$$= \quad 2x^2 \quad + \quad 8x \quad - \quad 3x \quad - \quad 12$$
$$= 2x^2 + 5x - 12$$

Thus, $(2x - 3)(x + 4) = 2x^2 + 5x - 12$.

Now Try Exercise 45

EXAMPLE 12 Multiply $(4 - 2x)(6 - 5x)$.

Solution

$$(4 - 2x)(6 - 5x)$$

$$\begin{array}{cccc} F & O & I & L \end{array}$$
$$= 4(6) + 4(-5x) + (-2x)(6) + (-2x)(-5x)$$
$$= \quad 24 \quad - \quad 20x \quad - \quad 12x \quad + \quad 10x^2$$
$$= 10x^2 - 32x + 24$$

Thus, $(4 - 2x)(6 - 5x) = 10x^2 - 32x + 24$.

Now Try Exercise 63

EXAMPLE 13 Multiply $(4p + 5)(4p - 5)$.

Solution

$$
\begin{array}{cccc}
 & F & O & I & L \\
(4p + 5)(4p - 5) = (4p)(4p) & + & (4p)(-5) & + & (5)(4p) & + & (5)(-5) \\
\end{array}
$$

$$= 16p^2 \quad - \quad 20p \quad + \quad 20p \quad - \quad 25$$

$$= 16p^2 - 25$$

Thus, $(4p + 5)(4p - 5) = 16p^2 - 25$.

Now Try Exercise 57

5 Multiply Binomials Using Formulas for Special Products

Example 13 illustrated a special product, the product of the sum and difference of the same two terms.

> **Special Product: Product of the Sum and Difference of the Same Two Terms**
>
> $$\underbrace{(a + b)}_{\substack{\text{sum of} \\ \text{2 terms}}}\underbrace{(a - b)}_{\substack{\text{difference} \\ \text{2 terms}}} = a^2 - b^2 \text{ where } a \text{ and } b \text{ represent terms.}$$

The expression on the right side of the equals sign is called **the difference of two squares**. Since multiplication is commutative, $(a + b)(a - b) = a^2 - b^2$ can also be written $(a - b)(a + b) = a^2 - b^2$.

EXAMPLE 14 Use the rule for finding the product of the sum and difference of two quantities to multiply each expression.

a) $(x + 5)(x - 5)$ **b)** $(2x + 3)(2x - 3)$ **c)** $(3x - 2y)(3x + 2y)$

Solution

a) If we let $x = a$ and $5 = b$, then

$$(a + b)(a - b) = a^2 - b^2$$
$$\downarrow \quad \downarrow \ \downarrow \quad \downarrow \qquad \downarrow \qquad \downarrow$$
$$(x + 5)(x - 5) = (x)^2 - (5)^2$$
$$= x^2 - 25$$

b)
$$(a + b)(a - b) = a^2 - b^2$$
$$\downarrow \quad \downarrow \ \downarrow \quad \downarrow \qquad \downarrow \qquad \downarrow$$
$$(2x + 3)(2x - 3) = (2x)^2 - (3)^2$$
$$= 4x^2 - 9$$

c)
$$(a - b)(a + b) = a^2 - b^2$$
$$\downarrow \quad \downarrow \ \downarrow \quad \downarrow \qquad \downarrow \qquad \downarrow$$
$$(3x - 2y)(3x + 2y) = (3x)^2 - (2y)^2$$
$$= 9x^2 - 4y^2$$

Now Try Exercise 77

Example 14 could also have been done using the FOIL method.

EXAMPLE 15 Using the FOIL method, multiply $(x + 3)^2$.

Solution $(x + 3)^2 = (x + 3)(x + 3)$

$$\begin{array}{cccc} \text{F} & \text{O} & \text{I} & \text{L} \end{array}$$

$$= x(x) + x(3) + 3(x) + (3)(3)$$
$$= x^2 + 3x + 3x + 9$$
$$= x^2 + 6x + 9$$

Now Try Exercise 59

Example 15 illustrates the **square of a binomial,** another special product.

Special Product: Square of Binomial Formulas

$$(a + b)^2 = (a + b)(a + b) = a^2 + 2ab + b^2$$
$$(a - b)^2 = (a - b)(a - b) = a^2 - 2ab + b^2$$

To square a binomial, add the square of the first term, twice the product of the terms, and the square of the second term.

EXAMPLE 16 Use the square of a binomial formula to multiply each expression.

a) $(x + 5)^2$ **b)** $(2x - 3)^2$ **c)** $(3r + 2s)^2$ **d)** $(x - 3)(x - 3)$

Solution

a) If we let $x = a$ and $5 = b$, then

$$(a + b)(a + b) = a^2 + 2\ a\ b + b^2$$
$$\downarrow\ \downarrow\ \downarrow\ \downarrow\quad \downarrow\quad\ \downarrow\ \downarrow\qquad \downarrow$$
$$(x + 5)^2 = (x + 5)(x + 5) = (x)^2 + 2(x)(5) + (5)^2$$
$$= x^2 + 10x + 25$$

b)
$$(a - b)\ (a - b) = a^2 - 2\ a\ b + b^2$$
$$\downarrow\ \downarrow\ \downarrow\ \downarrow\quad \downarrow\quad\ \downarrow\ \downarrow\qquad \downarrow$$
$$(2x - 3)^2 = (2x - 3)(2x - 3) = (2x)^2 - 2(2x)(3) + (3)^2$$
$$= 4x^2 - 12x + 9$$

c)
$$(a + b)\ (a + b) = a^2 + 2\ a\ b + b^2$$
$$\downarrow\ \searrow\ \downarrow\ \searrow\quad \downarrow\quad\ \downarrow\ \downarrow\qquad \downarrow$$
$$(3r + 2s)^2 = (3r + 2s)(3r + 2s) = (3r)^2 + 2(3r)(2s) + (2s)^2$$
$$= 9r^2 + 12rs + 4s^2$$

d)
$$(a - b)(a - b) = a^2 - 2\ a\ b + b^2$$
$$\downarrow\ \downarrow\ \downarrow\ \downarrow\quad \downarrow\quad\ \downarrow\ \downarrow\qquad \downarrow$$
$$(x - 3)(x - 3) = (x - 3)(x - 3) = (x)^2 - 2(x)(3) + (3)^2$$
$$= x^2 - 6x + 9$$

Now Try Exercise 83

Example 16 could also have been done using the FOIL method.

Avoiding Common Errors

CORRECT	INCORRECT
$(a + b)^2 = a^2 + 2ab + b^2$	$(a + b)^2 = a^2 + b^2$
$(a - b)^2 = a^2 - 2ab + b^2$	$(a - b)^2 = a^2 - b^2$

Do not forget the middle term when you square a binomial.

$$(x + 2)^2 \neq x^2 + 4$$
$$(x + 2)^2 = (x + 2)(x + 2)$$
$$= x^2 + 4x + 4$$

6 Multiply Any Two Polynomials

When multiplying any two polynomials, each term of one polynomial must be multiplied by each term of the other polynomial. For example.

$$(3x + 2)(4x^2 - 5x - 3)$$
$$= 3x\,(4x^2 - 5x - 3) \;+2\,(4x^2 - 5x - 3) \qquad \text{Use the distributive property.}$$
$$= 12x^3 - 15x^2 - 9x + 8x^2 - 10x - 6$$
$$= 12x^3 - 7x^2 - 19x - 6$$

Thus, $(3x + 2)(4x^2 - 5x - 3) = 12x^3 - 7x^2 - 19x - 6$.

Alternatively, you may prefer to multiply a polynomial by a polynomial using a vertical procedure. On page 259, we showed that when multiplying the number 43 by the number 12, we multiply each digit in the number 43 by each digit in the number 12. Review that example now. We can follow a similar procedure, being careful, however, to align like terms in the same column when performing the individual multiplications.

EXAMPLE 17 Multiply $(3x + 4)(2x + 5)$.

Solution   First write the polynomials one beneath the other.

$$3x + 4$$
$$2x + 5$$

Next, multiply each term in $(3x + 4)$ by 5.

$$
\begin{array}{r}
3x + \;\;4 \\
2x + \;\;5 \\
\hline
\end{array}
$$
$$5(3x + 4) \longrightarrow 15x + 20$$

Next, multiply each term in $(3x + 4)$ by $2x$ and align like terms.

$$
\begin{array}{r}
3x + 4 \\
2x + 5 \\
\hline
15x + 20 \\
\end{array}
$$
$$2x(3x + 4) \longrightarrow 6x^2 + \;\;8x$$
$$\overline{\qquad 6x^2 + 23x + 20} \qquad \text{Added like terms in columns.}$$

Now Try Exercise 55

The same answer for Example 17 would be obtained using the FOIL method.

EXAMPLE 18 Multiply $(4y + 3)(2y^2 - 7y - 5)$.

Solution   For convenience, we place the shorter expression on the bottom, as illustrated.

$$
\begin{array}{r}
2y^2 - 7y - 5 \\
4y + 3 \\
\hline
6y^2 - 21y - 15 \\
8y^3 - 28y^2 - 20y \\
\hline
8y^3 - 22y^2 - 41y - 15
\end{array}
$$

Multiplied the top polynomial by 3.

Multiplied the top polynomial by $4y$; aligned like terms.

Added like terms in columns.

Now Try Exercise 95

EXAMPLE 19 Multiply $(x^2 - 3x + 2)(2x^2 - 3)$.

Solution
$$
\begin{array}{r}
x^2 - 3x + 2 \\
2x^2 - 3 \\
\hline
-3x^2 + 9x - 6 \\
2x^4 - 6x^3 + 4x^2 \\
\hline
2x^4 - 6x^3 + x^2 + 9x - 6
\end{array}
$$

Multiplied the top polynomial by -3.

Multiplied the top polynomial by $2x^2$; aligned like terms.

Added like terms in columns.

Now Try Exercise 103

EXAMPLE 20 Multiply $(3x^3 - 2x^2 + 4x + 6)(x^2 - 5x)$.

Solution
$$
\begin{array}{r}
3x^3 - 2x^2 + 4x + 6 \\
x^2 - 5x \\
\hline
-15x^4 + 10x^3 - 20x^2 - 30x \\
3x^5 - 2x^4 + 4x^3 + 6x^2 \\
\hline
3x^5 - 17x^4 + 14x^3 - 14x^2 - 30x
\end{array}
$$

Multiplied the top polynomial by $-5x$.

Multiplied the top polynomial by x^2; aligned like terms.

Added like terms in columns.

Now Try Exercise 105

EXERCISE SET 4.5

MathXL
MathXL®

MyMathLab
MyMathLab

Warm-Up Exercises

Fill in the blanks with the appropriate word, phrase, or symbol(s) from the following list.

difference of two squares	trinomial	FOIL	False	True
$4t^2 + 4t + 1$	$4t^2 + 1$	$4t^2 - 1$	$4t^2 - 4t + 1$	align

1. When $(2x - 5)(3x + 4)$ is multiplied and simplified, the resulting expression is a(n) _____ .

2. When $(2t - 1)^2$ is multiplied and simplified, the result is _____ .

3. (True or False) $(x + 5)^2 = x^2 + 25$. _____

4. When $(2t + 1)(2t - 1)$ is multiplied and simplified, the result is _____ .

5. When multiplying polynomials vertically, it is important to _____ like terms.

6. When $(2t + 1)^2$ is multiplied and simplified, the result is _____ .

7. The result of multiplying $(x + 4)(x - 4)$ is an expression called the _____ .

8. When multiplying two binomials, a commonly used method is _____ .

Practice the Skills

Multiply.

9. $(3x^2)(5x^3)$

10. $(-3x^2)(-10x^3)$

11. $(6t^7)(-5t^3)$

12. $(-4z^{12})(5z^3)$

13. $4x^3(-5x^3)$

14. $(-13y^4)(-10y^3)$

15. $(3x^4)(-8x^2)$

16. $(-7p^5)(-2p^3)$

17. $5x^3y^5(4x^2y)$

18. $-5x^2y^4(2x^3y^2)$

19. $(4xy^6)(-7x^2y^9)$

20. $(4a^3b^7)(6a^2b)$

21. $9xy^6(6x^5y^8)$

22. $(6m^3n^4)(3n^5)$

23. $(6x^2y)\left(\dfrac{1}{2}x^4\right)$

24. $\dfrac{3}{4}x(8x^2y^3)$

25. $(3.3x^4)(1.8x^4y^3)$

26. $(2.3x^5)(4.1x^2y^4)$

Multiply.

27. $9(x-6)$

28. $4(x+3)$

29. $-3x(2x-2)$

30. $-4p(-3p+6)$

31. $-2(8y+5)$

32. $2x(x^2+3x-1)$

33. $-2x(x^2-2x+5)$

34. $-6c(-3c^2+5c-6)$

35. $5x(-4x^2+6x-4)$

36. $(3x^2+x-6)x$

37. $0.5x^2(x^3-6x^2-1)$

38. $2.3b^2(2b^2-b+3)$

39. $0.3x(2xy+5x-6y)$

40. $-\dfrac{1}{2}x^3(2x^2+4x-6y^2)$

41. $(x^2-4y^3-3)y^4$

42. $\dfrac{1}{4}y^4(y^2-12y+4x)$

Multiply.

43. $(5x-2)(x+4)$

44. $(2x-3)(x+5)$

45. $(2t+5)(3t-6)$

46. $(4a-1)(a+4)$

47. $(2x-4)(2x+4)$

48. $(4+5w)(3+w)$

49. $(8-5x)(6+x)$

50. $(-x+3)(2x+5)$

51. $(6x-1)(-2x+5)$

52. $(7n-3)(2n+1)$

53. $(x-2)(4x-2)$

54. $(2x+3)(x+5)$

55. $(3k-6)(4k-2)$

56. $(3d-5)(4d-1)$

57. $(x-2)(x+2)$

58. $(3x-8)(2x+3)$

59. $(2x-3)(2x-3)$

60. $(7x+3)(2x+4)$

61. $(6z-4)(7-z)$

62. $(6-2m)(5m-3)$

63. $(9-2x)(7-4x)$

64. $(2-5x)(7-2x)$

65. $(x+7)(y-3)$

66. $(z+2y)(4z-3)$

67. $(2x-3y)(3x+2y)$

68. $(2x+3)(2y-5)$

69. $(9x+y)(4-3x)$

70. $(2x-0.1)(x+2.4)$

71. $(x+0.6)(x+0.3)$

72. $(3x-6)\left(x+\dfrac{1}{3}\right)$

73. $(x+4)\left(x-\dfrac{1}{2}\right)$

74. $(2y-4)\left(\dfrac{1}{2}x-1\right)$

Multiply using a special product formula.

75. $(x+8)(x-8)$

76. $(x+3)^2$

77. $(3x-8)(3x+8)$

78. $(r-4)(r-4)$

79. $(x+y)^2$

80. $(2x-7)(2x+7)$

81. $(x-0.2)^2$

82. $(a+3b)(a-3b)$

83. $(4x+5)(4x+5)$

84. $(5x+4)(5x-4)$

85. $(0.4x+y)^2$

86. $\left(x-\dfrac{1}{2}y\right)^2$

87. $(4c-5d)(4c+5d)$

88. $(4+3w)(4-3w)$

89. $(-2x+6)(-2x-6)$

90. $(-3m+2n)(-3m-2n)$

91. $(7s-3t)^2$

92. $(7a+2)^2$

Multiply.

93. $(4m+3)(4m^2-5m+6)$

94. $(x+4)(3x^2+4x-1)$

95. $(3x+2)(4x^2-x+5)$

96. $(x-1)(3x^2+3x+2)$

97. $(-2x^2-4x+1)(7x-3)$

98. $(4x^2+9x-2)(x-2)$

99. $(a+b)(a^2-ab+b^2)$

100. $(a-b)(a^2+ab+b^2)$

101. $(3t^2 - 2t + 4)(2t^2 + 3t + 1)$

102. $(x^2 - 2x + 3)(x^2 - 4)$

103. $(x^2 - x + 3)(x^2 - 2x)$

104. $(6x + 4)(2x^2 + 2x - 4)$

105. $(2x^3 - 6x^2 + x - 3)(x^2 + 4x)$

106. $(3y^3 + 4y^2 - y + 7)(y^2 - 5y)$

Determine the cube of each expression by writing the expression as the square of an expression multiplied by another expression. For example, $(x + 3y)^3 = (x + 3y)^2 (x + 3y)$.

107. $(b - 1)^3$

108. $(x + 2)^3$

109. $(3a - 5)^3$

110. $(2z + 3)^3$

Concept/Writing Exercises

111. Will the product of a monomial and a monomial always be a monomial? Explain your answer.

112. Will the product of a monomial and a binomial ever be a trinomial? Explain your answer.

113. Will the product of two binomials after like terms are combined always be a trinomial? Explain your answer.

114. Will the product of any polynomial and a binomial always be a polynomial? Explain.

Problem Solving

Consider the multiplications in Exercises 115 and 116. Determine the exponents to be placed in the shaded areas.

115. $3x^2 (2x^{\square} - 5x^{\square} + 3x^{\square}) = 6x^8 - 15x^5 + 9x^3$.

116. $4x^3 (x^{\square} + 2x^{\square} - 5x^{\square}) = 4x^7 + 8x^5 - 20x^4$.

117. Suppose that one side of a rectangle is represented as $x + 2$ and a second side is represented as $2x + 1$.

   a) Express the area of the rectangle in terms of x.

   b) Find the area if $x = 4$ feet.

   c) What value of x, in feet, would result in the rectangle being a square? Explain how you determined your answer.

118. Consider the figure below.

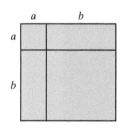

   a) Write an expression for the length of the top.

   b) Write an expression for the length of the left side.

   c) Is this figure a square? Explain.

   d) Express the area of this square as the square of a binomial.

   e) Determine the area of the square by summing the areas of the four individual pieces.

   f) Using the figure and your answer to part **e)**, complete the following.
   $$(a + b)^2 = ?$$

119. Suppose that a rectangular solid has length $x + 5$, width $3x + 4$, and height $2x - 2$ (see the figure).

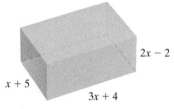

   a) Write a polynomial that represents the area of the base by multiplying the length by the width.

   b) The volume of the figure can be found by multiplying the area of the base by the height. Write a polynomial that represents the volume of the figure.

   c) Using the polynomial in part **b)**, find the volume of the figure if x is 4 feet.

   d) Using the binomials given for the length, width, and height, find the volume if x is 4 feet.

   e) Are your answers to parts **c)** and **d)** the same? If not, explain why.

Challenge Problems

Multiply.

120. $(2x^3 - 6x^2 + 5x - 3)(3x^3 - 6x + 4)$

121. $\left(\dfrac{1}{2}x + \dfrac{2}{3}\right)\left(\dfrac{2}{3}x - \dfrac{2}{5}\right)$

Group Activity

122. Consider the trinomial $2x^2 + 7x + 3$.

   a) As a group, determine whether there is a maximum number of pairs of binomials whose product is $2x^2 + 7x + 3$. That is, how many different pairs of binomials can go in the shaded areas?
   $$2x^2 + 7x + 3 = (\quad\quad)(\quad\quad)$$

   b) Individually, find a pair of binomials whose product is $2x^2 + 7x + 3$.

   c) Compare your answer to part **b)** with the other members of your group. If you did not all arrive at the same answer, explain why.

Cumulative Review Exercises

[2.5]   **123.** Solve the equation $3(x + 7) - 5 = 3x - 17$.

[3.3]   **124. Complementary Angles** Angles C and D are complementary angles, and angle D is $16°$ less than angle C. Find the measures of angle C and angle D.

[4.1]   **125.** Simplify $\left(\dfrac{3xy^4}{6y^6}\right)^4$.

[4.1–4.2]   **126.** Evaluate the following.

    a) -6^3

    b) 6^{-3}

[4.4]   **127.** Subtract $4x^2 - 4x - 9$ from $-x^2 - 6x + 5$.

4.6 Division of Polynomials

1   Divide a polynomial by a monomial.

2   Divide a polynomial by a binomial.

3   Check division of polynomial problems.

4   Write polynomials in descending order when dividing.

Now let's see how to divide polynomials.

1 Divide a Polynomial by a Monomial

To Divide a Polynomial by a Monomial

To divide a polynomial by a monomial, divide each term of the polynomial by the monomial.

EXAMPLE 1 Divide.

a) $\dfrac{4x + 20}{4}$ **b)** $\dfrac{9x^2 - 6x}{3x}$

Solution

a) $\dfrac{4x + 20}{4} = \dfrac{4x}{4} + \dfrac{20}{4} = x + 5$

b) $\dfrac{9x^2 - 6x}{3x} = \dfrac{9x^2}{3x} - \dfrac{6x}{3x} = 3x - 2$

Now Try Exercise 17

Avoiding Common Errors

CORRECT

$$\frac{x + 2}{2} = \frac{x}{2} + \frac{2}{2} = \frac{x}{2} + 1$$

$$\frac{x + 2}{x} = \frac{x}{x} + \frac{2}{x} = 1 + \frac{2}{x}$$

INCORRECT

$$\frac{x + \overset{1}{\cancel{2}}}{\underset{1}{\cancel{2}}} = \frac{x + 1}{1} = x + 1$$

$$\frac{\overset{1}{\cancel{x}} + 2}{\underset{1}{\cancel{x}}} = \frac{1 + 2}{1} = 3$$

Can you explain why the procedures on the right are not correct?

EXAMPLE 2 Divide $\dfrac{4t^5 - 6t^4 + 8t - 3}{2t^2}$.

Solution
$$\frac{4t^5 - 6t^4 + 8t - 3}{2t^2} = \frac{4t^5}{2t^2} - \frac{6t^4}{2t^2} + \frac{8t}{2t^2} - \frac{3}{2t^2}$$

$$= 2t^3 - 3t^2 + \frac{4}{t} - \frac{3}{2t^2}$$

Now Try Exercise 37

EXAMPLE 3 Divide $\dfrac{3x^3 - 6x^2 + 4x - 1}{-3x}$.

Solution A negative sign appears in the denominator. Usually, it is easier to divide if the divisor is positive. We multiply both numerator and denominator by -1 to get a positive denominator.

$$\frac{(-1)(3x^3 - 6x^2 + 4x - 1)}{(-1)(-3x)} = \frac{-3x^3 + 6x^2 - 4x + 1}{3x}$$

$$= \frac{-3x^3}{3x} + \frac{6x^2}{3x} - \frac{4x}{3x} + \frac{1}{3x}$$

$$= -x^2 + 2x - \frac{4}{3} + \frac{1}{3x}$$

Now Try Exercise 41

2 Divide a Polynomial by a Binomial

We divide a polynomial by a binomial in much the same way as we perform long division.

EXAMPLE 4 Divide $\dfrac{x^2 + 6x + 8}{x + 2}$. ⟵ Dividend
⟵ Divisor

Solution Rewrite the division problem in the following form:

$$x + 2 \overline{)x^2 + 6x + 8}$$

Divide x^2 (the first term in the dividend) by x (the first term in the divisor).

$$\frac{x^2}{x} = x$$

Place the quotient, x, above the like term containing x in the dividend.

$$\begin{array}{r} x \\ x + 2 \overline{)x^2 + 6x + 8} \end{array}$$

Next, multiply the x by $x + 2$ as you would do in long division and place the terms of the product under their like terms.

$$\begin{array}{r} \text{Times} \quad\quad x \\ x + 2 \overline{)x^2 + 6x + 8} \\ \text{Equals} \rightarrow x^2 + 2x \quad \leftarrow x(x+2) \end{array}$$

Now subtract $x^2 + 2x$ from $x^2 + 6x$. When subtracting, remember to change the sign of the terms being subtracted and then add the like terms.

$$\begin{array}{r} x \\ x + 2 \overline{)\; x^2 + 6x + 8} \\ \underline{x^2 + 2x} \\ 4x \end{array}$$

Next, bring down the 8, the next term in the dividend.

$$\begin{array}{r} x \\ x + 2 \overline{)x^2 + 6x + 8} \\ \underline{x^2 + 2x} \\ 4x + 8 \end{array}$$

Now divide $4x$, the first term at the bottom, by, x, the first term in the divisor.

$$\frac{4x}{x} = +4$$

Write the +4 in the quotient above the constant in the dividend.

$$
\begin{array}{r}
x + 4 \\
x + 2 \overline{\smash{)}x^2 + 6x + 8} \\
\underline{x^2 + 2x} \\
4x + 8
\end{array}
$$

Multiply the $x + 2$ by 4 and place the terms of the product under their like terms.

$$
\begin{array}{r}
x + 4 \\
x + 2 \overline{\smash{)}x^2 + 6x + 8} \\
\underline{x^2 + 2x} \\
4x + 8 \\
4x + 8 \quad \longleftarrow 4(x + 2)
\end{array}
$$

Now subtract.

$$
\begin{array}{r}
x + \ 4 \quad \longleftarrow \text{Quotient} \\
x + 2 \overline{\smash{)}x^2 + 6x + \ 8} \\
\underline{x^2 + 2x} \\
4x + \ 8 \\
\underline{4x + \ 8} \\
0 \quad \longleftarrow \text{Remainder}
\end{array}
$$

Thus,

$$
\frac{x^2 + 6x + 8}{x + 2} = x + 4
$$

There is no remainder.

Now Try Exercise 43

Understanding Algebra

Dividing by binomials is similar to long division in arithmetic. There are five major steps:

1. Enter term in quotient
2. Multiply
3. Subtract
4. Bring down
5. Repeat

EXAMPLE 5 Divide $\dfrac{3x^2 + x - 12}{x + 2}$.

Solution   First write the problem in the following form:

$$
x + 2 \overline{\smash{)}3x^2 + x - 12}
$$

Since $3x^2$ divided by x is $3x$, place $3x$ above the x-term in the dividend.

$$
\begin{array}{r}
3x \\
x + 2 \overline{\smash{)}3x^2 + x - 12}
\end{array}
$$

Then multiply $3x(x + 2)$ and write the product $3x^2 + 6x$ as shown below. Then subtract to get a difference of $-5x$.

$$
\begin{array}{r}
3x \\
x + 2 \overline{\smash{)}\ 3x^2 + \ x - 12} \\
\underline{3x^2 + 6x} \\
-5x
\end{array}
$$

Next bring down the -12. Then divide $-5x$ by x, which gives -5. Place -5 over -12 in the dividend, as shown below. Then multiply $-5(x + 2)$. Write the product, $-5x - 10$ below the $-5x - 12$. Then subtract to get a remainder of -2.

$$
\begin{array}{r}
3x - \ 5 \\
x + 2 \overline{\smash{)}3x^2 + \ x - 12} \\
\underline{3x^2 + 6x} \\
-5x - 12 \\
\underline{-5x - 10} \\
-2
\end{array}
$$

When there is a remainder, as in this example, list the quotient plus the remainder above the divisor. Thus,

$$\frac{3x^2 + x - 12}{x + 2} = 3x - 5 + \frac{-2}{x + 2} = 3x - 5 - \frac{2}{x + 2}$$

Now Try Exercise 45

EXAMPLE 6 Divide $\dfrac{6x^2 - 5x + 5}{2x + 3}$.

Solution

$$\frac{6x^2}{2x} \qquad \frac{-14x}{2x}$$

$$\begin{array}{r} 3x - 7 \\ 2x + 3 \overline{)\, 6x^2 - 5x + 5} \\ \underline{6x^2 + 9x} \leftarrow \quad 3x(2x+3) \\ -14x + 5 \\ \underline{+14x + 21} \leftarrow \quad -7(2x+3) \\ 26 \leftarrow \text{Remainder} \end{array}$$

Thus, $\dfrac{6x^2 - 5x + 5}{2x + 3} = 3x - 7 + \dfrac{26}{2x + 3}$.

Now Try Exercise 57

3 Check Division of Polynomial Problems

The answer to a division problem can be checked. Consider the division problem $13 \div 5$.

$$\begin{array}{r} 2 \\ 5 \overline{)\, 13} \\ \underline{10} \\ 3 \end{array}$$

Note that the divisor times the quotient, plus the remainder, equals the dividend:

$$(\text{divisor} \times \text{quotient}) + \text{remainder} = \text{dividend}$$
$$(5 \cdot 2) + 3 \overset{?}{=} 13$$
$$10 + 3 \overset{?}{=} 13$$
$$13 = 13 \qquad \text{True}$$

This same procedure can be used to check all division problems.

> **To Check Division of Polynomials**
>
> $$(\text{divisor} \times \text{quotient}) + \text{remainder} = \text{dividend}$$

Let's check the answer to Example 6. The divisor is $2x + 3$, the quotient is $3x - 7$, the remainder is 26, and the dividend is $6x^2 - 5x + 5$.

Check $(\text{divisor} \times \text{quotient}) + \text{remainder} = \text{dividend}$

$$(2x + 3)(3x - 7) + 26 \overset{?}{=} 6x^2 - 5x + 5$$

$$(6x^2 - 5x - 21) + 26 \overset{?}{=} 6x^2 - 5x + 5$$

$$6x^2 - 5x + 5 = 6x^2 - 5x + 5 \qquad \text{True}$$

4 Write Polynomials in Descending Order When Dividing

When dividing a polynomial by a binomial, both the polynomial and binomial should be listed in descending order. If there is no term for a certain power, we write that term with a numerical coefficient of 0 as a placeholder. This will help keep like terms aligned. For example, to divide $(6x^2 + x^3 - 4)/(x - 2)$, we begin by writing $(x^3 + 6x^2 + 0x - 4)/(x - 2)$.

EXAMPLE 7 Divide $(-x + 9x^3 - 28)$ by $(3x - 4)$.

Solution First we rewrite the dividend in descending order to get $(9x^3 - x - 28) \div (3x - 4)$. Since there is no x^2 term in the dividend, we will add $0x^2$ to help align like terms.

$$\frac{9x^3}{3x} \quad \frac{12x^2}{3x} \quad \frac{15x}{3x}$$
$$\downarrow \qquad \downarrow \qquad \downarrow$$

$$
\begin{array}{r}
3x^2 + 4x + 5 \\
3x - 4\overline{)9x^3 + 0x^2 - x - 28} \\
\underline{9x^3 - 12x^2} \longleftarrow 3x^2(3x-4) \\
12x^2 - x \\
\underline{12x^2 - 16x} \longleftarrow 4x(3x-4) \\
15x - 28 \\
\underline{15x - 20} \longleftarrow 5(3x-4) \\
-8 \longleftarrow \text{Remainder}
\end{array}
$$

> **Understanding Algebra**
>
> When a term in "missing", we can insert it with a zero coefficient as a placeholder.
>
> For example, $9x^3 - x - 28$ has no x^2 term. But we can write the expression as $9x^3 + 0x^2 - x - 28$ so terms align in the division process.

Thus, $\dfrac{-x + 9x^3 - 28}{3x - 4} = 3x^2 + 4x + 5 - \dfrac{8}{3x - 4}$. Check this division yourself using the procedure discussed on page 271.

Now Try Exercise 55

EXERCISE SET 4.6

  MathXL®   MyMathLab

Warm-Up Exercises

Fill in the blanks with the appropriate word, phrase, or symbol(s) from the following list.

divisor	$\dfrac{6x^2 - 7x - 20}{(2x - 5)} = (3x + 4)$	remainder	dividend
quotient		descending order	ascending order
$6x^3 + 8x^2 + 16 = (3x^2 - 2x + 4)(2x + 4)$	$6x^3 + 8x^2 + 0x + 16$	True	False

1. The multiplication statement $(2x - 5)(3x + 4) = 6x^2 - 7x - 20$, when written as a division problem, is _____.

2. In the division statement $(2x^2 + 11x + 12) \div (x + 5) = (2x + 1) + \dfrac{7}{x + 5}$, the quantity $2x^2 + 11x + 12$ is called the _____.

3. In the division statement $(2x^2 + 11x + 12) \div (x + 5) = (2x + 1) + \dfrac{7}{x + 5}$, the quantity $x + 5$ is called the _____.

4. In the division statement $(2x^2 + 11x + 12) \div (x + 5) = (2x + 1) + \dfrac{7}{x + 5}$, the quantity $2x + 1$ is called the _____.

5. In the division statement $(2x^2 + 11x + 12) \div (x + 5) = (2x + 1) + \dfrac{7}{x + 5}$, the quantity 7 is called the _____.

6. The division statement $(6x^3 + 8x^2 + 16) \div (3x^2 - 2x + 4) = 2x + 4$, when written as a multiplication problem is _____.

7. To prepare to do the division problem $\dfrac{6x^3 + 8x^2 + 16}{3x^2 - 2x + 4}$, the numerator $6x^3 + 8x^2 + 16$ is better written as _____ .

8. When dividing a polynomial by a binomial, the terms of each should be written in _____ .

9. (True or False) $\dfrac{2x + 8}{2} = x + 8$. _____

10. (True or False) $\dfrac{y + 5}{y} = 1 + \dfrac{5}{y}$. _____

Rewrite each multiplication problem as a division problem. There is more than one correct answer.

11. $(x - 7)(x + 6) = x^2 - x - 42$

12. $(x + 3)(3x - 1) = 3x^2 + 8x - 3$

13. $(2x + 3)(x + 1) = 2x^2 + 5x + 3$

14. $(2x - 5)(x + 1) = 2x^2 - 3x - 5$

15. $(2x + 3)(2x - 3) = 4x^2 - 9$

16. $(3n + 4)(n - 5) = 3n^2 - 11n - 20$

Practice the Skills

Divide.

17. $\dfrac{3t + 6}{3}$

18. $\dfrac{4x - 6}{2}$

19. $\dfrac{4n + 10}{4}$

20. $(-3x - 8) \div 4$

21. $\dfrac{7x + 6}{3}$

22. $\dfrac{5x - 10}{5}$

23. $\dfrac{-6x + 4}{2}$

24. $\dfrac{-5a + 4}{-3}$

25. $\dfrac{-9x - 3}{-3}$

26. $\dfrac{8x - 3}{-8}$

27. $\dfrac{2x + 16}{4}$

28. $\dfrac{2p - 3}{2p}$

29. $\dfrac{4 - 10w}{-4}$

30. $\dfrac{6 - 5x}{-3x}$

31. $(4x^2 + 8x - 12) \div 4x^2$

32. $\dfrac{12x^2 - 6x + 3}{3}$

33. $\dfrac{-4x^5 + 6x + 8}{2x^2}$

34. $\dfrac{6t^2 + 3t + 8}{2}$

35. $(x^5 + 3x^4 - 3) \div x^3$

36. $(6x^2 - 7x + 9) \div 3x$

37. $\dfrac{6x^5 - 4x^4 + 12x^3 - 5x^2}{2x^3}$

38. $\dfrac{9x^2 + 18x - 7}{-9}$

39. $\dfrac{8k^3 + 6k^2 - 8}{-4k}$

40. $\dfrac{-12x^4 + 6x^2 - 15x + 4}{-3x}$

41. $\dfrac{12x^5 + 3x^4 - 10x^2 - 9}{-3x^2}$

42. $\dfrac{-15m^3 - 6m^2 + 15}{-5m^3}$

Divide.

43. $\dfrac{x^2 + 4x + 3}{x + 1}$

44. $(2x^2 + 3x - 35) \div (x + 5)$

45. $\dfrac{5y^2 - 34y - 7}{y - 7}$

46. $\dfrac{2p^2 - 7p - 15}{p - 5}$

47. $\dfrac{6x^2 + 16x + 8}{3x + 2}$

48. $\dfrac{3r^2 + 5r - 8}{r - 1}$

49. $\dfrac{x^2 - 16}{-4 + x}$

50. $\dfrac{6t^2 - 7t - 20}{3t + 4}$

51. $(2x^2 + 7x - 18) \div (2x - 3)$

52. $(4a^2 - 25) \div (2a - 5)$

53. $\dfrac{x^2 - 36}{x - 6}$

54. $\dfrac{9x^2 - 16}{3x - 4}$

55. $\dfrac{-x + 9x^3 - 16}{3x - 4}$

56. $\dfrac{10x + 3x^2 + 6}{x + 2}$

57. $\dfrac{6x + 8x^2 - 12}{2x + 3}$

58. $\dfrac{x^3 + 5x^2 + 2x - 8}{x + 2}$

59. $\dfrac{7x^3 + 28x^2 - 5x - 20}{x + 4}$

60. $\dfrac{2x^3 - 3x^2 - 3x + 6}{x - 1}$

61. $\dfrac{2t^3 - 4t^2 + 12}{t - 2}$

62. $\dfrac{2x^3 + 6x - 4}{x + 4}$

63. $(w^3 - 8) \div (w - 3)$

64. $\dfrac{x^3 + 8}{x + 2}$

65. $\dfrac{x^3 - 27}{x - 3}$

66. $\dfrac{x^3 + 64}{x + 4}$

67. $\dfrac{4x^3 - 5x}{2x - 1}$

68. $\dfrac{9x^3 - x + 3}{3x - 2}$

69. $\dfrac{-m^3 - 6m^2 + 2m - 3}{m - 1}$

70. $\dfrac{-x^3 + 3x^2 + 14x + 16}{x + 3}$

71. $\dfrac{4t^3 - t + 4}{t + 2}$

72. $\dfrac{9n^3 - 6n + 4}{3n - 3}$

Concept/Writing Exercises

73. When dividing a binomial by a monomial, must the quotient be a binomial? Explain and give an example to support your answer.

74. When dividing a trinomial by a monomial, must the quotient be a trinomial? Explain and given an example to support your answer.

Problem Solving

75. If the divisor is $x + 4$, the quotient is $2x + 3$, and the remainder is 4, find the dividend (or the polynomial being divided).

76. If the divisor is $2x - 3$, the quotient is $3x - 1$, and the remainder is -2, find the dividend.

77. If a polynomial of degree 4 in x is divided by a polynomial of degree 1 in x, what will be the degree of the quotient? Explain.

78. If a polynomial of degree 2 in x is divided by a polynomial of degree 1 in x, what will be the degree of the quotient? Explain.

Determine the monomial to be placed in the shaded area to make a true statement. Explain how you determined your answer.

79. $\dfrac{16x^4 + 20x^3 - 4x^2 + 12x}{\rule{2em}{0.8em}} = 4x^3 + 5x^2 - x + 3$

80. $\dfrac{9x^5 - 6x^4 + 3x^2 + 12}{\rule{2em}{0.8em}} = 3x^3 - 2x^2 + 1 + \dfrac{4}{x^2}$

Determine the exponents to be placed in the shaded areas to make a true statement. Explain how you determined your answer.

81. $\dfrac{8x^{\square} + 4x^{\square} - 20x^{\square} - 5x^{\square}}{2x^2} = 4x^3 + 2x - 10 - \dfrac{5}{2x}$

82. $\dfrac{15x^{\square} + 25x^{\square} + 5x^{\square} + 10x^{\square}}{5x^2} = 3x^5 + 5x^4 + x^2 + 2$

Challenge Problems

Divide. The quotients in Exercises 83 and 84 will contain fractions.

83. $\dfrac{3x^3 - 5}{3x - 2}$

84. $\dfrac{4x^3 - 4x + 6}{2x + 3}$

85. $\dfrac{3x^2 + 6x - 10}{-x - 3}$

Group Activity

Discuss and answer Exercises 86 and 87 as a group. Determine the polynomial that when substituted in the shaded area results in a true statement. Explain how you determined your answer.

86. $\dfrac{\rule{2em}{0.8em}}{x + 4} = x + 2 + \dfrac{2}{x + 4}$

87. $\dfrac{\rule{2em}{0.8em}}{x + 3} = x + 1 - \dfrac{1}{x + 3}$

Cumulative Review Exercises

[1.4] **88.** Consider the set of numbers

$$\left\{ 2, -5, 0, \sqrt{7}, \frac{2}{5}, -6.3, \sqrt{3}, -\frac{23}{34} \right\}.$$

List those that are

a) natural numbers;

b) whole numbers;

c) rational numbers;

d) irrational numbers;

e) real numbers.

[1.8] **89. a)** To what is $\dfrac{0}{1}$ equal?

b) How do we refer to an expression like $\dfrac{1}{0}$?

[1.9] **90.** Give the order of operations to be followed when evaluating a mathematical expression.

[2.5] **91.** Solve the equation $2(x + 3) + 2x = x + 4$.

[3.2] **92. Sale** At a 30% off sale Jennifer Lucking purchased a sweater for $27.65. What was the original price of the sweater?

© Allen R. Angel

[4.2] **93.** Simplify $\dfrac{x^9}{x^{-4}}$.

Chapter 4 Summary

IMPORTANT FACTS AND CONCEPTS	EXAMPLES

Section 4.1

In the expression x^n, x is called the **base** and n is called the **exponent**.

base $\rightarrow 3^4 \nwarrow$ exponent

Rules of Exponents

Simplify.

1. Product Rule $\qquad x^m \cdot x^n = x^{m+n}$

1. $x^5 \cdot x^4 = x^{5+4} = x^9$

2. Quotient Rule $\qquad \dfrac{x^m}{x^n} = x^{m-n}, \qquad x \neq 0$

2. $\dfrac{x^{12}}{x^7} = x^{12-7} = x^5$

3. Zero Exponent Rule $\qquad x^0 = 1, \qquad x \neq 0$

3. $(-3ab^4)^0 = 1$

4. Power Rule $\qquad (x^m)^n = x^{m \cdot n}$

4. $(x^6)^3 = x^{6 \cdot 3} = x^{18}$

5. Power of a Product Rule $\quad (xy)^n = x^n y^n$

5. $(5t)^2 = 5^2 t^2 = 25t^2$

6. Power of a Quotient Rule $\left(\dfrac{x}{y}\right)^n = \dfrac{x^n}{y^n}, \quad y \neq 0$

6. $\left(\dfrac{x}{y}\right)^6 = \dfrac{x^6}{y^6}$

7. Expanded Power Rule $\left(\dfrac{ax}{by}\right)^m = \dfrac{a^m x^m}{b^m y^m}, \quad b \neq 0, \quad y \neq 0$

7. $\left(\dfrac{4x}{5y}\right)^2 = \dfrac{4^2 x^2}{5^2 y^2} = \dfrac{16x^2}{25y^2}$

Section 4.2

Negative Exponent Rule

$$x^{-m} = \dfrac{1}{x^m}, \qquad x \neq 0$$

$$x^{-2} = \dfrac{1}{x^2}$$

$$\dfrac{1}{y^{-6}} = y^6$$

A Fraction Raised to a Negative Exponent Rule

For a fraction of the form $\dfrac{a}{b}$, $a \neq 0$ and

$b \neq 0$, $\left(\dfrac{a}{b}\right)^{-m} = \left(\dfrac{b}{a}\right)^m$

$$\left(\dfrac{7}{8}\right)^{-2} = \left(\dfrac{8}{7}\right)^2 = \dfrac{8^2}{7^2} = \dfrac{64}{49}$$

Section 4.3

Each number written in **scientific notation** is written as a number greater than or equal to 1 and less than 10 multiplied by some power of 10.

$$1.3 \times 10^7$$

$$4.76 \times 10^{-2}$$

To Write a Number in Scientific Notation

1. Move the decimal point in the original number to the right of the first nonzero digit.
2. Count the number of places you moved the decimal point in step 1. If the original number was 10 or greater, the count is positive. If the original number was less than 1, the count is negative.
3. Multiply the number obtained in step 1 by 10 raised to the count (power) found in step 2.

$$25{,}700 = 2.57 \times 10^4$$

$$0.0000346 = 3.46 \times 10^{-5}$$

To Convert a Number from Scientific Notation to Decimal Form

1. Observe the exponent of the power of 10.
2. **a)** If the exponent is positive, move the decimal point in the number to the right the same number of places as the exponent.
   b) If the exponent is 0, do not move the decimal point.
   c) If the exponent is negative, move the decimal point in the number to the left the same number of places as the exponent.

$$9.8 \times 10^6 = 9{,}800{,}000$$

$$5.17 \times 10^{-3} = 0.00517$$

IMPORTANT FACTS AND CONCEPTS	EXAMPLES
Section 4.4	

A **polynomial in *x*** is an expression containing the sum of a finite number of terms of the form ax^n, for any real number a and any whole number n.	$\frac{1}{5}x - 2$ and $x^2 - 4x + 7$ are both polynomials in x.
A polynomial is written in **descending order** when the exponents on the variable decrease from left to right.	$5x^4 - 3x^3 + 7x^2 - 6x + 9$ is written in descending order.
A **monomial** is a polynomial with one term.	$-7y^2$ is a monomial.
A **binomial** is a two-termed polynomial.	$x^2 - 8$ is a binomial.
A **trinomial** is a three-termed polynomial.	$4z^2 - 9z + 1$ is a trinomial.
The **degree of a term** of a polynomial in **one variable** is the exponent on the variable in that term.	$2y^6$ has degree six.
The **degree of a term** of a polynomial in **two or more variables** is the sum of the exponents on those variables.	$3x^2y^5$ has degree seven.
The **degree of a polynomial** is the same as that of its highest-degree term.	$9x^3 + 2x^2 - 5x + 4$ has degree three.

To Add Polynomials

To add polynomials, combine the like terms of the polynomials.

$$(3x^2 - 9x + 4) + (2x^2 - 3x - 5) = \underbrace{3x^2 + 2x^2}\ \underbrace{-9x - 3x}\ \underbrace{+4 - 5}$$
$$= \quad 5x^2 \quad - 12x \quad - 1$$

To Subtract Polynomials

1. Use the distributive property to remove parentheses.
2. Combine like terms.

$$(9a^2 - 6a + 1) - (a^2 - 5a - 3)$$
$$= 9a^2 - 6a + 1 - a^2 + 5a + 3$$
$$= \underbrace{9a^2 - a^2}\ \underbrace{-6a + 5a}\ \underbrace{+1 + 3}$$
$$= \quad 8a^2 \quad - \quad a \quad + \quad 4$$

Section 4.5	

FOIL Method to Multiply Two Binomials (First, Outer, Inner, Last)

$$\overset{F\qquad O\qquad I\qquad L}{(3x - 5)(x + 4) = (3x)(x) + (3x)(4) + (-5)(x) + (-5)(4)}$$
$$= \quad 3x^2 \quad + \quad 12x \quad - \quad 5x \quad - \quad 20$$
$$= \quad 3x^2 + 7x - 20$$

Product of Sum and Difference of the Same Two Terms (also called the difference of two squares):
$$(a + b)(a - b) = a^2 - b^2$$

$$(y + 6)(y - 6) = (y)^2 - (6)^2$$
$$= y^2 - 36$$

Square of a Binomial
$$(a + b)^2 = a^2 + 2ab + b^2$$

$$(x + 7)^2 = (x)^2 + 2(x)(7) + (7)^2$$
$$= x^2 + 14x + 49$$

$$(a - b)^2 = a^2 - 2ab + b^2$$

$$(z - 3)^2 = (z)^2 - 2(z)(3) + (3)^2$$
$$= z^2 - 6z + 9$$

To Multiply Any Two Polynomials

To multiply any two polynomials, each term of one polynomial must multiply each term of the second polynomial.

$$(x^2 + 3x + 5)(x - 2) \text{ or}$$

$$\begin{array}{r} x^2 + 3x + 5 \\ \underline{x - 2} \\ -2x^2 - 6x - 10 \\ \underline{x^3 + 3x^2 + 5x} \\ x^3 + x^2 - x - 10 \end{array}$$

IMPORTANT FACTS AND CONCEPTS	EXAMPLES

Section 4.6

To Divide a Polynomial by a Monomial

To divide a polynomial by a monomial, divide each term of the polynomial by the monomial.

$$\frac{6x + 24}{6} = \frac{6x}{6} + \frac{24}{6} = x + 4$$

To Divide a Polynomial by a Binomial

To divide a polynomial by a binomial we perform division in much the same way as we perform long division.

$$\frac{x^2 - 4x + 3}{x + 2}$$

$$
\begin{array}{r}
x - 6 \\
x + 2\overline{)x^2 - 4x + 3} \\
\underline{x^2 + 2x} \\
-6x + 3 \\
\underline{-6x - 12} \\
15
\end{array}
$$

$$\frac{x^2 - 4x + 3}{x + 2} = x - 6 + \frac{15}{x + 2}$$

Chapter 4 Review Exercises

[4.1] *Simplify.*

1. $x^5 \cdot x^3$

2. $x^2 \cdot x^4$

3. $3^2 \cdot 3^3$

4. $2^4 \cdot 2$

5. $\dfrac{x^4}{x}$

6. $\dfrac{a^5}{a^5}$

7. $\dfrac{5^5}{5^3}$

8. $\dfrac{4^4}{4}$

9. $\dfrac{x^6}{x^8}$

10. $\dfrac{y^4}{y}$

11. x^0

12. $7y^0$

13. $(-6z)^0$

14. 6^0

15. $(5x)^2$

16. $(3a)^3$

17. $(-3x)^3$

18. $(6s)^3$

19. $(2x^2)^4$

20. $(-t^4)^6$

21. $(-p^8)^4$

22. $\left(-\dfrac{2x^3}{y}\right)^2$

23. $\left(-\dfrac{5y^2}{2b}\right)^2$

24. $6x^2 \cdot 4x^3$

25. $\dfrac{16x^2y}{4xy^2}$

26. $2x(3xy^3)^3$

27. $\left(\dfrac{9x^2y}{3xy}\right)^2$

28. $(2x^2y)^3 (3xy^4)$

29. $4x^2y^3 (2x^3y^4)^2$

30. $3c^2 (2c^4d^3)$

31. $\left(\dfrac{9a^3b^2}{3ab^7}\right)^3$

32. $\left(\dfrac{21x^4y^3}{7y^2}\right)^3$

[4.2] *Simplify.*

33. b^{-9}

34. 3^{-3}

35. 5^{-2}

36. $\dfrac{1}{z^{-2}}$

37. $\dfrac{1}{x^{-7}}$

38. $\dfrac{1}{4^{-2}}$

39. $y^5 \cdot y^{-8}$

40. $x^{-2} \cdot x^{-3}$

41. $p^{-6} \cdot p^4$

42. $a^{-2} \cdot a^{-3}$

43. $\dfrac{m^5}{m^{-5}}$

44. $\dfrac{x^5}{x^{-2}}$

45. $\dfrac{x^{-3}}{x^3}$

46. $(3x^4)^{-2}$

47. $(4x^{-3}y)^{-3}$

48. $(-2m^{-3}n)^2$

49. $6y^{-2} \cdot 2y^4$

50. $(-5y^{-3}z)^3$

51. $(-4x^{-2}y^3)^{-2}$

52. $2x(3x^{-2})$

53. $(5x^{-2}y)(2x^4y)$

54. $4y^{-2}(3x^2y)$

55. $4x^5(6x^{-7}y^2)$

56. $\dfrac{6xy^4}{2xy^{-1}}$

57. $\dfrac{12x^{-2}y^3}{3xy^2}$

58. $\dfrac{49x^2y^{-3}}{7x^{-3}y}$

59. $\dfrac{4x^8y^{-2}}{8x^7y^3}$

60. $\dfrac{36x^4y^7}{9x^5y^{-3}}$

[4.3]   *Express each number in scientific notation.*

61. 1,720,000

62. 0.153

63. 0.00763

64. 47,000

65. 5760

66. 0.000314

Express each number without exponents.

67. 7.5×10^{-3}

68. 6.52×10^{-4}

69. 8.9×10^{6}

70. 5.12×10^{4}

71. 3.14×10^{-5}

72. 1.103×10^{7}

Write each quantity as a base unit without metric prefixes and then write the quantity in scientific notation.

73. 92 milliliters

74. 6 gigameters

75. 12.8 micrograms

76. 19.2 kilograms

Perform each indicated operation and write your answer without exponents.

77. $(2.5 \times 10^{2})(3.4 \times 10^{-4})$

78. $(4.2 \times 10^{-3})(3.0 \times 10^{5})$

79. $(3.5 \times 10^{-2})(7.0 \times 10^{3})$

80. $\dfrac{7.94 \times 10^{6}}{2.0 \times 10^{-2}}$

81. $\dfrac{1.5 \times 10^{-2}}{5.0 \times 10^{2}}$

82. $\dfrac{6.5 \times 10^{4}}{2.0 \times 10^{6}}$

Convert each number to scientific notation. Then calculate. Express your answer in scientific notation.

83. $(14,000)(260,000)$

84. $(0.00053)(40,000)$

85. $(12,500)(400,000)$

86. $\dfrac{250}{500,000}$

87. $\dfrac{0.000068}{0.02}$

88. $\dfrac{850,000}{0.025}$

89. Milk Tank A milk tank holds 6.4×10^{6} fluid ounces of milk. If one gallon is 1.28×10^{2} fluid ounces, determine the number of gallons of milk the tank holds.

© Myska Brudnicka\Shutterstock

90. Social Security In 2008 there was about $4.3 trillion in the social security trust fund.

a) Write this amount without scientific notation.

b) Using scientific notation, determine the annual amount of interest obtained in a year if the interest rate is 2.5% per year. Write the answer in scientific notation.

[4.4]   *Indicate whether each expression is a polynomial. If the polynomial is not written in descending order, rewrite it in descending order. If the polynomial has a specific name, give that name. State the degree of each polynomial.*

91. $x^{-4} - 8$

92. 7

93. $x^{2} - 4 + 3x$

94. $-3 - x + 4x^{2}$

95. $4x^{1/2} - 6$

96. $13x^{3} - 4$

97. $x - 4x^{2}$

98. $y^{5} + y^{-3} - 9$

99. $2x^{3} - 7 + 4x^{2} - 3x$

[4.4–4.6]   *Perform each indicated operation.*

100. $(x + 8) + (4x - 11)$

101. $(2d - 3) + (5d + 7)$

102. $(-x - 10) + (-2x + 5)$

103. $(-3x^{2} + 9x + 5) + (-x^{2} + 2x - 12)$

104. $(-m^{2} + 5m - 8) + (6m^{2} - 5m - 2)$

105. $(6.2p - 4.3) + (1.9p + 7.1)$

106. $(-6y - 7) - (-3y + 8)$

107. $(4x^{2} - 9x) - (3x + 15)$

108. $(5a^{2} - 6a - 9) - (2a^{2} - a + 12)$

109. $(x^{2} + 7x - 3) - (x^{2} + 3x - 5)$

110. $(-2x^{2} + 8x - 7) - (3x^{2} + 12)$

111. $\dfrac{1}{7}x(21x + 21)$

112. $-3x(5x + 4)$

113. $3x(2x^2 - 4x + 7)$

114. $-c(2c^2 - 3c + 5)$

115. $-7b(-4b^2 - 3b - 5)$

116. $(x + 4)(x + 5)$

117. $(3x + 6)(-4x + 1)$

118. $(-5x + 3)^2$

119. $(6 - 2x)(2 + 3x)$

120. $(r + 5)(r - 5)$

121. $(x - 1)(3x^2 + 4x - 6)$

122. $(3x + 1)(x^2 + 2x + 4)$

123. $(-4x + 2)(3x^2 - x + 7)$

124. $\dfrac{2x + 4}{2}$

125. $\dfrac{12y + 18}{3}$

126. $\dfrac{8x^2 + 4x}{x}$

127. $\dfrac{6x^2 + 9x - 4}{3}$

128. $\dfrac{6w^2 - 5w + 3}{3w}$

129. $\dfrac{16x^6 - 8x^5 - 3x^3 + 1}{4x}$

130. $\dfrac{8m - 4}{-2}$

131. $\dfrac{5x^3 + 10x + 2}{2x^2}$

132. $\dfrac{5x^2 - 6x + 15}{3x}$

133. $\dfrac{x^2 + x - 12}{x - 3}$

134. $\dfrac{5x^2 + 28x - 10}{x + 6}$

135. $\dfrac{6n^2 + 19n + 3}{6n + 1}$

136. $\dfrac{4x^3 + 12x^2 + x - 12}{2x + 3}$

137. $\dfrac{4x^2 - 12x + 9}{2x - 3}$

Chapter 4 Practice Test

Chapter Test Prep Videos provide fully worked-out solutions to any of the exercises you want to review. Chapter Test Prep Videos are available via MyMathLab , or on YouTube (search "Angel Elementary Algebra" and click on "Channels").

Simplify each expression.

1. $5x^4 \cdot 3x^2$

2. $(3xy^2)^3$

3. $\dfrac{24p^7}{3p^2}$

4. $\left(\dfrac{3x^2y}{6xy^3}\right)^3$

5. $(2x^3y^{-2})^{-2}$

6. $(4x^0)(3x^2)^0$

7. $\dfrac{30x^6y^2}{45x^{-1}y}$

Convert each number to scientific notation and then determine the answer. Express your answer in scientific notation.

8. $(285,000)(50,000)$

9. $\dfrac{0.0008}{4000}$

Determine whether each expression is a polynomial. If the polynomial has a specific name, give that name.

10. $4x$

11. $-8c + 5$

12. $x^{-2} + 4$

13. Write the polynomial $-5 + 6x^3 - 2x^2 + 5x$ in descending order, and give its degree.

In Exercises 14–24, perform each indicated operation.

14. $(6x - 4) + (2x^2 - 5x - 3)$

15. $(y^2 - 7y + 3) - (4y^2 - 5y - 2)$

16. $(4x^2 - 5) - (x^2 + x - 8)$

17. $-5d(-3d + 8)$

18. $(5x + 8)(3x - 4)$

19. $(9 - 4c)(5 + 3c)$

20. $(3x - 5)(2x^2 + 4x - 5)$

21. $\dfrac{16x^2 + 8x - 4}{4}$

22. $\dfrac{-12x^2 - 6x + 5}{-3x}$

23. $\dfrac{8x^2 - 2x - 15}{2x - 3}$

24. $\dfrac{12x^2 + 7x - 12}{4x + 5}$

25. Half-Life The half-life of an element is the time it takes one half the amount of a radioactive element to decay. The half-life of carbon 14 (C^{14}) is 5730 years. The half-life of uranium 238 (U^{238}) is 4.46×10^9 years.

a) Write the half-life of C^{14} in scientific notation.

b) How many times longer is the half-life of U^{238} than C^{14}?

Cumulative Review Test

Take the following test and check your answers with those given in the back of the book. Review any questions that you answered incorrectly. The section where the material was covered is indicated after the answer.

1. Evaluate $12 + 8 \div 2^2 + 3$.

2. Simplify $7 - (2x - 3) + 2x - 8(1 - x)$.

3. Evaluate $-4x^2 + x - 7$ when $x = -2$.

4. Name each indicated property.

   a) $(5 + 2) + 7 = 5 + (2 + 7)$.

   b) $7 \cdot x = x \cdot 7$.

   c) $2(y + 9) = (y + 9)2$.

5. Solve the equation $5y + 7 = 2(y - 3)$.

6. Solve the equation $3(x + 2) + 3x - 5 = 4x + 1$.

7. Solve the inequality $3x - 11 < 5x - 2$ and graph the solution on a number line.

8. Solve the equation $3x - 2 = y - 7$ for y.

9. Solve $7x - 3y = 21$ for y, then find the value of y when $x = 6$.

10. Simplify $\left(\dfrac{5xy^{-3}}{x^{-2}y^5} \right)^2$.

11. Write the polynomial $-5x + 2 - 7x^2$ in descending order and give the degree.

Perform each indicated operation.

12. $(x^2 + 4x - 3) + (2x^2 + 5x + 1)$

13. $(6a^2 + 3a + 2) - (a^2 - 3a - 3)$

14. $(5t - 3)(2t - 1)$

15. $(2x - 1)(3x^2 - 5x + 2)$

16. $\dfrac{10d^2 + 12d - 8}{4d}$

17. $\dfrac{6x^2 + 11x - 10}{3x - 2}$

18. **Chicken Soup** At Art's Grocery Store, three cans of chicken soup sell for $1.25. Find the cost of eight cans.

19. **Average Speed** Bob Dolan drives from Jackson, Mississippi, to Tallulah, Louisiana, a distance of 60 miles. At the same time, Nick Reide starts driving from Tallulah to Jackson along the same route. If Bob and Nick meet after 0.5 hour and Nick's average speed was 7 miles per hour greater than Bob's, find the average speed of each car.

20. **Rectangle** The length of a rectangle is 2 less than 3 times the width. Find the dimensions of the rectangle if its perimeter is 28 feet.

Factoring

5.1   Factoring a Monomial from a Polynomial

5.2   Factoring by Grouping

5.3   Factoring Trinomials of the Form $ax^2 + bx + c$, $a = 1$

5.4   Factoring Trinomials of the Form $ax^2 + bx + c$, $a \neq 1$

       Mid-Chapter Test: Sections 5.1–5.4

5.5   Special Factoring Formulas and a General Review of Factoring

5.6   Solving Quadratic Equations Using Factoring

5.7   Applications of Quadratic Equations

       Chapter 5 Summary

       Chapter 5 Review Exercises

       Chapter 5 Practice Test

       Cumulative Review Test

Goals of This Chapter

The major emphasis of this chapter is to teach you how to factor polynomials. Factoring polynomials is the reverse process of multiplying polynomials.

In the first five sections of this chapter, you will learn how to factor a monomial from a polynomial, factor by grouping, factor trinomials of the form $ax^2 + bx + c$ when $a = 1$ and $a \neq 1$, and factor by using special factoring formulas. In the last two sections of this chapter, you will learn how to solve quadratic equations using factoring and how to solve applications of quadratic equations.

It is essential that you have a thorough understanding of factoring, especially Sections 5.3 through 5.5, to complete Chapter 6 successfully.

What do Donald Duck, the Scarecrow from The Wizard of Oz, and a baseball diamond all have in common? The answer is the Pythagorean Theorem! Donald Duck is on a postage stamp talking about the Pythagorean Theorem, the Scarecrow talks about the Pythagorean Theorem in the movie *The Wizard of Oz* (see Exercise 54 on page 330), and the Pythagorean Theorem can be used to find the distance between home plate and second base in a baseball diamond (see Exercise 54 on page 330).

© Allen R. Angel

5.1 Factoring a Monomial from a Polynomial

1 Identify factors.

2 Determine the greatest common factor of two or more numbers.

3 Determine the greatest common factor of two or more terms.

4 Factor a monomial from a polynomial.

Understanding Algebra

Factoring is the reverse process of multiplication.

Multiplying:

$3x(2x^2 + 5) \overset{\text{becomes}}{\longrightarrow} 6x^3 + 15x$

Factoring:

$6x^3 + 15x \overset{\text{becomes}}{\longrightarrow} 3x(2x^2 + 5)$

1 Identify Factors

In Chapter 4, you learned how to multiply polynomials. In this chapter, we focus on factoring, the reverse process of multiplication.

> **Factor**
>
> To **factor an expression** means to write the expression as a product of its factors.
>   In general, if $a \cdot b = c$, then a and b are called **factors** of c.

For example, in Section 4.5 we showed that $-12n^3 + 6n^2 + 3n$ can also be written as $-3n(4n^2 - 2n - 1)$. We say that $(-3n)$ and $(4n^2 - 2n - 1)$ are *factors* of $-12n^3 + 6n^2 + 3n$.

$3 \cdot 5 = 15$; so 3 and 5 are factors of 15.

$x^3 \cdot x^4 = x^7$; so x^3 and x^4 are factors of x^7.

$x(x + 2) = x^2 + 2x$; so x and $x + 2$ are factors of $x^2 + 2x$.

$(x - 1)(x + 3) = x^2 + 2x - 3$; so $x - 1$ and $x + 3$ are factors of $x^2 + 2x - 3$.

EXAMPLE 1   List the factors of $6x^3$.

Solution

Factors	Factors
$1 \cdot 6x^3 = 6x^3$	$x \cdot 6x^2 = 6x^3$
$2 \cdot 3x^3 = 6x^3$	$2x \cdot 3x^2 = 6x^3$
$3 \cdot 2x^3 = 6x^3$	$3x \cdot 2x^2 = 6x^3$
$6 \cdot x^3 = 6x^3$	$6x \cdot x^2 = 6x^3$

The factors of $6x^3$ are $1, 2, 3, 6, x, 2x, 3x, 6x, x^2, 2x^2, 3x^2, 6x^2, x^3, 2x^3, 3x^3$, and $6x^3$. The opposite (or negative) of each of these factors is also a factor, but these opposites are generally not listed unless specifically requested.

Now Try Exercise 7

Here are examples of multiplying and factoring. Notice again that factoring is the reverse process of multiplying.

Multiplying	Factoring
$3(2x + 5) = 6x + 15$	$6x + 15 = 3(2x + 5)$
$4y(y - 7) = 4y^2 - 28y$	$4y^2 - 28y = 4y(y - 7)$
$(x + 1)(x + 3) = x^2 + 4x + 3$	$x^2 + 4x + 3 = (x + 1)(x + 3)$

2 Determine the Greatest Common Factor of Two or More Numbers

To factor a monomial from a polynomial, we make use of the *greatest common factor* (GCF). If you wish to see additional material on obtaining the GCF, you may read Appendix B, where we also discuss finding the GCF.

Before we examine how to find the GCF, a discussion of **prime numbers** is appropriate.

Understanding Algebra

When we write $48 = 2^4 \cdot 3$, or $48 = 2 \cdot 2 \cdot 2 \cdot 2 \cdot 3$, we call $2^4 \cdot 3$ or $2 \cdot 2 \cdot 2 \cdot 2 \cdot 3$ the *prime factorization* of 48.

Prime Numbers and Composite Numbers

A **prime number** is an integer greater than 1 that has exactly two factors, itself and 1.
The first 15 prime numbers are:

$$2, 3, 5, 7, 11, 13, 17, 19, 23, 29, 31, 37, 41, 43, 47$$

A **composite** number is an integer greater than 1 that is not prime.
The first 15 composite numbers are:

$$4, 6, 8, 9, 10, 12, 14, 15, 16, 18, 20, 21, 22, 24, 25$$

The number 1 is neither prime nor composite.

Examples 2 and 3 present the procedure for writing composite numbers as the product of prime numbers.

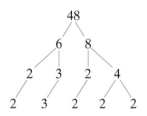

FIGURE 5.1

EXAMPLE 2 Write 48 as a product of prime numbers. ——————

Solution   Select any two numbers whose product is 48. Two possibilities are $6 \cdot 8$ and $4 \cdot 12$, but there are other choices. Continue breaking down the factors until all the factors are prime, as illustrated in **Figure 5.1**.
Note that no matter how you select your initial factors,

$$48 = 2 \cdot 2 \cdot 2 \cdot 2 \cdot 3 = 2^4 \cdot 3$$

Now Try Exercise 9

In Example 2, we found that $48 = 2 \cdot 2 \cdot 2 \cdot 2 \cdot 3 = 2^4 \cdot 3$. The $2 \cdot 2 \cdot 2 \cdot 2 \cdot 3$ or $2^4 \cdot 3$ may also be referred to as the **prime factorization** of 48.

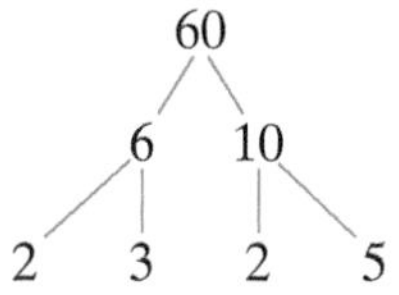

EXAMPLE 3 Write 60 as a product of its prime factors. ——————

Solution   One way to find the prime factors is shown in **Figure 5.2**. Therefore, $60 = 2 \cdot 2 \cdot 3 \cdot 5 = 2^2 \cdot 3 \cdot 5$.

Now Try Exercise 11

FIGURE 5.2

The **greatest common factor (GCF)** of two numbers is the greatest number that divides evenly into each of the numbers. The greatest common factor of 6 and 8 is 2 because 2 is the largest number that divides into both 6 and 8. To find the GCF of two or more numbers, a method involving the numbers' prime factorizations is used.

To Determine the GCF of Two or More Numbers

  1. Write each number as a product of prime factors.
  2. Determine the prime factors common to all the numbers.
  3. Multiply the common factors found in step 2. The product of these factors is the GCF.

EXAMPLE 4 Determine the greatest common factor of 48 and 60. ——————

Solution   From Examples 2 and 3, we know that

Step 1
$$48 = 2 \cdot 2 \cdot 2 \cdot 2 \cdot 3 = 2^4 \cdot 3$$
$$60 = 2 \cdot 2 \cdot 3 \cdot 5 = 2^2 \cdot 3 \cdot 5$$

Understanding Algebra

The greatest common factor (GCF) of 70 and 84 is 14 because 14 is the largest number that divides evenly into both 70 and 84.
$$70 = 2 \cdot 5 \cdot 7$$
$$84 = 2 \cdot 2 \cdot 3 \cdot 7$$

Step 2   The common factors are circled. Two factors of 2 and one factor of 3 are common to both numbers. The product of these factors is the GCF of 48 and 60:

Step 3   GCF $= 2 \cdot 2 \cdot 3 = 12$

The GCF of 48 and 60 is 12. Twelve is the greatest number that divides evenly into both 48 and 60.

Now Try Exercise 15

EXAMPLE 5 Determine the GCF of 18 and 24.

Solution

$$18 = 2 \cdot 3 \cdot 3 = 2 \cdot 3^2$$
$$24 = 2 \cdot 2 \cdot 2 \cdot 3 = 2^3 \cdot 3$$

One factor of 2 and one factor of 3 are common to both 18 and 24.

$$GCF = 2 \cdot 3 = 6$$

Now Try Exercise 19

3 Determine the Greatest Common Factor of Two or More Terms

Consider the terms $x^3, x^4, x^5,$ and x^6. The GCF of these terms is x^3, since x^3 is the largest number of x's common to all four terms. We can illustrate this by writing the terms in factored form, with x^3 as one factor.

$$x^3 = x^3 \cdot 1$$
$$x^4 = x^3 \cdot x$$
$$x^5 = x^3 \cdot x^2$$
$$x^6 = x^3 \cdot x^3$$

GCF of all four terms is x^3.

Notice that x^3 evenly divides all four terms,

$$\frac{x^3}{x^3} = 1, \quad \text{and} \quad \frac{x^4}{x^3} = x, \quad \text{and} \quad \frac{x^5}{x^3} = x^2, \quad \text{and} \quad \frac{x^6}{x^3} = x^3.$$

EXAMPLE 6 Determine the GCF of the terms $m^9, m^5, m^7,$ and m^4.

Solution The GCF is m^4 because m^4 is the largest factor common to all the terms.

Now Try Exercise 21

EXAMPLE 7 Determine the GCF of the terms x^2y^3, x^3y^2 and xy^4.

Solution

$$x^2y^3 = x \cdot x \cdot y \cdot y \cdot y$$
$$x^3y^2 = x \cdot x \cdot x \cdot y \cdot y$$
$$xy^4 = x \cdot y \cdot y \cdot y \cdot y$$

One x is common to each term   Two y's are common to each term

x^1 y^2

Thus, the GCF of the three terms is xy^2

Now Try Exercise 29

Greatest Common Factor of Two or More Terms

To determine the GCF of two or more terms

1. Find the GCF of the numerical coefficients of the terms.
2. Find the largest power of each variable that is common to all of the terms.
3. The GCF is the product of the number from step 1 and the variable expressions from step 2.

EXAMPLE 8 Determine the GCF of each group of terms.

   a) $18y^2, 15y^3, 27y^5$ **b)** $-20x^2, 12x, 40x^3$ **c)** $5s^4, s^7, s^3$

Solution   4, x, 4x   1, s³, s³

   a) The GCF of 18, 15, and 27 is 3. The GCF of $y^2, y^3,$ and y^5 is y^2. Therefore, the GCF of the three terms is $3y^2$.

b) The GCF of -20, 12, and 40 is 4. The GCF of x^2, x, and x^3 is x. Therefore, the GCF of the three terms is $4x$.

c) The GCF of 5, 1, and 1 is 1. The GCF of s^4, s^7, and s^3 is s^3. Therefore, the GCF of the three terms is $1s^3$, which we write as s^3.

Now Try Exercise 33

EXAMPLE 9 Determine the GCF of $48x^2yz$ and $60x^3y^3$.

Solution

1. The numerical coefficients are 48 and 60. From Example 4, the GCF of 48 and 60 is 12.
2. The variables x and y are common to both terms. The variable z does not appear in the second term. The largest power of x common to both terms is x^2. The largest power of y common to both terms is y.
3. Thus, the GCF is the product of 12, x^2, and y, or $12x^2y$.

Now Try Exercise 25

EXAMPLE 10 Determine the GCF of each pair of terms.

a) $a(a - 6)$ and $3(a - 6)$ $a-6$
b) $t(t + 4)$ and $t + 4$ $t+4$
c) $3(p + q)$ and $4p(p + q)$ $p+q$

Solution

a) The GCF is $(a - 6)$.
b) $t + 4$ can be written as $1(t + 4)$. Therefore, the GCF of $t(t + 4)$ and $1(t + 4)$ is $t + 4$.
c) The GCF is $(p + q)$.

Now Try Exercise 39

4 Factor a Monomial from a Polynomial

Factoring is the reverse process of multiplying factors. As mentioned earlier, to *factor an expression* means to write the expression as a product of its factors.

> **To Factor a Monomial from a Polynomial**
>
> 1. Determine the greatest common factor of all terms in the polynomial.
> 2. Write each term as the product of the GCF and its other factor.
> 3. Use the distributive property to factor out the GCF.

In step 3 of the process, where we indicate that we use the distributive property, we factor the GCF out of the terms in the polynomial. For example, to factor $4 \cdot x + 4 \cdot 2$, we factor out the GCF, 4, to write $4(x + 2)$.

EXAMPLE 11 Factor $6x + 18$.

Solution   The GCF is 6.

$$6x + 18 = \boxed{6} \cdot x + \boxed{6} \cdot 3$$ Write each term as a product of the GCF and its other factor.

$$= \boxed{6}(x + 3)$$ Distributive property

Now Try Exercise 49

> **Helpful Hint**
>
> Checking a factoring problem involves two steps. First, multiply the factored result—you should obtain the original expression. Second, be sure each factor in your factored result cannot be factored further. For example, if we factor $3x^2 + 6x$ as $x(3x + 6)$, the first part of the check—multiplying x by $(3x + 6)$—does in fact yield $3x^2 + 6x$. However, there is still a common factor, 3, in $(3x + 6)$, which needs to be factored out. The correct answer is that $3x^2 + 6x$ factors as $3x(x + 2)$. So, be sure the factors in your result do not have any remaining common factors.

EXAMPLE 12 Factor $15x - 20$.

Solution   The GCF is 5.

$$15x - 20 = 5 \cdot 3x - 5 \cdot 4$$
$$= 5(3x - 4)$$

The factored binomial no longer has any common factors and we can check that the factoring is correct by multiplying.

Now Try Exercise 51

EXAMPLE 13 Factor $6y^2 + 9y^5$.

Solution   The GCF is $3y^2$.

$$6y^2 + 9y^5 = 3y^2 \cdot 2 + 3y^2 \cdot 3y^3$$
$$= 3y^2(2 + 3y^3)$$

The factored binomial no longer has any common factors and we can check that the factoring is correct by multiplying.

Now Try Exercise 59

EXAMPLE 14 Factor $8q^3 - 20q^2 - 12q$.

Solution   The GCF is $4q$.

$$8q^3 - 20q^2 - 12q = 4q \cdot 2q^2 - 4q \cdot 5q - 4q \cdot 3$$
$$= 4q(2q^2 - 5q - 3)$$

Check $4q(2q^2 - 5q - 3) = 8q^3 - 20q^2 - 12q$

Now Try Exercise 81

EXAMPLE 15 Factor $35x^2 - 25x + 5$.

Solution   The GCF is 5.

$$35x^2 - 25x + 5 = 5 \cdot 7x^2 - 5 \cdot 5x + 5 \cdot 1$$
$$= 5(7x^2 - 5x + 1)$$

> **Understanding Algebra**
>
> In Example 15, notice we rewrite the constant term 5 as $5 \cdot 1$ so that when 5 is factored out, a 1 remains.

The factored trinomial no longer has any common factors and we can check that the factoring is correct by multiplying.

Now Try Exercise 85

EXAMPLE 16 Factor $4x^3 + x^2 + 8x^2y$.

Solution   The GCF is x^2.

$$4x^3 + x^2 + 8x^2y = x^2 \cdot 4x + x^2 \cdot 1 + x^2 \cdot 8y$$
$$= x^2(4x + 1 + 8y)$$

The factored trinomial no longer has any common factors and we can check that the factoring is correct by multiplying.

Now Try Exercise 89

Notice in Examples 15 and 16 that when one of the terms is itself the GCF, we express it in factored form as the product of the term itself and 1.

EXAMPLE 17   Factor $x(5x - 2) + 7(5x - 2)$. ————————

Solution   The GCF of $x(5x - 2)$ and $7(5x - 2)$ is $(5x - 2)$. Factoring out the GCF gives

$$x(5x - 2) + 7(5x - 2) = (5x - 2)(x + 7)$$

This factored result no longer has any common factors and we can check that the factoring is correct by multiplying.

Now Try Exercise 95

EXAMPLE 18   Factor $4x(3x - 5) - 7(3x - 5)$. ————————

Solution   The GCF of $4x(3x - 5)$ and $-7(3x - 5)$ is $(3x - 5)$. Factoring out the GCF gives

$$4x(3x - 5) - 7(3x - 5) = (3x - 5)(4x - 7)$$

This factored result no longer has any common factors and we can check that the factoring is correct by multiplying.

Recall from Section 1.10 that the commutative property of multiplication states that the order in which any two real numbers are multiplied does not matter. Therefore, $(3x - 5)(4x - 7)$ can also be written $(4x - 7)(3x - 5)$. In the book, we will place the common factor on the left.

Now Try Exercise 97

EXAMPLE 19   Factor $2x(x + 3) - 5(x + 3)$. ————————

Solution   The GCF of $2x(x + 3)$ and $-5(x + 3)$ is $(x + 3)$. Factoring out the GCF gives

$$2x(x + 3) - 5(x + 3) = (x + 3)(2x - 5)$$

The factored result no longer has any common factors and we can check that the factoring is correct by multiplying.

Now Try Exercise 93

Whenever you are factoring a polynomial by any of the methods presented in this chapter, the first step will always be to see if there is a common factor (other than 1) to all the terms in the polynomial. If so, factor the greatest common factor from each term using the distributive property.

EXERCISE SET 5.1

Math XL
MathXL®

MyMathLab
MyMathLab

Warm-Up Exercises

Fill in the blanks with the appropriate word, phrase, or symbol(s) from the following list.

~~composite~~	$4x^4$	$2x^2y^3$	~~1~~	~~2~~
~~12~~	prime	~~6~~	$40x^3y^6$	~~multiplying~~

1. The GCF of 24 and 42 is _____6_____ .

2. The positive integer that is neither prime nor composite is the number ____1____ .

3. The GCF of $4x^2y^6$, $10x^3y^4$, and $20x^3y^3$ is ___$2x^2y^3$___ .

4. Factoring is the reverse process of ___Multiplying___ .

5. The only even prime number is ____2____ .

6. An even integer greater than 2 is an example of a ___Composite___ number.

7. The positive factors of ___12___ are 1, 2, 3, 4, 6, and 12.

8. An integer greater than 1 that is divisible only by itself and 1 is called a ___prime___ number.

Practice the Skills

Write each number as a product of prime numbers.

9. 20 $2^2 \cdot 5$ **10.** 120   **11.** 90 $2 \cdot 3^2 \cdot 5$ **12.** 540   **13.** 248 $2^3 \cdot 31$ **14.** 144

Determine the greatest common factor for each pair of numbers.

15. 40, 56 8   **16.** 45, 27 9   **17.** 70, 98 7   **18.** 120, 96   **19.** 80, 126 2   **20.** 88, 160

Determine the greatest common factor for each group of terms.

21. x^5, x^3, x^2 x^2 **22.** y^3, y^5, y^2 **23.** $3x, 6x^2, 9x^3$ $3x$

24. $6p, 4p^2, 8p^3$ **25.** a, ab, ab^2 a **26.** x, y, z

27. q^3r, q^2r^2, qr^4 qr **28.** $4x^2y^2, 3xy^4, 2xy^2$ **29.** $x^3y^7, x^7y^{12}, x^5y^5$ x^3y^5

30. $6x, 12y, 18x^2$ **31.** $-3, 20x, 30x^2$ **32.** $24s^5, 6r^3s^3, 15rs^2$

33. $9x^3y^4, 8x^5y^4, 12x^4y^2$ x^2y^2 **34.** $16x^9y^{12}, 8x^5y^3, 20x^4y^2$ **35.** $40x^3, 27x, 30x^4y^2$ x

36. $6p^4q^3, 9p^2q^5, 9p^4q^2$ **37.** $8(x - 4), 7(x - 4)$ $x-4$ **38.** $4(x - 5), 3x(x - 5)$

39. $x^2(2x - 3), 5(2x - 3)$ $2x-3$ **40.** $x(9x - 3), 9x - 3$ **41.** $3w + 5, 6(3w + 5)$ $3w+5$

42. $b(b + 3), b + 3$ **43.** $x - 4, y(x - 4)$ $x-4$ **44.** $3y(x + 2), 3(x + 2)$

45. $3(x - 1), 5(x - 1)^2$ $x-1$ **46.** $5(n + 2), 7(n + 2)^2$ **47.** $(x - 9)(x + 6), (x - 9)(x + 3)$ $x-9$

48. $(a + 4)(a - 3), 5(a - 3)$

Factor the GCF from each term in the expression.

49. $4x - 80$ $4(x-20)$ **50.** $4x + 2$ **51.** $15x - 5$ $5(3x-1)$

52. $12x + 15$ **53.** $7q + 28$ $7(q+4)$ **54.** $3t^2 - 10t$

55. $9x^2 - 12x$ $3x(x-4)$ **56.** $24y - 6y^2$ **57.** $7x^5 - 9x^4$ $x^4(7x-9)$

58. $9x + 27x^3$ **59.** $3x^5 - 12x^2$ $3x^2(x^3-4)$ **60.** $26p^2 - 8p$

61. $36x^{12} + 24x^8$ $6x^8(6x^4 + 4)$ **62.** $45y^{12} + 30y^{10}$ **63.** $27y^{15} - 9y^3$ $9y^3(3y^{12}-1)$

64. $30w^5 + 25w^3$ **65.** $y + 6x^3y$ $y(6x^3)$ **66.** $4x^2y - 6x$

67. $7a^4 + 3a^2$ $a^2(7a^2+3)$ **68.** $3x^2y + 6x^2y^2$ **69.** $16xy^2z + 4x^3y$ $4x(4y^2z + x^2y)$

70. $48m^4n^2 - 16mn^2$ **71.** $80x^5y^3z^4 - 36x^2yz^3$

72. $56xy^5z^{13} - 24y^4z^2$ **73.** $25x^2yz^3 + 25x^3yz$

74. $13y^5z^3 - 11xy^2z^5$ **75.** $19x^4y^{12}z^{13} - 8x^5y^3z^9$

76. $16r^4s^5t^3 - 20r^5s^4t$ **77.** $8c^2 - 4c - 32$

78. $x^3 - 4x^2 - 3x$ **79.** $9x^2 + 18x + 3$

80. $4x^2 + 8x + 24$ **81.** $4x^3 - 8x^2 + 12x$

82. $12a^3 - 16a^2 - 4a$ **83.** $40b^2 - 48c + 24$

84. $5x^3 - xy^2 + x$ **85.** $15p^2 - 6p + 9$

86. $45y^3 - 63y^2 + 27y$ **87.** $9a^4 - 6a^3 + 3ab$

88. $45v^4w^2 + 10v^2x - 20vw^5$ **89.** $8x^2y + 12xy^2 + 5xy$

90. $52x^2y^2 + 16xy^3 + 26z$ **91.** $x(x - 7) + 6(x - 7)$

92. $9x(3x - 4) - 4(3x - 4)$ **93.** $3b(a - 2) - 4(a - 2)$

94. $3x(7x + 1) - 2(7x + 1)$ **95.** $4x(2x + 1) + 1(2x + 1)$

96. $4m(5m - 1) - 3(5m - 1)$ **97.** $5x(2x + 1) + 2x + 1$

98. $3x(4x - 5) + 4x - 5$ **99.** $3c(6c + 7) - 2(6c + 7)$

100. $5t(t - 2) - 3(t - 2)$

Problem Solving

Factor each expression, if possible. Treat the unknown symbol as if it were a variable.

101. $12\nabla - 6\nabla^2$ **102.** $3\star + 6$

103. $12\square^3 - 4\square^2 + 4\square$ **104.** $\copyright + 11\triangle$

Concept/Writing Exercises

105. Explain how to check a factoring problem.

106. What is the greatest common factor of two or more numbers?

Challenge Problems

107. Factor $6x^5(2x + 7) + 4x^3(2x + 7) - 2x^2(2x + 7)$.

108. Factor $4x^2(x - 3)^3 - 6x(x - 3)^2 + 4(x - 3)$.

109. Factor $x^2 + 2x + 3x + 6$. (*Hint:* Factor the first two terms, then factor the last two terms, then factor the resulting two terms. We will discuss factoring problems of this type in Section 5.2.)

Cumulative Review Exercises

[2.1] **110.** Simplify $2x - (x - 5) + 4(3 - x)$.

[2.5] **111.** Solve the equation $4 + 3(x - 8) = x - 4(x + 2)$.

[2.6] **112.** Solve the equation $4x - 5y = 20$ for y.

113. Find the volume of the cone shown below.

[3.2] **114.** The sum of two numbers is 41. Find the two numbers if the larger number is one less than twice the smaller number.

[4.1] **115.** Simplify $\left(\dfrac{3x^2y^3}{2x^5y^2}\right)^2$.

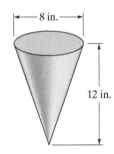

8 in.

12 in.

5.2 Factoring by Grouping

1 Factor a polynomial containing four terms by grouping.

1 Factor a Polynomial Containing Four Terms by Grouping

It may be possible to factor a polynomial containing four or more terms by removing common factors from groups of terms. This process is called **factoring by grouping**, which is illustrated in Example 1.

EXAMPLE 1   Factor $ax + ay + bx + by$ by grouping.

Solution   There is no factor (other than 1) common to all four terms. However, a is common to the first two terms and b is common to the last two terms. Factor a from the first two terms and b from the last two terms.

$$ax + ay + bx + by = a(x + y) + b(x + y)$$

This factoring gives two terms, and $(x + y)$ is common to both terms. Proceed to factor $(x + y)$ from each term, as shown below.

$$a(x + y) + b(x + y) = (x + y)(a + b)$$

Notice that when $(x + y)$ is factored out we are left with $a + b$, which becomes the other factor. Thus, $ax + ay + bx + by = (x + y)(a + b)$.

Now Try Exercise 7

Understanding Algebra

$(ax + ay) \xrightarrow{\text{factor out } a} a(x + y)$

$(bx + by) \xrightarrow{\text{factor out } b} b(x + y)$

$a(x + y) + b(x + y) \xrightarrow{\text{factor out } (x+y)}$

$\qquad\qquad (x + y)(a + b)$

To Factor a Four-Term Polynomial Using Grouping

1. Determine whether there are any factors common to all four terms. If so, factor the greatest common factor from each of the four terms.
2. If necessary, arrange the four terms so that the first two terms have a common factor and the last two have a common factor.
3. Use the distributive property to factor each group of two terms.
4. Factor the greatest common factor from the results of step 3.

EXAMPLE 2 Factor $x^2 + 3x + 4x + 12$ by grouping.

Solution   No factor is common to all four terms. However, you can factor x from the first two terms and 4 from the last two terms.

$$x^2 + 3x + 4x + 12 = x(x + 3) + 4(x + 3)$$

$$x + 3 \text{ is common}$$

$$x(x + 3) + 4(x + 3) = (x + 3)(x + 4)$$

Thus, $x^2 + 3x + 4x + 12 = (x + 3)(x + 4)$

Now Try Exercise 11

In Example 2, the $3x$ and $4x$ are like terms. However, if we were to combine them we would not be able to factor the four terms by grouping.

EXAMPLE 3 Factor $15x^2 + 10x + 12x + 8$ by grouping.

Solution

$$15x^2 + 10x + 12x + 8 = 5x(3x + 2) + 4(3x + 2)$$

Factor $5x$ from the first two terms and 4 from the last two terms.

$$= (3x + 2)(5x + 4)$$

Now Try Exercise 17

A factoring-by-grouping problem can be checked by multiplying the factors using the FOIL method. If you have not made a mistake, your result will be the polynomial you began with. Here is a check of Example 3.

Check   F   O   I   L

$$(3x + 2)(5x + 4) = (3x)(5x) + (3x)(4) + (2)(5x) + (2)(4)$$

$$= 15x^2 + 12x + 10x + 8$$

$$= 15x^2 + 10x + 12x + 8$$

We can write $12x + 10x$ as $10x + 12x$ because of the commutative property of addition. Since this is the polynomial we started with, the factoring is correct.

EXAMPLE 4 Factor $15x^2 + 12x + 10x + 8$ by grouping.

Solution $15x^2 + 12x + 10x + 8 = 3x(5x + 4) + 2(5x + 4)$

$$= (5x + 4)(3x + 2)$$

Now Try Exercise 19

Notice that Example 4 is the same as Example 3 with the two middle terms interchanged. The answers to Examples 3 and 4 are equivalent since only the order of the factors are changed.

EXAMPLE 5   Factor $x^2 - 3x + x - 3$ by grouping.

Solution   In the first two terms, x is the common factor. Is there a common factor in the last two terms? Yes; remember that 1 is a factor of every term. Factor 1 from the last two terms.

$$x^2 - 3x + x - 3 = x^2 - 3x + 1 \cdot x - 1 \cdot 3$$
$$= x(x - 3) + 1(x - 3)$$
$$= (x - 3)(x + 1)$$

Note that $x - 3$ was expressed as $1 \cdot x - 1 \cdot 3 = 1(x - 3)$.

Now Try Exercise 21

Understanding Algebra

In Example 5, notice that $x - 3$ can be rewritten as $1 \cdot x - 1 \cdot 3$ and then as $1(x - 3)$.

EXAMPLE 6   Factor $6x^2 - 3x - 2x + 1$ by grouping.

Solution   When $3x$ is factored from the first two terms, we get

$$6x^2 - 3x - 2x + 1 = 3x(2x - 1) - 2x + 1$$

What should we factor from the last two terms? We rewrite $-2x + 1$ as $-1(2x - 1)$.
Whenever we wish to change the sign of each term of an expression, we can factor out a negative number from each term. In this case, we factor out -1.

$$-2x + 1 = -1(2x - 1)$$

Next, we have

$$3x(2x - 1) - 2x + 1 = 3x(2x - 1) - 1(2x - 1)$$

Now we factor out the common factor $(2x - 1)$.

$$3x(2x - 1) - 1(2x - 1) = (2x - 1)(3x - 1)$$

Now Try Exercise 23

Understanding Algebra

It is important to recognize that $2x - 1$ is the opposite of $-2x + 1$. So, we can replace $-2x + 1$ with the equivalent $-1(2x - 1)$.

EXAMPLE 7   Factor $q^2 + 3q - q - 3$ by grouping.

Solution
$$
\begin{aligned}
q^2 + 3q - q - 3 &= q(q + 3) - q - 3 &&\text{Factored out } q. \\
&= q(q + 3) - 1(q + 3) &&\text{Factored out } -1 \\
&= (q + 3)(q - 1) &&\text{Factored out } (q + 3).
\end{aligned}
$$

Now Try Exercise 25

EXAMPLE 8   Factor $3x^2 - 6x - 4x + 8$ by grouping.

Solution
$$
\begin{aligned}
3x^2 - 6x - 4x + 8 &= 3x(x - 2) - 4(x - 2) \\
&= (x - 2)(3x - 4)
\end{aligned}
$$

Note: $-4x + 8 = -4(x - 2)$.

Now Try Exercise 27

Helpful Hint

When factoring four terms by grouping, if the coefficient of the third term is positive, as in Examples 2 through 5, you will generally factor out a positive coefficient from the last two terms. *If the coefficient of the third term is negative*, as in Examples 6 through 8, *you will generally factor out a negative coefficient from the last two terms.* The sign of the coefficient of the third term in the expression *must be included* so that the factoring results in two terms. For example,

$$2x^2 + 8x + 3x + 12 = 2x(x + 4) + 3(x + 4) = (x + 4)(2x + 3)$$
$$3x^2 - 15x - 2x + 10 = 3x(x - 5) - 2(x - 5) = (x - 5)(3x - 2)$$

When factoring four terms by grouping, the two middle terms need not be like terms. This is illustrated in Examples 9 and 10.

EXAMPLE 9 Factor $xy + 3x - 2y - 6$ by grouping.

Solution   This problem contains two variables, x and y. Factor x from the first two terms and -2 from the last two terms.

$$xy + 3x - 2y - 6 = x(y + 3) - 2(y + 3)$$
$$= (y + 3)(x - 2) \quad \text{Factored out } (y + 3).$$

Now Try Exercise 41

EXAMPLE 10 Factor $2xy + 4y + 3x + 6$.

Solution   We will factor out $2y$ from the first two terms and 3 from the last two terms.

$$2xy + 4y + 3x + 6 = 2y(x + 2) + 3(x + 2)$$

Factor out the common factor $(x + 2)$ from each term on the right.

$$2y(x + 2) + 3(x + 2) = (x + 2)(2y + 3)$$

Check   F   O   I   L

$$(x + 2)(2y + 3) = (x)(2y) + (x)(3) + (2)(2y) + (2)(3)$$
$$= 2xy + 3x + 4y + 6$$
$$= 2xy + 4y + 3x + 6$$

Now Try Exercise 29

If Example 10 were given as $2xy + 3x + 4y + 6$, would the results be the same? Try it and see.

EXAMPLE 11 Factor $15a^2 - 10ab + 12ab - 8b^2$.

Solution   Factor $5a$ from the first two terms and $4b$ from the last two terms.

$$15a^2 - 10ab + 12ab - 8b^2 = 5a(3a - 2b) + 4b(3a - 2b)$$
$$= (3a - 2b)(5a + 4b)$$

Now Try Exercise 31

EXAMPLE 12 Factor $3x^2 - 15x + 6x - 30$.

Solution   *The first step in any factoring problem is to determine whether all the terms have a common factor. If so, we factor out the greatest common factor (GCF).* In this polynomial, 3 is the GCF. Therefore, we begin by factoring out the 3.

$$3x^2 - 15x + 6x - 30 = 3(x^2 - 5x + 2x - 10)$$

Now we factor the expression in parentheses by grouping. We factor out x from the first two terms and 2 from the last two terms.

$$3(x^2 - 5x + 2x - 10) = 3[x(x - 5) + 2(x - 5)]$$
$$= 3[(x - 5)(x + 2)]$$
$$= 3(x - 5)(x + 2)$$

Thus, $3x^2 - 15x + 6x - 30 = 3(x - 5)(x + 2)$.

Now Try Exercise 49

EXERCISE SET 5.2

MathXL MathXL®   *MyMathLab* MyMathLab

Warm-Up Exercises

Fill in the blanks with the appropriate word, phrase, or symbol(s) from the following list.

FOIL $-1(x + 2)$ $-1(2x - 1)$ ~~factoring by grouping~~

$(x + 2)$ $2(x + 2)$ $(2x - 1)(x + 3)$ $(2x - 1)(x - 3)$

1. The technique used to factor $cx + dx + cy + dy$ is called ___*fbg*___ .

2. When factoring $6x^2 - 3x - 2x + 1$, the last two terms may be rewritten a _____ .

3. When $2x^2 + 6x - x - 3$ is factored, the result is _____ .

4. When factoring $x^2 + 2x - x - 2$, the last two terms may be rewritten as _____ .

5. A factoring-by-grouping problem can be checked by multiplying the result using the _____ method.

6. In $x^2 + 2x + 4x + 8$, there is a common factor in the first two terms and in the last two terms. That common factor is _____ .

Practice the Skills

Factor by grouping.

7. $x^2 + 3x + 2x + 6$ $x(x+3)+2(x+3)$

9. $t^2 + 5t + 4t + 20$ $t(t+5)+4(t+5)$

11. $x^2 + 2x + 5x + 10$ $x(x+2)+5(x+2)$

13. $c^2 - 4c + 7c - 28$

15. $4x^2 - 6x + 6x - 9$

17. $3x^2 + 9x + x + 3$

19. $6x^2 + 3x - 2x - 1$

21. $8x^2 + 32x + x + 4$

23. $12t^2 - 8t - 3t + 2$

25. $x^2 + 9x - x - 9$

27. $6p^2 + 15p - 4p - 10$

29. $x^2 + 2xy - 3xy - 6y^2$

31. $3x^2 + 2xy - 9xy - 6y^2$

33. $10x^2 - 12xy - 25xy + 30y^2$

35. $x^2 - bx - ax + ab$

37. $xy + 9x - 5y - 45$

39. $a^2 + 3a + ab + 3b$

41. $xy - x + 5y - 5$

43. $12 + 8y - 3x - 2xy$

45. $z^3 + 5z^2 + z + 5$

47. $x^3 - 5x^2 + 8x - 40$

49. $2x^2 - 12x + 8x - 48$

51. $4x^2 + 8x + 8x + 16$

53. $6x^3 + 9x^2 - 2x^2 - 3x$

55. $p^3 - 6p^2q + 2p^2q - 12pq^2$

8. $x^2 + 7x + 3x + 21$

10. $x^2 - x + 3x - 3$

12. $y^2 - 7y + 5y - 35$

14. $r^2 - 4r + 6r - 24$

16. $4b^2 - 10b + 10b - 25$

18. $a^2 + a + 3a + 3$

20. $5x^2 + 30x - 3x - 18$

22. $9w^2 - 6w - 6w + 4$

24. $12x^2 + 42x - 10x - 35$

26. $35x^2 - 40x + 21x - 24$

28. $10c^2 + 25c - 6c - 15$

30. $x^2 - 3xy + 4xy - 12y^2$

32. $3x^2 - 18xy + 4xy - 24y^2$

34. $6a^2 - 3ab + 4ab - 2b^2$

36. $x^2 + bx + ax + ab$

38. $x^2 - 2x + ax - 2a$

40. $3x^2 - 15x - 2xy + 10y$

42. $y^2 - yb + ya - ab$

44. $7y - 49 - xy + 7x$

46. $x^3 - 3x^2 + 2x - 6$

48. $y^3 - 3y + 2y^2 - 6$

50. $3x^2 - 3x - 3x + 3$

52. $3z^4 - 3z^3 - 7z^3 + 7z^2$

54. $9x^3 + 6x^2 - 45x^2 - 30x$

56. $18x^2 + 27xy + 12xy + 18y^2$

Rearrange the terms so that the first two terms have a common factor and the last two terms have a common factor (other than 1). Then factor by grouping. There may be more than one way to arrange the factors. However, the answer should be equivalent regardless of the arrangement selected.

57. $5x + 5y + xy + 25$

59. $6x + 5y + xy + 30$

61. $ax + by + ay + bx$

63. $rs - 42 + 6s - 7r$

65. $dc + 3c - ad - 3a$

58. $5m + 2w + mw + 10$

60. $ax - 10 - 5x + 2a$

62. $ax - 21 - 3a + 7x$

64. $ca - 2b + 2a - cb$

66. $ac - bd - ad + bc$

Problem Solving

67. If you know that a polynomial with four terms is factorable by a specific arrangement of the terms, then will *any* arrangement of the terms be factorable by grouping? Explain, and support your answer with an example.

Factor each expression, if possible. Treat the unknown symbol as if it were a variable.

68. $\heartsuit^2 + 3\heartsuit + 4\heartsuit + 12$

69. $\odot^2 + 3\odot - 5\odot - 15$

70. $\Delta^2 + 2\Delta - \Delta + 6$

Concept/Writing Exercises

71. A polynomial of four terms is factored by grouping and the result is $(x - 2y)(x - 3)$. Find the polynomial that was factored and explain how you determined the answer.

72. A polynomial of four terms is factored by grouping and the result is $(x - 2)(x + 4)$. Find the polynomial that was factored, and explain how you determined the answer.

Challenge Problems

In Section 5.4, we will factor trinomials of the form $ax^2 + bx + c, a \neq 1$, using grouping. To do this we rewrite the middle term of the trinomial, bx, as a sum or difference of two terms. Then we factor the resulting polynomial of four terms by grouping. For Exercises 73–78, **a)** *rewrite the trinomial as a polynomial of four terms by replacing the bx-term with the sum or difference given.* **b)** *Factor the polynomial of four terms. Note that the factors obtained are the factors of the trinomial.*

73. $2x^2 - 11x + 15, -11x = -5x - 6x$

74. $3x^2 + 10x + 8, 10x = 4x + 6x$

75. $2x^2 - 11x + 15, -11x = -6x - 5x$

76. $3x^2 + 10x + 8, 10x = 6x + 4x$

77. $4x^2 - 17x - 15, -17x = 3x - 20x$

78. $4x^2 - 17x - 15, -17x = -20x + 3x$

Factor each expression, if possible. Treat the unknown symbols as if they were variables.

79. $\bigstar\odot + 3\bigstar + 2\odot + 6$

80. $2\Delta^2 - 4\Delta\bigstar - 8\Delta\bigstar + 16\bigstar^2$

Cumulative Review Exercises

[2.5] **81.** Solve $5 - 3(2x - 7) = 4(x + 5) - 6$.

[3.4] **82. Mixture.** To celebrate the tenth anniversary of their candy store's opening, Harlan and Shelley Bricker decide to create a special candy mixture containing jelly beans and gumdrops. The jelly beans sell for $6.25 per pound and the gumdrops sell for $2.50 per pound. How many pounds of each type of candy will be needed to make a 50-pound mixture that will sell for $4.75 per pound?

[4.6] **83.** Divide $\dfrac{15x^3 - 6x^2 - 9x + 5}{3x}$.

84. Divide $\dfrac{a^2 - 16}{a + 4}$.

See Exercise 82.

5.3 Factoring Trinomials of the Form $ax^2 + bx + c, a = 1$

1 Factor trinomials of the form $ax^2 + bx + c$, where $a = 1$.

2 Remove the greatest common factor from a trinomial.

Understanding Algebra

We factor trinomials of the form $ax^2 + bx + c$ in this section and the next section.

In this section, $a = 1$ so the trinomials appear as $x^2 + bx + c$. In the next section, $a \neq 1$ and a different strategy will be employed.

1 Factor Trinomials of the Form $ax^2 + bx + c$, where $a = 1$

Now we discuss how to factor trinomials of the form $ax^2 + bx + c$, where a, the numerical coefficient of the squared term, is 1. Examples of such trinomials are

$$x^2 + 7x + 12 \qquad x^2 - 2x - 24$$
$$a = 1, b = 7, c = 12 \qquad a = 1, b = -2, c = -24$$

Recall that factoring is the reverse process of multiplication. We can show with the FOIL method of multiplying binomials that

$$(x + 3)(x + 4) = x^2 + 7x + 12 \quad \text{and} \quad (x - 6)(x + 4) = x^2 - 2x - 24$$

Therefore, $x^2 + 7x + 12$ and $x^2 - 2x - 24$ factor as follows:

$$x^2 + 7x + 12 = (x + 3)(x + 4) \quad \text{and} \quad x^2 - 2x - 24 = (x - 6)(x + 4)$$

In general, when we factor a trinomial of the form $x^2 + bx + c$ we will get a pair of binomial factors as follows:

$$x^2 + bx + c = (x + \_)(x + \_)$$

Numbers go here tha
add up to b and
multiply to c.

To determine the numbers to place in the shaded areas, try different sets of factors of the constant, c. We multiply each pair of factors using the FOIL method, and continue until we find the pair whose sum of the products of the outer and inner terms is the same as the x-term in the trinomial. This method for factoring is called **trial and error**.

EXAMPLE 1 Factor $x^2 + 7x + 12$ by trial and error.

Solution   Begin by listing the factors of 12. Then list the possible factors of the trinomial, and the products of these factors. Finally, determine which, if any, of these products gives the correct middle term, $7x$.

Factors of 12	Possible Factors of Trinomial	Product of Factors
$(1)(12)$	$(x + 1)(x + 12)$	$x^2 + 13x + 12$
$(2)(6)$	$(x + 2)(x + 6)$	$x^2 + 8x + 12$
$(3)(4)$	$(x + 3)(x + 4)$	$x^2 + 7x + 12$
$(-1)(-12)$	$(x - 1)(x - 12)$	$x^2 - 13x + 12$
$(-2)(-6)$	$(x - 2)(x - 6)$	$x^2 - 8x + 12$
$(-3)(-4)$	$(x - 3)(x - 4)$	$x^2 - 7x + 12$

In the last column, we find the trinomial we are seeking in the third line. Thus,

$$x^2 + 7x + 12 = (x + 3)(x + 4)$$

Now Try Exercise 17

Now let's consider an easier way to factor $x^2 + 7x + 12$. In Section 4.5, we illustrated how the FOIL method is used to multiply two binomials. Let's multiply $(x + 3)(x + 4)$ using the FOIL method.

$$
\begin{aligned}
(x + 3)(x + 4) &= x^2 + 4x + 3x + 12 \\
&= x^2 + 7x + 12
\end{aligned}
$$

We see that $(x + 3)(x + 4) = x^2 + 7x + 12$.

Note that the *sum of the outer and inner terms is 7x and the product of the last terms is 12*. To factor $x^2 + 7x + 12$, we look for two numbers whose product is 12 and whose sum is 7. We list the factors of 12 first and then list the sum of the factors.

Factors of 12	Sum of Factors
$(1)(12) = 12$	$1 + 12 = 13$
$(2)(6) = 12$	$2 + 6 = 8$
$(3)(4) = 12$	$3 + 4 = 7$
$(-1)(-12) = 12$	$-1 + (-12) = -13$
$(-2)(-6) = 12$	$-2 + (-6) = -8$
$(-3)(-4) = 12$	$-3 + (-4) = -7$

The only factors of 12 whose sum is a positive 7 are 3 and 4. The factors of $x^2 + 7x + 12$ will therefore be $(x + 3)$ and $(x + 4)$.

$$x^2 + 7x + 12 = (x + 3)(x + 4)$$

In the previous illustration, all the possible factors of 12 were listed so that you could see them. However, once you find the specific factors you are seeking when working a problem, you need go no further.

To Factor Trinomials of the Form $ax^2 + bx + c$, where $a = 1$

1. Find two numbers whose product equals the constant, c, and whose sum equals the coefficient of the x-term, b.
2. Use the two numbers found in step 1, including their signs, to write the trinomial in factored form. The trinomial in factored form will be

$$(x + \text{first number})(x + \text{second number})$$

The sign of the constant, c, is the key in finding the sign of the two numbers to be placed in parentheses. See the Helpful Hint below.

Helpful Hint

To factor a trinomial of the form $x^2 + bx + c$, first observe the sign of the constant.

a) If the constant, c, is positive, both numbers in the factors will have the same sign, either both positive or both negative. If b is positive, both factors will contain positive numbers, and if b is negative, both factors will contain negative numbers.

Example:

$$x^2 + 7x + 12 = (x + 3)(x + 4)$$

The coefficient, b, is positive   The constant, c, is positive   Positive Positive

Both factors have positive numbers.

Example:

$$x^2 - 5x + 6 = (x - 2)(x - 3)$$

The coefficient, b, is negative   The constant, c, is positive   Negative Negative

Both factors have negative numbers.

b) If the constant is negative, the two numbers in the factors will have opposite signs. That is, one number will be positive and the other number will be negative.

Example:

$$x^2 + x - 6 = (x + 3)(x - 2)$$

The coefficient, b, is positive   The constant, c, is negative   Positive Negative

One factor has a positive number and the other factor has a negative number.

Example:

$$x^2 - 3x - 10 = (x + 2)(x - 5)$$

The coefficient, b, is negative   The constant, c, is negative   Positive Negative

One factor has a positive number and the other factor has a negative number.

We will use this information as a starting point when factoring trinomials.

EXAMPLE 2 Consider a trinomial of the form $x^2 + bx + c$. Use the signs of b and c given below to determine the signs of the numbers in the factors.

  a) b is negative and c is positive

  b) b is negative and c is negative

  c) b is positive and c is negative

  d) b is positive and c is positive

> ## Understanding Algebra
>
> To factor $x^2 + bx + c$, first observe the sign of c, and then observe the sign of b:
> $x^2 + 11x + 18 \rightarrow (x + 9)(x + 2)$
> $x^2 - 11x + 18 \rightarrow (x - 9)(x - 2)$
>   ↑   ↑   ↑
> if c is positive, numbers have same sign
>
> $x^2 - 7x - 18 \rightarrow (x - 9)(x + 2)$
> $x^2 + 7x - 18 \rightarrow (x + 9)(x - 2)$
>   ↑   ↑   ↑
> if c is negative, numbers have different signs

Solution   In each case we look at the sign of the constant, c, first.

  a) Since c is positive, both numbers must have the same sign. Since b is negative, both factors will contain negative numbers.

  b) Since c is negative, one factor will contain a positive number and the other will contain a negative number.

  c) Since c is negative, one factor will contain a positive number and the other will contain a negative number.

  d) Since c is positive, both numbers must have the same sign. Since b is positive, both factors will contain positive numbers.

Now Try Exercise 1

EXAMPLE 3 Factor $x^2 + x - 6$.

Solution   We must find two numbers whose product is the constant, -6, and whose sum is the coefficient of the x-term, 1. Remember that x means $1x$. Since the constant is negative, one number must be positive and the other negative. We now list the factors of -6 and look for the two factors whose sum is 1.

Factors of -6	Sum of Factors
$1(-6) = -6$	$1 + (-6) = -5$
$2(-3) = -6$	$2 + (-3) = -1$
$3(-2) = -6$	$3 + (-2) = 1$
$6(-1) = -6$	$6 + (-1) = 5$

> ## Understanding Algebra
>
> Use FOIL to check the answer to Example 3.
>
> $(x + 3)(x - 2) = x^2 - 2x + 3x - 6$
> $\qquad\qquad\quad = x^2 + x - 6$
>
> Since the product of factors is identical to the original trinomial, the factoring is correct.

The numbers 3 and -2 have a product of -6 and a sum of 1. Thus, the factors are $(x + 3)$ and $(x - 2)$.

$$x^2 + x - 6 = (x + 3)(x - 2)$$

The order of the factors is not crucial. Therefore, $x^2 + x - 6 = (x - 2)(x + 3)$ is also an acceptable answer.

Now Try Exercise 19

EXAMPLE 4 Factor $x^2 - x - 6$.

Solution   The factors of -6 are illustrated in Example 3. The factors whose product is -6 and whose sum is -1 are 2 and -3.

Factors of -6	Sum of Factors
$2(-3) = -6$	$2 + (-3) = -1$

Therefore, $$x^2 - x - 6 = (x + 2)(x - 3)$$

Now Try Exercise 25

EXAMPLE 5 Factor $x^2 - 5x + 6$.

Solution   We must find two numbers whose product is 6 and whose sum is -5. Since the constant, 6, is positive, both numbers must have the same sign. Since the

Understanding Algebra

To factor a trinomial, write the trinomial in descending order. To factor $-5x + x^2 + 6$, we must first rewrite it as $x^2 - 5x + 6$.

coefficient of the x-term, -5, is negative, both numbers must be negative. We now list the negative factors of 6 and look for the pair whose sum is -5.

Factors of 6	Sum of Factors
$(-1)(-6)$	$-1 + (-6) = -7$
$(-2)(-3)$	$-2 + (-3) = -5$

The factors of 6 whose sum is -5 are -2 and -3.

$$x^2 - 5x + 6 = (x - 2)(x - 3)$$

Now Try Exercise 29

EXAMPLE 6 Factor $r^2 + 2r - 24$.

Solution   We must find the two factors of -24 whose sum is 2. Since the constant is negative, one factor will be positive and the other factor will be negative.

Factors of -24	Sum of Factors
$(1)(-24)$	$1 + (-24) = -23$
$(2)(-12)$	$2 + (-12) = -10$
$(3)(-8)$	$3 + (-8) = -5$
$(4)(-6)$	$4 + (-6) = -2$
$(6)(-4)$	$6 + (-4) = 2$

Since we have found the two numbers, 6 and -4, whose product is -24 and whose sum is 2, we need go no further.

$$r^2 + 2r - 24 = (r + 6)(r - 4)$$

Now Try Exercise 33

EXAMPLE 7 Factor $x^2 - 8x + 16$.

Solution   We must find the factors of 16 whose sum is -8. Both factors must be negative. The two factors whose product is 16 and whose sum is -8 are -4 and -4.

$$x^2 - 8x + 16 = (x - 4)(x - 4)$$
$$= (x - 4)^2$$

Now Try Exercise 41

EXAMPLE 8 Factor $x^2 - 11x - 60$.

Solution   We must find two numbers whose product is -60 and whose sum is -11. Since the constant is negative, one number must be positive and the other negative. The desired numbers are -15 and 4 because $(-15)(4) = -60$ and $-15 + 4 = -11$.

$$x^2 - 11x - 60 = (x - 15)(x + 4)$$

Now Try Exercise 47

Not all trinomials are factorable using integer coefficients as Example 9 will show.

Prime Polynomials

A **prime polynomial** is a polynomial that cannot be factored using only integer coefficients.
   For example, $x^2 + 3x + 8$ cannot be factored using integer coefficients because there are no two integers whose product is 8 and whose sum is 3. If asked to factor it, the correct answer is to say it is **prime**.

EXAMPLE 9 Factor $x^2 + 5x + 12$.

Solution   Let's first find the two numbers whose product is 12 and whose sum is 5. Since both the constant and the coefficient of the x-term are positive, the two numbers must also be positive.

Factors of 12	Sum of Factors
(1)(12)	$1 + 12 = 13$
(2)(6)	$2 + 6 = 8$
(3)(4)	$3 + 4 = 7$

Note that there are no two integers whose product is 12 and whose sum is 5. Thus, $x^2 + 5x + 12$ is prime.

Now Try Exercise 31

> **Understanding Algebra**
>
> When factoring a trinomial of the form $x^2 + bx + c$, there is at most one pair of factors whose product is $x^2 + bx + c$. For example, when factoring $x^2 - 12x + 32$, the only factors are $(x - 4)$ and $(x - 8)$.

In Examples 10 and 11, we will factor trinomials of the form $x^2 + bxy + cy^2$, where b and c are real numbers. An example of a trinomial in this form is $x^2 - 2xy - 15y^2$. When factoring trinomials of this form, the factors must be of the form as follows.

$$x^2 + bxy + cy^2 = (x + \blacksquare y)(x + \blacksquare y)$$

Numbers go here that
• add up to b
• multiply to c

EXAMPLE 10 Factor $x^2 + 3xy + 2y^2$.

Solution   In this problem, the second term contains two variables, x and y. The product of the first terms of the factors we are looking for must be x^2, and the product of the last terms of the factors must be $2y^2$.

We must find two numbers whose product is 2 (from $2y^2$) and whose sum is 3 (from $3xy$). The two numbers are 1 and 2. Thus,

$$x^2 + 3xy + 2y^2 = (x + 1y)(x + 2y) = (x + y)(x + 2y)$$

Now Try Exercise 65

> **Understanding Algebra**
>
> To factor $x^2 + 2xy + y^2$, we need to find two numbers whose product is 1 and whose sum is 2. The numbers are 1 and 1. So,
>
> $x^2 + 2xy + y^2 = (x + 1y)(x + 1y)$
>
> which we write as $(x + y)^2$.

EXAMPLE 11 Factor $x^2 - 2xy - 15y^2$.

Solution   Find two numbers whose product is -15 and whose sum is -2. The numbers are -5 and 3. The last terms must be $-5y$ and $3y$ to obtain $-15y^2$.

$$x^2 - 2xy - 15y^2 = (x - 5y)(x + 3y)$$

Now Try Exercise 69

2 Remove the Greatest Common Factor from a Trinomial

Sometimes each term of a trinomial has a common factor. When this occurs, factor out the greatest common factor (GCF) first, as explained in Section 5.1. *The first step in any factoring problem is to factor out the GCF.* After factoring out the GCF, you should factor the remaining trinomial further, if possible, until it is completely factored.

> **Understanding Algebra**
>
> *ALWAYS* factor out the GCF first.

EXAMPLE 12 Factor $2x^2 + 2x - 12$.

Solution   Since 2 is the GCF, we factor it out.

$$2x^2 + 2x - 12 = 2(x^2 + x - 6)$$

Now we factor the remaining trinomial $x^2 + x - 6$ into $(x + 3)(x - 2)$. Thus,

$$2x^2 + 2x - 12 = 2(x + 3)(x - 2).$$

Note that the trinomial $2x^2 + 2x - 12$ is now completely factored into *three* factors: two binomial factors, $x + 3$ and $x - 2$, and a monomial factor, 2. After 2 has been factored out, it plays no part in the factoring of the remaining trinomial.

Now Try Exercise 71

EXAMPLE 13 Factor $3n^3 + 24n^2 - 60n$.

Solution   The GCF is $3n$. After factoring out the $3n$, we factor the remaining trinomial.

$$3n^3 + 24n^2 - 60n = 3n(n^2 + 8n - 20) \quad \text{Factored out the GCF.}$$
$$= 3n(n + 10)(n - 2) \quad \text{Factored the remaining trinomial.}$$

Now Try Exercise 79

EXERCISE SET 5.3

MathXL MathXL®   MyMathLab MyMathLab

Warm-Up Exercises

Fill in the blanks with the appropriate word, phrase, or symbol(s) from the following list.

$2x^2 + 18$	prime	$2x^2 - 12x + 18$	factor out the GCF
$2(x - 5)(x - 1)$	$2(x - 2)(x - 3)$	$(2x - 4)(x - 3)$	$y(x - 1)(x - 5)$
one positive and one negative	$(x - y)(x - 5y)$	both positive	both negative

1. When the trinomial $x^2 - 20x + 36$ is factored, the signs that will appear in the binomial factors are _____ .

2. A polynomial that cannot be factored using integer coefficients is said to be _____ .

3. When $2x^2 - 10x + 12$ is factored, the result is _____ .

4. The first step in factoring is to _____ .

5. When $2x^2 - 12x + 10$ is factored, the result is _____ .

6. When $x^2 - 6xy + 5y^2$ is factored, the result is _____ .

7. When the trinomial $x^2 + 20x + 36$ is factored, the signs that will appear in the binomial factors are _____ .

8. When the trinomial $x^2 + 16x - 36$ is factored, the signs that will appear in the binomial factors are _____ .

9. When $x^2y - 6xy + 5y$ is factored, the result is _____ .

10. When the factored expression $2(x - 3)^2$ is multiplied out, the result is _____ .

Practice the Skills

Factor each polynomial. If the polynomial is prime, so state.

11. $x^2 + 11x + 24$

12. $t^2 + 10t + 21$

13. $y^2 - 10y + 16$

14. $x^2 - 11x + 24$

15. $x^2 - 7x + 10$

16. $x^2 + 8x + 15$

17. $x^2 + 6x + 8$

18. $x^2 - 3x + 2$

19. $x^2 + 5x - 24$

20. $x^2 - x - 12$

21. $x^2 + 4x - 6$

22. $y^2 - 6y + 8$

23. $y^2 - 13y + 12$

24. $x^2 + 3x - 54$

25. $a^2 - 2a - 8$

26. $p^2 + 3p - 10$

27. $r^2 - 2r - 15$

28. $x^2 - 6x + 8$

29. $b^2 - 11b + 18$

30. $x^2 + 11x - 30$

31. $x^2 - 8x - 15$

32. $x^2 - 8x + 7$

33. $q^2 + 4q - 45$

34. $x^2 + 10x + 25$

35. $x^2 - 7x - 30$

36. $b^2 - 9b - 36$

37. $x^2 + 4x + 4$

38. $x^2 - 4x + 4$

39. $s^2 - 8s + 16$

40. $u^2 + 2u + 1$

41. $p^2 - 12p + 36$

42. $x^2 - 10x - 25$

43. $-18w + w^2 + 45$

44. $-11x + x^2 + 10$

45. $10x - 39 + x^2$

46. $-3x + 8 + x^2$

47. $x^2 - x - 20$

48. $t^2 - 28t - 60$

49. $y^2 + 13y + 40$

50. $r^2 + 14r + 48$

51. $x^2 + 12x - 64$

52. $x^2 - 18x + 80$

53. $s^2 + 14s - 24$

54. $x^2 - 13x + 36$

55. $x^2 - 20x + 64$

56. $x^2 + 19x + 48$

57. $a^2 - 20a + 99$

58. $x^2 + 5x - 24$

59. $x^2 + 2 + 3x$

60. $m^2 - 11 - 10m$

61. $7w - 18 + w^2$

62. $30 + y^2 - 13y$

63. $x^2 - 8xy + 15y^2$

64. $x^2 - 2xy + y^2$

65. $m^2 - 6mn + 9n^2$

66. $b^2 - 2bc - 3c^2$

67. $x^2 + 8xy + 12y^2$

68. $x^2 + 16xy - 17y^2$

69. $m^2 - 5mn - 24n^2$

70. $c^2 + 2cd - 24d^2$

Factor completely.

71. $6x^2 - 30x + 24$

72. $2a^2 - 12a - 32$

73. $5x^2 + 20x + 15$

74. $4x^2 + 12x - 16$

75. $2x^2 - 18x + 40$

76. $3y^2 - 33y + 54$

77. $b^3 - 7b^2 + 10b$

78. $c^3 + 8c^2 - 48c$

79. $3z^3 - 21z^2 - 54z$

80. $3x^3 - 36x^2 + 33x$

81. $x^3 + 8x^2 + 16x$

82. $2x^3y - 12x^2y + 10xy$

83. $7a^2 - 35ab + 42b^2$

84. $3x^3 + 3x^2y - 18xy^2$

85. $3r^3 + 6r^2t - 24rt^2$

86. $r^2s + 7rs^2 + 12s^3$

87. $x^4 - 4x^3 - 21x^2$

88. $2z^5 + 14z^4 + 12z^3$

Problem Solving

89. The first two columns in the following table describe the signs of the coefficient of the x-term and constant term of a trinomial of the form $x^2 + bx + c$. Determine whether the third column should contain "both positive," "both negative," or "one positive and one negative."

Sign of Coefficient of x-term	Sign of Constant Term	Sign of Constant Terms in the Binomial Factors
−	+	
−	−	
+	−	
+	+	

90. Assume that a trinomial of the form $x^2 + bx + c$ is factorable. Determine whether the constant terms in the factors are "both positive," "both negative," or "one positive and one negative" for the given signs of b and c.

a) $b < 0, c > 0$

b) $b > 0, c > 0$

c) $b > 0, c < 0$

d) $b < 0, c < 0$

91. Write a trinomial whose binomial factors contain constant terms whose sum is -12 and have a product of 32. Show the factoring of the trinomial.

92. Write a trinomial whose binomial factors contain constant terms whose sum is 5 and have a product of 4. Show the factoring of the trinomial.

93. Write a trinomial whose binomial factors contain constant terms whose sum is -2 and have a product of -35. Show the factoring of the trinomial.

94. Write a trinomial whose binomial factors contain constant terms whose sum is 5 and have a product of -14. Show the factoring of the trinomial.

Concept/Writing Exercises

95. On an exam, a student factored $2x^2 - 6x + 4$ as $(2x - 4)(x - 1)$. Even though $(2x - 4)(x - 1)$ does multiply out to $2x^2 - 6x + 4$, why did his or her professor deduct points?

96. Explain how to determine the factors when factoring a trinomial of the form $x^2 + bx + c$.

Challenge Problems

Factor.

97. $x^2 + 0.6x + 0.08$

98. $x^2 - 0.5x - 0.06$

99. $x^2 + \frac{2}{5}x + \frac{1}{25}$

100. $x^2 - \frac{2}{7}x + \frac{1}{49}$

101. $x^2 - 24x - 256$

102. $x^2 + 5x - 300$

Cumulative Review Exercises

[2.5] **103.** Solve the equation $4(2x - 4) = 5x + 11$.

[3.4] **104.** **Mixing Solutions** Karen Moreau, a chemist, mixes 4 liters of an 18% acid solution with 1 liter of a 26% acid solution. Find the strength of the mixture.

[4.5] **105.** Multiply $(2x^2 + 5x - 6)(x - 2)$.

[4.6] **106.** Divide $3x^2 - 10x - 10$ by $x - 4$.

[5.2] **107.** Factor $20x^2 + 8x - 15x - 6$ by grouping.

See Exercise 104.

5.4 Factoring Trinomials of the Form $ax^2 + bx + c, a \neq 1$

1 Factor trinomials of the form $ax^2 + bx + c, a \neq 1$, by trial and error.

2 Factor trinomials of the form $ax^2 + bx + c, a \neq 1$, by grouping.

An Important Note

In this section, we discuss two methods of factoring trinomials of the form $ax^2 + bx + c$, $a \neq 1$. That is, we will be factoring trinomials whose squared term has a numerical coefficient not equal to 1, after removing any common factors. Examples of trinomials with $a \neq 1$ are

$$\overbrace{2x^2 + 11x + 12 \text{ (Notice } a = 2)}^{a \neq 1} \qquad 4x^2 - 3x + 1 \text{(Notice } a = 4)$$

The methods we discuss are (1) **factoring by trial and error** and (2) **factoring by grouping.** We present two different methods for factoring these trinomials because some students, and some instructors, prefer the first method, while others prefer the second method. You may use either method unless your instructor asks you to use a specific method. We will use the same examples to illustrate both methods so that you can make a comparison. Each method is treated independently of the other. Factoring by trial and error was introduced in Section 5.3 and factoring by grouping was introduced in Section 5.2.

1 Factor Trinomials of the Form $ax^2 + bx + c, a \neq 1$, by Trial and Error

Recall that factoring is the reverse of multiplying. Consider the product of the following two binomials:

$$
\begin{array}{cccc}
\text{F} & \text{O} & \text{I} & \text{L} \\
\end{array}
$$
$$
\begin{aligned}
(2x + 3)(x + 5) &= 2x(x) + (2x)(5) + 3(x) + 3(5) \\
&= 2x^2 + 10x + 3x + 15 \\
&= 2x^2 + 13x + 15
\end{aligned}
$$

> ### Understanding Algebra
>
> $$\begin{array}{cccc} \text{F} & \text{O} & \text{I} & \text{L} \end{array}$$
>
> Use FOIL to multiply $(2x + 3)(x + 5)$.
>
> Product of FIRST terms is $2x^2$.
> $$2x \cdot x = 2x^2$$
>
> Sum of OUTER and INNER products is $13x$.
> $$2x \cdot 5 + 3 \cdot x = 13x$$
>
> Product of LAST terms is 15.
> $$3 \cdot 5 = 15$$
> $$(2x + 3)(x + 5) = 2x^2 + 13x + 15$$

Note that $2x^2 + 13x + 15$ in factored form is $(2x + 3)(x + 5)$.

$$2x^2 + 13x + 15 = (2x + 3)(x + 5)$$

When factoring a trinomial of the form $ax^2 + bx + c$ by trial and error, the product of the x-terms in the binomial factors must equal the first term of the trinomial, ax^2. Also, the product of the constants in the binomial factors, including their signs, must equal the constant, c, of the trinomial.

Product of constants in factors must equal c.

$$ax^2 + bx + c = (x\text{-term} + 1\text{st constant})(x\text{-term} + 2\text{nd constant})$$

Product of x-terms in factors must equal ax^2.

For example, when factoring the trinomial $2x^2 + 7x + 6$, each of the following pairs of factors has a product of the first terms equal to $2x^2$ and a product of the last terms equal to 6.

Trinomial	Possible Factors	Product of First Terms	Product of Last Terms
$2x^2 + 7x + 6$	$(2x + 1)(x + 6)$	$2x(x) = 2x^2$	$1(6) = 6$
	$(2x + 2)(x + 3)$	$2x(x) = 2x^2$	$2(3) = 6$
	$(2x + 3)(x + 2)$	$2x(x) = 2x^2$	$3(2) = 6$
	$(2x + 6)(x + 1)$	$2x(x) = 2x^2$	$6(1) = 6$

How do we determine which is the correct factoring of the trinomial $2x^2 + 7x + 6$? The key lies in the x-term. We need to find the pair of factors whose sum of the products of the outer and inner terms is equal to the x-term of the trinomial.

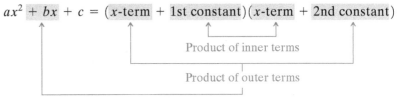

$$ax^2 + bx + c = (x\text{-term} + 1\text{st constant})(x\text{-term} + 2\text{nd constant})$$

Product of inner terms

Product of outer terms

Sum of products of outer and inner terms must equal bx.

Now look at the possible pairs of factors we obtained for $2x^2 + 7x + 6$ to see if any yield the correct x-term, $7x$.

Trinomial	Possible Factors	Product of the First Terms	Product of the Last Terms	Sum of the Products of Outer and Inner Terms
$2x^2 + 7x + 6$	$(2x + 1)(x + 6)$	$2x^2$	6	$2x(6) + 1(x) = 13x$
	$(2x + 2)(x + 3)$	$2x^2$	6	$2x(3) + 2(x) = 8x$
	$(2x + 3)(x + 2)$	$2x^2$	6	$2x(2) + 3(x) = 7x$
	$(2x + 6)(x + 1)$	$2x^2$	6	$2x(1) + 6(x) = 8x$

Since $(2x + 3)(x + 2)$ yields the correct x-term, $7x$, the factors of the trinomial $2x^2 + 7x + 6$ are $(2x + 3)$ and $(x + 2)$.

$$2x^2 + 7x + 6 = (2x + 3)(x + 2)$$

We can check this factoring using the FOIL method.

$$\begin{array}{cccc} \text{F} & \text{O} & \text{I} & \text{L} \end{array}$$

Check $(2x + 3)(x + 2) = 2x(x) + 2x(2) + 3(x) + 3(2)$

$$= 2x^2 + 4x + 3x + 6$$

$$= 2x^2 + 7x + 6$$

Since we obtained the original trinomial, our factoring is correct.

Understanding Algebra

Notice that $2x^2 + 13x + 15$ factors as $(2x + 3)(x + 5)$. The product $(2x + 5)(x + 3)$ will yield a $2x^2$ term and a 15 term, but the middle term is $11x$ and not $13x$!

Helpful Hint

When factoring a trinomial of the form $ax^2 + bx + c$, remember that the sign of the constant, c, and the sign of the x-term, bx, offer valuable information. When factoring a trinomial by trial and error, first check the sign of the constant. If it is positive, the signs in both factors will be the same as the sign of the x-term. If the constant is negative, one factor will contain a plus sign and the other a minus sign.

Now we outline the procedure to factor trinomials of the form $ax^2 + bx + c$, $a \neq 1$, by trial and error. Keep in mind that the more you practice, the better you will become at factoring.

To Factor Trinomials of the Form $ax^2 + bx + c, a \neq 1$, by Trial and Error

1. Factor out the greatest common factor (GCF), if any.
2. Write all pairs of factors of the coefficient of the squared term, a.
3. Write all pairs of factors of the constant term, c.
4. Try combinations of these factors until the correct middle term, bx, is found.

EXAMPLE 1   Factor $3x^2 + 20x + 12$. ———

Solution   We first determine that there is no GCF to factor out. Since the first term is $3x^2$, the factors will be of the form $(3x +)(x +)$. Now we must find the numbers to place in the shaded areas. The product of the last terms in the factors must be 12. Since the constant and the coefficient of the x-term are both positive, only the positive factors of 12 need be considered.

Factors of 12	Possible Factors of Trinomial	Sum of the Products of the Outer and Inner Terms
1(12)	$(3x + 1)(x + 12)$	$37x$
2(6)	$(3x + 2)(x + 6)$	$20x$
3(4)	$(3x + 3)(x + 4)$	$15x$
4(3)	$(3x + 4)(x + 3)$	$13x$
6(2)	$(3x + 6)(x + 2)$	$12x$
12(1)	$(3x + 12)(x + 1)$	$15x$

Since the product of $(3x + 2)$ and $(x + 6)$ yields the correct x-term, $20x$, they are the correct factors.

$$3x^2 + 20x + 12 = (3x + 2)(x + 6)$$

Now Try Exercise 5

EXAMPLE 2   Factor $5x^2 - 7x - 6$. ———

Solution   There is no GCF to factor out. Since the first term is $5x^2$, one factor must contain a $5x$ and the other an x. List the factors of -6 and look for the pair of factors that yields $-7x$.

Factors of -6	Possible Factors	Sum of the Products of the Outer and Inner Terms
$-1(6)$	$(5x - 1)(x + 6)$	$29x$
$-2(3)$	$(5x - 2)(x + 3)$	$13x$
$-3(2)$	$(5x - 3)(x + 2)$	$7x$
$-6(1)$	$(5x - 6)(x + 1)$	$-x$

Since we did not obtain the desired quantity, $-7x$, by writing the negative factor with the $5x$, we will now try listing the negative factor with the x.

Factors of -6	Possible Factors	Sum of the Products of the Outer and Inner Terms
1(-6)	$(5x + 1)(x - 6)$	$-29x$
2(-3)	$(5x + 2)(x - 3)$	$-13x$
3(-2)	$(5x + 3)(x - 2)$	$-7x$
6(-1)	$(5x + 6)(x - 1)$	x

We see that $(5x + 3)(x - 2)$ gives the $-7x$ we are looking for. Thus,

$$5x^2 - 7x - 6 = (5x + 3)(x - 2)$$

Again we listed all the possible combinations for you to study.

Now Try Exercise 9

> **Helpful Hint**
>
> In Example 2, we were asked to factor $5x^2 - 7x - 6$. When we considered $-3(2)$ in the first set of possible factors, we obtained
>
> | Factors of -6 | Possible Factors | Sum of the Products of the Outer and Inner Terms |
> |---|---|---|
> | $-3(2)$ | $(5x - 3)(x + 2)$ | $7x$ |
>
> Later in the solution we tried the factors $3(-2)$ and obtained the correct answer.
>
> | | Possible | Sum of the Products of the |
> | $3(-2)$ | $(5x + 3)(x - 2)$ | $-7x$ |
>
> When factoring a trinomial with a *negative constant*, if you obtain the x-term whose sign is the opposite of the one you are seeking, *reverse the signs on the constants* in the factors. This should give you the set of factors you are seeking.

EXAMPLE 3   Factor $8x^2 + 33x + 4$.

Solution   There is no GCF. Since the first term is $8x^2$, the possible factors may be of the form $(8x \quad)(x \quad)$ or $(4x \quad)(2x \quad)$. When this situation occurs, we will generally start with the middle-size pair of factors. Thus, we begin with $(4x \quad)(2x \quad)$. If this pair does not lead to the solution, we will then try $(8x \quad)(x \quad)$. We now list the factors of the constant, 4. Since all signs are positive, we list only the positive factors of 4.

Factors of 4	Possible Factors	Sum of the Products of the Outer and Inner Terms
$1(4)$	$(4x + 1)(2x + 4)$	$18x$
$2(2)$	$(4x + 2)(2x + 2)$	$12x$
$4(1)$	$(4x + 4)(2x + 1)$	$12x$

Since we did not obtain the correct factors with $(4x \quad)(2x \quad)$, we now try $(8x \quad)(x \quad)$.

Factors of 4	Possible Factors	Sum of the Products of the Outer and Inner Terms
$1(4)$	$(8x + 1)(x + 4)$	$33x$
$2(2)$	$(8x + 2)(x + 2)$	$18x$
$4(1)$	$(8x + 4)(x + 1)$	$12x$

Since the product of $(8x + 1)$ and $(x + 4)$ yields the correct x-term, $33x$, they are the correct factors.

$$8x^2 + 33x + 4 = (8x + 1)(x + 4)$$

Now Try Exercise 19

Understanding Algebra

In Example 3, another reason we can eliminate the factors

$(4x + 1)(2x + 4)$
$(4x + 2)(2x + 2)$
$(4x + 4)(2x + 1)$
$(8x + 2)(x + 2)$
$(8x + 4)(x + 1)$

is that each product has a binomial that contains a common factor.

Since the original trinomial did not have any common factors, there can be no common factors in the binomial factors.

EXAMPLE 4   Factor $25t^2 - 10t + 1$.

Solution   The factors must be of the form $(25t \quad)(t \quad)$ or $(5t \quad)(5t \quad)$. We will start with the middle-size factors $(5t \quad)(5t \quad)$. Since the constant is positive and the coefficient of the x-term is negative, both factors must be negative.

Factors of 1	Possible Factors	Sum of the Products of the Outer and Inner Terms
$(-1)(-1)$	$(5t - 1)(5t - 1)$	$-10t$

Since we found the correct factors, we can stop.

$$25t^2 - 10t + 1 = (5t - 1)(5t - 1) = (5t - 1)^2$$

Now Try Exercise 13

EXAMPLE 5 Factor $2x^2 + 3x + 7$.

Solution   The factors will be of the form $(2x\quad)(x\quad)$. We need only consider the positive factors of 7.

Factors of 7	Possible Factors	Sum of the Products of the Outer and Inner Terms
1(7)	$(2x + 1)(x + 7)$	$15x$
7(1)	$(2x + 7)(x + 1)$	$9x$

Since we have tried all possible combinations and we have not obtained the x-term, $3x$, this trinomial *cannot be factored using integer coefficients*. Thus, the trinomial $2x^2 + 3x + 7$ is a *prime polynomial*.

Now Try Exercise 17

EXAMPLE 6 Factor $6a^2 + 19ab + 3b^2$.

Solution   This trinomial is different from the other trinomials in that the last term is not a constant but contains b^2. The factoring process is the same, except that the second term of both factors will contain b. Consider factors of the form $(3a\quad)(2a\quad)$. If we cannot find the factors, then we try factors of the form $(6a\quad)(a\quad)$.

Factors of 3	Possible Factors	Sum of the Products of the Outer and Inner Terms
1(3)	$(3a + b)(2a + 3b)$	$11ab$
3(1)	$(3a + 3b)(2a + b)$	$9ab$
1(3)	$(6a + b)(a + 3b)$	$19ab$
3(1)	$(6a + 3b)(a + b)$	$9ab$

$$6a^2 + 19ab + 3b^2 = (6a + b)(a + 3b)$$

Check $(6a + b)(a + 3b) = 6a^2 + 18ab + ab + 3b^2 = 6a^2 + 19ab + 3b^2$

Now Try Exercise 55

EXAMPLE 7 Factor $6x^2 - 13xy - 8y^2$.

Solution   We begin with factors of the form $(3x\quad)(2x\quad)$. If we cannot find the solution from these, we will try $(6x\quad)(x\quad)$. Since the last term, $-8y^2$, is negative, one factor will contain a plus sign and the other will contain a minus sign.

Factors of −8	Possible Factors	Sum of the Products of the Outer and Inner Terms
1(−8)	$(3x + y)(2x - 8y)$	$-22xy$
2(−4)	$(3x + 2y)(2x - 4y)$	$-8xy$
4(−2)	$(3x + 4y)(2x - 2y)$	$2xy$
8(−1)	$(3x + 8y)(2x - y)$	$13xy$

We are looking for $-13xy$. When we considered $8(-1)$, we obtained $13xy$. As explained in the Helpful Hint on page 305, if we reverse the signs of the numbers in the factors, we will obtain the factors we are seeking.

$$(3x + 8y)(2x - y)\quad \text{Product is } 6x^2 + 13xy - 8y^2$$

$$(3x - 8y)(2x + y)\quad \text{Product is } 6x^2 - 13xy - 8y^2$$

Therefore, $6x^2 - 13xy - 8y^2 = (3x - 8y)(2x + y)$.

Now Try Exercise 57

EXAMPLE 8 Factor $6x^3 + 15x^2 - 36x$.

Solution   *The first step in any factoring problem is to factor out the GCF. In this example, $3x$ is common to all three terms. We begin by factoring out the $3x$. Then we continue factoring by trial and error.*

$$6x^3 + 15x^2 - 36x = 3x(2x^2 + 5x - 12)$$
$$= 3x(2x - 3)(x + 4)$$

Now Try Exercise 47

2 Factor Trinomials of the Form $ax^2 + bx + c, a \neq 1$, by Grouping

The steps in the box that follow give the procedure for factoring trinomials by grouping.

To Factor Trinomials of the Form $ax^2 + bx + c, a \neq 1$, by Grouping

1. Factor out the greatest common factor, if any.
2. Find two numbers whose product is equal to the product of *a* times *c*, and whose sum is equal to *b*.
3. Rewrite the middle term, *bx*, as the sum or difference of two terms using the numbers found in step 2.
4. Factor by grouping as explained in Section 5.2.

This process will be made clearer in Example 9. We will rework Examples 1 through 8 here using factoring by grouping. Example 9, which follows, is the same trinomial given in Example 1. After you study this method and try some exercises, you will gain a feel for which method you prefer using.

EXAMPLE 9 Factor $3x^2 + 20x + 12$.

Solution

1. There is no GCF to factor out.

$$a = 3 \quad b = 20 \quad c = 12$$

2. We must find two numbers whose product is $a \cdot c$ and whose sum is *b*. We must therefore find two numbers whose product equals $3 \cdot 12 = 36$ and whose sum equals 20. Only the positive factors of 36 need be considered since all signs of the trinomial are positive.

Factors of 36	Sum of Factors
(1)(36)	$1 + 36 = 37$
(2)(18)	$2 + 18 = 20$
(3)(12)	$3 + 12 = 15$
(4)(9)	$4 + 9 = 13$
(6)(6)	$6 + 6 = 12$

The desired factors are 2 and 18.

3. Rewrite $20x$ as the sum or difference of two terms using the values found in step 2. Therefore, we rewrite $20x$ as $2x + 18x$.

$$3x^2 + 20x + 12$$
$$= 3x^2 + 2x + 18x + 12$$

4. Now factor by grouping. Start by factoring out a common factor from the first two terms and a common factor from the last two terms. This procedure was discussed in Section 5.2.

$$\underbrace{3x^2 + 2x}_{x \text{ is common factor}} + \underbrace{18x + 12}_{6 \text{ is common factor}}$$

$$= x(3x + 2) + 6(3x + 2)$$
$$= (3x + 2)(x + 6)$$

Now Try Exercise 7

EXAMPLE 10 Factor $5x^2 - 7x - 6$.

Solution There are no common factors other than 1.
$$a = 5, \quad b = -7, \quad c = -6$$
The product of a times c is $5(-6) = -30$. We must find two numbers whose product is -30 and whose sum is -7.

Factors of -30	Sum of Factors
$(-1)(30)$	$-1 + 30 = 29$
$(-2)(15)$	$-2 + 15 = 13$
$(-3)(10)$	$-3 + 10 = 7$
$(-5)(6)$	$-5 + 6 = 1$
$(-6)(5)$	$-6 + 5 = -1$
$(-10)(3)$	$-10 + 3 = -7$
$(-15)(2)$	$-15 + 2 = -13$
$(-30)(1)$	$-30 + 1 = -29$

Rewrite the middle term of the trinomial, $-7x$, as $-10x + 3x$.

$$5x^2 - 7x - 6$$
$$= 5x^2 - 10x + 3x - 6 \qquad \text{Now factor by grouping.}$$
$$= 5x(x - 2) + 3(x - 2)$$
$$= (x - 2)(5x + 3)$$

Now Try Exercise 31

In Example 10, we could have expressed the $-7x$ as $3x - 10x$ and obtained the same answer. Try working Example 10 by rewriting $-7x$ as $3x - 10x$.

Helpful Hint

In Example 10 we were looking for two factors of -30 whose sum was -7. When we considered the factors -3 and 10, we obtained a sum of 7, which is the opposite of -7. When trying pairs of factors to obtain the middle term, if you obtain the opposite of the coefficient you are seeking, reverse the signs in the factors. This should give you the coefficient you are seeking.

EXAMPLE 11 Factor $8x^2 + 33x + 4$.

Solution There is no GCF to factor out. We must find two numbers whose product is $8 \cdot 4$ or 32 and whose sum is 33. The numbers are 1 and 32.

Factors of 32	Sum of Factors
$(1)(32)$	$1 + 32 = 33$

Rewrite $33x$ as $32x + x$. Then factor by grouping.

Understanding Algebra

In Example 11 we could also have written:

$$8x^2 + 33x + 4$$
$$= 8x^2 + x + 32x + 4$$
$$= x(8x + 1) + 4(8x + 1)$$
$$= (8x + 1)(x + 4)$$

$$8x^2 + 33x + 4$$
$$= 8x^2 + 32x + x + 4$$
$$= 8x(x + 4) + 1(x + 4)$$
$$= (x + 4)(8x + 1)$$

Now Try Exercise 25

EXAMPLE 12 Factor $25t^2 - 10t + 1$.

Solution There is no GCF to factor out. We must find two numbers whose product is $25 \cdot 1$ or 25 and whose sum is -10. Since the product of a times c is positive and the coefficient of the t-term is negative, both numerical factors must be negative.

Factors of 25	Sum of Factors
$(-1)(-25)$	$-1 + (-25) = -26$
$(-5)(-5)$	$-5 + (-5) = -10$

The desired factors are -5 and -5.

$$25t^2 - 10t + 1$$
$$= 25t^2 - 5t - 5t + 1 \qquad \text{Rewrote } -10t \text{ as } -5t - 5t.$$
$$= 5t(5t - 1) - 5t + 1$$
$$= 5t(5t - 1) - 1(5t - 1) \qquad \text{Rewrote } -5t + 1 \text{ as } -1(5t - 1).$$
$$= (5t - 1)(5t - 1) \text{ or } (5t - 1)^2$$

Now Try Exercise 29

Helpful Hint

When attempting to factor a trinomial, if there are no two integers whose product equals $a \cdot c$ and whose sum equals b, the trinomial is prime.

EXAMPLE 13 Factor $2x^2 + 3x + 7$.

Solution There are no common factors other than 1. We must find two numbers whose product is 14 and whose sum is 3. We need consider only positive factors of 14. Why?

Factors of 14	Sum of Factors
$(1)(14)$	$1 + 14 = 15$
$(2)(7)$	$2 + 7 = 9$

Since there are no factors of 14 whose sum is 3, we conclude that this trinomial cannot be factored with integers. This is an example of a *prime polynomial*.

Now Try Exercise 21

EXAMPLE 14 Factor $6a^2 + 19ab + 3b^2$.

Solution There is no GCF to factor out. This trinomial contains two variables. It is factored in basically the same manner as the previous examples. Find two numbers whose product is $6 \cdot 3$ or 18 and whose sum is 19. The two numbers are 18 and 1.

$$6a^2 + 19ab + 3b^2$$
$$= 6a^2 + 18ab + ab + 3b^2$$
$$= 6a(a + 3b) + b(a + 3b)$$
$$= (a + 3b)(6a + b)$$

Now Try Exercise 61

EXAMPLE 15 Factor $6x^2 - 13xy - 8y^2$.

Solution   There is no GCF to factor out. Find two numbers whose product is $6(-8)$ or -48 and whose sum is -13. Since the product is negative, one factor must be positive and the other negative. Some factors are given below.

Product of Factors	Sum of Factors
$(1)(-48)$	$1 + (-48) = -47$
$(2)(-24)$	$2 + (-24) = -22$
$(3)(-16)$	$3 + (-16) = -13$

There are many other factors, but we have found the pair we were looking for. The two numbers whose product is -48 and whose sum is -13 are 3 and -16.

$$6x^2 - 13xy - 8y^2$$
$$= 6x^2 + 3xy - 16xy - 8y^2$$
$$= 3x(2x + y) - 8y(2x + y)$$
$$= (2x + y)(3x - 8y)$$

Check $(2x + y)(3x - 8y)$

$$\begin{array}{cccc} \text{F} & \text{O} & \text{I} & \text{L} \end{array}$$
$$= (2x)(3x) + (2x)(-8y) \ \ + (y)(3x) + (y)(-8y)$$
$$= \ \ \ 6x^2 \ \ \ - \ \ \ 16xy \ \ \ + \ \ 3xy \ \ - \ \ 8y^2$$
$$= 6x^2 - 13xy - 8y^2$$

Now Try Exercise 63

Remember that in any factoring problem our first step is to factor the GCF from each term. We then continue to factor the trinomial, if possible.

EXAMPLE 16 Factor $6x^3 + 15x^2 - 36x$.

Solution   The factor $3x$ is common to all three terms. Factor the $3x$ from each term of the polynomial.

$$6x^3 + 15x^2 - 36x = 3x(2x^2 + 5x - 12)$$

Now continue by factoring $2x^2 + 5x - 12$. The two numbers whose product is $2(-12)$ or -24 and whose sum is 5 are 8 and -3.

$$3x(2x^2 + 5x - 12)$$
$$= 3x(2x^2 + 8x - 3x - 12)$$
$$= 3x[2x(x + 4) - 3(x + 4)]$$
$$= 3x(x + 4)(2x - 3)$$

Now Try Exercise 49

Helpful Hint

Which Method Should You Use to Factor a Trinomial?

If your instructor asks you to use a specific method, you should use that method. If your instructor does not require a specific method, you should use the method you feel most comfortable with. You may wish to start with the trial-and-error method if there are only a few possible factors to try. If you cannot find the factors by trial and error or if there are many possible factors to consider, you may wish to use the grouping procedure. With time and practice you will learn which method you feel most comfortable with and which method gives you greater success.

EXERCISE SET 5.4

Math XL
MathXL®

MyMathLab
MyMathLab

Warm-Up Exercises

Fill in the blanks with the appropriate word, phrase, or symbol(s) from the following list.

last   first   factoring by grouping

factor out the GCF   outer   inner

1. The two methods of factoring the trinomial $ax^2 + bx + c$, $a \neq 1$ are trial and error and _____ .

2. When factoring the trinomial $ax^2 + bx + c$ into two binomials, the product of the _____ terms of the binomials must equal ax^2.

3. The first step in factoring is to _____ .

4. When factoring the trinomial $ax^2 + bx + c$ into two binomials, the product of the _____ terms of the binomials must equal c.

Practice the Skills

Factor completely. If the polynomial is prime, so state.

5. $2x^2 + 11x + 5$

6. $2x^2 + 9x + 4$

7. $3x^2 + 14x + 8$

8. $7x^2 + 37x + 10$

9. $5x^2 - 9x - 2$

10. $3y^2 + 17y + 10$

11. $3r^2 + 13r - 10$

12. $3x^2 - 2x - 8$

13. $4z^2 - 12z + 9$

14. $4n^2 - 9n + 5$

15. $6z^2 + z - 12$

16. $5m^2 - 17m + 6$

17. $5a^2 - 12a + 6$

18. $2x^2 - x - 6$

19. $8x^2 + 19x + 6$

20. $6y^2 - 11y + 4$

21. $3x^2 + 11x + 4$

22. $3a^2 + 7a - 20$

23. $5y^2 - 16y + 3$

24. $5x^2 + 2x + 9$

25. $7x^2 + 43x + 6$

26. $7x^2 - 8x + 1$

27. $4x^2 + 4x - 15$

28. $15x^2 - 19x + 6$

29. $49t^2 - 14t + 1$

30. $16z^2 - 8z + 1$

31. $5z^2 - 6z - 8$

32. $3z^2 - 11z - 6$

33. $4y^2 + 5y - 6$

34. $5y^2 - 3y - 1$

35. $10x^2 - 27x + 5$

36. $6a^2 + 7a - 10$

37. $10d^2 - 7d - 12$

38. $6x^2 + 13x + 3$

39. $8x^2 - 46x - 12$

40. $12x^2 - 13x - 35$

41. $10t + 3 + 7t^2$

42. $n - 30 + n^2$

43. $6x^2 + 16x + 10$

44. $12z^2 + 32z + 20$

45. $6x^3 - 5x^2 - 4x$

46. $8x^3 + 8x^2 - 6x$

47. $12x^3 + 28x^2 + 8x$

48. $18x^3 - 21x^2 - 9x$

49. $4x^3 - 2x^2 - 12x$

50. $300x^2 - 400x - 400$

51. $48c^2 + 8c - 16$

52. $28x^2 - 28x + 7$

53. $4p - 12 + 8p^2$

54. $72 + 3r^2 - 30r$

55. $8c^2 + 41cd + 5d^2$

56. $8x^2 - 8xy - 6y^2$

57. $15x^2 - xy - 6y^2$

58. $2x^2 - 7xy + 3y^2$

59. $12x^2 + 10xy - 8y^2$

60. $12a^2 - 34ab + 24b^2$

61. $7p^2 + 13pq + 6q^2$

62. $24x^2 - 92x + 80$

63. $6m^2 - mn - 2n^2$

64. $8m^2 + 4mn - 4n^2$

65. $8x^3 + 10x^2y + 3xy^2$

66. $8a^2b + 10ab^2 + 3b^3$

67. $4x^4 + 8x^3y + 3x^2y^2$

68. $26u^2v + 6uv^2 + 24u^3$

Problem Solving

For Exercises 69–74, write a polynomial whose factors are listed.

69. $3x + 1, x - 7$

70. $6y - 5, 4y - 3$

71. $5, x + 3, 2x + 1$

72. $3, 2x + 3, x - 4$

73. $t^2, t + 4, 3t - 1$

74. $5x^2, 3x - 7, 2x + 3$

75. a) If you know one binomial factor of a trinomial, explain how you can use division to find the second binomial factor of the trinomial (see Section 4.6).

   b) One factor of $18x^2 + 93x + 110$ is $3x + 10$. Use division to find the second factor.

76. One factor of $30x^2 - 17x - 247$ is $6x - 19$. Find the other factor.

Concept/Writing Exercises

77. Explain the relationship between the process of factoring trinomials and the process of multiplying binomials.

78. When factoring a trinomial of the form $ax^2 + bx + c$,

a) What must the product of the first terms of the binomial factors equal?

b) What must the product of the constants in the binomial factors equal?

Challenge Problems

Factor each trinomial.

79. $18x^2 + 9x - 20$

80. $9p^2 - 104p + 55$

81. $15x^2 - 124x + 160$

82. $16x^2 - 62x - 45$

83. $105a^2 - 220a - 160$

84. $72x^2 + 417x - 420$

85. Two factors of $6x^3 + 235x^2 + 2250x$ are x and $3x + 50$. Determine the other factor. Explain how you determined your answer.

86. Two factors of the polynomial $2x^3 + 11x^2 + 3x - 36$ are $x + 3$ and $2x - 3$. Determine the third factor. Explain how you determined your answer.

Cumulative Review Exercises

[1.9] **87.** Evaluate $-x^2 - 4(y + 3) + 2y^2$ when $x = -3$ and $y = -5$.

[2.6] **88. Daytona 500** Ryan Newman won the 2008 Dayton 500 in a time of about 3.27 hours. If the race covered 507.5 miles, find the average speed of Newman's car.

[5.1] **89.** Factor $36x^4y^3 - 12xy^2 + 24x^5y^6$.

[5.3] **90.** Factor $b^2 + 4b - 96$.

See Exercise 88. Ryan Newman after winning the Daytona 500.

Mid-Chapter Test: 5.1–5.4

To find out how well you understand the chapter material to this point, take this brief test. The answers, and the section where the material was initially discussed, are given in the back of the book. Review any questions that you answered incorrectly.

1. How may any factoring problem be checked?

2. Determine the greatest common factor of $18xy^2, 27x^3y^4$, and $12x^2y^3$.

In Exercises 3–5, factor the GCF from each term in the expression.

3. $4a^2b^3 - 24a^3b$

4. $5c(d - 6) - 3(d - 6)$

5. $7x(2x + 9) + 2x + 9$

In Exercises 6–10, factor by grouping.

6. $x^2 + 4x + 7x + 28$

7. $x^2 + 5x - 3x - 15$

8. $6a^2 + 15ab - 2ab - 5b^2$

9. $5x^2 - 2xy - 45x + 18y$

10. $8x^3 + 4x^2 - 48x^2 - 24x$

In Exercises 11–20, factor each polynomial completely. If the polynomial is prime, so state.

11. $x^2 - 10x + 21$

12. $t^2 + 9t + 20$

13. $p^2 - 3p - 8$

14. $x^2 + 16x + 64$

15. $m^2 - 4mn - 45n^2$

16. $3x^2 + 17x + 10$

17. $4z^2 - 11z + 6$

18. $3y^2 + 13y + 6$

19. $9x^2 - 6x + 1$

20. $6a^2 + 3ab - 3b^2$

5.5 Special Factoring Formulas and a General Review of Factoring

1 **Factor the difference of two squares.**

2 **Factor the sum and difference of two cubes.**

3 **Learn the general procedure for factoring a polynomial.**

Understanding Algebra

$x^2 - y^2$ Difference of two squares; is factorable

$x^2 + y^2$ Sum of two squares; is *not* factorable

The special formulas, for certain types of factoring problems, we focus on in this section are the *difference of two squares, the sum of two cubes, and the difference of two cubes. You will need to memorize the three highlighted formulas in this section* so that you can use them whenever you need them.

1 Factor the Difference of Two Squares

Consider the binomial $x^2 - 9$. Note that each term of the binomial can be expressed as the square of some expression.

$$x^2 - 9 = x^2 - 3^2$$

This is an example of a **difference of two squares**.

> **Difference of Two Squares**
>
> $$a^2 - b^2 = (a + b)(a - b)$$

EXAMPLE 1 Factor $x^2 - 9$.

Solution   If we write $x^2 - 9$ as a difference of two squares, we have $(x)^2 - (3)^2$. Using the difference of two squares formula, where a is replaced by x and b is replaced by 3, we obtain the following:

$$a^2 - b^2 = (a + b)(a - b)$$
$$x^2 - 9 = (x)^2 - (3)^2 = (x + 3)(x - 3)$$

Thus, $x^2 - 9 = (x + 3)(x - 3)$.

Now Try Exercise 13

EXAMPLE 2 Factor using the difference of two squares formula.

a) $x^2 - 16$ **b)** $25x^2 - 4$ **c)** $36x^2 - 49y^2$

Solution

a) $x^2 - 16 = (x)^2 - (4)^2$
$$= (x + 4)(x - 4)$$

b) $25x^2 - 4 = (5x)^2 - (2)^2$
$$= (5x + 2)(5x - 2)$$

c) $36x^2 - 49y^2 = (6x)^2 - (7y)^2$
$$= (6x + 7y)(6x - 7y)$$

Now Try Exercise 21

EXAMPLE 3 Factor each difference of two squares.

a) $16x^4 - 9y^4$ **b)** $x^6 - y^4$

Solution

a) $16x^4 - 9y^4 = (4x^2)^2 - (3y^2)^2$ Rewrote as a difference of two squares.

$$= (4x^2 + 3y^2)(4x^2 - 3y^2)$$ Difference of two squares formula was used.

b) Rewrite x^6 as $(x^3)^2$ and y^4 as $(y^2)^2$, then use the difference of two squares formula.

$$x^6 - y^4 = (x^3)^2 - (y^2)^2$$
$$= (x^3 + y^2)(x^3 - y^2)$$

Now Try Exercise 29

EXAMPLE 4 Factor $9x^2 - 36y^2$ using the difference of two squares formula.

Solution

$$9x^2 - 36y^2 = 9(x^2 - 4y^2) \qquad \text{Factor out the GCF, 9}$$
$$9(x^2 - 4y^2) = 9[(x)^2 - (2y)^2] \qquad \text{Rewrote as difference of two squares.}$$
$$= 9(x + 2y)(x - 2y) \quad \text{Difference of two squares formula was used.}$$

Now Try Exercise 23

Notice in Example 4 that $9x^2 - 36y^2$ is the difference of two squares, $(3x)^2 - (6y)^2$. If you factor this difference of squares without first factoring out the GCF, 9, the factoring may be more difficult. After you factor this difference of squares you will need to factor out the GCF, 3, from each binomial factor, as illustrated below.

$$9x^2 - 36y^2 = (3x)^2 - (6y)^2$$
$$= (3x + 6y)(3x - 6y)$$
$$= 3(x + 2y)3(x - 2y)$$
$$= 9(x + 2y)(x - 2y)$$

We obtain the same answer as we did in Example 4. However, since we did not factor out the common factor 9 first, we had to work a little harder to obtain the answer.

EXAMPLE 5 Factor $z^4 - 16$ using the difference of two squares formula.

Solution   We rewrite z^4 as $(z^2)^2$ and 16 as $(4)^2$, then use the difference of two squares formula.

$$z^4 - 16 = (z^2)^2 - (4)^2$$
$$= (z^2 + 4)(z^2 - 4)$$

Notice that the second factor, $z^2 - 4$, is also the difference of two squares. To complete the factoring, we use the difference of two squares formula again to factor $z^2 - 4$.

$$= (z^2 + 4)(z^2 - 4)$$
$$= (z^2 + 4)(z + 2)(z - 2)$$

Now Try Exercise 35

Avoiding Common Errors

The difference of two squares can be factored. However, a sum of two squares, where there is no common factor to the two terms, cannot be factored using real numbers.

CORRECT

$$a^2 - b^2 = (a + b)(a - b)$$

INCORRECT

$$\cancel{a^2 + b^2 = (a + b)(a + b)}$$

2 Factor the Sum and Difference of Two Cubes

Consider the product of $(a + b)(a^2 - ab + b^2)$.

$$
\begin{array}{r}
a^2 - ab + b^2 \\
a + b \\
\hline
a^2b - ab^2 + b^3 \qquad \leftarrow b(a^2 - ab + b^2) \\
a^3 - a^2b + ab^2 \qquad\qquad \leftarrow a(a^2 - ab + b^2) \\
\hline
a^3 \qquad\qquad\quad + b^3 \quad \leftarrow \text{Sum of terms}
\end{array}
$$

Thus, $(a + b)(a^2 - ab + b^2) = a^3 + b^3$. Since factoring is the opposite of multiplying, we may factor $a^3 + b^3$ as follows:

$$a^3 + b^3 = (a + b)(a^2 - ab + b^2)$$

We see, using the same procedure, that $a^3 - b^3 = (a - b)(a^2 + ab + b^2)$. The expression $a^3 + b^3$ is a sum of two cubes and the expression $a^3 - b^3$ is a difference of two cubes.

Sum of Two Cubes

$$a^3 + b^3 = (a + b)(a^2 - ab + b^2)$$

Difference of Two Cubes

$$a^3 - b^3 = (a - b)(a^2 + ab + b^2)$$

Note that the trinomials $a^2 - ab + b^2$ and $a^2 + ab + b^2$ cannot be factored further. Now let's solve some factoring problems using the sum and the difference of two cubes.

EXAMPLE 6 Factor $x^3 + 8$.

Solution   We rewrite $x^3 + 8$ as a sum of two cubes: $x^3 + 8 = (x)^3 + (2)^3$. Using the sum of two cubes formula, where a is replaced by x and b is replaced by 2, we get

$$a^3 + b^3 = (a + b)(a^2 - a \cdot b + b^2)$$
$$x^3 + 8 = (x)^3 + (2)^3 = (x + 2)(x^2 - x \cdot 2 + 2^2)$$
$$= (x + 2)(x^2 - 2x + 4)$$

You can check the factoring by multiplying $(x + 2)(x^2 - 2x + 4)$. If factored correctly, the product of the factors will equal the original expression, $x^3 + 8$. Try it and see.

Now Try Exercise 41

Helpful Hint

To help remember the signs in the sum or difference of two cubes formulas, consider

$$a^3 + b^3 = (a + b)(a^2 - ab + b^2)$$

Same sign   Opposite sign   Always positive

$$a^3 - b^3 = (a - b)(a^2 + ab + b^2)$$

Same sign   Opposite sign   Always positive

EXAMPLE 7 Factor $y^3 - 125$.

Solution   We rewrite $y^3 - 125$ as a difference of two cubes: $(y)^3 - (5)^3$. Using the difference of two cubes formula, where a is replaced by y and b is replaced by 5, we get

$$a^3 - b^3 = (a - b)(a^2 + a \cdot b + b^2)$$
$$y^3 - 125 = (y)^3 - (5)^3 = (y - 5)(y^2 + y \cdot 5 + 5^2)$$
$$= (y - 5)(y^2 + 5y + 25)$$

Now Try Exercise 43

EXAMPLE 8 Factor $64a^3 - b^3$.

Solution   We rewrite $64a^3 - b^3$ as a difference of two cubes. Since $(4a)^3 = 64a^3$, we write

$$64a^3 - b^3 = (4a)^3 - (b)^3$$
$$= (4a - b)[(4a)^2 + (4a)(b) + b^2]$$
$$= (4a - b)(16a^2 + 4ab + b^2)$$

Now Try Exercise 49

EXAMPLE 9 Factor $8r^3 + 27s^3$.

Solution We rewrite $8r^3 + 27s^3$ as a sum of two cubes. Since $8r^3 = (2r)^3$ and $27s^3 = (3s)^3$, we write

$$8r^3 + 27s^3 = (2r)^3 + (3s)^3$$
$$= (2r + 3s)[(2r)^2 - (2r)(3s) + (3s)^2]$$
$$= (2r + 3s)(4r^2 - 6rs + 9s^2)$$

Now Try Exercise 53

Avoiding Common Errors

Recall that $a^2 + b^2 \neq (a + b)^2$ and $a^2 - b^2 \neq (a - b)^2$. The same principle applies to the sum and difference of two cubes.

CORRECT	INCORRECT
$a^3 + b^3 = (a + b)(a^2 - ab + b^2)$	~~$a^3 + b^3 = (a + b)^3$~~
$a^3 - b^3 = (a - b)(a^2 + ab + b^2)$	~~$a^3 - b^3 = (a - b)^3$~~

Since $(a + b)^3 = (a + b)(a + b)(a + b)$, it cannot possibly equal $a^3 + b^3$. Also, since $(a - b)^3 = (a - b)(a - b)(a - b)$, it cannot possibly equal $a^3 - b^3$.

It may be easier to see that, for example, $a^3 + b^3 = (a + b)(a^2 - ab + b^2)$ and not $(a + b)^3$ by substituting numbers for a and b. Suppose $a = 3$ and $b = 4$, then

$$a^3 + b^3 = (a + b)(a^2 - ab + b^2)$$
$$3^3 + 4^3 = (3 + 4)[3^2 - 3(4) + 4^2]$$
$$27 + 64 = 7(13)$$
$$91 = 91$$

but $a^3 + b^3 \neq (a + b)^3$
$$3^3 + 4^3 \neq (3 + 4)^3$$
$$91 \neq 343$$

---

3 Learn the General Procedure for Factoring a Polynomial

In this chapter, we have presented several methods of factoring. We now combine techniques from this and previous sections to give you an overview of a general factoring procedure.

Here is a general procedure for factoring any polynomial:

General Procedure for Factoring a Polynomial

1. If all the terms of the polynomial have a greatest common factor other than 1, factor it out.
2. If the polynomial has two terms (or is a binomial), determine whether it is a difference of two squares or a sum or a difference of two cubes. If so, factor using the appropriate formula.
3. If the polynomial has three terms, factor the trinomial using the methods discussed in Sections 5.3 and 5.4.
4. If the polynomial has more than three terms, try factoring by grouping.
5. As a final step, examine your factored polynomial to determine whether the terms in any factors have a common factor. If you find a common factor, factor it out at this point.

Understanding Algebra

Be careful! $16x^2 - 64$ is the difference of two squares. There is, however, a GCF, 16. Factor the 16 out first then use the formula:

$16x^2 - 64 = 16(x^2 - 4)$
$= 16(x + 2)(x - 2)$

EXAMPLE 10 Factor $3x^4 - 27x^2$.

Solution First determine whether the terms have a greatest common factor other than 1. Since $3x^2$ is common to both terms, factor it out.

$$3x^4 - 27x^2 = 3x^2(x^2 - 9)$$
$$= 3x^2(x + 3)(x - 3) \quad \text{Difference of two squares formula was used.}$$

Note that $x^2 - 9$ is a difference of two squares.

Now Try Exercise 69

EXAMPLE 11   Factor $2m^2n^2 + 6m^2n - 36m^2$.

Solution   Begin by factoring the GCF, $2m^2$, from each term. Then factor the remaining trinomial.

$$2m^2n^2 + 6m^2n - 36m^2 = 2m^2(n^2 + 3n - 18)$$
$$= 2m^2(n + 6)(n - 3)$$

Now Try Exercise 81

EXAMPLE 12   Factor $15c^2d - 10cd + 20d$.

Solution

$$15c^2d - 10cd + 20d = 5d(3c^2 - 2c + 4)$$

Since $3c^2 - 2c + 4$ cannot be factored, we stop here.

Now Try Exercise 77

EXAMPLE 13   Factor $3xy + 6x + 3y + 6$.

Solution   Always begin by determining whether all the terms in the polynomial have a common factor. In this example, 3 is the GCF. Factor 3 from each term.

$$3xy + 6x + 3y + 6 = 3(xy + 2x + y + 2)$$

Now factor by grouping.

$$= 3[x(y + 2) + 1(y + 2)]$$
$$= 3(y + 2)(x + 1)$$

Now Try Exercise 79

In Example 13, what would happen if we forgot to factor out the common factor 3? Let's rework the problem without first factoring out the 3, and see what happens. Factor $3x$ from the first two terms, and 3 from the last two terms.

$$3xy + 6x + 3y + 6 = 3x(y + 2) + 3(y + 2)$$
$$= (y + 2)(3x + 3)$$

In step 5 of the general factoring procedure on page 316, we are reminded to examine the factored polynomial to see whether the terms in any factor have a common factor. If we study the factors, we see that the factor $3x + 3$ has the common factor 3. If we factor out the 3 from $3x + 3$, we will obtain the same answer obtained in Example 13.

$$(y + 2)(3x + 3) = 3(y + 2)(x + 1)$$

EXAMPLE 14   Factor $12x^2 + 12x - 9$.

Solution   First factor out the GCF, 3. Then factor the remaining trinomial by one of the methods discussed in Section 5.4 (either by grouping or trial and error).

$$12x^2 + 12x - 9 = 3(4x^2 + 4x - 3)$$
$$= 3(2x + 3)(2x - 1)$$

Now Try Exercise 59

EXAMPLE 15   Factor $2x^4y + 54xy$.

Solution   First factor out the GCF, $2xy$.

$$2x^4y + 54xy = 2xy(x^3 + 27)$$
$$= 2xy(x + 3)(x^2 - 3x + 9)$$

Note that $x^3 + 27$ is a sum of two cubes.

Now Try Exercise 95

EXERCISE SET 5.5

MathXL MathXL®   MyMathLab MyMathLab

Warm-Up Exercises

Fill in the blanks with the appropriate word, phrase, or symbol(s) from the following list.

the sum of two squares

factor out the greatest common factor

the difference of two squares

the difference of two cubes

prime polynomial

call your instructor

the sum of two cubes

use a formula

1. $x^2 - 1$ is an example of a binomial that is _____ .

2. $x^3 - 1$ is an example of a binomial that is _____ .

3. $x^2 + 1$ is an example of a binomial that is _____ .

4. $x^3 + 1$ is an example of a binomial that is _____ .

5. The first step in any factoring problem is to _____ .

6. $x^2 + x - 7$ is an example of a _____ .

In Exercises 7–12, the binomial is a sum of squares. There is no formula for factoring the sum of squares. However, sometimes a common factor can be factored out from a sum of squares. Factor those polynomials that are factorable. If the polynomial is not factorable, write the word prime.

7. $x^2 + 9$

8. $4y^2 + 1$

9. $9b^2 + 81$

10. $16s^2 + 64t^2$

11. $16m^2 + 36n^2$

12. $9y^2 + 16z^2$

Practice the Skills

Factor each difference of two squares.

13. $y^2 - 25$

14. $t^2 - 4$

15. $81 - z^2$

16. $64 - z^2$

17. $x^2 - 49$

18. $c^2 - d^2$

19. $x^2 - y^2$

20. $16x^2 - 9$

21. $9y^2 - 25z^2$

22. $64z^2 - 9$

23. $64a^2 - 36b^2$

24. $100x^2 - 81y^2$

25. $36 - 49x^2$

26. $100 - y^4$

27. $z^4 - 81x^2$

28. $9x^4 - 81y^2$

29. $25x^4 - 49y^4$

30. $4x^4 - 25y^4$

31. $36m^4 - 49n^2$

32. $10x^2 - 160$

33. $2x^4 - 50y^2$

34. $4x^3 - xy^2$

35. $5x^4 - 405$

36. $36x^4 - 4y^2$

Factor each sum or difference of two cubes.

37. $x^3 + y^3$

38. $a^3 - b^3$

39. $x^3 - y^3$

40. $a^3 + b^3$

41. $x^3 + 64$

42. $x^3 - 8$

43. $x^3 - 27$

44. $a^3 + 27$

45. $a^3 + 1$

46. $t^3 - 1$

47. $27x^3 - 1$

48. $64y^3 + 125$

49. $27a^3 - 125$

50. $125 + q^3$

51. $27 - 8y^3$

52. $8 + 27y^3$

53. $64m^3 + 27n^3$

54. $64x^3 - 125y^3$

55. $8a^3 - 27b^3$

56. $27c^3 + 125d^3$

Factor completely.

57. $4t^2 - 24t + 36$

58. $3x^2 - 9x - 12$

59. $50x^2 - 10x - 12$

60. $3x^2 - 48$

61. $2d^2 + 16d + 32$

62. $3x^2 + 9x + 12x + 36$

63. $5x^2 - 10x - 15$

64. $3xy - 6x + 9y - 18$

65. $5x^2 - 20$

66. $x^2y + 2xy - 6xy - 12y$

67. $2x^2 - 50$

68. $4a^2y - 64y^3$

69. $2x^2y - 18y$

70. $3x^3 - 147x$

71. $3x^3y^2 + 3y^2$

72. $x^4 - 125x$

73. $2x^3 - 16$

74. $x^3 - 27y^3$

75. $18x^2 - 50$

76. $54a^3 - 16$

77. $6t^2r - 15tr + 21r$

78. $12n^2 + 4n - 16$

79. $6x^2 - 4x + 24x - 16$

80. $4ab^2 + 4ab - 24a$

81. $2rs^2 - 10rs - 48r$

82. $4x^4 - 26x^3 + 30x^2$

83. $4x^2 + 5x - 6$

84. $12a^2 + 36a + 27$

85. $25b^2 - 100$

86. $3b^2 - 75c^2$

87. $a^5b^2 - 4a^3b^4$

88. $12x^2 + 36x - 3x - 9$

89. $5x^4 + 10x^3 + 5x^2$

90. $3c^6 + 12c^4d^2$

91. $x^3 + 25x$

92. $8y^2 - 23y - 3$

93. $y^4 - 16$

94. $36a^2 - 15ab - 6b^2$

95. $16m^3 + 250$

96. $2ab - 3b + 4a - 6$

97. $ac + 2a + bc + 2b$

98. $x^3 - 100x$

99. $9 - 9y^4$

Problem Solving

Factor each expression. Treat the unknown symbols as if they were variables.

100. ◆✹ + 2◆ + ☺✹ + 2☺

101. $2◆^6 + 4◆^4✹^2$

102. $4◆^2✹ - 6◆✹ - 20✹◆ + 30✹$

Concept/Writing Exercises

103. Explain why the sum of two squares, $a^2 + b^2$, cannot be factored using real numbers.

104. Have you ever seen the proof that 1 is equal to 2? Here it is.

Let $a = b$, then square both sides of the equation:

$$a^2 = b^2$$
$$a^2 = b \cdot b$$
$$a^2 = ab \qquad \text{Substituted because } a = b.$$
$$a^2 - b^2 = ab - b^2 \qquad \text{Subtract } b^2 \text{ from both sides of the equation.}$$
$$(a + b)(a - b) = b(a - b) \qquad \text{Factored both sides of the equation.}$$
$$\frac{(a + b)\cancel{(a - b)}}{\cancel{(a - b)}} = \frac{b\cancel{(a - b)}}{\cancel{(a - b)}} \qquad \text{Divide both sides of the equation by } (a - b) \text{ and divide out common factors.}$$
$$a + b = b$$
$$b + b = b \qquad \text{Substituted because } a = b.$$
$$2b = b$$
$$\frac{\overset{1}{\cancel{2b}}}{\underset{1}{\cancel{b}}} = \frac{\overset{1}{\cancel{b}}}{\underset{1}{\cancel{b}}} \qquad \text{Divide both sides of the equation by } b.$$
$$2 = 1$$

Obviously, $2 \neq 1$. Therefore, we must have made an error somewhere. Can you find it?

Challenge Problems

105. Factor $x^6 - 27y^9$.

106. Factor $x^6 + 1$.

107. Factor $x^2 - 6x + 9 - 4y^2$. (*Hint:* Write the first three terms as the square of a binomial.)

108. Factor $x^6 - y^6$. (*Hint:* Factor initially as the difference of two squares.)

109. Factor $x^2 + 10x + 25 - y^2 + 4y - 4$. (*Hint:* Group the first three terms and the last three terms.)

Cumulative Review Exercises

[2.8] **110.** Solve the inequality $3x - 2(x + 4) \geq 2x - 9$ and graph the solution on a number line.

[2.6] **111.** Use the formula $A = \frac{1}{2}h(b + d)$ to find h in the following trapezoid if the area of the trapezoid is 36 square inches.

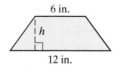

[4.1] **112.** Simplify $-9\,(a^3b^2c^6)^0$.

[4.1] **113.** Simplify $\left(\dfrac{4x^4y}{6xy^5}\right)^3$.

[4.2] **114.** Simplify $a^{-4}a^{-7}$.

5.6 Solving Quadratic Equations Using Factoring

1 Recognize quadratic equations.

2 Solve quadratic equations using factoring.

1 Recognize Quadratic Equations

In this section, we introduce **quadratic equations**, which are equations that contain a second-degree term and no term of a higher degree.

Quadratic Equation

Quadratic equations have the form

$$ax^2 + bx + c = 0$$

where a, b, and c are real numbers, $a \neq 0$.

Examples of Quadratic Equations

$$x^2 + 4x - 12 = 0$$
$$2x^2 - 5x = 0$$
$$3x^2 - 2 = 0$$

Quadratic equations like these, in which one side of the equation is written in descending order and the other side of the equation is 0, are said to be in **standard form**.

Some quadratic equations can be solved by factoring. To solve a quadratic equation by factoring, we use the **zero-factor property**.

Zero-Factor Property

If $ab = 0$, then $a = 0$ or $b = 0$.

Understanding Algebra

If you multiply any number by 0, the product is 0. That is, if $a = 0$ or $b = 0$, then $ab = 0$. The reverse is also true. If a product equals 0, at least one of its factors must be 0.

We now illustrate how the zero-factor property is used in solving equations.

EXAMPLE 1 Solve the equation $(x + 3)(x + 4) = 0$.

Solution   Since the product of the factors equals 0, according to the zero-factor property, one or both factors must equal 0. Set each factor equal to 0, and solve each resulting equation.

$$
\begin{array}{ccc}
x + 3 = 0 & \text{or} & x + 4 = 0 \\
x + 3 - 3 = 0 - 3 & & x + 4 - 4 = 0 - 4 \\
x = -3 & & x = -4
\end{array}
$$

Thus, if x is either -3 or -4, the product of the factors is 0. The solutions to the equation are -3 and -4.

Check
$$
\begin{array}{cc}
x = -3 & x = -4 \\
(x + 3)(x + 4) = 0 & (x + 3)(x + 4) = 0 \\
(-3 + 3)(-3 + 4) \stackrel{?}{=} 0 & (-4 + 3)(-4 + 4) \stackrel{?}{=} 0 \\
0(1) \stackrel{?}{=} 0 & -1(0) \stackrel{?}{=} 0 \\
0 = 0 \quad \text{True} & 0 = 0 \quad \text{True}
\end{array}
$$

Now Try Exercise 7

EXAMPLE 2 Solve the equation $(3x - 2)(4x + 1) = 0$.

Solution   Set each factor equal to 0 and solve for x.

$$
\begin{array}{ccc}
3x - 2 = 0 & \text{to} & 4x + 1 = 0 \\
3x = 2 & & 4x = -1 \\
x = \dfrac{2}{3} & & x = -\dfrac{1}{4}
\end{array}
$$

The solutions to the equation are $\dfrac{2}{3}$ and $-\dfrac{1}{4}$.

Now Try Exercise 11

2 Solve Quadratic Equations Using Factoring

General Rules to Solve a Quadratic Equation Using Factoring

1. Write the equation in standard form with the squared term having a positive coefficient. This will result in one side of the equation being 0.
2. Factor the side of the equation that is not 0.
3. Set each factor *containing a variable* equal to 0 and solve each equation.
4. Check each solution found in step 3 in the *original* equation.

Now we will use factoring to solve quadratic equations.

EXAMPLE 3 Solve the equation $3x^2 = 12x$.

Solution

$$3x^2 = 12x$$
$$3x^2 - 12x = 12x - 12x \qquad \text{Subtract } 12x \text{ from both sides}$$
$$\text{to make one side 0.}$$
$$3x^2 - 12x = 0$$
$$3x(x - 4) = 0 \qquad \text{Factored out the GCF, } 3x.$$

Now set each factor equal to 0.

$$3x = 0 \qquad \text{or} \qquad x - 4 = 0$$
$$x = \frac{0}{3} \qquad\qquad\qquad x = 4$$
$$x = 0$$

The solutions to the quadratic equation are 0 and 4. Check by substituting $x = 0$, then $x = 4$, in $3x^2 = 12x$.

Now Try Exercise 47

EXAMPLE 4 Solve the equation $x^2 + 10x + 28 = 4$.

Solution

$$x^2 + 10x + 28 = 4$$
$$x^2 + 10x + 24 = 0 \qquad \text{Subtracted 4 from both sides.}$$
$$(x + 4)(x + 6) = 0 \qquad \text{Factored}$$
$$x + 4 = 0 \qquad \text{or} \qquad x + 6 = 0 \qquad \text{Set each factor equal to 0.}$$
$$x = -4 \qquad\qquad x = -6$$

The solutions are -4 and -6. We will check these values in the original equation.

Check

$x = -4$	$x = -6$
$x^2 + 10x + 28 = 4$	$x^2 + 10x + 28 = 4$
$(-4)^2 + 10(-4) + 28 \stackrel{?}{=} 4$	$(-6)^2 + 10(-6) + 28 \stackrel{?}{=} 4$
$16 - 40 + 28 \stackrel{?}{=} 4$	$36 - 60 + 28 \stackrel{?}{=} 4$
$-24 + 28 \stackrel{?}{=} 4$	$-24 + 28 \stackrel{?}{=} 4$
$4 = 4$ True	$4 = 4$ True

Now Try Exercise 23

Understanding Algebra

To solve $x^2 = 8x$ it is *not* correct to divide both sides of the equation by x. Since it is a quadratic equation, we solve it this way:

$$x^2 = 8x$$
$$x^2 - 8x = 0$$
$$x(x - 8) = 0$$
$$x = 0 \quad \text{or} \quad x = 8$$

EXAMPLE 5 Solve the equation $4y^2 + 5y - 20 = -11y$.

Solution   Since all terms are not on the same side of the equation, add $11y$ to both sides of the equation.

$$4y^2 + 5y - 20 = -11y$$
$$4y^2 + 16y - 20 = 0 \qquad \text{Added } 11y \text{ to both sides.}$$
$$4(y^2 + 4y - 5) = 0 \qquad \text{Factored out GCF, 4.}$$
$$4(y + 5)(y - 1) = 0 \qquad \text{Factored}$$
$$y + 5 = 0 \qquad \text{or} \qquad y - 1 = 0 \qquad \text{Set each factor equal to 0.}$$
$$y = -5 \qquad\qquad y = 1$$

Since 4 is a factor that does not contain a variable, we do not set it equal to 0. The solutions to the quadratic equation are -5 and 1.

Now Try Exercise 25

EXAMPLE 6 Solve the equation $-x^2 + 5x + 6 = 0$.

Solution   When the squared term is negative, we generally make it positive by multiplying both sides of the equation by -1.

$$-1(-x^2 + 5x + 6) = -1 \cdot 0$$
$$x^2 - 5x - 6 = 0$$
$$(x - 6)(x + 1) = 0$$

$x - 6 = 0$ or $x + 1 = 0$ Set each factor equal to 0.
$x = 6$ $x = -1$

A check using the original equation will show that the solutions are 6 and -1.

Now Try Exercise 33

Avoiding Common Errors

Be careful not to confuse factoring a polynomial with using factoring as a method to solve an equation.

CORRECT	INCORRECT

Factor: $x^2 + 3x + 2$ Factor: $x^2 + 3x + 2$
$(x + 2)(x + 1)$ $(x + 2)(x + 1)$
~~$x + 2 = 0$ or $x + 1 = 0$~~
~~$x = -2$ $x = -1$~~

The expression $x^2 + 3x + 2$ is a polynomial, not an equation. Since it is not an equation, it cannot be solved.

CORRECT

Solve: $x^2 + 3x + 2 = 0$
$(x + 2)(x + 1) = 0$
$x + 2 = 0$ or $x + 1 = 0$
$x = -2$ $x = -1$

EXAMPLE 7 Solve the equation $x^2 = 49$.

Solution

$$x^2 = 49$$
$$x^2 - 49 = 0 \qquad \text{49 was subtracted from both sides.}$$
$$(x + 7)(x - 7) = 0 \qquad \text{Factored using the difference of two squares.}$$

$x + 7 = 0$ or $x - 7 = 0$ Set each factor equal to 0.
$x = -7$ $x = 7$

The solutions are -7 and 7.

Now Try Exercise 45

EXAMPLE 8 Solve the equation $(x - 3)(x + 1) = 5$.

Solution

$$(x - 3)(x + 1) = 5$$
$$x^2 - 2x - 3 = 5 \qquad \text{Factors were multiplied.}$$
$$x^2 - 2x - 8 = 0 \qquad \text{Wrote the equation in standard form.}$$
$$(x - 4)(x + 2) = 0 \qquad \text{Trinomial was factored.}$$

$x - 4 = 0$ or $x + 2 = 0$ Zero-factor property
$x = 4$ $x = -2$

The solutions are 4 and -2. We will check these values in the original equation.

Check

$$x = 4$$
$$(x - 3)(x + 1) = 5$$
$$(4 - 3)(4 + 1) \overset{?}{=} 5$$
$$1(5) \overset{?}{=} 5$$
$$5 = 5 \quad \text{True}$$

$$x = -2$$
$$(x - 3)(x + 1) = 5$$
$$(-2 - 3)(-2 + 1) \overset{?}{=} 5$$
$$(-5)(-1) \overset{?}{=} 5$$
$$5 = 5 \quad \text{True}$$

Now Try Exercise 51

Helpful Hint

In Example 8, you might have been tempted to start the problem by writing

$$x - 3 = 5 \quad \text{or} \quad x + 1 = 5.$$

This would lead to an incorrect solution. Remember, the zero-factor property only holds when one side of the equation is equal to 0. In Example 8, once we obtained $(x - 4)(x + 2) = 0$, we were able to use the zero-factor property.

EXERCISE SET 5.6

Warm-Up Exercises

Fill in the blanks with the appropriate word, phrase, or symbol(s) from the following list.

$x = 0$ or $x = 2$ $x = -2$ or $x = 2$ $x = 3$ or $x = -2$ or $x = 2$ $x = -2$ or $x = 3$

standard form   zero-factor property $x = -2$ or $x = 0$

1. "If $ab = 0$ then either $a = 0$ or $b = 0$" is called the _____ .

2. When $x^2 + 12 = 7x$ is rewritten as $x^2 - 7x + 12 = 0$, we say that the quadratic equation is now in _____ .

3. The solution to $x^2 = 2x$ is _____ .

4. The solution to $x^2 + 2x = 0$ is _____ .

5. The solution to $3(x + 2)(x - 2) = 0$ is _____ .

6. The solution to $(x + 1)(x - 2) = 4$ is _____ .

Practice the Skills

Solve.

7. $(x + 8)(x - 7) = 0$

8. $-2x(x + 9) = 0$

9. $7x(x - 8) = 0$

10. $(t + 3)(t + 5) = 0$

11. $(3x + 7)(2x - 11) = 0$

12. $(3x - 2)(x - 5) = 0$

13. $x^2 - 16 = 0$

14. $y^2 - 9 = 0$

15. $x^2 - 12x = 0$

16. $9x^2 + 27x = 0$

17. $x^2 + 7x = 0$

18. $a^2 - 4a - 12 = 0$

19. $x^2 - 8x + 16 = 0$

20. $x^2 + 12x + 36 = 0$

21. $x^2 + 12x = -20$

22. $3y^2 - 4 = -4y$

23. $x^2 + 12x + 22 = 2$

24. $3x^2 = -21x - 18$

25. $2x^2 + 3x - 24 = 5x$

26. $x^2 = 4x + 21$

27. $23p - 24 = -p^2$

28. $3x^2 - 9x - 30 = 0$

29. $33w + 90 = -3w^2$

30. $t^2 + 44 + 15t = 0$

31. $-2x - 15 = -x^2$

32. $-9x + 20 = -x^2$

33. $-x^2 + 29x + 30 = 0$

34. $12y - 11 = y^2$

35. $-15 = 4m^2 + 17m$

36. $z^2 + 8z = -16$

37. $9p^2 = -21p - 6$

38. $2x^2 - 5 = 3x$

39. $3r^2 + 13r = 10$

40. $3x^2 = 7x + 20$

41. $4x^2 + 4x - 48 = 0$

42. $6x^2 - 7x - 5 = 0$

43. $8x^2 + 2x = 3$

44. $2x^2 + 4x - 6 = 0$

45. $c^2 = 64$

46. $2n^2 + 36 = -18n$

47. $2x^2 = 50x$

48. $4x^2 - 25 = 0$

49. $x^2 = 100$

50. $3x^2 - 48 = 0$

51. $(x - 2)(x - 1) = 12$

52. $(x + 2)(x + 5) = -2$

53. $(3x + 2)(x + 1) = 4$

54. $(x - 1)(2x - 5) = 9$

55. $2(a^2 + 9) = 15a$

56. $x(x + 5) = 6$

Problem Solving

In Exercises 57–60, create a quadratic equation with the given solutions. Explain how you determined your answers.

57. $6, -4$ **58.** $-3, -5$ **59.** $6, 0$ **60.** $0, -9$

61. The solutions to a quadratic equation are $\frac{1}{2}$ and $-\frac{1}{3}$.

    a) Give two possible factors with integer coefficients that were set equal to 0 to obtain these solutions.

    b) Write a quadratic equation whose solutions are $\frac{1}{2}$ and $-\frac{1}{3}$.

62. The solutions to a quadratic equation are $\frac{2}{3}$ and $-\frac{3}{4}$.

    a) Give two possible factors with integer coefficients that were set equal to 0 to obtain these solutions.

    b) Write a quadratic equation whose solutions are $\frac{2}{3}$ and $-\frac{3}{4}$.

Concept/Writing Exercises

63. Carefully observe the quadratic equations $x^2 - 7x + 12 = 0$, $2x^2 - 14x + 24 = 0$, and $3x^2 - 21x + 36 = 0$. Explain how you know that all three equations have the same solution.

64. Write the steps to the method you would use to solve $(x + 1)(x - 2) = 4$ as if you were writing an email to a friend taking an algebra course.

Challenge Problems

65. Solve the equation $(2x - 3)(x - 4) = (x - 5)(x + 3) + 7$.

66. Solve the equation $(x - 3)(x - 2) = (x + 5)(2x - 3) + 21$.

67. Solve the equation $x(x - 3)(x + 2) = 0$.

68. Solve the equation $x^3 - 10x^2 + 24x = 0$.

Cumulative Review Exercises

[1.7] **69.** Subtract $\frac{3}{5} - \frac{2}{9}$.

[2.5] **70. a)** What is the name given to an equation that has an infinite number of solutions?

    b) What is the name given to an equation that has no solution?

[2.7] **71. Cypress Gardens** At Cypress Gardens, there is a long line of people waiting to go through the entrance. If 160 people are admitted in 13 minutes, how many people will be admitted in 60 minutes? Assume the rate stays the same.

[4.1] **72.** Simplify $\left(\dfrac{3p^5q^7}{p^9q^8}\right)^2$.

Cypress Gardens; see Exercise 71.

[4.4] *Identify the following as a monomial, binomial, trinomial or not a polynomial. If an expression is not a polynomial, explain why.*

73. $2x$ **74.** $x - 3$ **75.** $\dfrac{1}{x}$ **76.** $x^2 - 6x + 9$

5.7 Applications of Quadratic Equations

1 Solve applications by factoring quadratic equations.

2 Learn the Pythagorean Theorem.

1 Solve Applications by Factoring Quadratic Equations

In Section 5.6, we learned how to solve quadratic equations by factoring. In this section, we will discuss and solve application problems that require solving quadratic equations to obtain the answer. In Example 1, we will solve a problem involving a relationship between two numbers.

EXAMPLE 1 Number Problem The product of two numbers is 78. Find the two numbers if one number is 7 more than the other.

Solution Understand and Translate Our goal is to find the two numbers.

            Let x = smaller number.
          $x + 7$ = larger number.

$$x(x + 7) = 78 \quad \text{"Product" refers to multiplication.}$$
$$x^2 + 7x = 78$$

Carry Out
$$x^2 + 7x - 78 = 0$$
$$(x - 6)(x + 13) = 0$$
$$x - 6 = 0 \quad \text{or} \quad x + 13 = 0$$
$$x = 6 \qquad\qquad x = -13$$

Remember that x represents the smaller of the two numbers. This problem has two possible solutions.

	Solution 1	Solution 2
Smaller number	6	−13
Larger number	$x + 7 = 6 + 7 = 13$	$x + 7 = -13 + 7 = -6$

Thus, the two possible solutions are 6 and 13, and −13 and −6.

Check	6 and 13	−13 and −6
Product of the two numbers is 78.	$6 \cdot 13 = 78$	$(-13)(-6) = 78$
One number is 7 more than the other number.	13 is 7 more than 6.	−6 is 7 more than −13.

Answer   One solution is: smaller number 6, larger number 13. A second solution is: smaller number −13, larger number −6. You must give both solutions. If the question had stated "the product of two *positive* numbers is 78," the only solution would be 6 and 13.

Now Try Exercise 13

Now let us work an application problem involving geometry.

EXAMPLE 2 **Advertising** The marketing department of a large publishing company is planning to make a large rectangular sign to advertise a new book at a convention. They want the length of the sign to be 3 feet longer than the width (**Fig. 5.3**). Signs at the convention may have a maximum area of 54 square feet. Find the length and width of the sign if the area is to be 54 square feet.

Solution   Understand and Translate   We need to find the length and width of the sign. We will use the formula for the area of a rectangle.

$$\text{Let } x = \text{width.}$$
$$x + 3 = \text{length.}$$
$$\text{area} = \text{length} \cdot \text{width}$$
$$54 = (x + 3)x$$

Carry Out
$$54 = x^2 + 3x$$
$$0 = x^2 + 3x - 54 \quad \text{Standard quadratic form}$$
$$\text{or} \quad x^2 + 3x - 54 = 0 \quad \text{Also standard quadratic form}$$
$$(x - 6)(x + 9) = 0$$
$$x - 6 = 0 \quad \text{or} \quad x + 9 = 0$$
$$x = 6 \qquad\qquad x = -9 \quad \text{Reject } -9 \text{ because width cannot be negative.}$$

FIGURE 5.3

Check and Answer   Since the width of the sign cannot be a negative number, the only solution is

$$\text{width} = x = 6 \text{ feet, length} = x + 3 = 6 + 3 = 9 \text{ feet}$$

The area, length $\cdot$ width, is 54 square feet, and the length is 3 feet more than the width, so the answer checks.

Now Try Exercise 21

EXAMPLE 3 **Earth's Gravitational Field** In Earth's gravitational field, the distance, d, in feet, that an object falls t seconds after it has been released is given by the formula $d = 16t^2$. While at the top of a roller coaster, a rider's eyeglasses slide off his head and fall out of the cart. How long does it take the eyeglasses to reach the ground 64 feet below?

Solution   Understand and Translate Substitute 64 for d in the formula and then solve for t.

$$d = 16t^2$$
$$64 = 16t^2$$

Carry Out

$$\frac{64}{16} = t^2$$
$$4 = t^2$$

Now subtract 4 from both sides of the equation and write the equation with 0 on the right side to put the quadratic equation in standard form.

$$4 - 4 = t^2 - 4$$
$$0 = t^2 - 4$$
$$\text{or} \quad t^2 - 4 = 0$$
$$(t + 2)(t - 2) = 0$$

$t + 2 = 0 \quad$ or $\quad t - 2 = 0 \quad$ Reject -2 because time
$t = -2 \qquad\qquad t = 2 \quad$ cannot be negative.

Check and Answer Since t represents the number of seconds, it must be a positive number. Thus, the only possible answer is 2 seconds. It takes 2 seconds for the eyeglasses (or any other object falling under the influence of gravity) to fall 64 feet.

Now Try Exercise 25

Pythagoras of Samos

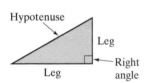

Hypotenuse

Leg

Right angle

Leg

FIGURE 5.4

2 Learn The Pythagorean Theorem

We now introduce the Pythagorean Theorem, which describes an important relationship between the length of the sides of a right triangle. The Pythagorean Theorem is named after Pythagoras of Samos ($\approx$569 B.C.–475 B.C.) who was born in Samos, Ionia. Pythagoras is often described as the first pure mathematician. Now let's discuss the Pythagorean Theorem.

A **right triangle** is a triangle that contains a right, or 90°, angle (**Fig. 5.4**). The two shorter sides of a right triangle are called the **legs** and the largest side, which is always opposite the right angle, is called the **hypotenuse**. The **Pythagorean Theorem** expresses the relationship between the lengths of the legs of a right triangle and its hypotenuse.

Understanding Algebra

The proof of the Pythagorean Theorem is often expressed visually:

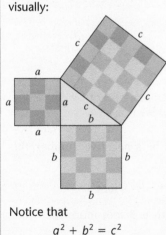

Notice that
$$a^2 + b^2 = c^2$$
$$3^2 + 4^2 = 5^2$$

Pythagorean Theorem

The square of the hypotenuse of a right triangle is equal to the sum of the squares of the two legs.

$$(\text{leg})^2 + (\text{leg})^2 = (\text{hypotenuse})^2$$

If a and b represent the legs, and c represents the hypotenuse, then

$$a^2 + b^2 = c^2$$

When you use the Pythagorean Theorem, it makes no difference which leg you designate as a and which leg you designate as b, but the hypotenuse, the longest side is always designated as c.

EXAMPLE 4 **Verifying Right Triangles** Determine if a right triangle can have the following sides.

a) 3 inches, 4 inches, 5 inches   **b)** 2 inches, 5 inches, 7 inches

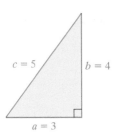

FIGURE 5.5

Solution

a) Understand   To determine if a right triangle can have the sides given, we will use the Pythagorean Theorem.

Translate   We must always select the largest size to represent the hypotenuse, c. We will designate the length of leg a to be 3 inches and the length of leg b to be 4 inches. The length of the hypotenuse, c, will be 5 inches. See **Figure 5.5**.

$$a^2 + b^2 = c^2$$
$$3^2 + 4^2 \stackrel{?}{=} 5^2$$

Carry Out
$$9 + 16 \stackrel{?}{=} 25$$
$$25 = 25 \quad \text{True}$$

Check and Answer   Since using the Pythagorean Theorem results in a true statement, a right triangle can have the given sides.

b) We will let leg a have a length of 2 inches, leg b have a length of 5 inches, and the hypotenuse, c, have a length of 7 inches.

$$a^2 + b^2 = c^2$$
$$2^2 + 5^2 \stackrel{?}{=} 7^2$$
$$4 + 25 \stackrel{?}{=} 49$$
$$29 = 49 \quad \text{False}$$

Since 29 is not equal to 49, the Pythagorean Theorem does not hold for these lengths. Therefore, no right triangle can have sides with lengths of 2 inches, 5 inches and 7 inches.

Now Try Exercise 27

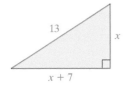

FIGURE 5.6

EXAMPLE 5 Using the Pythagorean Theorem One leg of a right triangle is 7 feet longer than the other leg. The hypotenuse is 13 feet. Find the dimensions of the right triangle.

Solution   Understand and Translate   We will first draw a diagram of the situation. See **Figure 5.6**.

Now we will use the Pythagorean Theorem to determine the dimensions of the right triangle.

$$a^2 + b^2 = c^2$$
$$x^2 + (x + 7)^2 = 13^2$$

Carry Out
$$x^2 + (x^2 + 14x + 49) = 169$$
$$2x^2 + 14x - 120 = 0$$
$$2(x^2 + 7x - 60) = 0$$
$$2(x + 12)(x - 5) = 0$$
$$x + 12 = 0 \quad \text{or} \quad x - 5 = 0$$
$$x = -12 \qquad\qquad x = 5$$

Check and Answer   Since a length cannot be a negative number, the only answer is 5. The dimensions of the right triangle are: one leg is 5 feet, the other leg is $x + 7$ or 12 feet, and the hypotenuse is 13 feet. Since $5^2 + 12^2 = 25 + 144 = 169$, which is 13^2, the answer checks.

Now Try Exercise 35

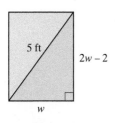

FIGURE 5.7

EXAMPLE 6 Sand and Water Table Clayton Jackson is building a rectangular table for his son to hold sand in one area and water in a different area (**Fig. 5.7**). The length of the table will be 2 feet less than twice the width. He is placing a divider that is 5 feet in length along the diagonal of the table to separate the sand from the water. Find the dimensions of the table.

Solution   Understand and Translate   Our goal is to find the dimensions of the table. **Figure 5.7** shows a right triangle. Therefore, we will use the Pythagorean Theorem to answer the question.

$$\text{Let } w = \text{width of the table.}$$
$$\text{Then } 2w - 2 = \text{length of the table.}$$

Now we use the Pythagorean Theorem. We will let w represent leg a, $2w - 2$ represent leg b, and 5 represent the hypotenuse, c.

$$a^2 + b^2 = c^2$$
$$w^2 + (2w - 2)^2 = 5^2$$

Carry Out
$$w^2 + 4w^2 - 8w + 4 = 25$$
$$5w^2 - 8w + 4 = 25$$
$$5w^2 - 8w - 21 = 0$$
$$(5w + 7)(w - 3) = 0$$
$$5w + 7 = 0 \quad \text{or} \quad w - 3 = 0$$
$$5w = -7 \qquad\quad w = 3$$
$$w = -\frac{7}{5}$$

Check and Answer   Since the width of the table cannot be a negative number, the only solution is 3. Therefore, the width of the table is 3 feet. The length of the table is $2w - 2 = 2(3) - 2 = 6 - 2 = 4$ feet.

Now Try Exercise 37

In the exercise set, we use the terms consecutive integers, consecutive even integers, and consecutive odd integers. Recall from Section 3.1 that **consecutive integers** may be represented as x and $x + 1$. **Consecutive even** or **consecutive odd integers** may be represented as x and $x + 2$.

EXERCISE SET 5.7

Math XL
MathXL®

MyMathLab
MyMathLab

Warm-Up Exercises

Fill in the blanks with the appropriate word, phrase, or symbol(s) from the following list.

90°	hypotenuse	The Pythagorean Theorem
45°	legs	10 5

1. The longest side of a right triangle is called its _____ .

2. "The hypotenuse squared is equal to the sum of the squares of the other two sides" is called _____ .

3. Every right triangle contains exactly one angle of measure _____ .

4. The two shorter sides of a right triangle are called its _____ .

Practice the Skills

In Exercises 5–8, determine the value of the question mark.

5.

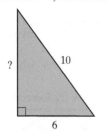

6.

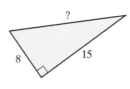

7.

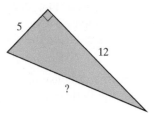

8.

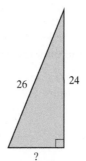

In Exercises 9–12, a and b represent two legs of a right triangle and c represents the hypotenuse. Determine the value of the question mark (?).

9. $a = 24, c = 26, b = ?$

10. $a = 12, b = 16, c = ?$

11. $a = 15, b = 36, c = ?$

12. $b = 20, c = 25, a = ?$

Problem Solving

Express each problem as an equation, then solve.

13. **Product of Numbers** The product of two positive numbers is 221. Determine the two numbers if one is 4 more than the other.

14. **Positive Numbers** The product of two positive numbers is 245. Determine the two numbers if one number is 5 times the other.

15. **Positive Numbers** The product of two positive numbers is 84. Find the two numbers if one number is 2 more than twice the other.

16. **Consecutive Integers** The product of two consecutive positive integers is 56. Find the two integers.

17. **Consecutive Even Integers** The product of two consecutive positive even integers is 288. Find the two integers.

18. **Consecutive Odd Integers** The product of two consecutive positive odd integers is 143. Determine the two integers.

 19. **Area of Rectangle** The area of a rectangle is 36 square feet. Determine the length and width if the length is 4 times the width.

20. **Rectangular Scrapbook** A scrapbook page has an area of 180 square inches. Find the length and width if the width is 3 inches less than the length.

21. **Rectangular Garden** Maureen Woolhouse has a rectangular garden whose width is two-thirds its length. If its area is 150 square feet, determine the length and width of the garden.

22. **Buying Wallpaper** Alejandro Ibanez wishes to buy a wallpaper border to go along the top of one wall in his living room. The length of the wall is 7 feet greater than its height.

   a) Find the length and height of the wall if the area of the wall is 120 square feet.

   b) What is the length of the border he will need?

   c) If the border costs $4 per linear foot, how much will the border cost?

See Exercise 21.

23. **Square** If each side of a square is increased by 4 meters, the area becomes 81 square meters. Determine the length of a side of the original square.

24. **Sign** If the length of the sign in Example 2 is to be 2 feet longer than the width and the area is to be 35 square feet, determine the dimensions of the sign.

25. **Dropped Egg** How long would it take for an egg dropped from a helicopter to fall 256 feet to the ground? See Example 3.

26. **Falling Rock** How long would it take a rock that falls from a cliff 400 feet above the sea to hit the sea? See Example 3.

In Exercises 27–30, determine if a right triangle can have the following sides where a and b represent the legs and c represents the hypotenuse. Explain your answer.

27. $a = 7, b = 24, c = 25$

28. $a = 16, c = 20, b = 22$

29. $a = 9, b = 40, c = 41$

30. $a = 13, b = 18, c = 28$

In Exercises 31–34, find the value of the question mark.

31.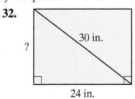

32.

33.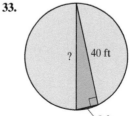

34.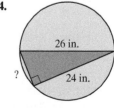

35. **Triangle** One leg of a right triangle is 2 feet longer than the other leg. The hypotenuse is 10 feet. Find the lengths of the three sides of the triangle.

36. **Triangle** One leg of a right triangle is two inches more than twice the other leg. The hypotenuse is 13 inches. Find the lengths of the three sides of the triangle.

37. Artwork Rachel bought a framed piece of artwork as a souvenir from her trip to Disney World. The diagonal of the frame is 15 inches. If the length of the frame is 3 inches greater than its width, find the dimensions of the frame.

38. Laptop The top of a new experimental rectangular laptop computer has a diagonal of 17 inches. If the length of the computer is 1 inch less than twice its width, find the dimensions of the computer.

39. Rectangular Garden Mary Ann Tuerk has constructed a rectangular garden. The length of the garden is 3 feet more than three times its width. The diagonal of the garden is 4 feet more than three times the width. Find the length and width of the garden.

40. Height of Tree A tree is supported by ropes. One rope goes from the top of the tree to a point on the ground. The height of the tree is 4 feet more than twice the distance between the base of the tree and the rope anchored in the ground. The length of the rope is 6 feet more than twice the distance between the base of the tree and the rope anchored in the ground. Find the height of the tree.

41. Book Store A book store owner finds that her daily profit, P, is approximated by the formula $P = x^2 - 15x - 50$, where x is the number of books she sells. How many books must she sell in a day for her profit to be $400?

42. Water Sprinklers The cost, C, for manufacturing x water sprinklers is given by the formula $C = x^2 - 27x - 20$. Determine the number of water sprinklers manufactured at a cost of $70.

43. Sum of Numbers The sum, s, of the first n even numbers is given by the formula $s = n^2 + n$. Determine n for the given sums:
a) $s = 20$ **b)** $s = 90$

44. Telephone Lines For a switchboard that handles n telephone lines, the maximum number of telephone connections, C, that it can make simultaneously is given by the formula
$$C = \frac{n(n - 1)}{2}.$$
a) How many telephone connections can a switchboard make simultaneously if it handles 15 lines?
b) How many lines does a switchboard have if it can make 55 telephone connections simultaneously?

45. Backyard Baseball In baseball, the infield is called the "diamond"; it is actually a square. But the DeVito brothers had to improvise in their backyard for infield practice. They made the distance from home to first base 60 feet, the distance from first base to second base 80 feet, the distance from second base to third base 60 feet, and the distance from third base to home 80 feet as depicted in the rectangle below. How far is the distance from second base to home plate?

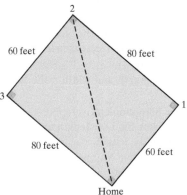

46. Refer to Exercise 45. If they had moved all the bases counterclockwise (so that home is where first is in the diagram and first is where second is in the diagram, etc.), would the distance from home to second base change?

Challenge Problems

47. Area Determine the area of the rectangle.

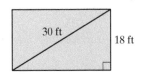

48. Area Determine the area of the circle.

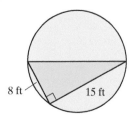

49. Solve the equation $x^3 - 4x^2 - 32x = 0$.

50. Solve the equation $x^3 + 2x^2 - 15x = 0$.

51. Create an equation whose solutions are $-2, 0,$ and 3. Explain how you determined your answer.

52. Numbers The product of two numbers is -63. Determine the numbers if their sum is -2.

53. Numbers The sum of two numbers is 9. The sum of the squares of the two numbers is 45. Determine the two numbers.

54. Wizard of Oz Near the end of the movie *The Wizard of Oz*, when the scarecrow receives his diploma, he starts talking rapidly and seems to impress us with his new found intelligence. One of the things that the scarecrow *attempts* to say is the Pythagorean Theorem. The only problem is that he says it incorrectly! Rent or borrow a videotape or DVD of the movie and write down exactly what the scarecrow says about the Pythagorean Theorem. Then see if you can rewrite the script to make it mathematically correct.

Group Activity

Discuss and solve Exercises 55 and 56 in groups.

55. Cost and Revenue The break-even point for a manufacturer occurs when its cost of production, C, is equal to its revenue, R. The cost equation for a company is $C = 2x^2 - 20x + 600$ and its revenue equation is $R = x^2 + 50x - 400$, where x is the number of units produced and sold. How many units must be produced and sold for the manufacturer to break even? There are two values.

56. Cannonball When a certain cannon is fired, the height, in feet, of the cannonball at time t can be found by using the formula $h = -16t^2 + 128t$.

a) Determine the height of the cannonball 3 seconds after being fired.

b) Determine the time it takes for the cannonball to hit the ground. (*Hint:* What is the value of h at impact?)

Cumulative Review Exercises

[3.1] **57.** Express the statement "seven less than three times a number" as a mathematical expression.

[4.4] **58.** Subtract $x^2 - 4x + 6$ from $3x + 2$.

[4.5] **59.** Multiply $(3x^2 + 2x - 4)(2x - 1)$.

[4.6] **60.** Divide $\dfrac{6x^2 - 19x + 15}{3x - 5}$ by dividing the numerator by the denominator.

[5.4] **61.** Divide $\dfrac{6x^2 - 19x + 15}{3x - 5}$ by factoring the numerator and dividing out common factors.

Chapter 5 Summary

IMPORTANT FACTS AND CONCEPTS	EXAMPLES
Section 5.1	
To **factor an expression** means to write the expression as a product of its factors.	$x^2 + 2x - 35 = (x + 7)(x - 5)$
If $a \cdot b = c$, then a and b are **factors** of c.	6 and 4 are factors of 24.
The **greatest common factor (GCF)** of two or more numbers is the greatest number that divides into all the numbers.	The GCF of 36 and 48 is 12.
A **prime number** is an integer greater than 1 that has exactly two factors, itself and 1. A positive integer (other than 1) that is not prime is called **composite**. The number 1 is neither prime nor composite; it is called a **unit**.	23 is a prime number. 72 is a composite number.
To Determine the GCF of Two or More Numbers 1. Write each number as a product of prime factors. 2. Determine the prime factors common to all the numbers. 3. Multiply the common factors found in step 2. The product is the GCF.	$40 = 2^3 \cdot 5 \quad \text{and} \quad 140 = 2^2 \cdot 5 \cdot 7$ The GCF of 40 and 140 is $2^2 \cdot 5 = 4 \cdot 5 = 20$.
To Determine the Greatest Common Factor of Two or More Terms 1. Find the GCF of the numerical coefficients of the terms. 2. Find the largest power of each variable that is common to all of the terms. 3. The GCF is product of the number from step 1 and the variable expressions from step 2.	The GCF of $6xy^2$, $4x^3y^4$, and $8x^2y^3$ is $2xy^2$.
To Factor a Monomial from a Polynomial 1. Determine the greatest common factor of all terms in the polynomial. 2. Write each term as the product of the GCF and its other factor. 3. Use the distributive property to factor out the GCF.	$6a^4 + 27a^3 - 18a^2 = 3a^2(2a^2 + 9a - 6)$

IMPORTANT FACTS AND CONCEPTS	EXAMPLES

Section 5.2

To Factor a Four-Term Polynomial Using Grouping

1. If all the terms have a GCF other than 1, factor it out.
2. If necessary, arrange the four terms so that the first two terms have a common factor and the last two have a common factor.
3. Use the distributive property to factor each group of two terms.
4. Factor the GCF from the results of step 3.

$$xy + 5x - 3y - 15 = x(y + 5) - 3(y + 5)$$
$$= (y + 5)(x - 3)$$

Section 5.3

To Factor Trinomials of the Form $ax^2 + bx + c$, where $a = 1$

1. Find two numbers whose product equals the constant, c, and whose sum equals the coefficient of the x-term, b.
2. Use the two numbers found in step 1, including their signs, to write the trinomial in factored form. The trinomial in factored form will be
$$(x + \text{first number})(x + \text{second number}).$$

Factor $x^2 + 5x - 36$.

The two numbers whose product is -36 and whose sum is 5 are 9 and -4.

Therefore,
$$x^2 + 5x - 36 = (x + 9)(x - 4).$$

A **prime polynomial** is a polynomial that cannot be factored using only integer coefficients

$x^2 - 7x + 11$ is a prime polynomial.

Section 5.4

To Factor Trinomials of the Form $ax^2 + bx + c, a \neq 1$, by Trial and Error

1. If all the terms have a GCF other than 1, factor it out.
2. Write all pairs of factors of the coefficient of the squared term, a.
3. Write all pairs of factors of the constant term, c.
4. Try various combinations of these factors until the correct middle term, bx, is found.

Factor $3x^2 - 2x - 8$.

Factors of -8	Possible Factors	Sum of the Products of the Outer and Inner Terms
$-1(8)$	$(3x - 1)(x + 8)$	$23x$
$-2(4)$	$(3x - 2)(x + 4)$	$10x$
$-4(2)$	$(3x - 4)(x + 2)$	$2x$
$-8(1)$	$(3x - 8)(x + 1)$	$-5x$
$4(-2)$	$(3x + 4)(x - 2)$	$-2x$

Therefore, $3x^2 - 2x - 8 = (3x + 4)(x - 2)$.

To Factor Trinomials of the Form $ax^2 + bx + c, a \neq 1$, by Grouping

1. If all the terms have a GCF other than 1, factor it out.
2. Find two numbers whose product is equal to the product of a times c, and whose sum is equal to b.
3. Rewrite the middle term, bx, as the sum or difference of two terms using the numbers found in step 2.
4. Factor by grouping as explained in Section 5.2.

Factor $4x^2 + 19x - 30$.

$$ac = 4(-30) = -120$$

Two numbers whose product is ac, or -120, and whose sum is b, or 19, are 24 and -5.

$$4x^2 + 19x - 30 = 4x^2 + \overbrace{24x - 5x}^{19x} - 30$$
$$= 4x(x + 6) - 5(x + 6)$$
$$= (x + 6)(4x - 5)$$

Section 5.5

Difference of Two Squares
$$a^2 - b^2 = (a + b)(a - b)$$

$$y^2 - 49 = (y + 7)(y - 7)$$

Sum of Two Cubes
$$a^3 + b^3 = (a + b)(a^2 - ab + b^2)$$

$$8p^3 + q^3 = (2p)^3 + (q)^3$$
$$= (2p + q)[(2p)^2 - (2p)(q) + (q)^2]$$
$$= (2p + q)(4p^2 - 2pq + q^2)$$

IMPORTANT FACTS AND CONCEPTS	EXAMPLES

Section 5.5 (cont.)

Difference of Two Cubes

$$a^3 - b^3 = (a - b)(a^2 + ab + b^2)$$

$$8p^3 - q^3 = (2p)^3 - (q)^3$$
$$= (2p - q)[(2p)^2 + (2p)(q) + (q)^2]$$
$$= (2p - q)(4p^2 + 2pq + q^2)$$

General Procedure for Factoring a Polynomial

1. If all the terms have a GCF other than 1, factor it out.

2. If the polynomial has two terms, determine whether it is a difference of two squares or a sum or a difference of two cubes. If so, factor using the appropriate formula from Section 5.5.

3. If the polynomial has three terms, factor the trinomial using the methods discussed in Sections 5.3 and 5.4.

4. If the polynomial has more than three terms, try factoring by grouping as discussed in Section 5.2.

5. Examine your factored polynomial to determine whether the terms in any factors have a common factor. If you find a common factor, factor it out.

Factor $3x^2 - 48$.
$$3x^2 - 48 = 3(x^2 - 16)$$
$$= 3(x + 4)(x - 4)$$

Section 5.6

Quadratic Equation

Quadratic equations have the form
$$ax^2 + bx + c = 0$$
where a, b, and c are real numbers, $a \neq 0$.

$6x^2 - 7x + 3 = 0$ is a quadratic equation in **standard form**.

Zero-Factor Property

If $ab = 0$, then $a = 0$ or $b = 0$.

If $(x + 3)(x - 1) = 0$, then $x + 3 = 0$ or $x - 1 = 0$.

To Solve a Quadratic Equation Using Factoring

1. Write the equation in standard form with the squared term having a positive coefficient.

2. Factor the side of the equation that is not 0.

3. Set each factor *containing a variable* equal to 0 and solve each equation.

4. Check each solution found in step 3 in the *original* equation.

Solve the equation $x^2 - 3x - 52 = -12$.
$$x^2 - 3x - 52 = -12$$
$$x^2 - 3x - 40 = 0$$
$$(x - 8)(x + 5) = 0$$
$$x - 8 = 0 \quad \text{or} \quad x + 5 = 0$$
$$x = 8 \qquad\qquad x = -5$$

Section 5.7

A **right triangle** is a triangle that contains a right, or 90°, angle.

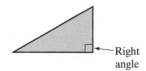
Right angle

Pythagorean Theorem

If a and b represent the legs of a right triangle, and c represents the hypotenuse, then

$$a^2 + b^2 = c^2$$

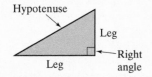
Hypotenuse
Leg
Right angle
Leg

c
b
a

Determine the value of x.

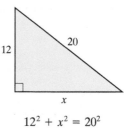
12
20
x

$$12^2 + x^2 = 20^2$$
$$144 + x^2 = 400$$
$$x^2 = 256$$
$$x = 16$$

Chapter 5 Review Exercises

[5.1]   *Find the greatest common factor for each set of terms.*

1. $3y^5, y^4, 2y^3$

2. $3p, 6p^2, 9p^3$

3. $18c^4, 12c^2, 30c^5$

4. $20x^2y^3, 25x^3y^4, 10x^5y^2z$

5. $9xyz, 12xz, 36, x^2y$

6. $9st, 16s^2t, 24s, s^3t^3$

7. $8(x - 3), x - 3$

8. $x(x + 5), x + 5$

Factor each expression. If an expression is prime, so state.

9. $7x - 35$

10. $35x - 5$

11. $24y^2 - 4y$

12. $55p^3 - 20p^2$

13. $60a^2b - 36ab^2$

14. $9xy - 36x^3y^2$

15. $20x^3y^2 + 8x^9y^3 - 16x^5y^2$

16. $24x^2 - 13y^2 + 6xy$

17. $14a^2b - 7b - a^3$

18. $x(5x + 3) - 2(5x + 3)$

19. $3t(t - 1) + 4(t - 1)$

20. $2x(4x - 3) + 4x - 3$

[5.2]   *Factor by grouping.*

21. $x^2 + 6x + 2x + 12$

22. $x^2 - 5x + 4x - 20$

23. $y^2 - 6y - 6y + 36$

24. $3xy + 3x + 2y + 2$

25. $4a^2 - 4ab - a + b$

26. $2x^2 + 12x - x - 6$

27. $x^2 + 3x - 2xy - 6y$

28. $5x^2 - xy + 20xy - 4y^2$

29. $4x^2 + 12xy - 5xy - 15y^2$

30. $6a^2 - 10ab - 3ab + 5b^2$

31. $pq - 3q + 4p - 12$

32. $3x^2 - 9xy + 2xy - 6y^2$

33. $7a^2 + 14ab - ab - 2b^2$

34. $8x^2 - 4x + 6x - 3$

[5.3]   *Factor completely. If an expression is prime, so state.*

35. $x^2 + 5x + 6$

36. $x^2 + 4x - 15$

37. $x^2 + 11x + 18$

38. $n^2 + 3n - 40$

39. $b^2 + b - 20$

40. $x^2 - 15x + 56$

41. $c^2 - 10c - 20$

42. $y^2 - 10y - 22$

43. $x^3 - 17x^2 + 72x$

44. $t^3 - 5t^2 - 36t$

45. $x^2 - 2xy - 15y^2$

46. $4x^3 + 32x^2y + 60xy^2$

[5.4]   *Factor completely. If an expression is prime, so state.*

47. $2x^2 - x - 15$

48. $6x^2 - 29x - 5$

49. $4x^2 - 9x + 5$

50. $5m^2 - 14m + 8$

51. $16y^2 + 8y - 3$

52. $5x^2 - 32x + 12$

53. $2t^2 + 14t + 9$

54. $5x^2 + 37x - 24$

55. $6s^2 + 13s + 5$

56. $6x^2 + 11x - 10$

57. $12x^2 + 2x - 4$

58. $25x^2 - 30x + 9$

59. $9x^3 - 12x^2 + 4x$

60. $18x^3 + 12x^2 - 16x$

61. $4a^2 - 16ab + 15b^2$

62. $16a^2 - 22ab - 3b^2$

[5.5]   *Factor completely.*

63. $x^2 - 100$

64. $x^2 - 36$

65. $3x^2 - 48$

66. $81x^2 - 9y^2$

67. $81 - a^2$

68. $64 - x^2$

69. $16x^4 - 49y^2$

70. $64x^6 - 49y^6$

71. $a^3 + b^3$

72. $x^3 - y^3$

73. $x^3 - 1$

74. $x^3 + 8$

75. $a^3 + 27$

76. $b^3 - 64$

77. $125a^3 + b^3$

78. $27 - 8y^3$

79. $3x^3 - 192y^3$

80. $27x^4 - 75y^2$

[5.1–5.5]   *Factor completely.*

81. $x^2 - 14x + 48$

82. $3x^2 - 18x + 27$

83. $5q^2 - 5$

84. $8x^2 + 16x - 24$

85. $4y^2 - 36$

86. $x^2 - 6x - 27$

87. $9x^2 - 6x + 1$

88. $7x^2 + 25x - 12$

89. $6b^3 - 6$

90. $x^3y - 27y$

91. $a^2b - 2ab - 15b$

92. $6x^3 + 30x^2 + 9x^2 + 45x$

93. $x^2 - 4xy + 3y^2$

94. $3m^2 + 2mn - 8n^2$

95. $4x^2 + 12xy + 9y^2$

96. $25a^2 - 49b^2$

97. $xy - 7x + 2y - 14$

98. $16y^5 - 25y^7$

99. $6x^2 + 5xy - 21y^2$

100. $4x^3 + 18x^2y + 20xy^2$

101. $16x^4 - 8x^3 - 3x^2$

102. $d^4 - 16$

[5.6]   *Solve.*

103. $x(x + 9) = 0$

104. $(a - 2)(a + 6) = 0$

105. $(x + 5)(4x - 3) = 0$

106. $x^2 + 7x = 0$

107. $6x^2 + 30x = 0$

108. $6x^2 + 18x = 0$

109. $r^2 + 9r + 18 = 0$

110. $x^2 - 3x = -2$

111. $x^2 - 12 = -x$

112. $15x + 12 = -3x^2$

113. $x^2 - 6x + 8 = 0$

114. $3p^2 + 6p = 45$

115. $8x^2 - 3 = -10x$

116. $3p^2 - 11p = 4$

117. $4x^2 - 16 = 0$

118. $49x^2 - 100 = 0$

119. $8x^2 - 14x + 3 = 0$

120. $-48x = -12x^2 - 45$

[5.7]

121. State the Pythagorean Theorem.

122. What is the longest side of a right triangle called?

In Exercises 123 and 124, determine the value of the question mark (?).

123.

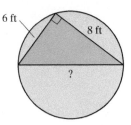

6 ft, 8 ft, ?

124.

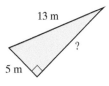

13 m, ?, 5 m

Express each problem as an equation, then solve.

125. Product of Integers The product of two consecutive positive odd integers is 99. Determine the two integers.

126. Product of Integers The product of two positive integers is 56. Determine the integers if the larger is 6 more than twice the smaller.

127. Area of Rectangle The area of a rectangle is 180 square feet. Determine the length and width of the rectangle if the length is 3 feet greater than the width.

128. Right Triangle One leg of a right triangle is 7 feet longer than the other leg. The hypotenuse is 9 feet longer than the shortest leg. Find the lengths of the three sides of the triangle.

129. Square The length of each side of a square is made smaller by 4 inches. If the area of the resulting square is 25 square inches, determine the length of a side of the original square.

130. Table Brian has a rectangular table. The length of the table is 2 feet greater than the width of the table. A diagonal across the table is 4 feet greater than the width of the table. Find the length of the diagonal across the table.

131. Falling Pear How long would it take a pear that falls off a 16-foot tree to hit the ground?

132. Baking Cookies The Pine Hills Neighborhood Association has determined that the cost, C, to make x dozen cookies can be estimated by the formula $C = x^2 - 79x + 20$. If they have \$100 to be used to make the cookies, how many dozen cookies can the association make to sell at a fund-raiser?

© Jaimie Duplass\Shutterstock

Chapter 5 Practice Test

CHAPTER
Test Prep
VIDEOS

Chapter Test Prep Videos provide fully worked-out solutions to any of the exercises you want to review. Chapter Test Prep Videos are available via MyMathLab , or on You Tube (search "Angel Elementary Algebra" and click on "Channels").

1. Determine the greatest common factor of $9y^5, 15y^3$, and $27y^4$.

2. Determine the greatest common factor of $8p^3q^2, 32p^2q^5$, and $24p^4q^3$.

Factor completely.

3. $5x^2y^3 - 15x^5y^2$

4. $8a^3b - 12a^2b^2 + 28a^2b$

5. $4x^2 - 20x + x - 5$

6. $a^2 - 4ab - 5ab + 20b^2$

7. $r^2 + 5r - 24$

8. $25a^2 - 5ab - 6b^2$

9. $4x^2 - 16x - 48$

10. $2y^3 - y^2 - 3y$

11. $12x^2 - xy - 6y^2$

12. $x^2 - 9y^2$

13. $x^3 - 64$

Solve.

14. $(6x - 5)(x + 3) = 0$

15. $x^2 - 6x = 0$

16. $x^2 = 64$

17. $x^2 + 18x + 81 = 0$

18. $x^2 - 7x + 12 = 0$

19. $x^2 + 6 = -5x$

20. Right Triangle Find the length of the side indicated with a question mark.

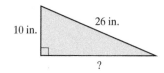

10 in.   26 in.   ?

21. Right Triangle In a right triangle, one leg is 2 feet less than twice the length of the smaller leg. The hypotenuse is 2 feet more than twice the length of the smaller leg. Determine the hypotenuse of the triangle.

22. Product of Integers The product of two positive integers is 36. Determine the two integers if the larger is 1 more than twice the smaller.

23. Consecutive Even Integers The product of two positive consecutive even integers is 168. Determine the integers.

24. Rectangle The area of a rectangle is 24 square meters. Determine the length and width of the rectangle if its length is 2 meters greater than its width.

25. Fallen Object How long would it take for an object dropped from a hot air balloon to fall 1600 feet to the ground?

© Thomas Barrat\Shutterstock

Cumulative Review Test

Take the following test and check your answers with those given in the back of the book. Review any questions that you answered incorrectly. The section where the material was covered is indicated after the answer.

1. Evaluate $4 - 5(2x + 4x^2 - 21)$ when $x = -4$.

2. Evaluate $5x^2 - 3y + 7(2 + y^2 - 4x)$ when $x = 3$ and $y = -2$.

3. Motel Room The cost of a motel room including a 12% state tax and 3% county tax is $103.50. Determine the cost of the room before tax.

4. Consider the set of numbers

$$\left\{ -6, -0.2, \frac{3}{5}, \sqrt{7}, -\sqrt{2}, 7, 0, -\frac{5}{9}, 1.34 \right\}$$

List the elements that are

a) natural numbers.

b) rational numbers.

c) irrational numbers.

d) real numbers.

5. Which is greater, $|-8|$ or $-|8|$? Explain your answer.

6. Solve the equation $4x - 2 = 4(x - 7) + 2x$ for x.

7. Solve the proportion $\frac{5}{12} = \frac{8}{x}$ for x by cross-multiplying.

8. Solve the inequality $3x - 5 \geq 10(6 - x)$, and graph the solution on a number line.

9. Solve the equation $4x + 3y = 7$ for y. Write your answer in $y = mx + b$ form.

10. Acid Solution How many liters of a 10% acid solution must be mixed with three liters of a 4% acid solution to get an 8% acid solution?

11. Consecutive Odd Integers The sum of two consecutive odd integers is 96. Find the two integers.

12. Cross-Country Skiing Two cross-country skiers follow the same trail in a local park. Brooke Stoner skis at a rate of 8 kilometers per hour and Bob Thoresen skis at a rate of 4 kilometers per hour. How long will it take Brooke to catch Bob if she leaves 15 minutes after he does?

© Steve Mason\Getty Images, Inc.-Photodisc/Royalty Free

13. Simplify $\left(\frac{4x^3}{9y^4} \right)^2$.

14. Simplify $(2x^{-3})^{-2}(4x^{-3}y^2)^3$.

15. Subtract $(4x^3 - 3x^2 + 7)$ from $(x^3 - x^2 + 6x - 5)$.

Perform the operations indicated.

16. $(3x - 2)(x^2 + 5x - 6)$

17. $\dfrac{x^2 - 2x + 6}{x + 3}$

18. Factor $qr + 2q - 8r - 16$ by grouping.

19. Factor $5x^2 - 7x - 6$.

20. Factor $7y^3 - 63y$.

6 Rational Expressions and Equations

6.1   Simplifying Rational Expressions

6.2   Multiplication and Division of Rational Expressions

6.3   Addition and Subtraction of Rational Expressions with a Common Denominator and Finding the Least Common Denominator

6.4   Addition and Subtraction of Rational Expressions

       Mid-Chapter Test: Sections 6.1–6.4

6.5   Complex Fractions

6.6   Solving Rational Equations

6.7   Rational Equations: Applications and Problem Solving

6.8   Variation

       Chapter 6 Summary

       Chapter 6 Review Exercises

       Chapter 6 Practice Test

       Cumulative Review Test

Goals of This Chapter

You worked with rational numbers when you worked with fractions in arithmetic. Fractions that contain variables are often referred to as rational expressions. The same basic procedures that you used with arithmetic fractions will be used with rational expressions. You might wish to review Section 1.3 since the material presented in this chapter builds upon the procedures presented there.

Equations that contain rational expressions are called rational equations. We will solve rational equations in Section 6.6.

To be successful in this chapter, you need to have a complete understanding of factoring, which was presented in Chapter 5. Sections 5.3 and 5.4 are especially important.

When two people paint a house, the job gets done faster than if each person painted the house separately. In Exercise 31 on page 388, we will see how algebra can be used to determine how much faster the job gets done.

© Konstantin Shevtsov\Shutterstock

6.1 Simplifying Rational Expressions

1 Determine the values for which a rational expression is defined.

2 Understand the three signs of a fraction.

3 Simplify rational expressions.

4 Factor a negative 1 from a polynomial.

1 Determine the Values for Which a Rational Expression Is Defined

We begin this chapter by defining a *rational expression*.

> **Rational Expression**
>
> A **rational expression** is an expression of the form $\frac{p}{q}$, where p and q are polynomials and $q \neq 0$.

Examples of Rational Expressions

$$\frac{4}{5}, \quad \frac{x+3}{x}, \quad \frac{x^2+8x}{x-3}, \quad \frac{x}{x^2-4}$$

The denominator of a rational expression cannot equal 0 since division by 0 is not defined.

Expression	Defined	Undefined
$\dfrac{x+3}{x}$	for all real numbers except 0	when $x = 0$
$\dfrac{x^2+8x}{x-3}$	for all real numbers except 3	when $x = 3$
$\dfrac{x}{x^2-4}$	for all real numbers except 2 and -2	when $x = 2$ or $x = -2$

Whenever a rational expression has a variable in the denominator, we always assume that the value or values of the variable that make the denominator 0 are excluded.

One method that can be used to determine the value or values of the variable that are excluded is to set the denominator equal to 0 and then solve the resulting equation for the variable.

EXAMPLE 1 Determine the value or values of the variable for which the rational expression is defined.

a) $\dfrac{7}{x-4}$ **b)** $\dfrac{3x+4}{2x-7}$ **c)** $\dfrac{x+5}{x^2+6x-7}$

Solution

a) To determine the conditions for which the denominator is zero, we set $x - 4$ equal to 0.

$$x - 4 = 0$$
$$x = 4$$

We say $\dfrac{7}{x-4}$ is defined for all real numbers except 4, or simply $x \neq 4$.

b) In $\dfrac{3x+4}{2x-7}$, we set the denominator $2x - 7$ equal to 0 to find values we need to exclude.

$$2x - 7 = 0$$
$$2x = 7$$
$$x = \frac{7}{2}$$

Thus when we consider the rational expression $\dfrac{3x+4}{2x-7}$, we say x cannot equal $\dfrac{7}{2}$, or $x \neq \dfrac{7}{2}$.

c) Again, we set the denominator of $\dfrac{x+5}{x^2+6x-7}$ equal to zero.

$$x^2 + 6x - 7 = 0$$
$$(x+7)(x-1) = 0$$
$$x + 7 = 0 \quad \text{or} \quad x - 1 = 0$$
$$x = -7 \qquad\qquad x = 1$$

Thus, for $\dfrac{x+5}{x^2+6x-7}$, we say $x \neq -7$ and $x \neq 1$.

Now Try Exercise 15

Now Try Exercise 15

Understanding Algebra

Since changing any two of a fraction's three signs does not change the fraction, we can write the following:

$$\frac{3}{-4} = \frac{-3}{4} = -\frac{3}{4}$$

$$\frac{-2x}{-3y^2} = -\frac{-2x}{3y^2} = \frac{2x}{3y^2}$$

$$-\frac{-4a}{-5b} = \frac{-4a}{5b} = -\frac{4a}{5b}$$

---

2 Understand the Three Signs of a Fraction

Three **signs** are associated with any fraction: the sign of the numerator, the sign of the denominator, and the sign of the fraction.

Sign of numerator

$$\text{Sign of fraction} \longrightarrow +\frac{-a}{+b}$$

Sign of denominator

Whenever any of the three signs is omitted, we assume it to be positive. For example,

$$\frac{a}{b} \quad \text{means} \quad +\frac{+a}{+b}$$

$$\frac{-a}{b} \quad \text{means} \quad +\frac{-a}{+b}$$

$$-\frac{a}{b} \quad \text{means} \quad -\frac{+a}{+b}$$

Negative Fractions

Changing any two of the three signs of a fraction does not change the value of a fraction.

$$\frac{-a}{b} = -\frac{a}{b} = \frac{a}{-b}$$

Generally, we do not write a fraction with a negative denominator. For example, the expression $\dfrac{2}{-5}$ would be written as either $\dfrac{-2}{5}$ or $-\dfrac{2}{5}$. The expression $\dfrac{x}{-(4-x)}$ can be written $\dfrac{x}{x-4}$ since $-(4-x) = -4 + x$ or $x - 4$.

3 Simplify Rational Expressions

A rational expression is **simplified** or **reduced to its lowest terms** when the numerator and denominator have no common factors other than 1. The fraction $\dfrac{9}{12}$ is not simplified because 9 and 12 both contain the common factor 3. When the 3 is factored out, the simplified fraction is $\dfrac{3}{4}$.

$$\frac{9}{12} = \frac{\overset{1}{\cancel{3}} \cdot 3}{\underset{1}{\cancel{3}} \cdot 4} = \frac{3}{4}$$

Not simplified ⟶   ⟵ Simplified

The rational expression $\dfrac{ab - b^2}{2b}$ is not simplified because both the numerator and denominator have a common factor, b. To simplify this expression, factor b from each term in the numerator, then divide it out.

$$\frac{ab - b^2}{2b} = \frac{\overset{1}{\cancel{b}}(a - b)}{2\underset{1}{\cancel{b}}} = \frac{a - b}{2}$$

Thus, $\dfrac{ab - b^2}{2b}$ becomes $\dfrac{a - b}{2}$ when simplified.

Understanding Algebra

We say that the simplified form of

$$\frac{ab - b^2}{2b} \text{ is } \frac{a - b}{2}.$$

We should keep in mind that in both original and simplified expressions, b cannot equal 0 because that would make the original denominator 0.

To Simplify Rational Expressions

1. Factor both the numerator and denominator as completely as possible.
2. Divide out any factors common to both the numerator and denominator.

EXAMPLE 2 Simplify $\dfrac{5x^3 + 10x^2 - 35x}{10x^2}$.

Solution

$$\frac{5x^3 + 10x^2 - 35x}{10x^2} \qquad \leftarrow \text{Observe that the GCF is } 5x.$$

$$= \frac{\overset{1}{\cancel{5x}}(x^2 + 2x - 7)}{\underset{1}{\cancel{5x}} \cdot 2x} \qquad \leftarrow \begin{array}{l}\text{Factor } 5x \text{ from the numerator and the} \\ \text{denominator and divide it out.}\end{array}$$

$$= \frac{x^2 + 2x - 7}{2x}$$

Now Try Exercise 33

Helpful Hint

In Example 2 we *simplified* a polynomial divided by a monomial using factoring. In Section 4.6 we *divided* polynomials by monomials by writing each term in the numerator over the expression in the denominator. For example,

$$\frac{5x^3 + 10x^2 - 35x}{10x^2} = \frac{5x^3}{10x^2} + \frac{10x^2}{10x^2} - \frac{35x}{10x^2}$$

$$= \frac{x}{2} + 1 - \frac{7}{2x}$$

The answer above, $\dfrac{x}{2} + 1 - \dfrac{7}{2x}$, is equivalent to the answer $\dfrac{x^2 + 2x - 7}{2x}$, which was obtained by factoring in Example 2. We show this below.

$$\frac{x}{2} + 1 - \frac{7}{2x}$$

$$= \frac{x}{x} \cdot \frac{x}{2} + \frac{2x}{2x} \cdot 1 - \frac{7}{2x} \qquad \text{Write each term with LCD } 2x.$$

$$= \frac{x^2}{2x} + \frac{2x}{2x} - \frac{7}{2x}$$

$$= \frac{x^2 + 2x - 7}{2x}$$

When asked to *simplify* an expression we will factor numerators and denominators, when possible, then divide out common factors. This process was illustrated in Example 2 and will be further illustrated in Examples 3 through 5.

EXAMPLE 3 Simplify $\dfrac{x^2 - x - 12}{x + 3}$.

Solution Factor the numerator; then divide out the common factor.

$$\frac{x^2 - x - 12}{x + 3} = \frac{\overset{1}{\cancel{(x + 3)}}(x - 4)}{\underset{1}{\cancel{x + 3}}} = x - 4$$

Now Try Exercise 35

EXAMPLE 4 Simplify $\dfrac{r^2 - 25}{r - 5}$.

Solution Factor the numerator; then divide out common factors.

$$\frac{r^2 - 25}{r - 5} = \frac{(r + 5)\overset{1}{\cancel{(r - 5)}}}{\underset{1}{\cancel{r - 5}}} = r + 5$$

Now Try Exercise 61

EXAMPLE 5 Simplify $\dfrac{3x^2 - 10x - 8}{x^2 + 3x - 28}$.

Solution Factor both the numerator and denominator, then divide out common factors.

$$\frac{3x^2 - 10x - 8}{x^2 + 3x - 28} = \frac{(3x + 2)\overset{1}{\cancel{(x - 4)}}}{(x + 7)\underset{1}{\cancel{(x - 4)}}} = \frac{3x + 2}{x + 7}.$$

Note that $\dfrac{3x + 2}{x + 7}$ cannot be simplified any further.

Now Try Exercise 41

Avoiding Common Errors

Remember: Only common factors can be divided out from expressions.

CORRECT

$$\frac{\overset{5}{\cancel{20}}\overset{x}{\cancel{x^2}}}{\underset{1}{\cancel{4}}\underset{1}{\cancel{x}}} = 5x$$

INCORRECT

In the denominator of the example on the left, $4x$, the 4 and x are factors since they are *multiplied* together. The 4 and the x are also both factors of the numerator $20x^2$, since $20x^2$ can be written $4 \cdot x \cdot 5x$.

Some students incorrectly divide out *terms*. In the expression $\dfrac{x^2 - 20}{x - 4}$, the x and -4 are *terms* of the denominator, not factors, and therefore cannot be divided out.

4 Factor a Negative 1 from a Polynomial

Recall from Section 5.2 that when -1 is factored from a polynomial, the sign of each term in the polynomial changes.

Examples

$$-3x + 10 = -1(3x - 10) = -(3x - 10)$$
$$5 - 2x = -1(-5 + 2x) = -(2x - 5)$$
$$-2x^2 + 3x - 4 = -1(2x^2 - 3x + 4) = -(2x^2 - 3x + 4)$$

Whenever the terms in a numerator and denominator differ only in their signs, we can factor out −1 from either the numerator or denominator and then divide out the common factor.

Understanding Algebra

An expression divided by its *additive inverse* (or *opposite*) is −1:

$$\frac{a - b}{b - a} = -1 \text{ (provided } a \neq b)$$

EXAMPLE 6   Simplify $\dfrac{3x - 8}{8 - 3x}$.

Solution   Since each term in the numerator differs only in sign from its like term in the denominator, we will factor −1 from each term in the denominator.

$$\frac{3x - 8}{8 - 3x} = \frac{3x - 8}{-1(-8 + 3x)}$$

$$= \frac{\overset{1}{\cancel{3x - 8}}}{-\underset{1}{\cancel{(3x - 8)}}}$$

$$= -1$$

Now Try Exercise 43

Understanding Algebra

In Example 7 we simplified $\dfrac{4n^2 - 23n - 6}{6 - n}$ to $-(4n + 1)$.

Notice $n \neq 6$ in the original expression. Therefore, it is assumed that $n \neq 6$ in the simplified expression, $-(4n + 1)$, as well.

EXAMPLE 7   Simplify $\dfrac{4n^2 - 23n - 6}{6 - n}$.

Solution

$$\frac{4n^2 - 23n - 6}{6 - n} = \frac{(4n + 1)(n - 6)}{6 - n}$$ The terms in $n - 6$ differ only in sign from the terms in $6 - n$.

$$= (4n + 1)(-1)$$ Replaced $\dfrac{n - 6}{6 - n}$ with -1.

$$= -(4n + 1)$$

Note that $-4n - 1$ is also an acceptable answer.

Now Try Exercise 49

EXERCISE SET 6.1

MathXL
MathXL®

MyMathLab
MyMathLab

Warm-Up Exercises

Fill in the blanks with the appropriate word, phrase, or symbol(s) from the following list.

−4	reduced to lowest terms	$\dfrac{4}{x}$	$4x - 1$	$x - 4$
1	rational expression	4	$\dfrac{5 - 2x^2}{2x^2}$	$\dfrac{-4}{x}$
−1				

1. An expression of the form $\dfrac{p}{q}$ where p and q are polynomials $(q \neq 0)$ is called a(n) _____.

2. The expression $\dfrac{x - 1}{4 - x}$ is defined for all values of x except _____.

3. When a fraction's numerator and denominator have no common factor (other than 1), we say the fraction is _____.

4. When $\dfrac{25 - 10x^2}{10x^2}$ is simplified, the result is _____.

5. When $\dfrac{x^2 - x - 12}{x + 3}$ is simplified, the result is _____.

6. If $x \neq 8$, then $-\dfrac{8 - x}{x - 8}$ simplifies to _____.

7. If $x \neq 2$, then $\dfrac{x - 2}{2 - x}$ simplifies to _____.

8. The expression $\dfrac{4}{-x}$ can be written as _____.

9. When $\dfrac{4x^2 - 13x - 3}{x - 3}$ is simplified, the result is _____.

10. The expression $\dfrac{2x}{x + 4}$ is defined for all values of x except _____.

Practice the Skills

Determine the value or values of the variable for which each expression is defined.

11. $\dfrac{5}{x-1}$

12. $\dfrac{x+1}{4-x}$

13. $\dfrac{x-2}{x}$

14. $\dfrac{8}{r+3}$

15. $\dfrac{7}{4n-16}$

16. $\dfrac{7}{2x-3}$

17. $\dfrac{x+4}{x^2-4}$

18. $\dfrac{9}{x^2+4x-5}$

19. $\dfrac{2x-3}{2x^2-9x+9}$

20. $\dfrac{x^2+2}{2x^2-13x+15}$

21. $\dfrac{x}{x^2+36}$

22. $\dfrac{4}{9+x^2}$

23. $\dfrac{p+8}{4p^2-25}$

24. $\dfrac{10}{9r^2-16}$

Simplify the following rational expressions that contain a monomial divided by a monomial. This material was covered in Sections 4.1 and 4.2, and it will help prepare you for the next section.

25. $\dfrac{8x^3y}{24x^2y^5}$

26. $\dfrac{18x^3y^2}{30x^4y^5}$

27. $\dfrac{(2a^4b^5)^3}{2a^{12}b^{20}}$

28. $\dfrac{(5r^2s^3)^2}{(3r^4s)^3}$

Simplify.

29. $\dfrac{5x}{x+xy}$

30. $\dfrac{12t}{3t+9}$

31. $\dfrac{5x+15}{x+3}$

32. $\dfrac{3x^2+6x}{3x^2+9x}$

33. $\dfrac{x^3+6x^2+7x}{2x}$

34. $\dfrac{x^2y^2-2xy+5y}{y}$

35. $\dfrac{r^2-r-2}{r-2}$

36. $\dfrac{b-6}{b^2-8b+12}$

37. $\dfrac{x^2+2x}{x^2+4x+4}$

38. $\dfrac{x^2+3x-18}{4x-12}$

39. $\dfrac{z^2-10z+25}{z^2-25}$

40. $\dfrac{k^2-6k+9}{k^2-9}$

41. $\dfrac{x^2-2x-3}{x^2-x-6}$

42. $\dfrac{4x^2-12x-40}{2x^2-16x+30}$

43. $\dfrac{4x-8}{8-4x}$

44. $\dfrac{10a-6}{3-5a}$

45. $\dfrac{x^2-2x-8}{4-x}$

46. $\dfrac{7-s}{s^2-12s+35}$

47. $\dfrac{x^2+3x-18}{-2x^2+6x}$

48. $\dfrac{3p^2-13p-10}{3p+2}$

49. $\dfrac{2x^2+5x-3}{1-2x}$

50. $\dfrac{x^2-25}{x^2-2x-15}$

51. $\dfrac{m-2}{4m^2-13m+10}$

52. $\dfrac{2x^2-13x+21}{(x-3)^2}$

53. $\dfrac{x^2-25}{(x+5)^2}$

54. $\dfrac{16x^2+24x+9}{4x+3}$

55. $\dfrac{6x^2-13x+6}{3x-2}$

56. $\dfrac{6t^2-7t-5}{3t-5}$

57. $\dfrac{x^2-3x+4x-12}{x+4}$

58. $\dfrac{x^2-2x+4x-8}{2x^2+3x+8x+12}$

59. $\dfrac{2x^2-8x+3x-12}{2x^2+8x+3x+12}$

60. $\dfrac{x^3-125}{x^2-25}$

61. $\dfrac{a^3-8}{a-2}$

62. $\dfrac{y^3+1}{y+1}$

63. $\dfrac{9s^2-16t^2}{3s-4t}$

64. $\dfrac{a+6b}{a^2-36b^2}$

65. $\dfrac{6x+9y}{2x^2+xy-3y^2}$

66. $\dfrac{3k^2+6kr-9r^2}{k^2+5kr+6r^2}$

Problem Solving

Simplify the following expressions, if possible. Treat the unknown symbol as if it were a variable.

67. $\dfrac{3\text{☺}}{15}$

68. $\dfrac{\text{☺}}{\text{☺}+8\text{☺}^2}$

69. $\dfrac{7\Delta}{14\Delta+63}$

70. $\dfrac{\Delta^2 + 2\Delta}{\Delta^2 + 4\Delta + 4}$

71. $\dfrac{3\Delta - 4}{4 - 3\Delta}$

72. $\dfrac{(\Delta - 3)^2}{\Delta^2 - 6\Delta + 9}$

Determine the denominator that will make each statement true. Explain how you obtained your answer.

73. $\dfrac{x^2 - x - 6}{\rule{1.5em}{0.8em}} = x - 3$

74. $\dfrac{2x^2 + 11x + 12}{\rule{1.5em}{0.8em}} = 2x + 3$

Determine the numerator that will make the statement true. Explain how you obtained your answer.

75. $\dfrac{\rule{1.5em}{0.8em}}{x + 4} = x + 5$

Concept/Writing Exercises

76. Explain how to simplify a rational expression.

77. Explain how to determine the value or values of the variable that makes a rational expression undefined.

Challenge Problems

In Exercises 78 and 79, **a)** *determine the value or values that x cannot represent.* **b)** *Simplify the expression.*

78. $\dfrac{x - 4}{2x^2 - 5x - 8x + 20}$

79. $\dfrac{x + 5}{2x^3 + 7x^2 - 15x}$

Simplify. Explain how you determined your answer.

80. $\dfrac{\dfrac{1}{6}x^5 - \dfrac{2}{3}x^4}{x^4}$

81. $\dfrac{\dfrac{1}{5}x^5 - \dfrac{2}{3}x^4}{\dfrac{1}{5}x^5 - \dfrac{2}{3}x^4}$

82. $\dfrac{\dfrac{1}{5}x^5 - \dfrac{2}{3}x^4}{\dfrac{2}{3}x^4 - \dfrac{1}{5}x^5}$

Group Activity

Discuss and answer Exercise 83 as a group.

83. a) As a group, determine the values of the variable where the expression $\dfrac{x^2 - 25}{x^3 + 2x^2 - 15x}$ is undefined.

b) As a group, simplify the rational expression.

c) Group member 1: Substitute 6 in the *original expression* and evaluate.

d) Group member 2: Substitute 6 in the *simplified expression* from part **b)** and compare your result to that of Group member 1.

e) Group member 3: Substitute −2 in the original expression and in the simplified expression in part **b)**. Compare your answers.

f) As a group, discuss the results of your work in parts **c)–e)**.

g) Now, as a group, substitute −5 in the original expression and in the simplified expression. Discuss your results.

h) Is $\dfrac{x^2 - 25}{x^3 + 2x^2 - 15x}$ always equal to its simplified form for *any* value of *x*? Explain your answer.

Cumulative Review Exercises

[2.6] **84.** Solve the formula $z = \dfrac{x - y}{4}$ for *y*.

[3.3] **85.** **Triangle** Find the measures of the three angles of a triangle if one angle is 30° greater than the smallest angle, and the third angle is 10° greater than 3 times the smallest angle.

[4.1] **86.** Simplify $\left(\dfrac{5x^2 y^2}{9x^4 y^3}\right)^2$.

[4.4] **87.** Subtract $3x^2 - 4x - 8 - (-5x^2 + 6x + 11)$.

[5.3] **88.** Factor $3a^2 - 6a - 72$ completely.

[5.7] **89.** Find the length of the hypotenuse of the right triangle.

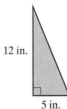

12 in.

5 in.

6.2 Multiplication and Division of Rational Expressions

1 Multiply rational expressions.

2 Divide rational expressions.

Understanding Algebra

Multiplying fractions in algebra is just like multiplying fractions in arithmetic.

Simplify by dividing out common factors first, then multiply numerators and multiply denominators.

Arithmetic:

$$\frac{2}{3} \times \frac{6}{7} = \frac{2 \times \overset{2}{\cancel{6}}}{\underset{1}{\cancel{3}} \times 7} = \frac{4}{7}$$

Algebra:

$$\frac{x}{3} \cdot \frac{6}{7} = \frac{x \cdot \overset{2}{\cancel{6}}}{\underset{1}{\cancel{3}} \cdot 7} = \frac{2x}{7}$$

1 Multiply Rational Expressions

In Section 1.3 we reviewed multiplication of numerical fractions. Recall that to multiply two fractions we multiply their numerators together and multiply their denominators together.

> **To Multiply Two Fractions**
>
> $$\frac{a}{b} \cdot \frac{c}{d} = \frac{a \cdot c}{b \cdot d}, \quad b \neq 0 \quad \text{and} \quad d \neq 0$$

EXAMPLE 1 Multiply $\left(\dfrac{3}{5}\right)\left(\dfrac{-2}{9}\right)$.

Solution   First divide out common factors; then multiply.

$$\frac{\overset{1}{\cancel{3}}}{5} \cdot \frac{-2}{\underset{3}{\cancel{9}}} = \frac{1 \cdot (-2)}{5 \cdot 3} = -\frac{2}{15}$$

Now Try Exercise 7

The same principles apply when multiplying rational expressions containing variables. Before multiplying, you should first divide out any factors common to both a numerator and a denominator.

> **To Multiply Rational Expressions**
>
> 1. Factor all numerators and denominators completely.
> 2. Divide out common factors.
> 3. Multiply numerators together and multiply denominators together.

EXAMPLE 2 Multiply $\dfrac{3x^2}{2y} \cdot \dfrac{4y^3}{3x}$.

Solution   This problem can be represented as

$$\frac{3x^2}{2y} \cdot \frac{4y^3}{3x} = \frac{3xx}{2y} \cdot \frac{4yyy}{3x}$$

$$= \frac{\overset{1}{\cancel{3}}\overset{1}{\cancel{x}}x}{2y} \cdot \frac{4yyy}{\underset{1}{\cancel{3}}\underset{1}{\cancel{x}}} \qquad \text{Divide out the 3's and } x\text{'s.}$$

$$= \frac{\overset{12}{\cancel{3}}\overset{1}{\cancel{x}}x}{\underset{1}{\cancel{2}}\underset{1}{\cancel{y}}} \cdot \frac{\overset{2}{\cancel{4}}\overset{1}{\cancel{y}}yy}{\underset{1}{\cancel{3}}\underset{1}{\cancel{x}}} \qquad \begin{array}{l}\text{Divide both the 4 and the 2}\\\text{by 2, and divide out the } y\text{'s.}\end{array}$$

Now we multiply the remaining numerators together and the remaining denominators together.

$$= \frac{2xy^2}{1} \quad \text{or} \quad 2xy^2$$

Now Try Exercise 19

Rather than illustrating this entire process when multiplying rational expressions, we will often proceed as follows:

$$\frac{3x^2}{2y} \cdot \frac{4y^3}{3x}$$

$$= \frac{\overset{1}{\cancel{3}}\overset{x}{\cancel{x^2}}}{\underset{1}{\cancel{2}}\underset{1}{\cancel{y}}} \cdot \frac{\overset{2}{\cancel{4}}\overset{y^2}{\cancel{y^3}}}{\underset{1}{\cancel{3}}\underset{1}{\cancel{x}}} = 2xy^2$$

EXAMPLE 3 Multiply $-\dfrac{5y^2}{2x^3} \cdot \dfrac{3x^2}{7y^2}$.

Solution

$$-\dfrac{5\overset{1}{\cancel{y^2}}}{\underset{x}{\cancel{2x^3}}} \cdot \dfrac{3\overset{1}{\cancel{x^2}}}{7\underset{1}{\cancel{y^2}}} = -\dfrac{15}{14x}$$

Now Try Exercise 53

Understanding Algebra

When we divide out common factors, it is not necessary to write the 1's as was done in Examples 2 and 3.

From this point on, instead of showing

$$\dfrac{5y^{2^{\,1}}}{2x^3{}_x} \cdot \dfrac{3x^{2^{\,1}}}{7y^2{}_1} = -\dfrac{15}{14x}$$

we will generally show

$$-\dfrac{5y^2}{2x^3{}_x} \cdot \dfrac{3x^2}{7y^2} = \dfrac{15}{14x}.$$

EXAMPLE 4 Multiply $(x-6) \cdot \dfrac{4}{x^3 - 6x^2}$.

Solution

$$(x-6) \cdot \dfrac{4}{x^3 - 6x^2} = \dfrac{\cancel{x-6}}{1} \cdot \dfrac{4}{x^2\cancel{(x-6)}} = \dfrac{4}{x^2}$$

Now Try Exercise 27

EXAMPLE 5 Multiply $\dfrac{(x+2)^2}{6x^2} \cdot \dfrac{3x}{x^2 - 4}$.

Solution

$$\dfrac{(x+2)^2}{6x^2} \cdot \dfrac{3x}{x^2 - 4} = \dfrac{(x+2)(x+2)}{6x^2} \cdot \dfrac{3x}{(x+2)(x-2)}$$

$$= \dfrac{\cancel{(x+2)}(x+2)}{\underset{2\,x}{\cancel{6x^2}}} \cdot \dfrac{\cancel{3x}}{\cancel{(x+2)}(x-2)} = \dfrac{x+2}{2x(x-2)}$$

Now Try Exercise 61

In the answer to Example 5 we could have multiplied the factors in the denominator to get $\dfrac{x+2}{2x^2 - 4x}$. This is also a correct answer. In this section we will leave rational answers with the numerator as a polynomial (in unfactored form) and the denominators in factored form, as was given in Example 5.

EXAMPLE 6 Multiply $\dfrac{b-4}{5b} \cdot \dfrac{10b}{4-b}$.

Solution

$$\dfrac{b-4}{\cancel{5b}} \cdot \dfrac{\overset{2}{\cancel{10b}}}{4-b} = \dfrac{2(b-4)}{4-b}.$$

Next, we rewrite $4-b$ as $-1(b-4)$. Thus,

$$\dfrac{2(b-4)}{4-b} = \dfrac{2\cancel{(b-4)}}{-1\cancel{(b-4)}} = -2$$

Now Try Exercise 23

Helpful Hint

When only the signs differ in a numerator and denominator in a multiplication problem, factor out -1 *from either the numerator or denominator*; then divide out the common factor.

$$\dfrac{a-b}{x} \cdot \dfrac{y}{b-a} = \dfrac{\cancel{a-b}}{x} \cdot \dfrac{y}{-1\cancel{(a-b)}} = -\dfrac{y}{x}$$

EXAMPLE 7 Multiply $\dfrac{3x + 2}{2x - 1} \cdot \dfrac{4 - 8x}{3x + 2}$.

Solution

$$\dfrac{3x + 2}{2x - 1} \cdot \dfrac{4 - 8x}{3x + 2} = \dfrac{3x + 2}{2x - 1} \cdot \dfrac{4(1 - 2x)}{3x + 2} \qquad \text{Factor.}$$

$$= \dfrac{\cancel{3x + 2}}{2x - 1} \cdot \dfrac{4(1 - 2x)}{\cancel{3x + 2}}. \qquad \text{Divide out common factors.}$$

Note that the factor $(1 - 2x)$ in the numerator of the second fraction differs only in sign from $2x - 1$, the denominator of the first fraction. We will therefore factor -1 from each term of the $(1 - 2x)$ in the numerator of the second fraction.

$$= \dfrac{\cancel{3x + 2}}{2x - 1} \cdot \dfrac{4(-1)(2x - 1)}{\cancel{3x + 2}} \qquad \text{Factored } -1 \text{ from the second numerator.}$$

$$= \dfrac{\cancel{3x + 2}}{\cancel{2x - 1}} \cdot \dfrac{-4\cancel{(2x - 1)}}{\cancel{3x + 2}} \qquad \text{Divide out common factors.}$$

$$= \dfrac{-4}{1} = -4$$

Now Try Exercise 25

EXAMPLE 8 Multiply $\dfrac{2x^2 + 5x - 12}{6x^2 - 11x + 3} \cdot \dfrac{3x^2 + 2x - 1}{x^2 + 5x + 4}$.

Solution   Factor all numerators and denominators, and then divide out common factors.

$$\dfrac{2x^2 + 5x - 12}{6x^2 - 11x + 3} \cdot \dfrac{3x^2 + 2x - 1}{x^2 + 5x + 4} = \dfrac{(2x - 3)(x + 4)}{(2x - 3)(3x - 1)} \cdot \dfrac{(3x - 1)(x + 1)}{(x + 1)(x + 4)}$$

$$= \dfrac{\cancel{(2x - 3)}\cancel{(x + 4)}}{\cancel{(2x - 3)}\cancel{(3x - 1)}} \cdot \dfrac{\cancel{(3x - 1)}\cancel{(x + 1)}}{\cancel{(x + 1)}\cancel{(x + 4)}} = 1$$

Now Try Exercise 67

EXAMPLE 9 Multiply $\dfrac{2x^3 - 18x^2 + 16x}{6y^2} \cdot \dfrac{-2y}{3x^2 - 3x}$.

Solution

$$\dfrac{2x^3 - 18x^2 + 16x}{6y^2} \cdot \dfrac{-2y}{3x^2 - 3x} = \dfrac{2x(x^2 - 9x + 8)}{6y^2} \cdot \dfrac{-2y}{3x(x - 1)}$$

$$= \dfrac{2x(x - 8)(x - 1)}{6y^2} \cdot \dfrac{-2y}{3x(x - 1)}$$

$$= \dfrac{\cancel{2}x(x - 8)\cancel{(x - 1)}}{\underset{3\ y}{\cancel{6}\cancel{y^2}}} \cdot \dfrac{-2\cancel{y}}{3\cancel{x}\cancel{(x - 1)}}$$

$$= \dfrac{-2(x - 8)}{9y} = \dfrac{-2x + 16}{9y}$$

Now Try Exercise 29

EXAMPLE 10 Multiply $\dfrac{x^2 - y^2}{x + y} \cdot \dfrac{x + 2y}{2x^2 - 3xy + y^2}$.

Solution $\dfrac{x^2 - y^2}{x + y} \cdot \dfrac{x + 2y}{2x^2 - 3xy + y^2} = \dfrac{(x + y)(x - y)}{x + y} \cdot \dfrac{x + 2y}{(2x - y)(x - y)}$

$$= \dfrac{\cancel{(x + y)}\cancel{(x - y)}}{\cancel{x + y}} \cdot \dfrac{x + 2y}{(2x - y)\cancel{(x - y)}}$$

$$= \dfrac{x + 2y}{2x - y}$$

Now Try Exercise 33

2 Divide Rational Expressions

Recall that to divide one fraction by a second fraction, we multiply the first fraction by the reciprocal of the second fraction (or by the reciprocal of the divisor).

To Divide Two Fractions

$$\frac{a}{b} \div \frac{c}{d} = \frac{a}{b} \cdot \frac{d}{c} = \frac{ad}{bc}, \quad b \neq 0, \quad d \neq 0, \quad \text{and} \quad c \neq 0$$

EXAMPLE 11 Divide.

a) $\dfrac{2}{7} \div \dfrac{9}{7}$ **b)** $\dfrac{3}{4} \div \dfrac{10}{6}$

Solution

a) $\dfrac{2}{7} \div \dfrac{9}{7} = \dfrac{2}{\overset{1}{\cancel{7}}} \cdot \dfrac{\overset{1}{\cancel{7}}}{9} = \dfrac{2 \cdot 1}{1 \cdot 9} = \dfrac{2}{9}$

b) $\dfrac{3}{4} \div \dfrac{10}{6} = \dfrac{3}{\underset{2}{\cancel{4}}} \cdot \dfrac{\overset{3}{\cancel{6}}}{10} = \dfrac{3 \cdot 3}{2 \cdot 10} = \dfrac{9}{20}$

Now Try Exercise 13

The same principles are used to **divide rational expressions**.

To Divide Rational Expressions

Multiply the first fraction by the reciprocal of the second fraction.

EXAMPLE 12 Divide $\dfrac{8x^3}{z} \div \dfrac{5z^3}{3}$.

Solution $\dfrac{8x^3}{z} \div \dfrac{5z^3}{3} = \dfrac{8x^3}{z} \cdot \dfrac{3}{5z^3}$ Multiply $\dfrac{8x^3}{z}$ by $\dfrac{3}{5z^3}$, the reciprocal of $\dfrac{5z^3}{3}$.

$$= \dfrac{24x^3}{5z^4}$$ There are no common factors to divide out.

Now Try Exercise 35

EXAMPLE 13 Divide $\dfrac{x^2 - 9}{x + 4} \div \dfrac{x - 3}{x + 4}$.

Solution

$$\dfrac{x^2 - 9}{x + 4} \div \dfrac{x - 3}{x + 4} = \dfrac{x^2 - 9}{x + 4} \cdot \dfrac{x + 4}{x - 3}$$ Multiply the first fraction by the reciprocal of the second fraction.

$$= \dfrac{(x + 3)\cancel{(x - 3)}}{\cancel{x + 4}} \cdot \dfrac{\cancel{x + 4}}{\cancel{x - 3}}$$ Factor, and divide out common factors.

$$= x + 3$$

Now Try Exercise 49

Understanding Algebra

Dividing fractions in algebra is just like dividing fractions in arithmetic. Multiply the first fraction by the reciprocal of the second fraction, dividing out any common factors.

Arithmetic:

$$\frac{2}{3} \div \frac{6}{7} = \frac{2}{3} \cdot \frac{7}{6} = \frac{2 \cdot 7}{3 \cdot \underset{3}{\cancel{6}}} = \frac{7}{9}$$

Algebra:

$$\frac{x}{3} \div \frac{5}{6} = \frac{x}{3} \cdot \frac{\overset{2}{\cancel{6}}}{5} = \frac{2x}{5}$$

EXAMPLE 14 Divide $\dfrac{-1}{2x - 3} \div \dfrac{8}{3 - 2x}$.

Solution

$$\dfrac{-1}{2x - 3} \div \dfrac{8}{3 - 2x} = \dfrac{-1}{2x - 3} \cdot \dfrac{3 - 2x}{8}$$

Multiply the first fraction by the reciprocal of the second fraction.

$$= \dfrac{-1}{\cancel{2x - 3}} \cdot \dfrac{-1\cancel{(2x - 3)}}{8}$$

Factor out −1, then divide out common factors.

$$= \dfrac{(-1)(-1)}{(1)(8)} = \dfrac{1}{8}$$

Now Try Exercise 41

EXAMPLE 15 Divide $\dfrac{w^2 - 11w + 30}{w^2} \div (w - 5)^2$.

Solution $(w - 5)^2$ means $\dfrac{(w - 5)^2}{1}$.

$$\dfrac{w^2 - 11w + 30}{w^2} \div (w - 5)^2 = \dfrac{w^2 - 11w + 30}{w^2} \cdot \dfrac{1}{(w - 5)^2}$$

$$= \dfrac{(w - 6)\cancel{(w - 5)}}{w^2} \cdot \dfrac{1}{\cancel{(w - 5)}(w - 5)}$$

$$= \dfrac{w - 6}{w^2(w - 5)}$$

Now Try Exercise 43

EXAMPLE 16 Divide $\dfrac{12x^2 - 22x + 8}{7x} \div \dfrac{3x^2 + 2x - 8}{2x^2 + 4x}$.

Solution

$$\dfrac{12x^2 - 22x + 8}{7x} \div \dfrac{3x^2 + 2x - 8}{2x^2 + 4x} = \dfrac{12x^2 - 22x + 8}{7x} \cdot \dfrac{2x^2 + 4x}{3x^2 + 2x - 8}$$

$$= \dfrac{2(6x^2 - 11x + 4)}{7x} \cdot \dfrac{2x(x + 2)}{(3x - 4)(x + 2)}$$

$$= \dfrac{2\cancel{(3x - 4)}(2x - 1)}{7\cancel{x}} \cdot \dfrac{2\cancel{x}\cancel{(x + 2)}}{\cancel{(3x - 4)}\cancel{(x + 2)}}$$

$$= \dfrac{4(2x - 1)}{7} = \dfrac{8x - 4}{7}$$

Now Try Exercise 45

EXERCISE SET 6.2

Math XL
MathXL®

MyMathLab
MyMathLab

Warm-Up Exercises

Fill in the blanks with the appropriate word, phrase, or symbol(s) from the following list.

$\dfrac{10}{x - 4}$	factor	reciprocal	additive inverse
$\dfrac{10}{x^3 - 4}$	divide out	$x + 4$	$x - 3$

1. When multiplying two rational expressions, the first step should be to _____ numerators and denominators.

2. When dividing two fractions, we multiply the first fraction by the _____ of the second fraction.

3. When multiplying two rational expressions, prior to multiplying the numerators and the denominators, you should _____ common factors.

4. When $\dfrac{10}{x^3 - 4x^2}$ is multiplied by x^2, the result is _____ .

5. When $\dfrac{x^2 - 16}{x - 2}$ is divided by $\dfrac{x - 4}{x - 2}$, the result is _____ .

6. When $\dfrac{x^2 + x - 12}{x + 5}$ is divided by $\dfrac{x^2 - x - 20}{x^2 - 25}$, the result is _____ .

Practice the Skills

Multiply or divide as indicated.

7. $\left(\dfrac{1}{5}\right)\left(\dfrac{15}{19}\right)$

8. $\left(\dfrac{3}{8}\right)\left(-\dfrac{9}{33}\right)$

9. $\left(\dfrac{6}{8}\right)\left(-\dfrac{10}{14}\right)$

10. $\left(\dfrac{7}{9}\right)\left(\dfrac{81}{98}\right)$

11. $\left(-\dfrac{4}{11}\right)\left(-\dfrac{55}{64}\right)$

12. $\left(-\dfrac{12}{13}\right)\left(-\dfrac{65}{42}\right)$

13. $\dfrac{3}{7} \div \dfrac{5}{7}$

14. $\dfrac{3}{8} \div \dfrac{15}{44}$

15. $-\dfrac{2}{9} \div \dfrac{32}{39}$

16. $\left(-\dfrac{3}{4}\right) \div \left(-\dfrac{15}{16}\right)$

Multiply.

17. $\dfrac{6x}{4y} \cdot \dfrac{y^2}{12}$

18. $\dfrac{15x^3 y^2}{2z} \cdot \dfrac{2z}{5xy^3}$

19. $\dfrac{14x^2}{y^4} \cdot \dfrac{5x^2}{y^2}$

20. $\dfrac{7n^3}{16m} \cdot \dfrac{-4}{21m^2 n^3}$

21. $\dfrac{6x^5 y^3}{5z^3} \cdot \dfrac{6x^4}{5yz^4}$

22. $\dfrac{x^2 - 4}{x^2 - 16} \cdot \dfrac{x - 4}{x - 2}$

23. $\dfrac{3x - 2}{3x + 2} \cdot \dfrac{x - 1}{1 - x}$

24. $\dfrac{m - 5}{2m + 5} \cdot \dfrac{8m}{-m + 5}$

25. $\dfrac{x^2 + 7x + 6}{x + 6} \cdot \dfrac{1}{x + 1}$

26. $\dfrac{b^2 + 7b + 12}{6b} \cdot \dfrac{b^2 - 4b}{b^2 - b - 12}$

27. $\dfrac{a}{a^2 - b^2} \cdot \dfrac{a + b}{a^2 + ab}$

28. $\dfrac{t^2 - 36}{t^2 + t - 30} \cdot \dfrac{t - 5}{4t}$

29. $\dfrac{6x^2 - 14x - 12}{6x + 4} \cdot \dfrac{2x + 4}{2x^2 - 2x - 12}$

30. $\dfrac{2x^2 - 9x + 9}{8x - 12} \cdot \dfrac{4x}{x^2 - 3x}$

31. $\dfrac{3x^2 - 13x - 10}{x^2 - 2x - 15} \cdot \dfrac{x^2 + x - 2}{3x^2 - x - 2}$

32. $\dfrac{2t^2 - t - 6}{2t^2 - 3t - 2} \cdot \dfrac{2t^2 - 5t - 3}{2t^2 + 11t + 12}$

33. $\dfrac{x + 9}{x - 3} \cdot \dfrac{x^3 - 27}{x^2 + 3x + 9}$

34. $\dfrac{x^3 + 8}{x^2 - x - 6} \cdot \dfrac{x + 5}{x^2 - 2x + 4}$

Divide.

35. $\dfrac{12x^3}{y^2} \div \dfrac{3x}{y^3}$

36. $\dfrac{9x^3}{5} \div \dfrac{1}{20x^2}$

37. $\dfrac{15xy^2}{4z} \div \dfrac{5x^2 y^2}{12z^2}$

38. $\dfrac{36y}{5z^2} \div \dfrac{3xy}{2z}$

39. $\dfrac{11xy}{7ab^2} \div \dfrac{6xy}{7}$

40. $3xz \div \dfrac{6xy}{z}$

41. $\dfrac{12r + 6}{r} \div \dfrac{2r + 1}{r^3}$

42. $\dfrac{x - 3}{10y^2} \div \dfrac{x^2 - 9}{5xy}$

43. $\dfrac{x^2 + 11x + 18}{x} \div \dfrac{x + 2}{x}$

44. $\dfrac{1}{x^2 + 7x - 18} \div \dfrac{1}{x^2 - 17x + 30}$

45. $\dfrac{x^2 - 12x + 32}{x^2 - 6x - 16} \div \dfrac{x^2 - x - 12}{x^2 - 5x - 24}$

46. $\dfrac{a - b}{9a + 9b} \div \dfrac{a^2 - b^2}{a^2 + 2a + 7}$

47. $\dfrac{2x^2 + 9x + 4}{x^2 + 7x + 12} \div \dfrac{2x^2 - x - 1}{(x + 3)^2}$

48. $\dfrac{a^2 - b^2}{9} \div \dfrac{3a - 3b}{27x^2}$

49. $\dfrac{x^2 - y^2}{x^2 - 2xy + y^2} \div \dfrac{x + y}{y - x}$

50. $\dfrac{9x^2 - 9y^2}{18x^2 y^2} \div \dfrac{3x + 3y}{12x^2 y^5}$

51. $\dfrac{5x^2 - 4x - 1}{5x^2 + 6x + 1} \div \dfrac{x^2 - 5x + 4}{x^2 + 2x + 1}$

52. $\dfrac{7n^2 - 15n + 2}{n^2 + n - 6} \div \dfrac{n^2 - 3n - 10}{n^2 - 2n - 15}$

Perform each indicated operation.

53. $\dfrac{11z}{6y^2} \cdot \dfrac{24x^2 y^4}{11z}$

54. $\dfrac{5z^3}{7} \cdot \dfrac{9x^2}{15z}$

55. $\dfrac{63a^2 b^3}{20c^3} \cdot \dfrac{4c^4}{9a^3 b^5}$

56. $\dfrac{-2xw}{y^5} \div \dfrac{8x^2}{y^6}$

57. $\dfrac{-xy}{a} \div \dfrac{-2ax}{6y}$

58. $\dfrac{27x}{8y^2} \div 3x^2 y^2$

59. $\dfrac{64m^6}{21x^5 y^7} \cdot \dfrac{14x^{12} y^5}{16m^5}$

60. $\dfrac{-18x^2 y}{11z^2} \cdot \dfrac{22z^3}{x^2 y^5}$

61. $\dfrac{(x + 3)^2}{5x^2} \cdot \dfrac{10x}{x^2 - 9}$

62. $\dfrac{1}{4x - 3} \cdot (24x - 18)$

63. $\dfrac{1}{5x^2 y^2} \div \dfrac{1}{35x^3 y}$

64. $\dfrac{x^2 y^5}{3z} \div \dfrac{7z}{2x}$

65. $\dfrac{(4m)^2}{8n^3} \div \dfrac{m^6 n^8}{2}$

66. $\dfrac{11r^5 s^2}{(r^2 s^3)^3} \cdot \dfrac{6r^4}{4s}$

67. $\dfrac{r^2 + 5r + 6}{r^2 + 9r + 18} \cdot \dfrac{r^2 + 4r - 12}{r^2 - 5r + 6}$

68. $\dfrac{z^2 - z - 20}{z^2 - 3z - 10} \cdot \dfrac{(z + 2)^2}{(z + 4)^2}$

69. $\dfrac{x^2 - 12x + 36}{x^2 - 8x + 12} \div \dfrac{x^2 - 7x + 12}{x^2 - 6x + 8}$

70. $\dfrac{p^2 - 5p + 6}{p^2 - 10p + 16} \div \dfrac{p^2 + 2p}{p^2 - 6p - 16}$

71. $\dfrac{2w^2 + 3w - 35}{w^2 - 7w - 8} \cdot \dfrac{w^2 - 5w - 24}{w^2 + 8w + 15}$

72. $\dfrac{3z^2 - 4z - 4}{z^2 - 4} \cdot \dfrac{2z^2 + 5z + 2}{2z^2 - 3z - 2}$

73. $\dfrac{q^2 - 11q + 30}{2q^2 - 7q - 15} \div \dfrac{q^2 - 2q - 24}{q^2 - q - 20}$

74. $\dfrac{2x^2 - 19x + 24}{x^2 - 12x + 32} \div \dfrac{2x^2 + x - 6}{x^2 + 7x + 10}$

75. $\dfrac{4n^2 - 9}{9n^2 - 1} \cdot \dfrac{3n^2 - 2n - 1}{2n^2 - 5n + 3}$

76. $\dfrac{2z^2 + 9z + 9}{4z^2 - 9} \div \dfrac{(z + 3)^2}{(2z - 3)^2}$

Problem Solving

Perform each indicated operation. Treat Δ and ☺ as if they were variables.

77. $\dfrac{6\Delta^2}{13} \cdot \dfrac{13}{36\Delta^5}$

78. $\dfrac{\Delta - 7}{2\Delta + 5} \cdot \dfrac{3\Delta}{-\Delta + 7}$

79. $\dfrac{\Delta - ☺}{9\Delta - 9☺} \div \dfrac{\Delta^2 - ☺^2}{\Delta^2 + 2\Delta☺ + ☺^2}$

80. $\dfrac{\Delta^2 - ☺^2}{\Delta^2 - 2\Delta☺ + ☺^2} \div \dfrac{\Delta + ☺}{☺ - \Delta}$

For each equation, fill in the shaded area with a binomial or trinomial to make the statement true. Explain how you determined your answer.

81. $\dfrac{\rule{0.6cm}{0.4cm}}{x + 2} = x + 3$

82. $\dfrac{x + 5}{\rule{0.6cm}{0.4cm}} = \dfrac{1}{x - 5}$

83. $\dfrac{\rule{0.6cm}{0.4cm}}{x - 6} = x + 2$

84. $\dfrac{\rule{0.6cm}{0.4cm}}{x^2 - 7x + 10} = \dfrac{1}{x - 2}$

85. $\dfrac{\rule{0.6cm}{0.4cm}}{x^2 - 4} \cdot \dfrac{x + 2}{x - 1} = 1$

86. $\dfrac{x + 4}{x^2 + 9x + 20} \cdot \dfrac{\rule{0.6cm}{0.4cm}}{x - 2} = 1$

Concept/Writing Exercises

87. Explain how to multiply two rational expressions.

88. Explain how to divide two rational expressions.

Challenge Problems

Simplify.

89. $\left(\dfrac{x^2 - x - 6}{2x^2 - 9x + 9} \div \dfrac{x^2 + x - 12}{x^2 + 3x - 4} \right) \cdot \dfrac{2x^2 - 5x + 3}{x^2 + x - 2}$

90. $\left(\dfrac{x^2 + 4x + 3}{x^2 - 6x - 16} \div \dfrac{x^2 + 5x + 6}{x^2 - 9x + 8} \right) \cdot \left(\dfrac{x^2 - 1}{x^2 + 4x + 4} \right)$

For Exercises 91 and 92, determine the polynomials that when placed in the shaded areas make the statement true. Explain how you determined your answer.

91. $\dfrac{\rule{0.6cm}{0.4cm}}{\rule{0.6cm}{0.4cm}} \cdot \dfrac{x^2 + 3x - 4}{x^2 - 4x + 3} = \dfrac{x - 2}{x - 5}$

92. $\dfrac{\rule{0.6cm}{0.4cm}}{x^2 + x - 2} \cdot \dfrac{x^2 + 6x + 8}{\rule{0.6cm}{0.4cm}} = \dfrac{x + 3}{x + 5}$

Group Activity

93. Consider the three problems that follow:

1. $\left(\dfrac{x + 2}{x - 3} \right) \div \left(\dfrac{x^2 - 5x + 6}{x - 2} \cdot \dfrac{x + 2}{x - 3} \right)$

2. $\left(\dfrac{x + 2}{x - 3} \div \dfrac{x^2 - 5x + 6}{x - 2} \right) \cdot \left(\dfrac{x + 2}{x - 3} \right)$

3. $\left(\dfrac{x + 2}{x - 3} \right) \div \left(\dfrac{x^2 - 5x + 6}{x - 2} \cdot \left(\dfrac{x + 2}{x - 3} \right) \right)$

a) Without working the problem, decide as a group which of the problems will have the same answer. Explain.

b) Individually, simplify each of the three problems.

c) Compare your answers to part **b)** with those of the other members of your group. If you did not get the same answers, determine why.

Cumulative Review Exercises

[3.4]   **94. White Water Rafting** Jon and Louis leave Idaho Falls paddling downstream at an average speed of 15 miles per hour toward Pocatello. On the return trip, paddling against the current, they average 5 miles per hour. If the trip back to Idaho Falls took 2 hours longer than the trip out, find the time it took them to reach Pocatello.

© Monkey Business Images\Shutterstock

[4.5]   **95.** Multiply $(4x^3y^2z^4)(3xy^3z^7)$.

[4.6]   **96.** Divide $\dfrac{4x^3 - 5x}{2x - 1}$.

[5.4]   **97.** Factor $6x^2 - 18x - 60$.

[5.6]   **98.** Solve $3x^2 - 9x - 30 = 0$.

6.3 Addition and Subtraction of Rational Expressions with a Common Denominator and Finding the Least Common Denominator

1 Add and subtract rational expressions with a common denominator.

2 Find the least common denominator.

1 Add and Subtract Rational Expressions with a Common Denominator

Recall that when adding or subtracting two fractions with a common denominator we add or subtract the numerators while keeping the common denominator.

> **To Add or Subtract Two Fractions with a Common Denominator**
>
> Adding: $\dfrac{a}{c} + \dfrac{b}{c} = \dfrac{a + b}{c}, c \neq 0$ Subtracting: $\dfrac{a}{c} - \dfrac{b}{c} = \dfrac{a - b}{c}, c \neq 0$

EXAMPLE 1   **a)** Add $\dfrac{7}{16} + \dfrac{8}{16}$.   **b)** Subtract $\dfrac{4}{9} - \dfrac{1}{9}$.

Solution

a) $\dfrac{7}{16} + \dfrac{8}{16} = \dfrac{7 + 8}{16} = \dfrac{15}{16}$

b) $\dfrac{4}{9} - \dfrac{1}{9} = \dfrac{4 - 1}{9} = \dfrac{3}{9} = \dfrac{1}{3}$

Now Try Exercise 13

When adding or subtracting rational expressions, we use the same principles that we use when adding or subtracting fractions.

> **To Add or Subtract Rational Expressions with a Common Denominator**
>
> 1. Add or subtract the numerators.
> 2. Place the sum or difference of the numerators found in step 1 over the common denominator.
> 3. Simplify the fraction if possible.

EXAMPLE 2 Add $\dfrac{3}{x-4} + \dfrac{x+8}{x-4}$.

Solution

$$\dfrac{3}{x-4} + \dfrac{x+8}{x-4} = \dfrac{3+(x+8)}{x-4} = \dfrac{x+11}{x-4}$$

Now Try Exercise 19

EXAMPLE 3 Add $\dfrac{2x^2+7}{x+3} + \dfrac{6x-7}{x+3}$.

Solution

$$\dfrac{2x^2+7}{x+3} + \dfrac{6x-7}{x+3} = \dfrac{(2x^2+7)+(6x-7)}{x+3}$$

$$= \dfrac{2x^2+7+6x-7}{x+3}$$

$$= \dfrac{2x^2+6x}{x+3}$$

Now factor $2x$ from each term in the numerator and simplify.

$$= \dfrac{2x\cancel{(x+3)}}{\cancel{x+3}} = 2x$$

Now Try Exercise 21

EXAMPLE 4 Add $\dfrac{x^2+2x-2}{(x+5)(x-2)} + \dfrac{5x+12}{(x+5)(x-2)}$.

Solution

$$\dfrac{x^2+2x-2}{(x+5)(x-2)} + \dfrac{5x+12}{(x+5)(x-2)} = \dfrac{(x^2+2x-2)+(5x+12)}{(x+5)(x-2)} \quad \text{Write as a single fraction.}$$

$$= \dfrac{x^2+2x-2+5x+12}{(x+5)(x-2)} \quad \begin{array}{l}\text{Parentheses}\\ \text{were removed in}\\ \text{the numerator.}\end{array}$$

$$= \dfrac{x^2+7x+10}{(x+5)(x-2)} \quad \begin{array}{l}\text{Like terms}\\ \text{were combined.}\end{array}$$

$$= \dfrac{\cancel{(x+5)}(x+2)}{\cancel{(x+5)}(x-2)} \quad \begin{array}{l}\text{Factor, divide}\\ \text{out common}\\ \text{factor.}\end{array}$$

$$= \dfrac{x+2}{x-2}$$

Now Try Exercise 27

When subtracting rational expressions, be sure to subtract the *entire numerator of the fraction being subtracted*.

Avoiding Common Errors

Consider the subtraction

$$\dfrac{4x}{x-2} - \dfrac{2x+1}{x-2}$$

Many people begin problems of this type incorrectly. Here are the correct and incorrect ways of working this problem.

CORRECT

$$\dfrac{4x}{x-2} - \dfrac{2x+1}{x-2} = \dfrac{4x-(2x+1)}{x-2}$$

$$= \dfrac{4x-2x-1}{x-2}$$

$$= \dfrac{2x-1}{x-2}$$

INCORRECT

$$\cancel{\dfrac{4x}{x-2} - \dfrac{2x+1}{x-2} = \dfrac{4x-2x+1}{x-2}}$$

Note that the entire numerator of the second fraction, not just the first term, must be subtracted. Also note that the sign of *each* term of the numerator being subtracted will change when the parentheses are removed.

EXAMPLE 5 Subtract $\dfrac{x^2 - 6x + 3}{x^2 + 7x + 12} - \dfrac{x^2 - 8x - 5}{x^2 + 7x + 12}$.

Solution

$$\dfrac{x^2 - 6x + 3}{x^2 + 7x + 12} - \dfrac{x^2 - 8x - 5}{x^2 + 7x + 12} = \dfrac{(x^2 - 6x + 3) - (x^2 - 8x - 5)}{x^2 + 7x + 12} \quad \text{Write as a single fraction.}$$

$$= \dfrac{x^2 - 6x + 3 - x^2 + 8x + 5}{x^2 + 7x + 12} \quad \text{Removed parentheses.}$$

$$= \dfrac{2x + 8}{x^2 + 7x + 12} \quad \text{Combined like terms.}$$

$$= \dfrac{2\cancel{(x + 4)}}{(x + 3)\cancel{(x + 4)}} \quad \text{Factor, divide out common factor.}$$

$$= \dfrac{2}{x + 3}$$

Now Try Exercise 43

EXAMPLE 6 Subtract $\dfrac{6r}{r - 5} - \dfrac{4r^2 - 17r + 15}{r - 5}$.

Solution

$$\dfrac{6r}{r - 5} - \dfrac{4r^2 - 17r + 15}{r - 5} = \dfrac{6r - (4r^2 - 17r + 15)}{r - 5} \quad \text{Write as a single fraction.}$$

$$= \dfrac{6r - 4r^2 + 17r - 15}{r - 5} \quad \text{Parentheses were removed.}$$

$$= \dfrac{-4r^2 + 23r - 15}{r - 5} \quad \text{Like terms were combined.}$$

$$= \dfrac{-(4r^2 - 23r + 15)}{r - 5} \quad \text{Factored out } -1$$

$$= \dfrac{-(4r - 3)\cancel{(r - 5)}}{\cancel{r - 5}} \quad \text{Factor, divide out common factor.}$$

$$= -(4r - 3) \quad \text{or} \quad -4r + 3$$

Now Try Exercise 31

2 Find the Least Common Denominator

To add two fractions with unlike denominators, we first obtain the least common denominator. Now we explain how to find the *least common denominator* for rational expressions.

EXAMPLE 7 Add $\dfrac{4}{7} + \dfrac{2}{3}$.

Solution   The least common denominator (LCD) of the fractions $\dfrac{4}{7}$ and $\dfrac{2}{3}$ is 21 because it is the smallest number that is divisible by both denominators, 7 and 3. Rewrite each fraction so that its denominator is 21.

$$\dfrac{4}{7} + \dfrac{2}{3} = \dfrac{3}{3} \cdot \dfrac{4}{7} + \dfrac{2}{3} \cdot \dfrac{7}{7}$$

$$= \dfrac{12}{21} + \dfrac{14}{21}$$

$$= \dfrac{26}{21}$$

Now Try Exercise 95

> **To Find the Least Common Denominator of Rational Expressions**
>
> 1. Factor each denominator completely. Any factors that occur more than once should be expressed as powers. For example, $(x - 3)(x - 3)$ should be expressed as $(x - 3)^2$.
> 2. List all different factors (other than 1) that appear in any of the denominators. When the same factor appears in more than one denominator, write that factor with the highest power that appears on it.
> 3. The least common denominator is the product of all the factors listed in step 2.

EXAMPLE 8 Find the least common denominator.

$$\frac{1}{7} + \frac{1}{y}$$

Solution   The only factor (other than 1) of the first denominator is 7. The only factor (other than 1) of the second denominator is y. The LCD is therefore $7 \cdot y = 7y$.

Now Try Exercise 53

EXAMPLE 9 Find the LCD.

$$\frac{8}{x^2} - \frac{3}{5x}$$

Solution   The factors that appear in the denominators are 5 and x. List each factor with its highest power. The LCD is the product of these factors.

Highest power of 5 ⌐   ⌐ Highest power of x

$$\text{LCD} = 5^1 \cdot x^2 = 5x^2$$

Now Try Exercise 59

EXAMPLE 10 Find the LCD.

$$\frac{11}{18x^3y} + \frac{5}{27x^2y^3}$$

Solution   We first write the denominators in factored form. To determine the LCD, we multiply the highest power of each factor.

$18x^3y = 2 \cdot 3^2 \cdot x^3 \cdot y$ The prime factorization of 18 is $2 \cdot 3 \cdot 3$ or $2 \cdot 3^2$

$27x^2y^3 = \quad 3^3 \cdot x^2 \cdot y^3$ The prime factorization of 27 is $3 \cdot 3 \cdot 3$ or 3^3

Highest power of 3 ⌐   ⌐ Highest power of x

$$\text{LCD} = 2 \cdot 3^3 \cdot x^3 \cdot y^3$$

Highest power of 2 ⌐   Highest power of y ⌐

Thus, the LCD is $2 \cdot 3^3 \cdot x^3 \cdot y^3 = 54x^3y^3$

Now Try Exercise 61

> **Understanding Algebra**
>
> Numerical coefficients like those in Example 10 need to be factored also. To help you write numbers in their prime factored form, you may want to review Section 5.1 or consult Appendix B.

EXAMPLE 11 Find the LCD.

$$\frac{9}{x} - \frac{2z}{x + 3}$$

Solution   The factors in the denominators are x and $x + 3$. *Note that the x in the second denominator, $x + 3$, is a term, not a factor.*

$$\text{LCD} = x(x + 3)$$

Now Try Exercise 65

EXAMPLE 12 Find the LCD.

$$\frac{7}{3x^2 - 6x} + \frac{8x^2}{x^2 - 4x + 4}$$

Solution Factor both denominators.

$$\frac{7}{3x^2 - 6x} + \frac{8x^2}{x^2 - 4x + 4} = \frac{7}{3x(x - 2)} + \frac{8x^2}{(x - 2)(x - 2)}$$

$$= \frac{7}{3x(x - 2)} + \frac{8x^2}{(x - 2)^2}$$

The factors in the denominators are $3, x,$ and $x - 2$. List the highest power of each of these factors.

$$\text{LCD} = 3 \cdot x \cdot (x - 2)^2 = 3x(x - 2)^2.$$

Now Try Exercise 85

EXAMPLE 13 Find the LCD.

$$\frac{11x}{x^2 - x - 12} - \frac{6x^2}{x^2 - 7x + 12}$$

Solution Factor both denominators.

$$\frac{11x}{x^2 - x - 12} - \frac{6x^2}{x^2 - 7x + 12} = \frac{11x}{(x + 3)(x - 4)} - \frac{6x^2}{(x - 3)(x - 4)}$$

The factors in the denominators are $x + 3, x - 4,$ and $x - 3$.

$$\text{LCD} = (x + 3)(x - 4)(x - 3)$$

Although $x - 4$ is a common factor of each denominator, the highest power of that factor that appears in each denominator is 1.

Now Try Exercise 81

EXAMPLE 14 Find the LCD.

$$\frac{6w}{w^2 - 14w + 45} + w + 8$$

Solution Factor the denominator of the first term.

$$\frac{6w}{w^2 - 14w + 45} + w + 8 = \frac{6w}{(w - 5)(w - 9)} + w + 8$$

Since the denominator of $w + 8$ is 1, the expression can be rewritten as

$$\frac{6w}{(w - 5)(w - 9)} + \frac{w + 8}{1}$$

The LCD is therefore $1(w - 5)(w - 9)$ or simply $(w - 5)(w - 9)$.

Now Try Exercise 89

EXERCISE SET 6.3

MathXL
MathXL®

MyMathLab
MyMathLab

Warm-Up Exercises

Fill in the blanks with the appropriate word, phrase, or symbol(s) from the following list.

$\dfrac{3x - 2}{y}$	True	False	$\dfrac{3x + 2}{y}$	$12x^3$	$x + 4$	x^3

1. The result of the subtraction problem $\dfrac{4x}{y} - \dfrac{(x - 2)}{y}$ is
_____ .

2. (True or False) When adding two fractions with the same denominator, we add the numerators and we add the denominators. _____

3. (True or False) When adding two rational expressions, after the addition takes place, there may remain the possibility of further simplification. _____

4. The LCD of $4x^2, 6x^3,$ and $12x$ is _____ .

Determine the LCD to be used to perform each indicated operation. Explain how you determined the LCD. Do not perform the operations.

5. $\dfrac{9}{x+6} - \dfrac{2}{x}$

6. $\dfrac{10}{x-2} + \dfrac{3}{7}$

7. $\dfrac{2}{x+3} + \dfrac{1}{x} + \dfrac{1}{4}$

8. $\dfrac{6}{x-3} + \dfrac{1}{x} - \dfrac{1}{8}$

In Exercises 9–12, **a)** *explain why the expression on the left side of the not-equal-to sign is not equal to the expression on the right side.* **b)** *Show what the expression on the right side should be for it to be equal to the one on the left.*

9. $\dfrac{4x-3}{5x+4} - \dfrac{2x-9}{5x+4} \neq \dfrac{4x-3-2x-9}{5x+4}$

10. $\dfrac{5x}{2x-3} - \dfrac{-3x-7}{2x-3} \neq \dfrac{5x+3x-7}{2x-3}$

11. $\dfrac{8x-2}{x^2-4x+3} - \dfrac{3x^2-4x+5}{x^2-4x+3} \neq \dfrac{8x-2-3x^2-4x+5}{x^2-4x+3}$

12. $\dfrac{2x+5}{x^2-6x} - \dfrac{-x^2+3x+6}{x^2-6x} \neq \dfrac{2x+5+x^2+3x+6}{x^2-6x}$

Practice the Skills

Add or subtract.

13. $\dfrac{1}{7} + \dfrac{4}{7}$

14. $\dfrac{8}{5} - \dfrac{6}{5}$

15. $\dfrac{5r+2}{4} - \dfrac{3}{4}$

16. $\dfrac{3x+6}{2} - \dfrac{x}{2}$

17. $\dfrac{2}{x} + \dfrac{x+4}{x}$

18. $\dfrac{3x+1}{x+1} + \dfrac{6x+8}{x+1}$

19. $\dfrac{6}{n+1} + \dfrac{n+2}{n+1}$

20. $\dfrac{7}{t-2} - \dfrac{t+4}{t-2}$

21. $\dfrac{x}{x-3} + \dfrac{4x+9}{x-3}$

22. $\dfrac{4x-3}{x-7} - \dfrac{2x+8}{x-7}$

23. $\dfrac{4t+7}{5t^2} - \dfrac{3t+4}{5t^2}$

24. $\dfrac{3w+6}{w^2+2w+1} + \dfrac{-2w-5}{w^2+2w+1}$

25. $\dfrac{5x+4}{x^2-x-12} + \dfrac{-4x-1}{x^2-x-12}$

26. $\dfrac{-x-6}{x^2-16} + \dfrac{2(x+5)}{x^2-16}$

27. $\dfrac{2m+5}{(m+4)(m-3)} - \dfrac{m+1}{(m+4)(m-3)}$

28. $\dfrac{x^2+3x}{(x+6)(x-3)} - \dfrac{x+15}{(x+6)(x-3)}$

29. $\dfrac{2p-6}{p-5} - \dfrac{p+6}{p-5}$

30. $\dfrac{x^2-6}{3x} - \dfrac{x^2+4x-11}{3x}$

31. $\dfrac{x^2+4x+1}{x+2} - \dfrac{5x+7}{x+2}$

32. $\dfrac{-4x+2}{3x+6} + \dfrac{4(x-1)}{3x+6}$

33. $\dfrac{3x+13}{2x+10} - \dfrac{2(x+4)}{2x+10}$

34. $\dfrac{x^2}{x+4} - \dfrac{16}{x+4}$

35. $\dfrac{b^2-2b-2}{b^2-b-6} + \dfrac{b-4}{b^2-b-6}$

36. $\dfrac{4x+17}{3-x} - \dfrac{3x+20}{3-x}$

37. $\dfrac{t-3}{t+3} - \dfrac{-3t-15}{t+3}$

38. $\dfrac{x+8}{3x+2} - \dfrac{x+8}{3x+2}$

39. $\dfrac{3x^2+15x}{x^3+2x^2-8x} + \dfrac{2x^2+5x}{x^3+2x^2-8x}$

40. $\dfrac{x^2-12}{x+5} - \dfrac{13}{x+5}$

41. $\dfrac{3x^2-9x}{4x^2-8x} + \dfrac{3x}{4x^2-8x}$

42. $\dfrac{x^3-10x^2+35x}{x(x-6)} - \dfrac{x^2+5x}{x(x-6)}$

43. $\dfrac{3x^2-4x+6}{3x^2+7x+2} - \dfrac{10x+11}{3x^2+7x+2}$

44. $\dfrac{x^2-2}{x^2+6x-7} - \dfrac{-4x+19}{x^2+6x-7}$

45. $\dfrac{x^2+3x-6}{x^2-5x+4} - \dfrac{-2x^2+4x-4}{x^2-5x+4}$

46. $\dfrac{4x^2+15}{9x^2-64} - \dfrac{x^2-x+39}{9x^2-64}$

47. $\dfrac{5x^2+30x+8}{x^2-64} + \dfrac{x^2+19x}{x^2-64}$

48. $\dfrac{20x^2+8x+1}{6x^2+x-2} - \dfrac{8x^2-9x-5}{6x^2+x-2}$

Find the least common denominator for each expression.

49. $\dfrac{x}{5} + \dfrac{x+4}{5}$

50. $\dfrac{2+r}{17} - \dfrac{12}{17}$

51. $\dfrac{3}{n} + \dfrac{1}{9n}$

52. $\dfrac{6}{x+1} - \dfrac{4}{7}$

53. $\dfrac{3}{5x} + \dfrac{7}{3}$

54. $\dfrac{1}{8} + \dfrac{1}{z}$

55. $\dfrac{6}{p} + \dfrac{9}{p^3}$

56. $\dfrac{2x}{x+3} + \dfrac{6}{x-9}$

57. $\dfrac{m+3}{3m-4} + m$

58. $\dfrac{x+4}{2x} + \dfrac{8}{7x}$

59. $\dfrac{t}{6t} + \dfrac{4}{t^2}$

60. $\dfrac{x}{5x^2} + \dfrac{9}{7x^3}$

61. $\dfrac{x+1}{12x^2y} - \dfrac{7}{9x^3}$

62. $\dfrac{-3}{8x^2y^2} + \dfrac{5}{12x^4y^5}$

63. $\dfrac{4}{2r^4s^5} - \dfrac{5}{9r^3s^7}$

64. $\dfrac{5}{4w^5z^4} + \dfrac{4}{9wz^2}$

65. $\dfrac{3}{m} - \dfrac{17m}{m+2}$

66. $\dfrac{x-3}{17} - \dfrac{6}{x-5}$

67. $\dfrac{5x-2}{x^2+x} - \dfrac{13}{x}$

68. $\dfrac{3t}{t-5} + \dfrac{2}{5-t}$

69. $\dfrac{n}{4n-1} + \dfrac{n-8}{1-4n}$

70. $\dfrac{3}{-2a+3b} - \dfrac{10}{2a-3b}$

71. $\dfrac{3}{4k-5r} - \dfrac{10}{-4k+5r}$

72. $\dfrac{p}{4p^2+2p} - \dfrac{7}{2p+1}$

73. $\dfrac{4}{2q^2+2q} - \dfrac{5}{9q}$

74. $\dfrac{10}{(x+4)(x+2)} - \dfrac{6+x}{x+2}$

75. $\dfrac{21}{24x^2y} + \dfrac{x+4}{15xy^3}$

76. $\dfrac{p^2+4}{p^2-25} + \dfrac{9}{p-5}$

77. $\dfrac{11}{3x+12} + \dfrac{3x+1}{2x+4}$

78. $6x^2 + \dfrac{8x}{x-7}$

79. $\dfrac{9x+4}{x+1} - \dfrac{2x-6}{x+8}$

80. $\dfrac{x+3}{x^2+11x+18} - \dfrac{x^2-11}{x^2-3x-10}$

81. $\dfrac{x-2}{x^2-5x-24} + \dfrac{3}{x^2+11x+24}$

82. $\dfrac{6n}{n^2-4} - \dfrac{n-3}{n^2-5n-14}$

83. $\dfrac{5}{(a-4)^2} - \dfrac{a+2}{a^2-7a+12}$

84. $\dfrac{3x+5}{x^2-1} + \dfrac{x^2-18}{(x+1)^2}$

85. $\dfrac{9x}{x^2+6x+5} - \dfrac{5x^2}{x^2+4x+3}$

86. $\dfrac{6x+5}{x+2} + \dfrac{3x}{(x+2)^2}$

87. $\dfrac{3x-5}{x^2-6x+9} + \dfrac{3}{x-3}$

88. $\dfrac{2n+11}{(n+5)(n+2)} - \dfrac{3n-5}{(n-3)(n+5)}$

89. $\dfrac{8x^2}{x^2-7x+6} + x - 9$

90. $\dfrac{2x-1}{x^2-25} + x - 10$

91. $\dfrac{t-1}{3t^2+10t-8} - \dfrac{11}{3t^2+11t-4}$

92. $\dfrac{-4x+9}{2x^2+5x+2} + \dfrac{x^2}{3x^2+4x-4}$

93. $\dfrac{3x-1}{4x^2+4x+1} + \dfrac{x^2+x-9}{8x^2+10x+3}$

94. $\dfrac{3x+7}{6x^2+11x-10} + \dfrac{x^2-8}{9x^2-12x+4}$

Add or subtract using the technique from Example 7.

95. $\dfrac{1}{7} + \dfrac{2}{5}$

96. $\dfrac{3}{8} + \dfrac{1}{4}$

97. $\dfrac{2}{9} + \dfrac{3}{4}$

98. $\dfrac{5}{6} - \dfrac{1}{3}$

99. $\dfrac{5}{9} - \dfrac{1}{2}$

100. $\dfrac{6}{5} - \dfrac{3}{10}$

Problem Solving

List the polynomial to be placed in each shaded area to make a true statement. Explain how you determined your answer.

101. $\dfrac{x^2-6x+3}{x+3} + \dfrac{\blacksquare}{x+3} = \dfrac{2x^2-5x-6}{x+3}$

102. $\dfrac{4x^2-6x-7}{x^2-4} - \dfrac{\blacksquare}{x^2-4} = \dfrac{2x^2+x-3}{x^2-4}$

103. $\dfrac{-x^2-4x+3}{2x+5} + \dfrac{\blacksquare}{2x+5} = \dfrac{5x-7}{2x+5}$

104. $\dfrac{-3x^2-9}{(x+4)(x-2)} - \dfrac{\blacksquare}{(x+4)(x-2)} = \dfrac{x^2+3x}{(x+4)(x-2)}$

Find the least common denominator of each expression.

105. $\dfrac{3}{\text{☺}} + \dfrac{4}{5\text{☺}}$

106. $\dfrac{5}{8\Delta^2\text{☺}^2} + \dfrac{6}{5\Delta^4\text{☺}^5}$

107. $\dfrac{8}{\Delta^2-9} - \dfrac{2}{\Delta+3}$

108. $\dfrac{6}{\Delta+3} - \dfrac{\Delta+5}{\Delta^2-4\Delta+3}$

Concept/Writing Exercises

109. Explain how to add or subtract rational expressions with a common denominator.

110. Explain how to find the least common denominator of two rational expressions.

Challenge Problems

Perform each indicated operation.

111. $\dfrac{4x-1}{x^2-25} - \dfrac{3x^2-8}{x^2-25} + \dfrac{8x-7}{x^2-25}$

112. $\dfrac{x^2-8x+2}{x+7} + \dfrac{2x^2-5x}{x+7} - \dfrac{3x^2+7x+10}{x+7}$

Find the least common denominator for each expression.

113. $\dfrac{17}{6x^5y^9} - \dfrac{9}{2x^3y} + \dfrac{6}{5x^{12}y^2}$

114. $\dfrac{2x}{x-3} - \dfrac{3}{x^2-9} + \dfrac{5}{x+3}$

115. $\dfrac{3x}{x^2-x-12} + \dfrac{2}{x^2-6x+8} + \dfrac{3}{x^2+x-6}$

116. $\dfrac{9}{x^2-4} - \dfrac{8}{3x^2+5x-2} + \dfrac{7}{3x^2-7x+2}$

Cumulative Review Exercises

[1.3] **117.** Subtract $4\dfrac{3}{5} - 2\dfrac{5}{9}$.

[2.5] **118.** Solve $6x + 4 = -(x+2) - 3x + 4$.

[2.7] **119.** **Hummingbird Food** The instructions on a bottle of concentrated hummingbird food indicate that 6 ounces of the concentrate should be mixed with 1 gallon (128 ounces) of water. If you wish to mix the concentrate with only 48 ounces of water, how much concentrate should you use?

[3.2] **120.** **Tennis Club** A Tennis Club has two payment plans. Plan 1 is a yearly membership fee of $250 plus $5.00 per hour for use of the tennis court. Plan 2 is an annual membership fee of $600 with no charge for court time. How many hours would Malcolm Wu have to play in a year to make the cost of plan 1 equal to the cost of plan 2?

© Michael Woodruff\Shutterstock

[4.3] **121.** Use scientific notation to evaluate $\dfrac{840,000,000}{0.0021}$. Leave your answer in scientific notation.

[5.6] **122.** Solve $2x^2 - 3 = x$.

6.4 Addition and Subtraction of Rational Expressions

1 Add and subtract rational expressions.

In Section 6.3 we discussed how to add and subtract rational expressions with a common denominator. Now we discuss adding and subtracting rational expressions that are not given with a common denominator.

1 Add and Subtract Rational Expressions

The method used to add and subtract rational expressions with unlike denominators is outlined in Example 1.

EXAMPLE 1 Add $\dfrac{7}{x} + \dfrac{6}{y}$.

Solution First we determine the LCD as outlined in Section 6.3.

$$\text{LCD} = xy$$

We write each fraction with the LCD. We do this by multiplying *both* the numerator and denominator of each fraction by any factors needed to obtain the LCD.

$$\frac{7}{x} + \frac{6}{y} = \frac{7}{x} \cdot \boxed{\frac{y}{y}} + \frac{6}{y} \cdot \boxed{\frac{x}{x}}$$

$$= \frac{7y}{xy} + \frac{6x}{xy}$$

$\left\{\begin{array}{l}\text{Multiply } \dfrac{7}{x} \text{ by } \dfrac{y}{y} \text{ and} \\[6pt] \text{multiply } \dfrac{6}{y} \text{ by } \dfrac{x}{x}. \\[6pt] \text{Values do not change since } \dfrac{x}{x} = 1 \text{ and } \dfrac{y}{y} = 1.\end{array}\right.$

Understanding Algebra

The concept of adding rational expressions is the same as adding fractions in arithmetic. Rewrite the fractions as equivalent fractions with the least common denominator.

Arithmetic:

$$\frac{1}{8} + \frac{1}{2} = \frac{1}{8} + \frac{4}{8} = \frac{1+4}{8} = \frac{5}{8}$$

Algebra:

$$\frac{3}{x^2} + \frac{2}{x^3} = \frac{3x}{x^3} + \frac{2}{x^3} = \frac{3x+2}{x^3}$$

Now we add the numerators, and keep the LCD, xy.

$$\frac{7y}{xy} + \frac{6x}{xy} = \frac{7y + 6x}{xy} \quad \text{or} \quad \frac{6x + 7y}{xy}$$

Now Try Exercise 7

To Add or Subtract Two Rational Expressions with Unlike Denominators

1. Determine the LCD.
2. Rewrite each fraction as an equivalent fraction with the LCD. This is done by multiplying both the numerator and denominator of each fraction by any factors needed to obtain the LCD.
3. Add or subtract the numerators while maintaining the LCD.
4. When possible, factor the remaining numerator and simplify the fraction.

EXAMPLE 2 Add $\dfrac{1}{4x^2y} + \dfrac{3}{14xy^3}$.

Solution   The LCD is $28x^2y^3$. We must write each fraction with the denominator $28x^2y^3$.

$$\frac{1}{4x^2y} + \frac{3}{14xy^3} = \frac{1}{4x^2y} \cdot \boxed{\frac{7y^2}{7y^2}} + \frac{3}{14xy^3} \cdot \boxed{\frac{2x}{2x}}$$

$$\left\{\begin{array}{l} \text{Multiply } \dfrac{1}{4x^2y} \text{ by } \dfrac{7y^2}{7y^2} \text{ and} \\[2mm] \text{multiply } \dfrac{3}{14xy^3} \text{ by } \dfrac{2x}{2x} \\[2mm] \text{to obtain the LCD of } 28x^2y^3. \end{array}\right.$$

$$= \frac{7y^2}{28x^2y^3} + \frac{6x}{28x^2y^3}$$

$$= \frac{7y^2 + 6x}{28x^2y^3} \quad \text{or} \quad \frac{6x + 7y^2}{28x^2y^3}$$

Now Try Exercise 15

EXAMPLE 3 Add $\dfrac{3}{x+2} + \dfrac{5}{x}$.

Solution   The LCD is $x(x+2)$.

$$\frac{3}{x+2} + \frac{5}{x} = \frac{3}{x+2} \cdot \boxed{\frac{x}{x}} + \frac{5}{x} \cdot \boxed{\frac{x+2}{x+2}}$$

$$\left\{\begin{array}{l} \text{Multiply } \dfrac{3}{x+2} \text{ by } \dfrac{x}{x} \text{ and} \\[2mm] \text{multiply } \dfrac{5}{x} \text{ by } \dfrac{x+2}{x+2} \\[2mm] \text{to obtain the LCD of } x(x+2). \end{array}\right.$$

$$= \frac{3x}{x(x+2)} + \frac{5(x+2)}{x(x+2)} \qquad \text{Each fraction has been written as an equivalent fraction with the LCD of } x(x+2)$$

$$= \frac{3x}{x(x+2)} + \frac{5x+10}{x(x+2)} \qquad \text{Distributive property was used.}$$

$$= \frac{3x + (5x+10)}{x(x+2)} \qquad \text{Rewrote as a single fraction.}$$

$$= \frac{3x + 5x + 10}{x(x+2)} \qquad \text{Parentheses were removed in the numerator.}$$

$$= \frac{8x + 10}{x(x+2)} \qquad \text{Like terms were combined in the numerator.}$$

Now Try Exercise 25

Helpful Hint

Look at the answer to Example 3, $\dfrac{8x + 10}{x(x + 2)}$. Notice that the numerator could have been

factored to obtain $\dfrac{2(4x + 5)}{x(x + 2)}$. Also notice that the denominator could have been multiplied

to get $\dfrac{8x + 10}{x^2 + 2x}$. All three of these answers are equivalent and each is correct. In this section, *when writing answers, unless there is a common factor in the numerator and denominator we will leave the numerator in unfactored form and the denominator in factored form.* If both the numerator and denominator have a common factor, we will factor the numerator and simplify the fraction.

EXAMPLE 4 Subtract $\dfrac{w}{w - 7} - \dfrac{6}{w - 4}$.

Solution   The LCD is $(w - 7)(w - 4)$.

$$\frac{w}{w - 7} - \frac{6}{w - 4} = \frac{w - 4}{w - 4} \cdot \frac{w}{w - 7} - \frac{6}{w - 4} \cdot \frac{w - 7}{w - 7} \qquad \begin{array}{l} \text{Multiply} \dfrac{w}{w - 7} \text{ by } \dfrac{w - 4}{w - 4} \text{ and} \\ \text{multiply} \dfrac{6}{w - 4} \text{ by } \dfrac{w - 7}{w - 7}. \end{array}$$

$$= \frac{w(w - 4)}{(w - 4)(w - 7)} - \frac{6(w - 7)}{(w - 4)(w - 7)} \qquad \begin{array}{l} \text{Rewrote each fraction as} \\ \text{an equivalent fraction with} \\ \text{the LCD.} \end{array}$$

$$= \frac{w^2 - 4w}{(w - 4)(w - 7)} - \frac{6w - 42}{(w - 4)(w - 7)} \qquad \begin{array}{l} \text{Distributive property was} \\ \text{used in the numerators.} \end{array}$$

$$= \frac{(w^2 - 4w) - (6w - 42)}{(w - 4)(w - 7)} \qquad \text{Wrote as a single fraction.}$$

$$= \frac{w^2 - 4w - 6w + 42}{(w - 4)(w - 7)} \qquad \begin{array}{l} \text{Parentheses were removed} \\ \text{in the numerator.} \end{array}$$

$$= \frac{w^2 - 10w + 42}{(w - 4)(w - 7)} \qquad \begin{array}{l} \text{Like terms were combined} \\ \text{in the numerator.} \end{array}$$

Now Try Exercise 29

Avoiding Common Errors

Remember: When subtracting fractions, the subtraction symbol changes the sign of each term in the numerator following it.

CORRECT

$$\frac{5x}{x + 2} - \frac{x - 3}{x + 2} = \frac{5x - x + 3}{x + 2} = \frac{4x + 3}{x + 2}$$

INCORRECT

$$\frac{5x}{x + 2} - \frac{x - 3}{x + 2} = \frac{5x - x - 3}{x + 2} = \frac{4x - 3}{x + 2}$$

EXAMPLE 5 Subtract $\dfrac{x + 2}{x - 4} - \dfrac{x + 3}{x + 4}$.

Solution   The LCD is $(x - 4)(x + 4)$.

$$\frac{x + 2}{x - 4} - \frac{x + 3}{x + 4} = \frac{x + 4}{x + 4} \cdot \frac{x + 2}{x - 4} - \frac{x + 3}{x + 4} \cdot \frac{x - 4}{x - 4}$$

$$= \frac{(x + 4)(x + 2)}{(x + 4)(x - 4)} - \frac{(x + 3)(x - 4)}{(x + 4)(x - 4)} \qquad \begin{array}{l} \text{Rewrote each fraction} \\ \text{as an equivalent} \\ \text{fraction with the LCD.} \end{array}$$

Use the FOIL method to multiply each numerator.

$$= \frac{x^2 + 6x + 8}{(x + 4)(x - 4)} - \frac{x^2 - x - 12}{(x + 4)(x - 4)}$$

$$= \frac{(x^2 + 6x + 8) - (x^2 - x - 12)}{(x + 4)(x - 4)}$$ Wrote as a single fraction.

$$= \frac{x^2 + 6x + 8 - x^2 + x + 12}{(x + 4)(x - 4)}$$ Parentheses were removed in the numerator.

$$= \frac{7x + 20}{(x + 4)(x - 4)}$$ Like terms were combined in the numerator.

Now Try Exercise 37

Consider the problem

$$\frac{4}{x - 2} + \frac{x + 3}{2 - x}$$

Because the denominators are opposites, we can proceed by converting one of the denominators to the other by multiplying by -1. See the Helpful Hint below.

Understanding Algebra

The expressions $a - b$ and $b - a$ are opposites and, therefore, differ only by a factor of -1. Thus,

$(b - a)(-1) = -b + a = a - b.$

Helpful Hint

When adding or subtracting fractions whose denominators are opposites, multiply both the numerator *and* the denominator of *either* fraction by -1. Then both fractions will have the same denominator.

$$\frac{x}{a - b} + \frac{y}{b - a} = \frac{x}{a - b} + \frac{y}{b - a} \cdot \frac{-1}{-1}$$

$$= \frac{x}{a - b} + \frac{-y}{a - b}$$

$$= \frac{x - y}{a - b}$$

EXAMPLE 6 Add $\dfrac{4}{x - 2} + \dfrac{x + 3}{2 - x}$.

Solution Since the denominators differ only in sign, we may multiply both the numerator and the denominator of either fraction by -1.

$$\frac{4}{x - 2} + \frac{x + 3}{2 - x} = \frac{4}{x - 2} + \frac{x + 3}{2 - x} \cdot \frac{-1}{-1}$$ Multiply numerator and denominator of the second fraction by -1.

$$= \frac{4}{x - 2} + \frac{(-x - 3)}{x - 2}$$ Notice $(2 - x)(-1) = x - 2$.

$$= \frac{4 + (-x - 3)}{x - 2}$$ Wrote as a single fraction.

$$= \frac{4 - x - 3}{x - 2}$$ Parentheses were removed in the numerator.

$$= \frac{-x + 1}{x - 2}$$ Like terms were combined in the numerator.

Now Try Exercise 31

Let's work another example where the denominators differ only in sign.

EXAMPLE 7 Subtract $\dfrac{a - 9}{3a - 4} - \dfrac{2a - 5}{4 - 3a}$.

Solution The denominators of the two fractions differ only in sign.

$$\frac{a - 9}{3a - 4} - \frac{2a - 5}{4 - 3a} = \frac{a - 9}{3a - 4} - \frac{2a - 5}{4 - 3a} \cdot \frac{-1}{-1}$$ Multiply numerator and denominator of the second fraction by -1.

$$= \frac{a - 9}{3a - 4} - \frac{(-2a + 5)}{3a - 4} \qquad \text{The common denominator is } 3a - 4.$$

$$= \frac{(a - 9) - (-2a + 5)}{3a - 4} \qquad \text{Wrote as a single fraction.}$$

$$= \frac{a - 9 + 2a - 5}{3a - 4} \qquad \text{Parentheses were removed in the numerator.}$$

$$= \frac{3a - 14}{3a - 4} \qquad \text{Like terms were combined in the numerator.}$$

Now Try Exercise 33

EXAMPLE 8 Add $\dfrac{3}{x^2 + 5x + 6} + \dfrac{1}{3x^2 + 8x - 3}$.

Solution

$$\frac{3}{x^2 + 5x + 6} + \frac{1}{3x^2 + 8x - 3} = \frac{3}{(x + 2)(x + 3)} + \frac{1}{(3x - 1)(x + 3)}$$

The LCD is $(x + 2)(x + 3)(3x - 1)$.

$$= \frac{3x - 1}{3x - 1} \cdot \frac{3}{(x + 2)(x + 3)} + \frac{1}{(3x - 1)(x + 3)} \cdot \frac{x + 2}{x + 2}$$

$$= \frac{9x - 3}{(3x - 1)(x + 2)(x + 3)} + \frac{x + 2}{(3x - 1)(x + 2)(x + 3)}$$

$$= \frac{(9x - 3) + (x + 2)}{(3x - 1)(x + 2)(x + 3)}$$

$$= \frac{9x - 3 + x + 2}{(3x - 1)(x + 2)(x + 3)}$$

$$= \frac{10x - 1}{(3x - 1)(x + 2)(x + 3)}$$

Now Try Exercise 55

EXAMPLE 9 Subtract $\dfrac{5}{x^2 - 5x} - \dfrac{x}{5x - 25}$.

Solution

$$\frac{5}{x^2 - 5x} - \frac{x}{5x - 25} = \frac{5}{x(x - 5)} - \frac{x}{5(x - 5)}$$

The LCD is $5x(x - 5)$.

$$= \frac{5}{5} \cdot \frac{5}{x(x - 5)} - \frac{x}{5(x - 5)} \cdot \frac{x}{x}$$

$$= \frac{25}{5x(x - 5)} - \frac{x^2}{5x(x - 5)}$$

$$= \frac{25 - x^2}{5x(x - 5)} \qquad \text{Factor the numerator.}$$

$$= \frac{(5 - x)(5 + x)}{5x(x - 5)}$$

$$= \frac{-1(x - 5)(x + 5)}{5x(x - 5)} \qquad 5 - x = -1(x - 5)$$

$$= \frac{-1\cancel{(x - 5)}(x + 5)}{5x\cancel{(x - 5)}} \qquad \text{Simplify.}$$

$$= \frac{-1(x + 5)}{5x} \quad \text{or} \quad -\frac{x + 5}{5x}$$

Now Try Exercise 65

Avoiding Common Errors

1. A common error in an addition or subtraction problem is to add or subtract the numerators and the denominators. Here is one such example.

CORRECT

$$\frac{1}{x} + \frac{x}{1} = \frac{1}{x} + \frac{x}{1} \cdot \frac{x}{x}$$

$$= \frac{1}{x} + \frac{x^2}{x}$$

$$= \frac{1 + x^2}{x} \quad \text{or} \quad \frac{x^2 + 1}{x}$$

INCORRECT

$$\frac{1}{x} + \frac{x}{1} = \frac{1+x}{x+1}$$

$$\frac{1}{x} - \frac{x}{1} = \frac{1-x}{x-1}$$

Remember that to add or subtract fractions you must first have a common denominator. Then you add or subtract the numerators while maintaining the common denominator.

2. Another common mistake is to treat an addition or subtraction problem as a multiplication problem. You can divide out common factors only when *multiplying* expressions, not when adding or subtracting them.

CORRECT

$$\frac{1}{x} \cdot \frac{x}{1} = \frac{1}{\cancel{x}} \cdot \frac{\cancel{x}^{1}}{1}$$

$$= 1 \cdot 1 = 1$$

INCORRECT

$$\frac{1}{x} + \frac{x}{1} = \frac{1}{\cancel{x}} + \frac{\cancel{x}}{1}$$

$$= 1 + 1 = 2$$

EXERCISE SET 6.4

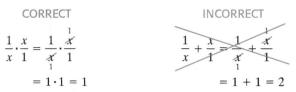

Warm-Up Exercises

Fill in the blanks with the appropriate word, phrase, or symbol(s) from the following list.

$24z^2$	you are multiplying by 1	x	$\dfrac{y+5}{12z^2}$
$\dfrac{3yz+10}{12z^2}$	$12z^2$	opposites	the LCD

1. When adding two fractions whose denominators are _____ , multiply the numerator and denominator of either fraction by -1.

2. The first step in adding two rational expressions with unlike denominators is to determine _____ .

3. The value of a fraction does not change when you multiply the numerator and denominator by the same quantity because _____ .

4. When adding $\dfrac{2}{x^2-4x} + \dfrac{5}{x-4}$ the numerator and denominator of the second fraction should be multiplied by _____ .

5. When adding $\dfrac{y}{4z} + \dfrac{5}{6z^2}$, the LCD is _____ .

6. $\dfrac{y}{4z} + \dfrac{5}{6z^2} =$ _____ .

Practice the Skills

Add or subtract.

7. $\dfrac{2}{x} + \dfrac{5}{y}$

8. $\dfrac{5}{x} - \dfrac{1}{y}$

9. $\dfrac{5}{t^2} + \dfrac{1}{2t}$

10. $7 - \dfrac{1}{x^2}$

11. $3 + \dfrac{8}{x}$

12. $\dfrac{5}{6y} + \dfrac{3}{5y^2}$

13. $\dfrac{2}{x^2} + \dfrac{3}{5x}$

14. $\dfrac{6}{x} - \dfrac{5}{x^2}$

15. $\dfrac{9}{4x^2y} + \dfrac{3}{5xy^2}$

16. $\dfrac{7}{12x^4y} - \dfrac{1}{5x^2y^3}$

17. $4y + \dfrac{x}{y}$

18. $x + \dfrac{2x}{y}$

19. $\dfrac{3a-1}{2a} + \dfrac{5}{3a}$

20. $\dfrac{11}{n} + 5$

21. $\dfrac{6x}{y} + \dfrac{2y}{xy}$

22. $\dfrac{4}{5p} - \dfrac{5}{2p^2}$

23. $\dfrac{9}{b} - \dfrac{4}{5a^2}$

24. $\dfrac{x-3}{x} - \dfrac{7}{6x}$

25. $\dfrac{4}{x} + \dfrac{9}{x-3}$

26. $10 - \dfrac{3}{x-3}$

27. $\dfrac{9}{p+3} + \dfrac{2}{p}$

28. $\dfrac{2a}{a+b} + \dfrac{a-b}{a}$

29. $\dfrac{5}{d+1} - \dfrac{d}{3d+5}$

30. $\dfrac{2}{x-3} - \dfrac{5}{x-1}$

31. $\dfrac{8}{p-3} + \dfrac{2}{3-p}$

32. $\dfrac{3}{n-5} - \dfrac{7}{5-n}$

33. $\dfrac{9}{x+7} - \dfrac{5}{-x-7}$

34. $\dfrac{6}{7x-1} - \dfrac{3}{1-7x}$

35. $\dfrac{8}{a-2} + \dfrac{a}{2a-4}$

36. $\dfrac{4}{y-1} + \dfrac{3}{y+1}$

37. $\dfrac{x+5}{x-5} - \dfrac{x-5}{x+5}$

38. $\dfrac{x+7}{x+3} - \dfrac{x+3}{x+7}$

39. $\dfrac{5}{6n+3} - \dfrac{2}{n}$

40. $\dfrac{x}{4x-4} - \dfrac{1}{3x}$

41. $\dfrac{3}{2w+10} + \dfrac{6}{w+2}$

42. $\dfrac{5k}{4k-8} - \dfrac{k}{k+2}$

43. $\dfrac{z}{z^2-16} + \dfrac{4}{z+4}$

44. $\dfrac{5}{(x+4)^2} + \dfrac{3}{x+4}$

45. $\dfrac{x+2}{x^2-4} - \dfrac{2}{x+2}$

46. $\dfrac{3}{(x-2)(x+3)} + \dfrac{5}{(x+2)(x+3)}$

47. $\dfrac{3r+4}{r^2-10r+24} - \dfrac{2}{r-6}$

48. $\dfrac{x+9}{x^2-3x-10} - \dfrac{2}{x-5}$

49. $\dfrac{x^2-3}{x^2+2x-8} - \dfrac{x-4}{x+4}$

50. $\dfrac{x+8}{x^2-4x+4} - \dfrac{x+1}{x-2}$

51. $\dfrac{x-6}{x^2+10x+25} + \dfrac{x-3}{x+5}$

52. $\dfrac{x}{x^2-xy} - \dfrac{y}{xy-x^2}$

53. $\dfrac{5}{a^2-9a+8} - \dfrac{6}{a^2-6a-16}$

54. $\dfrac{4}{a^2+2a-15} - \dfrac{1}{a^2-9}$

55. $\dfrac{2}{x^2+6x+9} + \dfrac{7}{x^2+x-6}$

56. $\dfrac{x}{2x^2+7x-4} + \dfrac{4}{x^2-x-20}$

57. $\dfrac{x}{2x^2+7x+3} - \dfrac{5}{3x^2+7x-6}$

58. $\dfrac{x}{6x^2+7x+2} + \dfrac{5}{2x^2-3x-2}$

59. $\dfrac{x}{4x^2+11x+6} - \dfrac{2}{8x^2+2x-3}$

60. $\dfrac{x}{5x^2-9x-2} - \dfrac{1}{3x^2-7x+2}$

61. $\dfrac{3w+12}{w^2+w-12} - \dfrac{2}{w-3}$

62. $\dfrac{5x+10}{x^2-5x-14} - \dfrac{4}{x-7}$

63. $\dfrac{4r}{2r^2-10r+12} + \dfrac{4}{r-2}$

64. $\dfrac{6m}{3m^2-24m+48} - \dfrac{2}{m-4}$

65. $\dfrac{4}{x^2-4x} - \dfrac{x}{4x-16}$

66. $\dfrac{6}{x^2-6x} - \dfrac{x}{6x-36}$

Problem Solving

For what value(s) of x is each expression defined?

67. $\dfrac{8}{x} + 6$

68. $\dfrac{6}{x-1} - \dfrac{5}{x}$

69. $\dfrac{3}{x-4} + \dfrac{7}{x+6}$

70. $\dfrac{4}{x^2-9} - \dfrac{9}{x+3}$

Add or subtract. Treat the unknown symbols as if they were variables.

71. $\dfrac{3}{\Delta-2} - \dfrac{4}{2-\Delta}$

72. $\dfrac{\Delta}{2\Delta^2+7\Delta-4} + \dfrac{2}{\Delta^2-\Delta-20}$

Challenge Problems

Under what conditions is each expression defined? Explain your answers.

73. $\dfrac{5}{a+b} + \dfrac{4}{a}$

74. $\dfrac{x+2}{x+5y} - \dfrac{y-2}{3x}$

Perform each indicated operation.

75. $\dfrac{x}{x^2 - 9} + \dfrac{2x}{x + 3} + \dfrac{2x^2 - 5x}{9 - x^2}$

76. $\dfrac{8x + 9}{x^2 + x - 6} + \dfrac{x}{x + 3} - \dfrac{5}{x - 2}$

77. $\dfrac{x + 6}{4 - x^2} - \dfrac{x + 3}{x + 2} + \dfrac{x - 3}{2 - x}$

78. $\dfrac{3x - 1}{x + 2} + \dfrac{x}{x - 3} - \dfrac{4}{2x + 3}$

79. $\dfrac{2}{x^2 - x - 6} + \dfrac{3}{x^2 - 2x - 3} + \dfrac{1}{x^2 + 3x + 2}$

80. $\dfrac{3x}{x^2 - 4} + \dfrac{4}{x^3 + 8}$

Group Activity

Discuss and answer Exercise 81 as a group.

81. a) As a group, find the LCD of

$$\frac{x + 3y}{x^2 + 3xy + 2y^2} + \frac{y - x}{2x^2 + 3xy + y^2}$$

    b) As a group, perform the indicated operation, but do not simplify your answer.

    c) As a group, simplify your answer.

    d) Group member 1: Substitute 2 for x and 1 for y in the fraction on the left in part **a)** and evaluate.

    e) Group member 2: Substitute 2 for x and 1 for y in the fraction on the right in part **a)** and evaluate.

    f) Group member 3: Add the numerical fractions found in parts **d)** and **e)**.

    g) Individually, substitute 2 for x and 1 for y in the expression obtained in part **b)** and evaluate.

    h) Individually, substitute 2 for x and 1 for y in the expression obtained in part **c)**, evaluate, and compare your answers.

    i) As a group, discuss what you discovered from this activity.

    j) Do you think your results would have been similar for any numbers substituted for x and y (for which the denominator is not 0)? Why?

Cumulative Review Exercises

[2.7] **82. White Pass Railroad** The White Pass Railroad is a narrow gauge railroad that travels slowly through the mountains of Alaska. If the train travels 22 miles in 0.8 hours, how long will it take to travel 42 miles? Assume the train travels at the same rate throughout the trip.

[2.8] **83.** Solve the inequality $3(x - 2) + 2 < 4(x + 1)$ and graph the solution on a number line.

[4.6] **84.** Divide $(8x^2 + 6x - 15) \div (2x + 3)$.

[6.2] **85.** Multiply $\dfrac{x^2 + xy - 6y^2}{x^2 - xy - 2y^2} \cdot \dfrac{y^2 - x^2}{x^2 + 2xy - 3y^2}$.

© Allen R. Angel

Mid-Chapter Test: 6.1–6.4

To find out how well you understand the chapter material to this point, take this brief test. The answers, and the section where the material was initially discussed, are given in the back of the book. Review any questions that you answered incorrectly.

Determine the value or values of the variable where each expression is defined.

1. $\dfrac{9}{3x - 2}$

2. $\dfrac{2x + 1}{x^2 - 5x - 14}$

Simplify each rational expression.

3. $\dfrac{9x + 18}{x + 2}$

4. $\dfrac{2x^2 + 13x + 15}{3x^2 + 14x - 5}$

5. $\dfrac{25r^2 - 36t^2}{5r - 6t}$

Multiply or divide as indicated.

6. $\dfrac{15x^2}{2y} \cdot \dfrac{4y^4}{5x^5}$

7. $\dfrac{m - 3}{m + 4} \cdot \dfrac{m^2 + 8m + 16}{3 - m}$

8. $\dfrac{x^3 + 27}{x^2 - 2x - 15} \cdot \dfrac{x^2 - 7x + 10}{x^2 - 3x + 9}$

9. $\dfrac{5x - 1}{x^2 + 11x + 10} \div \dfrac{10x - 2}{x^2 + 17x + 70}$

10. $\dfrac{5x^2 + 7x + 2}{x^2 + 6x + 5} \div \dfrac{7x^2 - 39x - 18}{x^2 - x - 30}$

Add or subtract as indicated.

11. $\dfrac{x^2}{x + 6} - \dfrac{36}{x + 6}$

12. $\dfrac{2x^2 - 2x}{2x + 5} + \dfrac{x - 15}{2x + 5}$

13. $\dfrac{3t^2 - t}{4t^2 - 9t + 2} - \dfrac{3t + 4}{4t^2 - 9t + 2}$

Find the least common denominator.

14. $\dfrac{2m}{6m^2 + 3m} + \dfrac{m + 7}{2m + 1}$

15. $\dfrac{9x + 8}{2x^2 - 5x - 12} + \dfrac{2x + 3}{x^2 - 9x + 20}$

For Exercises 16–19, add or subtract as indicated.

16. $\dfrac{x + 1}{2x} + \dfrac{4x - 3}{5x}$

17. $\dfrac{2a + 5}{a + 3} - \dfrac{3a + 1}{a - 4}$

18. $\dfrac{x^2 + 5}{2x^2 + 13x + 6} + \dfrac{3x - 1}{2x + 1}$

19. $\dfrac{x}{x^2 + 3x + 2} - \dfrac{4}{x^2 - x - 6}$

20. To add the rational expressions $\dfrac{7}{x + 1} + \dfrac{8}{x}$, Samuel Ditsi decided to add both numerators and then add both denominators to get $\dfrac{7 + 8}{(x + 1) + x}$, which simplified to $\dfrac{15}{2x + 1}$. This procedure is wrong. Why is it wrong? Explain your answer. Then add the rational expressions $\dfrac{7}{x + 1} + \dfrac{8}{x}$ correctly.

6.5 Complex Fractions

1 Simplify complex fractions by combining terms.

2 Simplify complex fractions using multiplication first to clear fractions.

1 Simplify Complex Fractions by Combining Terms

Complex Fraction

A **complex fraction** is one that has a fraction in its numerator or its denominator or in both its numerator and denominator.

Examples of Complex Fractions

$$\dfrac{\frac{3}{5}}{7} \qquad \dfrac{x + 9}{\dfrac{x}{4x}} \qquad \dfrac{\frac{x}{y}}{x + 1} \qquad \dfrac{\frac{a + b}{a}}{\dfrac{a - b}{b}}$$

The expression above the **main fraction bar** is the numerator of the complex fraction, and the expression below the main fraction bar is the denominator of the complex fraction.

Numerator of complex fraction $\Big\{$ $\dfrac{a + b}{a}$

$\longleftarrow$ Main fraction bar

Denominator of complex fraction $\Big\{$ $\dfrac{a - b}{b}$

Understanding Algebra

The complex fraction

$$\dfrac{\dfrac{a + b}{c}}{\dfrac{d + e}{f}}$$

is another way to represent the division

$$\dfrac{a + b}{c} \div \dfrac{d + e}{f}.$$

We perform the division by multiplying the first fraction by the reciprocal of the second fraction:

$$\dfrac{a + b}{c} \cdot \dfrac{f}{d + e}$$

There are two methods to simplify complex fractions. The first reinforces many of the concepts used in this chapter because we may need to add, subtract, multiply, and divide simpler fractions as we simplify the complex fraction. Many students prefer to use the second method because the answer may be obtained more quickly.

Method 1—To Simplify a Complex Fraction by Combining Terms

1. Add or subtract the fractions in both the numerator and denominator of the complex fraction to obtain single fractions in both the numerator and the denominator.

2. Multiply the fraction in the numerator by the reciprocal of the fraction in the denominator.

3. Simplify further if possible.

EXAMPLE 1 Simplify $\dfrac{\dfrac{ab^2}{c^3}}{\dfrac{a}{bc^2}}$.

Solution Since both numerator and denominator are already single fractions, we begin with step 2.

$$\frac{\dfrac{ab^2}{c^3}}{\dfrac{a}{bc^2}} = \frac{ab^2}{c^3} \div \frac{a}{bc^2} \qquad \text{A fraction bar means "divided by."}$$

$$= \frac{ab^2}{c_c^3} \cdot \frac{bc^2}{a} \qquad \text{Multiply by } \frac{bc^2}{a}, \text{ the reciprocal of } \frac{a}{bc^2}.$$

$$= \frac{b^3}{c} \qquad \begin{array}{l}\text{Both } a \text{ and } c^2 \text{ were factored out of the}\\\text{numerator and denominator.}\end{array}$$

Thus the expression simplifies to $\dfrac{b^3}{c}$.

Now Try Exercise 11

EXAMPLE 2 Simplify $\dfrac{a + \dfrac{1}{x}}{x + \dfrac{1}{a}}$.

Solution Step 1 is to express the numerator and denominator as single fractions. To obtain one fraction in the numerator, we notice that the LCD is x. Multiply a by $\dfrac{x}{x}$.

$$a + \frac{1}{x} = a \cdot \frac{x}{x} + \frac{1}{x} = \frac{ax + 1}{x} \qquad \text{We use this as the numerator.}$$

To obtain one fraction in the denominator, we notice that the LCD is a. Multiply x by $\dfrac{a}{a}$.

$$x + \frac{1}{a} = x \cdot \frac{a}{a} + \frac{1}{a} = \frac{ax + 1}{a} \qquad \text{We use this as the denominator.}$$

So

$$\frac{a + \dfrac{1}{x}}{x + \dfrac{1}{a}} = \frac{\dfrac{ax + 1}{x}}{\dfrac{ax + 1}{a}} = \frac{ax + 1}{x} \div \frac{ax + 1}{a}$$

$$= \frac{ax + 1}{x} \cdot \frac{a}{ax + 1} = \frac{a}{x}$$

Now Try Exercise 25

In Example 4 we will rework Example 2 using the second method.

2 Simplify Complex Fractions Using Multiplication First to Clear Fractions

Method 2—To Simplify a Complex Fraction Using Multiplication First

1. Find the least common denominator of *all* the denominators appearing in the complex fraction.
2. Multiply both the numerator and denominator of the complex fraction by the LCD found in step 1.
3. Simplify when possible.

EXAMPLE 3 Simplify $\dfrac{\dfrac{2}{3} + \dfrac{1}{5}}{\dfrac{4}{5} - \dfrac{1}{3}}$.

Solution   The denominators in the complex fraction are 3 and 5. Multiply both the numerator and denominator of the complex fraction by 15, the LCD of the complex fraction.

$$\frac{\dfrac{2}{3} + \dfrac{1}{5}}{\dfrac{4}{5} - \dfrac{1}{3}} = \frac{15}{15} \cdot \frac{\left(\dfrac{2}{3} + \dfrac{1}{5}\right)}{\left(\dfrac{4}{5} - \dfrac{1}{3}\right)} = \frac{15\left(\dfrac{2}{3}\right) + 15\left(\dfrac{1}{5}\right)}{15\left(\dfrac{4}{5}\right) - 15\left(\dfrac{1}{3}\right)}$$

Now simplify.

$$= \frac{10 + 3}{12 - 5} = \frac{13}{7}$$

Now Try Exercise 9

> **Understanding Algebra**
>
> The LCD of the complex fraction
> $$\dfrac{\dfrac{a + b}{c}}{\dfrac{d + e}{f}}$$
> is *cf* (*c* from the numerator and *f* from the denominator). To eliminate fractions within the complex fraction, we multiply both the numerator and the denominator by *cf*:
> $$\frac{cf}{cf} \cdot \frac{\left(\dfrac{a + b}{c}\right)}{\left(\dfrac{d + e}{f}\right)} = \frac{(a + b)f}{(d + e)c}$$

Now we will rework Example 2 using method 2.

EXAMPLE 4 Simplify $\dfrac{a + \dfrac{1}{x}}{x + \dfrac{1}{a}}$.

Solution   The denominators in the complex fraction are *x* and *a*. Multiply both the numerator and denominator of the complex fraction by *ax*, the LCD of the complex fraction.

$$\frac{a + \dfrac{1}{x}}{x + \dfrac{1}{a}} = \frac{ax}{ax} \cdot \frac{\left(a + \dfrac{1}{x}\right)}{\left(x + \dfrac{1}{a}\right)} = \frac{a^2 x + a}{ax^2 + x}$$

$$= \frac{a\,\cancel{(ax + 1)}}{x\,\cancel{(ax + 1)}} = \frac{a}{x}$$

Now Try Exercise 25

Note that the answers to Examples 2 and 4 are the same.

EXAMPLE 5 Simplify $\dfrac{y^2}{\dfrac{1}{x} + \dfrac{1}{y}}$.

Solution   The denominators in the complex fraction are *x* and *y*. Multiply both the numerator and denominator of the complex fraction by *xy*, the LCD of the complex fraction.

$$\frac{y^2}{\dfrac{1}{x} + \dfrac{1}{y}} = \frac{xy}{xy} \cdot \frac{y^2}{\left(\dfrac{1}{x} + \dfrac{1}{y}\right)}$$

$$= \frac{xy^3}{xy\left(\dfrac{1}{x}\right) + xy\left(\dfrac{1}{y}\right)}$$

$$= \frac{xy^3}{y + x}$$

Now Try Exercise 33

> **Helpful Hint**
>
> We have presented two methods for simplifying complex fractions. Which method should you use? Although either method can be used to simplify complex fractions, most students prefer to use method 1 when both the numerator and denominator consist of a single term, as in Example 1. When the complex fraction has a sum or difference of expressions in either the numerator or denominator, as in Examples 2, 3, 4, or 5, most students prefer to use method 2.

EXERCISE SET 6.5   *MathXL*   *MyMathLab*
MathXL®   MyMathLab

Warm-Up Exercises

Fill in the blanks with the appropriate word, phrase, or symbol(s) from the following list.

complex fraction   denominator   numerator   5 $\dfrac{5}{3}$ $x^2 + 5x + 6$

1. The numerator of the complex fraction $\dfrac{\frac{5}{3}}{x^2 + 5x + 6}$ is

_____ .

2. A fraction that contains a fraction in its numerator or its denominator or in both is called a _____ .

3. The numerator of the complex fraction $\dfrac{\frac{5}{3}}{x^2 + 5x + 6}$ is

_____ .

4. To simplify a complex fraction using multiplication, multiply both the numerator and _____ of the complex fraction by the LCD of the complex fraction.

Practice the Skills

Simplify.

5. $\dfrac{1 + \frac{2}{3}}{5 + \frac{1}{3}}$

6. $\dfrac{2 + \frac{4}{5}}{1 - \frac{9}{16}}$

7. $\dfrac{2 + \frac{3}{8}}{1 + \frac{1}{3}}$

8. $\dfrac{\frac{1}{4} + \frac{5}{6}}{\frac{2}{3} + \frac{3}{5}}$

9. $\dfrac{\frac{2}{3} + \frac{1}{4}}{\frac{5}{6} - \frac{1}{3}}$

10. $\dfrac{\frac{5}{8} + \frac{1}{3}}{\frac{11}{12} - \frac{1}{6}}$

11. $\dfrac{\frac{xy^2}{7}}{\frac{3}{x^2}}$

12. $\dfrac{\frac{11a}{b^3}}{\frac{b^2}{4}}$

13. $\dfrac{\frac{6a^2b}{7}}{\frac{9ac^2}{b^2}}$

14. $\dfrac{\frac{18x^4}{5y^4z^5}}{\frac{9xy^2}{15z^5}}$

15. $\dfrac{a - \frac{a}{b}}{\frac{3 + a}{b}}$

16. $\dfrac{a + \frac{2}{b}}{\frac{a}{b}}$

17. $\dfrac{\frac{9}{t} + \frac{3}{t^2}}{3 + \frac{1}{t}}$

18. $\dfrac{\frac{4}{a} + \frac{1}{2a}}{a + \frac{a}{2}}$

19. $\dfrac{5 - \frac{1}{x}}{4 - \frac{1}{x}}$

20. $\dfrac{\frac{2x}{x - y}}{\frac{x^2}{y}}$

21. $\dfrac{\frac{m}{n} - \frac{n}{m}}{\frac{m + n}{n}}$

22. $\dfrac{5}{\frac{1}{x} + y}$

23. $\dfrac{\frac{a^2}{b} - b}{\frac{b^2}{a} - a}$

24. $\dfrac{\frac{1}{x^2} - \frac{8}{x}}{3 + \frac{1}{x^2}}$

25. $\dfrac{2 - \frac{a}{b}}{\frac{a}{b} - 2}$

26. $\dfrac{\frac{x}{y} - 9}{\frac{-x}{y} + 9}$

27. $\dfrac{\frac{4}{t^2} + \frac{4}{t}}{\frac{4}{t} + \frac{4}{t^2}}$

28. $\dfrac{\frac{a^2 - b^2}{a}}{\frac{a + b}{a^4}}$

29. $\dfrac{\frac{1}{a} - \frac{1}{b}}{\frac{1}{ab}}$

30. $\dfrac{\frac{1}{a} - \frac{1}{b}}{\frac{1}{a} + \frac{1}{b}}$

31. $\dfrac{\frac{a}{b} + \frac{1}{a}}{\frac{b}{a} + \frac{1}{a}}$

32. $\dfrac{\frac{2}{a} + \frac{3}{b}}{\frac{1}{a}}$

33. $\dfrac{x}{\dfrac{1}{x} - \dfrac{1}{y}}$

34. $\dfrac{\dfrac{1}{a} + \dfrac{1}{b}}{ab}$

35. $\dfrac{\dfrac{5}{a} + \dfrac{5}{a^2}}{\dfrac{5}{b} + \dfrac{5}{b^2}}$

36. $\dfrac{\dfrac{x}{y} - \dfrac{2}{x}}{\dfrac{y}{x} + \dfrac{1}{y}}$

Problem Solving

For the complex fractions in Exercises 37–40,

 a) *Determine which of the two methods discussed in this section you would use to simplify the fraction. Explain why.*

 b) *Simplify by the method you selected in part **a**).*

 c) *Simplify by the method you did not select in part **a**). If your answers to parts **b**) and **c**) are not the same, explain why.*

37. $\dfrac{5 + \dfrac{3}{5}}{\dfrac{1}{8} - 4}$

38. $\dfrac{\dfrac{x + y}{x^3} - \dfrac{1}{x}}{\dfrac{x - y}{x^5} + 5}$

39. $\dfrac{\dfrac{x - y}{x + y} + \dfrac{6}{x + y}}{2 - \dfrac{7}{x + y}}$

40. $\dfrac{\dfrac{25}{x - y} + \dfrac{2}{x + y}}{\dfrac{5}{x - y} - \dfrac{3}{x + y}}$

*In Exercises 41 and 42, **a**) write the complex fraction, and **b**) simplify the complex fraction.*

41. The numerator of the complex fraction consists of one term: 5 is divided by $12x$. The denominator of the complex fraction consists of two terms: 4 divided by $3x$ is subtracted from 8 divided by x^2.

42. The numerator of the complex fraction consists of two terms: 3 divided by $2x$ is subtracted from 6 divided by x. The denominator of the complex fraction consists of two terms: the sum of x and the quantity 1 divided by x.

Concept/Writing Exercises

43. Explain what a complex number is.

44. a) Select the method you prefer to simplify complex fractions and then write down a step-by-step procedure for simplifying complex fractions using that method.

 b) Using your answer to part **a**), simplify $\dfrac{\dfrac{4}{x} - \dfrac{3}{y}}{x + \dfrac{1}{y}}$.

Challenge Problems

Simplify. (Hint: Refer to Section 4.2, which discusses negative exponents.)

45. $\dfrac{x^{-1} + y^{-1}}{3}$

46. $\dfrac{x^{-1} + y^{-1}}{y^{-1}}$

47. $\dfrac{x^{-1} + y^{-1}}{x^{-1}y^{-1}}$

48. $\dfrac{x^{-2} - y^{-2}}{y^{-1} - x^{-1}}$

49. Jack The efficiency of a jack, E, is expressed by the formula

$$E = \dfrac{\dfrac{1}{2}h}{h + \dfrac{1}{2}},$$ where h is determined by the pitch of the jack's

thread. Determine the efficiency of a jack if h is

 a) $\dfrac{2}{3}$ **b)** $\dfrac{4}{5}$

Pitch

Simplify.

50. $\dfrac{\dfrac{x}{y} + \dfrac{y}{x} + \dfrac{2}{x}}{\dfrac{x}{y} + y}$

51. $\dfrac{\dfrac{a}{b} + b - \dfrac{1}{a}}{\dfrac{a}{b^2} - \dfrac{b}{a} + \dfrac{3}{a^2}}$

52. $\dfrac{x}{4 + \dfrac{x}{1 + x}}$

Cumulative Review Exercises

[2.5] **53.** Solve the equation

$$2x - 8(5 - x) = 9x - 3(x + 2).$$

[4.4] **54.** What is a polynomial?

[5.3] **55.** Factor $x^2 - 13x + 40$.

[6.4] **56.** Subtract $\dfrac{x}{3x^2 + 17x - 6} - \dfrac{2}{x^2 + 3x - 18}$.

6.6 Solving Rational Equations

1 Solve rational equations with integer denominators.

2 Solve rational equations where a variable appears in a denominator.

1 Solve Rational Equations with Integer Denominators

A **rational equation** is one that contains one or more rational expressions. A rational equation may contain rational coefficients, such as $\frac{1}{2}x + \frac{3}{5}x = 8$ or $\frac{x}{2} + \frac{3x}{5} = 8$. A rational equation may also have a variable in a denominator, such as $\frac{4}{x-2} = 5$.

The emphasis of this section will be on solving rational equations where a variable appears in a denominator.

> **To Solve Rational Equations**
>
> 1. Determine the least common denominator (LCD) of all fractions in the equation.
> 2. Multiply *both* sides of the equation by the LCD. *This will result in every term in the equation being multiplied by the LCD.*
> 3. Remove any parentheses and combine like terms on each side of the equation.
> 4. Solve the equation using the properties discussed in earlier chapters.
> 5. Check your solution in the *original* equation.

The purpose of multiplying both sides of the equation by the LCD (step 2) is to eliminate all fractions from the equation. After both sides of the equation are multiplied by the LCD, the resulting equation should contain no fractions.

EXAMPLE 1 Solve $\frac{t}{4} - \frac{t}{5} = 1$ for t. ──────

Solution   The LCD of 4 and 5 is 20. Multiply both sides of the equation by 20.

$$\frac{t}{4} - \frac{t}{5} = 1$$

$$20\left(\frac{t}{4} - \frac{t}{5}\right) = 20 \cdot 1 \quad \text{Multiply both sides by the LCD, 20.}$$

$$20\left(\frac{t}{4}\right) - 20\left(\frac{t}{5}\right) = 20 \quad \text{Distributive property}$$

$$5t - 4t = 20$$

$$t = 20$$

Check $$\frac{t}{4} - \frac{t}{5} = 1$$

$$\frac{20}{4} - \frac{20}{5} \overset{?}{=} 1$$

$$5 - 4 \overset{?}{=} 1$$

$$1 = 1 \quad \text{True}$$

The solution is 20.

Now Try Exercise 13

EXAMPLE 2 Solve $\frac{x-5}{30} = \frac{4}{5} - \frac{x-1}{10}$. ──────

Solution   Multiply both sides of the equation by the LCD, 30.

$$\frac{x-5}{30} = \frac{4}{5} - \frac{x-1}{10}$$

$$30\left(\frac{x-5}{30}\right) = 30\left(\frac{4}{5} - \frac{x-1}{10}\right) \qquad \text{Multiply both sides by the LCD, 30.}$$

$$x - 5 = 30\left(\frac{4}{5}\right) - 30\left(\frac{x-1}{10}\right) \qquad \text{Distributive property}$$

$$x - 5 = 24 - 3(x-1)$$

$$x - 5 = 24 - 3x + 3 \qquad \text{Distributive property}$$

$$x - 5 = -3x + 27 \qquad \text{Combined like terms.}$$

$$4x - 5 = 27 \qquad 3x \text{ was added to both sides.}$$

$$4x = 32 \qquad 5 \text{ was added to both sides.}$$

$$x = 8 \qquad \text{Both sides were divided by 4.}$$

A check will show that the answer is 8.

Now Try Exercise 27

2 Solve Rational Equations Where a Variable Appears in a Denominator

When solving a rational equation where a variable appears in any denominator, you *must* check your answer. *Whenever a variable appears in any denominator of a rational equation, it is necessary to check your answer in the original equation. If the answer obtained makes any denominator equal to zero, that value is not a solution to the equation.* Such values are called **extraneous roots** or **extraneous solutions**.

EXAMPLE 3 Solve $4 - \dfrac{5}{x} = \dfrac{3}{2}$.

Solution   Multiply both sides of the equation by the LCD, $2x$.

$$2x\left(4 - \frac{5}{x}\right) = \left(\frac{3}{2}\right) \cdot 2x \qquad \text{Multiply both sides by the LCD, } 2x.$$

$$2x(4) - 2x\left(\frac{5}{x}\right) = \left(\frac{3}{2}\right) \cdot 2x \qquad \text{Distributive property}$$

$$8x - 10 = 3x$$

$$5x - 10 = 0 \qquad 3x \text{ was subtracted from both sides.}$$

$$5x = 10 \qquad 10 \text{ was added to both sides.}$$

$$x = 2$$

Check

$$4 - \frac{5}{x} = \frac{3}{2}$$

$$4 - \frac{5}{2} \stackrel{?}{=} \frac{3}{2}$$

$$\frac{8}{2} - \frac{5}{2} \stackrel{?}{=} \frac{3}{2}$$

$$\frac{3}{2} = \frac{3}{2} \qquad \text{True}$$

Since 2 does check, it is the solution to the equation.

Now Try Exercise 17

EXAMPLE 4 Solve $\dfrac{p-5}{p+3} = \dfrac{1}{5}$.

Solution The LCD is $5(p+3)$. Multiply both sides of the equation by the LCD.

$$5(p+3) \cdot \dfrac{(p-5)}{p+3} = \dfrac{1}{5} \cdot 5(p+3)$$

$$5(p-5) = 1(p+3)$$
$$5p - 25 = p + 3$$
$$4p - 25 = 3$$
$$4p = 28$$
$$p = 7$$

A check will show that 7 is the solution.

Now Try Exercise 43

In Section 2.7 we illustrated that proportions of the form

$$\dfrac{a}{b} = \dfrac{c}{d}$$

can be cross-multiplied to obtain $a \cdot d = b \cdot c$. Example 4 is a proportion and can also be solved by cross-multiplying, as we will do in Example 5.

EXAMPLE 5 Use cross-multiplication to solve $\dfrac{9}{x+1} = \dfrac{5}{x-3}$.

Solution

$$\dfrac{9}{x+1} = \dfrac{5}{x-3}$$

$$9(x-3) = 5(x+1) \quad \text{Cross-multiplied.}$$
$$9x - 27 = 5x + 5 \quad \text{Distributive property was used.}$$
$$4x - 27 = 5$$
$$4x = 32$$
$$x = 8$$

A check will show that 8 is the solution to the equation.

Now Try Exercise 41

The following examples involve quadratic equations. Recall from Section 5.6 that quadratic equations have the form $ax^2 + bx + c = 0$, where $a \neq 0$.

EXAMPLE 6 Solve $x + \dfrac{12}{x} = -7$.

Solution

$$x + \dfrac{12}{x} = -7$$

$$x \cdot \left(x + \dfrac{12}{x} \right) = -7 \cdot x \quad \text{Multiply both sides by } x.$$

$$x(x) + x\left(\dfrac{12}{x} \right) = -7x \quad \text{Distributive property was used.}$$

$$x^2 + 12 = -7x$$

$$x^2 + 7x + 12 = 0 \quad \text{7x was added to both sides.}$$

$$(x+3)(x+4) = 0 \quad \text{Factored.}$$

$$x + 3 = 0 \quad \text{or} \quad x + 4 = 0 \quad \text{Zero-factor property}$$

$$x = -3 \qquad\qquad x = -4$$

Check

$$x = -3$$

$$x + \frac{12}{x} = -7$$

$$-3 + \frac{12}{-3} \stackrel{?}{=} -7$$

$$-3 + (-4) \stackrel{?}{=} -7$$

$$-7 = -7 \quad \text{True}$$

$$x = -4$$

$$x + \frac{12}{x} = -7$$

$$-4 + \frac{12}{-4} \stackrel{?}{=} -7$$

$$-4 + (-3) \stackrel{?}{=} -7$$

$$-7 = -7 \quad \text{True}$$

The solutions are -3 and -4.

Now Try Exercise 57

EXAMPLE 7 Solve $\dfrac{x^2 - 2x}{x - 6} = \dfrac{24}{x - 6}$.

Solution   If we try to solve this equation using cross-multiplication we will get a cubic equation. We will solve this equation by multiplying both sides of the equation by the LCD, $x - 6$.

$$\frac{x^2 - 2x}{x - 6} = \frac{24}{x - 6}$$

$$\cancel{x - 6} \cdot \frac{x^2 - 2x}{\cancel{x - 6}} = \frac{24}{\cancel{x - 6}} \cdot \cancel{x - 6} \qquad \text{Multiply both sides by the LCD, } x - 6.$$

$$x^2 - 2x = 24$$

$$x^2 - 2x - 24 = 0 \qquad \text{24 was subtracted from both sides.}$$

$$(x + 4)(x - 6) = 0 \qquad \text{Factored}$$

$$x + 4 = 0 \quad \text{or} \quad x - 6 = 0 \qquad \text{Zero-factor property}$$

$$x = -4 \qquad\qquad x = 6$$

Understanding Algebra

When multiplying both sides of an equation by a variable expression, checking answers is crucial to determine if any of your answers are extraneous solutions that must be eliminated from the final answer.

Check

$$x = -4$$

$$\frac{x^2 - 2x}{x - 6} = \frac{24}{x - 6}$$

$$\frac{(-4)^2 - 2(-4)}{-4 - 6} \stackrel{?}{=} \frac{24}{-4 - 6}$$

$$\frac{16 + 8}{-10} \stackrel{?}{=} \frac{24}{-10}$$

$$\frac{24}{-10} = \frac{24}{-10} \quad \text{True}$$

$$x = 6$$

$$\frac{x^2 - 2x}{x - 6} = \frac{24}{x - 6}$$

$$\frac{6^2 - 2(6)}{6 - 6} \stackrel{?}{=} \frac{24}{6 - 6}$$

$$\frac{24}{0} = \frac{24}{0}$$

$\uparrow \qquad \uparrow$

Since the denominator is 0, and we cannot divide by 0, 6 is not a solution.

Since $\dfrac{24}{0}$ is not a real number, 6 is an extraneous solution. Thus, this equation has only one solution, -4.

Now Try Exercise 47

Helpful Hint

Remember, when solving a rational equation in which a variable appears in a denominator, you must check *all* your answers to make sure that none is an extraneous root. If any of your answers make any denominator 0, that answer is an extraneous root and not a true solution.

EXAMPLE 8 Solve $\dfrac{5w}{w^2 - 4} + \dfrac{1}{w - 2} = \dfrac{4}{w + 2}$.

Solution   First factor $w^2 - 4$.

$$\frac{5w}{(w + 2)(w - 2)} + \frac{1}{w - 2} = \frac{4}{w + 2}$$

Multiply both sides of the equation by the LCD, $(w + 2)(w - 2)$.

$$(w + 2)(w - 2)\left[\frac{5w}{(w + 2)(w - 2)} + \frac{1}{w - 2}\right] = \frac{4}{w + 2} \cdot (w + 2)(w - 2)$$

$$(w + 2)(w - 2) \cdot \frac{5w}{(w + 2)(w - 2)} + (w + 2)(w - 2) \cdot \frac{1}{w - 2} = \frac{4}{w + 2} \cdot (w + 2)(w - 2)$$

$$(w + 2)(w - 2) \cdot \frac{5w}{(w + 2)(w - 2)} + (w + 2)(w - 2) \cdot \frac{1}{w - 2} = \frac{4}{w + 2} \cdot (w + 2)(w - 2)$$

$$5w + (w + 2) = 4(w - 2)$$

$$6w + 2 = 4w - 8$$

$$2w + 2 = -8$$

$$2w = -10$$

$$w = -5$$

A check will show that -5 is the solution to the equation.

Now Try Exercise 65

Helpful Hint

Some students confuse adding and subtracting rational expressions with solving rational equations. When adding or subtracting rational expressions, we must rewrite each expression with a common denominator. When solving a rational equation, we multiply both sides of the equation by the LCD to eliminate fractions from the equation. Consider the following two problems. Note that the one on the right is an equation because it contains an equals sign. We will work both problems. The LCD for both problems is $x(x + 4)$.

Adding Rational Expressions	Solving Rational Equations
$$\frac{x + 2}{x + 4} + \frac{3}{x}$$	$$\frac{x + 2}{x + 4} = \frac{3}{x}$$

We rewrite each fraction with the LCD, $x(x + 4)$.

We eliminate fractions by multiplying both sides of the equation by the LCD, $x(x + 4)$.

$$= \frac{x}{x} \cdot \frac{x + 2}{x + 4} + \frac{3}{x} \cdot \frac{x + 4}{x + 4}$$

$$(x)(x + 4)\left(\frac{x + 2}{x + 4}\right) = \frac{3}{x}(x)(x + 4)$$

$$= \frac{x(x + 2)}{x(x + 4)} + \frac{3(x + 4)}{x(x + 4)}$$

$$x(x + 2) = 3(x + 4)$$

$$= \frac{x^2 + 2x}{x(x + 4)} + \frac{3x + 12}{x(x + 4)}$$

$$x^2 + 2x = 3x + 12$$

$$= \frac{x^2 + 2x + 3x + 12}{x(x + 4)}$$

$$x^2 - x - 12 = 0$$

$$= \frac{x^2 + 5x + 12}{x(x + 4)}$$

$$(x - 4)(x + 3) = 0$$

$$x - 4 = 0 \quad \text{or} \quad x + 3 = 0$$

$$x = 4 \qquad\qquad x = -3$$

The numbers 4 and -3 on the right will both check and are thus solutions to the equation.

Understanding Algebra

When adding and subtracting rational expressions, we usually end up with an algebraic expression.

When solving rational equations, the solution, if one exists, will be a numerical value or values.

EXERCISE SET 6.6   Math XL   MyMathLab

Warm-Up Exercises

Fill in the blanks with the appropriate word, phrase, or symbol(s) from the following list.

LCD   check   rational expression   No $(x + 1)(x - 3)$

rational equation   multiplied $x + 1$ Yes

1. When solving rational equations, both sides of the equation are _____ by the LCD.

2. When solving rational equations with variable denominators, it is very important to _____ your answers.

3. $\frac{x}{2} - \frac{x}{3} + \frac{5}{2x + 7}$ is an example of a _____ .

4. The first step in solving a rational equation is determining the _____ of all fractions.

5. $\frac{x}{2} - \frac{x}{3} = \frac{5}{2x + 7}$ is an example of a _____ .

6. (Yes or No) Is $x = 2$ a solution to the equation $\frac{3}{x - 2} + \frac{2}{x + 2} = \frac{4x}{x^2 - 4}$? _____

7. (Yes or No) Is $x = 1$ a solution to the equation $\frac{3}{x - 2} + \frac{2}{x + 2} = \frac{7x}{x^2 - 4}$? _____

8. The first step in solving the equation $\frac{9}{x + 1} = \frac{5}{x - 3}$ is to multiply both sides of the equation by the algebraic expression _____ .

Practice the Skills

Solve each equation and check your solution. See Examples 1 and 2.

9. $\frac{x}{3} + \frac{x}{2} = 10$

10. $\frac{x}{3} - \frac{x}{2} = 10$

11. $\frac{y}{6} - \frac{y}{4} = \frac{1}{2}$

12. $\frac{x}{4} - \frac{x}{6} = \frac{1}{2}$

13. $\frac{x}{3} - \frac{x}{4} = 1$

14. $\frac{t}{5} - \frac{t}{6} = 2$

15. $\frac{r}{6} = \frac{r}{4} + \frac{1}{3}$

16. $\frac{n}{5} = \frac{n}{6} + \frac{2}{3}$

17. $\frac{z}{2} + 6 = \frac{z}{5}$

18. $\frac{3w}{5} - 6 = w$

19. $\frac{z}{6} + \frac{2}{3} = \frac{z}{5} - \frac{1}{3}$

20. $\frac{m - 2}{6} = \frac{2}{3} + \frac{m}{12}$

21. $d + 7 = \frac{3}{2}d + 5$

22. $\frac{q}{5} + \frac{q}{2} = \frac{21}{10}$

23. $3k + \frac{1}{6} = 4k - 4$

24. $\frac{p}{4} + \frac{1}{4} = \frac{p}{3} - \frac{1}{2}$

25. $\frac{n + 6}{3} = \frac{5(n - 8)}{10}$

26. $\frac{3(x - 6)}{5} = \frac{4(x + 2)}{8}$

27. $\frac{x - 5}{15} = \frac{3}{5} - \frac{x - 4}{10}$

28. $\frac{z + 4}{6} = \frac{3}{2} - \frac{2z + 2}{12}$

29. $\frac{-p + 1}{4} + \frac{13}{20} = \frac{p}{5} - \frac{p - 1}{2}$

30. $\frac{1}{10} - \frac{n + 1}{6} = \frac{1}{5} - \frac{n + 10}{15}$

31. $\frac{d - 3}{4} + \frac{1}{15} = \frac{2d + 1}{3} - \frac{34}{15}$

32. $\frac{t + 4}{5} = \frac{5}{8} + \frac{t + 7}{40}$

Solve each equation and check your solution. See Examples 3–8.

33. $2 + \frac{3}{x} = \frac{11}{4}$

34. $3 - \frac{1}{x} = \frac{14}{5}$

35. $7 - \frac{5}{x} = \frac{9}{2}$

36. $4 + \frac{3}{z} = \frac{9}{2}$

37. $\frac{4}{n} - \frac{3}{2n} = \frac{1}{2}$

38. $\frac{5}{3x} + \frac{2}{x} = 1$

39. $\frac{x - 1}{x - 5} = \frac{4}{x - 5}$

40. $\frac{2x + 3}{x + 2} = \frac{3}{2}$

41. $\frac{5}{a + 3} = \frac{4}{a + 1}$

42. $\frac{5}{x + 2} = \frac{1}{x - 4}$

43. $\frac{y + 3}{y - 3} = \frac{6}{4}$

44. $\frac{x}{x + 6} = \frac{2}{5}$

45. $\frac{2x - 3}{x - 4} = \frac{5}{x - 4}$

46. $\frac{3}{x} + 9 = \frac{3}{x}$

47. $\frac{x^2}{x - 3} = \frac{9}{x - 3}$

48. $\frac{x^2}{x + 5} = \frac{25}{x + 5}$

49. $\frac{n - 3}{n + 2} = \frac{n + 4}{n + 10}$

50. $\frac{x + 5}{x + 1} = \frac{x - 6}{x - 3}$

51. $\frac{1}{r} = \frac{3r}{8r + 3}$

52. $\frac{1}{r} = \frac{2r}{r + 15}$

53. $\frac{k}{k + 2} = \frac{3}{k - 2}$

54. $\frac{3a - 2}{2a + 2} = \frac{3}{a - 1}$

55. $\frac{4}{r} + r = \frac{20}{r}$

56. $a + \frac{5}{a} = \frac{14}{a}$

57. $x + \frac{20}{x} = -9$

58. $x - \frac{32}{x} = 4$

59. $\frac{3y - 2}{y + 1} = 4 - \frac{y + 2}{y - 1}$

60. $\frac{2b}{b + 1} = 2 - \frac{5}{2b}$

61. $\frac{1}{x + 3} + \frac{1}{x - 3} = \frac{-5}{x^2 - 9}$

62. $\frac{t + 2}{t - 5} - \frac{3}{4} = \frac{6}{t - 5}$

63. $\frac{x}{x - 3} + \frac{3}{2} = \frac{3}{x - 3}$

64. $\frac{y}{2y + 2} + \frac{2y - 16}{4y + 4} = \frac{y - 3}{y + 1}$

65. $\frac{3}{x - 5} - \frac{4}{x + 5} = \frac{11}{x^2 - 25}$

66. $\frac{2n^2 - 15}{n^2 + n - 6} = \frac{n + 1}{n + 3} + \frac{n - 3}{n - 2}$

67. $\dfrac{3x}{x^2 - 9} + \dfrac{1}{x - 3} = \dfrac{3}{x + 3}$

68. $\dfrac{3}{x + 3} + \dfrac{5}{x + 4} = \dfrac{12x + 7}{x^2 + 7x + 12}$

69. $\dfrac{1}{y - 1} + \dfrac{1}{2} = \dfrac{2}{y^2 - 1}$

70. $\dfrac{2y}{y + 2} = \dfrac{y}{y + 3} - \dfrac{3}{y^2 + 5y + 6}$

71. $\dfrac{3t}{6t + 6} + \dfrac{t}{2t + 2} = \dfrac{2t - 3}{t + 1}$

72. $\dfrac{2}{x - 2} - \dfrac{1}{x + 1} = \dfrac{2}{x^2 - x - 2}$

Problem Solving

In Exercises 73–78, determine the solution by observation. Explain how you determined your answer.

73. $\dfrac{3}{x - 2} = \dfrac{x - 2}{x - 2}$

74. $\dfrac{1}{2} + \dfrac{x}{2} = \dfrac{5}{2}$

75. $\dfrac{x}{x - 6} + \dfrac{x}{x - 6} = 0$

76. $\dfrac{x}{4} + \dfrac{3x}{4} = x$

77. $\dfrac{x - 2}{3} + \dfrac{x - 2}{3} = \dfrac{2x - 4}{3}$

78. $\dfrac{3}{x} - \dfrac{1}{x} = \dfrac{2}{x}$

79. Optics A formula frequently used in optics is

$$\frac{1}{p} + \frac{1}{q} = \frac{1}{f}$$

where p represents the distance of the object from a mirror (or lens), q represents the distance of the image from the mirror (or lens), and f represents the focal length of the mirror (or lens). If a mirror has a focal length of 10 centimeters, how far from the mirror will the image appear when the object is 30 centimeters from the mirror?

© Kellie. L. Folkerts\Shutterstock

Challenge Problems

80. a) Explain why the equation $\dfrac{x^2}{x - 3} = \dfrac{9}{x - 3}$ cannot be solved by cross-multiplying using the material presented in the book.

b) Solve the equation given in part **a)**.

81. Solve the equation $\dfrac{x - 4}{x^2 - 2x} = \dfrac{-4}{x^2 - 4}$

82. Electrical Resistance In electronics the total resistance R_T, of resistors wired in a parallel circuit is determined by the formula

$$\frac{1}{R_T} = \frac{1}{R_1} + \frac{1}{R_2} + \frac{1}{R_3} + \cdots + \frac{1}{R_n}$$

where $R_1, R_2, R_3, \ldots, R_n$ are the resistances of the individual resistors (measured in ohms) in the circuit.

a) Find the total resistance if two resistors, one of 200 ohms and the other of 300 ohms, are wired in a parallel circuit.

b) If three identical resistors are to be wired in parallel, what should be the resistance of each resistor if the total resistance of the circuit is to be 300 ohms?

83. Can an equation of the form $\dfrac{a}{x} + 1 = \dfrac{a}{x}$ have a real number solution for any real number a? Explain your answer.

Group Activity

Discuss and answer Exercise 84 as a group.

84. a) As a group, discuss two different methods you can use to solve the equation $\dfrac{x + 3}{5} = \dfrac{x}{4}$.

b) Group member 1: Solve the equation by obtaining a common denominator.

Group member 2: Solve the equation by cross-multiplying.

Group member 3: Check the results of group member 1 and group member 2.

c) Individually, create another equation by taking the reciprocal of each term in the equation in part **a)**. Compare your results. Do you think that the reciprocal of the answer you found in part **b)** will be the solution to this equation? Explain.

d) Individually, solve the equation you found in part **c)** and check your answer. Compare your work with the other group members. Was the conclusion you came to in part **c)** correct? Explain.

e) As a group, solve the equation $\dfrac{1}{x} + \dfrac{1}{3} = \dfrac{2}{x}$. Check your result.

f) As a group, create another equation by taking the reciprocal of each term of the equation in part **e)**. Do you think that the reciprocal of the answer you found in part **e)** will be the solution to this equation? Explain.

g) Individually, solve the equation you found in part **f)** and check your answer. Compare your work with the other group members. Did your group make the correct conclusion in part **f)**? Explain.

h) As a group, discuss the relationship between the solution to the equation $\dfrac{7}{x - 9} = \dfrac{3}{x}$ and the solution to the equation $\dfrac{x - 9}{7} = \dfrac{x}{3}$. Explain your answer.

Cumulative Review Exercises

[3.2]   **85. Internet Plans** An Internet service offers two plans for its customers. One plan includes 5 hours of use and costs $7.95 per month. Each additional minute after the 5 hours costs $0.15. The second plan costs $19.95 per month and provides unlimited Internet access. How many hours would Jake LaRue have to use the Internet monthly to make the second plan the less expensive?

86. Filling a Hot Tub How long will it take to fill a 600-gallon hot tub if water is flowing into the hot tub at a rate of 4 gallons a minute?

[3.3]   **87. Supplementary Angles** Two angles are supplementary angles if the sum of their measures is 180°. Find the two supplementary angles if the smaller angle is 30° less than half the larger angle.

See Exercise 86.

[4.6]   **88.** Multiply $(3.4 \times 10^{-5})(2 \times 10^{13})$.

6.7 Rational Equations: Applications and Problem Solving

1 Set up and solve applications containing rational expressions.

2 Set up and solve motion problems.

3 Set up and solve work problems.

FIGURE 6.1

1 Set Up and Solve Applications Containing Rational Expressions

Many applications of algebra involve rational equations. After we represent the application as an equation, we solve the rational equation as we did in Section 6.6.

The first type of application we will consider is a *geometry problem*.

EXAMPLE 1 A New Rug Mary and Larry Armstrong are interested in purchasing a carpet whose area is 60 square feet. Determine the length and width if the width is 5 feet less than $\frac{3}{5}$ of the length. See **Figure 6.1**.

Solution

Understand and Translate

Let x = length.

Then $\frac{3}{5}x - 5$ = width.

$$\text{area} = \text{length} \cdot \text{width}$$

$$60 = x\left(\frac{3}{5}x - 5\right)$$

Carry Out

$$60 = \frac{3}{5}x^2 - 5x$$

$$5\,(60) = 5\left(\frac{3}{5}x^2 - 5x\right) \qquad \text{Multiply both sides by 5.}$$

$$300 = 3x^2 - 25x \qquad \text{Distributive property was used.}$$

$$0 = 3x^2 - 25x - 300 \qquad \text{Subtracted 300 from both sides.}$$

$$\text{or} \quad 3x^2 - 25x - 300 = 0$$

$$(3x + 20)(x - 15) = 0 \qquad \text{Factored.}$$

$$3x + 20 = 0 \quad \text{or} \quad x - 15 = 0 \qquad \text{Zero-factor property}$$

$$3x = -20 \qquad\qquad x = 15$$

$$x = -\frac{20}{3}$$

Check and Answer Since the length of a rectangle cannot be negative, we can eliminate $-\dfrac{20}{3}$ as an answer to our problem.

$$\text{length} = x = 15 \text{ feet}$$

$$\text{width} = \dfrac{3}{5}(15) - 5 = 4 \text{ feet}$$

Check
$$a = lw$$
$$60 \overset{?}{=} 15(4)$$
$$60 = 60 \qquad \text{True}$$

Therefore, the length is 15 feet and the width is 4 feet.

Now Try Exercise 5

Now we will work with a problem that expresses the relationship between two numbers. Problems like this are sometimes referred to as *number problems*.

EXAMPLE 2 **Reciprocals** One number is 4 times another number. The sum of their reciprocals is $\dfrac{5}{2}$. Determine the numbers.

Solution Understand and Translate

$$\text{Let } x = \text{first number.}$$
$$\text{Then } 4x = \text{second number.}$$

The reciprocal of the first number is $\dfrac{1}{x}$ and the reciprocal of the second number is $\dfrac{1}{4x}$. The sum of their reciprocals is $\dfrac{5}{2}$, thus, $\dfrac{1}{x} + \dfrac{1}{4x} = \dfrac{5}{2}$.

Carry Out
$$\dfrac{1}{x} + \dfrac{1}{4x} = \dfrac{5}{2}$$

$$4x\left(\dfrac{1}{x} + \dfrac{1}{4x}\right) = 4x\left(\dfrac{5}{2}\right) \qquad \text{Multiply both sides by the LCD, } 4x.$$

$$4x\left(\dfrac{1}{x}\right) + 4x\left(\dfrac{1}{4x}\right) = 10x \qquad \text{Distributive property}$$

$$4 + 1 = 10x$$
$$5 = 10x$$
$$\dfrac{5}{10} = x$$
$$\dfrac{1}{2} = x$$

Check The first number is $\dfrac{1}{2}$. The second number is therefore $4x = 4\left(\dfrac{1}{2}\right) = 2$.

Let's now check if the sum of the reciprocals is $\dfrac{5}{2}$. The reciprocal of $\dfrac{1}{2}$ is 2. The reciprocal of 2 is $\dfrac{1}{2}$. The sum of the reciprocals is

$$2 + \dfrac{1}{2} = \dfrac{4}{2} + \dfrac{1}{2} = \dfrac{5}{2}$$

Answer Since the sum of the reciprocals is $\dfrac{5}{2}$, the two numbers are 2 and $\dfrac{1}{2}$.

Now Try Exercise 11

Understanding Algebra

The distance formula is usually written as:

$$\text{distance} = \text{rate} \cdot \text{time}$$

However, it is sometimes convenient to solve the formula for *time*:

$$\frac{\text{distance}}{\text{rate}} = \frac{\text{rate} \cdot \text{time}}{\text{rate}}$$

$$\frac{\text{distance}}{\text{rate}} = \text{time}$$

or $\text{time} = \dfrac{\text{distance}}{\text{rate}}$

2 Set Up and Solve Motion Problems

In Chapter 3 we discussed *motion problems.* Recall that

$$\text{distance} = \text{rate} \cdot \text{time}$$

If we solve this equation for time, we obtain

$$\text{time} = \frac{\text{distance}}{\text{rate}} \quad \text{or} \quad t = \frac{d}{r}$$

This equation is useful in solving motion problems when the total time of travel for two objects or the time of travel between two points is known.

EXAMPLE 3   Canoeing Cindy Kilborn went canoeing in the Colorado River. The current in the river was 2 miles per hour. If it took Cindy the same amount of time to travel 10 miles downstream as 2 miles upstream, determine the speed at which Cindy's canoe would travel in still water.

Solution   Understand and Translate

Let $r = $ the canoe's speed in still water.

Then $r + 2 = $ the canoe's speed traveling downstream (with current)

and $r - 2 = $ the canoe's speed traveling upstream (against current.)

Direction	Distance	Rate	Time
Downstream	10	$r + 2$	$\dfrac{10}{r + 2}$
Upstream	2	$r - 2$	$\dfrac{2}{r - 2}$

Since the time it takes to travel 10 miles downstream is the same as the time to travel 2 miles upstream, we set the times equal to each other and then solve the resulting equation.

$$\text{time downstream} = \text{time upstream}$$

$$\frac{10}{r + 2} = \frac{2}{r - 2}$$

Carry Out
$$10(r - 2) = 2(r + 2) \qquad \text{Cross-multiplied.}$$
$$10r - 20 = 2r + 4$$
$$8r = 24$$
$$r = 3$$

Check and Answer   A check will show that 3 satisfies the equation. Thus, the canoe would travel at 3 miles per hour in still water.

Now Try Exercise 15

EXAMPLE 4   Scenic Route Shelby Kaylor drives along Route 72 in Oahu, Hawaii. Because of the beautiful scenery she drives an average of 20 miles per hour. Then she drives inland and averages 65 miles per hour. If the total distance she drove was 100 miles and the total time she drove was 3.5 hours, how long did she drive at each speed?

Solution   Understand and Translate

Let $d = $ distance traveled at 20 miles per hour.

Then $100 - d = $ distance traveled at 65 miles per hour.

Direction	Distance	Rate	Time
Shoreline	d	20	$\dfrac{d}{20}$
Inland	$100 - d$	65	$\dfrac{100 - d}{65}$

Since the total time spent driving is 3.5 hours, we write

$$\text{time along shoreline} + \text{time inland} = 3.5 \text{ hours}$$

$$\frac{d}{20} + \frac{100 - d}{65} = 3.5$$

Carry Out
$$260\left(\frac{d}{20} + \frac{100 - d}{65}\right) = 260(3.5) \qquad \text{Multiply both sides by the LCD, 260.}$$

$$\overset{13}{\cancel{260}}\left(\frac{d}{\cancel{20}}\right) + \overset{4}{\cancel{260}}\left(\frac{100 - d}{\cancel{65}}\right) = 910 \qquad \text{Distributive property}$$

$$13d + 4(100 - d) = 910$$

$$13d + 400 - 4d = 910$$

$$9d + 400 = 910$$

$$9d = 510$$

$$d = \frac{510}{9}$$

$$d \approx 57$$

Answer   Remember that the question asked us to find the *time* spent traveling at each speed. The variable d represents the distance traveled at 20 miles per hour. To find the time traveled and to answer the question asked, we need to evaluate $\frac{d}{20}$ and $\frac{100 - d}{65}$ for $d = 57$.

Time at 20 mph
$$\frac{d}{20} = \frac{57}{20} \approx 2.9$$

Time at 65 mph
$$\frac{100 - d}{65} = \frac{100 - 57}{65} = \frac{43}{65} \approx 0.6$$

Thus, Shelby drove about 2.9 hours along the shoreline and about 0.6 hours inland. The total time was $2.9 + 0.6$ or 3.5 hours.

Now Try Exercise 17

EXAMPLE 5   **Distance of a Race**   At a fund-raising race participants can either bike, walk, or run. Kim Clark, who rode a bike, completed the entire distance of the race with an average speed of 16 kilometers per hour (kph). Steve Schwartz, who jogged, completed the entire distance with an average speed of 5 kph. If Kim completed the race in 2.75 hours less time than Steve did, determine the distance the race covered.

Solution   Understand and Translate   Let d = the distance from the start to the finish of the race. Then we can construct the following table. To determine the time, we divide the distance by the rate.

Person	Distance	Rate	Time
Kim	d	16	$\frac{d}{16}$
Steve	d	5	$\frac{d}{5}$

We are given that Kim completed the race in 2.75 hours less time than Steve did. Therefore, to make Kim's and Steve's times equal, we need to subtract 2.75 hours from Steve's time (or add 2.75 hours to Kim's time).

$$\text{Time for Kim} = \text{Time for Steve} - 2.75 \text{ hours}$$

$$\frac{d}{16} = \frac{d}{5} - 2.75$$

Carry Out
$$80\left(\frac{d}{16}\right) = 80\left(\frac{d}{5} - 2.75\right)$$ Multiply both sides by the LCD, 80.

$$5d = 80\left(\frac{d}{5}\right) - 80(2.75)$$ Distributive property was used.

$$5d = 16d - 220$$

$$-11d = -220$$

$$d = 20$$

Check and Answer To check this answer we will determine the times it took Kim and Steve to complete the race and see if the difference between the times is 2.75 hours. To determine the times, divide the distance, 20 kilometers, by the rate.

$$\text{Kim's time} = \frac{d}{16} = \frac{20}{16} = 1.25 \text{ hours}$$

$$\text{Steve's time} = \frac{d}{5} = \frac{20}{5} = 4 \text{ hours}$$

Since $4 - 1.25 = 2.75$ hours, the answer checks. Therefore the distance the race covered is 20 kilometers.

Now Try Exercise 25

3 Set Up and Solve Work Problems

When two machines or two people work together to get a job done, the situation leads to solving a *work problem*. To solve work problems, we use the fact summarized in the following diagram:

$$\left(\begin{array}{c}\text{part of task done}\\\text{by one person}\\\text{or machine}\end{array}\right) + \left(\begin{array}{c}\text{part of task done}\\\text{by second person}\\\text{or machine}\end{array}\right) = \left(\begin{array}{c}1\\(\text{one completed})\\\text{task}\end{array}\right)$$

To determine the part of the task done by each person or machine, we use the following formula:

rate of work · time worked = part of task completed

An important step in solving these problems is determining the *rate* of work. Consider the following examples:

- If Joe can do a task by himself in 5 hours, his *rate* is $\frac{1}{5}$ of the task per hour.

- If Yoko can do a task by herself in 4 hours, her *rate* is $\frac{1}{4}$ of the task per hour.

- If a pump can empty a 10-gallon tank in 1 hour, its *rate* is $\frac{1}{10}$ of a gallon per hour.

In general, if a task can get done in x hours, then the *rate* for completing that task is $\frac{1}{x}$ of the task per hour.

Understanding Algebra

Problems where two or more people or machines work together to complete a task are referred to as *work problems*

Understanding Algebra

If JoAnn can perform a task in 6 hours, then her *rate* of work is $\frac{1}{6}$ task per hour.

If she then works t hours, the *amount* of work she has completed is represented as $\frac{1}{6} \cdot t$ or $\frac{t}{6}$ of the task.

EXAMPLE 6 **Plowing a Field** Bob can plow a field by himself in 20 hours. His wife, Mary, can plow the same field by herself in 30 hours. How long will it take them to plow the field if they work together?

Solution Understand and Translate Let $t =$ the time, in hours, for Bob and Mary working together to plow the field. We will construct a table to help us in finding the part of the task completed by Bob and Mary in t hours.

Person	Rate of Work (part of the task completed per hour)	Time Worked	Part of Task
Bob	$\dfrac{1}{20}$	t	$\dfrac{t}{20}$
Mary	$\dfrac{1}{30}$	t	$\dfrac{t}{30}$

$$\left(\begin{array}{c}\text{part of the field plowed}\\\text{by Bob in } t \text{ hours}\end{array}\right) + \left(\begin{array}{c}\text{part of the field plowed}\\\text{by Mary in } t \text{ hours}\end{array}\right) = 1(\text{entire field plowed})$$

$$\frac{t}{20} \quad + \quad \frac{t}{30} \quad = 1$$

Carry Out Now multiply both sides of the equation by the LCD, 60.

$$60\left(\frac{t}{20} + \frac{t}{30}\right) = 60 \cdot 1$$

$$\overset{3}{60}\left(\frac{t}{20}\right) + \overset{2}{60}\left(\frac{t}{30}\right) = 60 \qquad \text{Distributive property}$$

$$3t + 2t = 60$$

$$5t = 60$$

$$t = 12$$

Answer Thus, Bob and Mary working together can plow the field in 12 hours. We leave the check for you.

Now Try Exercise 27

Helpful Hint

In Example 6, Bob could plow the field by himself in 20 hours, and Mary could plow the field by herself in 30 hours. We determined that together they could plow the field in 12 hours. Does this answer make sense? Since you would expect the time to plow the field together to be less than the time either of them could plow it alone, the answer makes sense.

EXAMPLE 7 **Storing Wine** At a winery in Napa Valley, California, one pipe can fill a tank with wine in 3 hours and another pipe can empty the tank in 5 hours. If the valves to both pipes are open, how long will it take to fill the empty tank?

Solution Understand and Translate Let $t =$ amount of time to fill the tank with the values to both pipes open.

Pipe	Rate of Work	Time	Part of Task
Pipe filling tank	$\dfrac{1}{3}$	t	$\dfrac{t}{3}$
Pipe emptying tank	$\dfrac{1}{5}$	t	$\dfrac{t}{5}$

As one pipe is filling, the other is emptying the tank. Therefore, instead of adding the parts of the task, we will subtract the parts of the task.

$$\left(\begin{array}{c}\text{part of tank}\\\text{filled in } t \text{ hours}\end{array}\right) - \left(\begin{array}{c}\text{part of tank}\\\text{emptied in } t \text{ hours}\end{array}\right) = 1(\text{total tank filled})$$

$$\frac{t}{3} - \frac{t}{5} = 1$$

Carry Out
$$15\left(\frac{t}{3} - \frac{t}{5}\right) = 15 \cdot 1 \qquad \text{Multiply both sides by the LCD, 15.}$$

$$\overset{5}{\cancel{15}}\left(\frac{t}{\cancel{3}}\right) - \overset{3}{\cancel{15}}\left(\frac{t}{\cancel{5}}\right) = 15 \qquad \text{Distributive property was used.}$$

$$5t - 3t = 15$$

$$2t = 15$$

$$t = 7\frac{1}{2}$$

Check and Answer   The tank will be filled in $7\frac{1}{2}$ hours. This answer is reasonable because we expect it to take longer than 3 hours when the tank is being drained at the same time.

Now Try Exercise 35

EXAMPLE 8 Cleaning Service Linda and John Franco own a house cleaning service. When Linda cleans Damon's house by herself, it takes 7 hours. When Linda and John work together, they can clean the house in 4 hours. How long will it take John to clean the house by himself?

Solution   Let t = time for John to clean the house by himself. Then John's rate is $\frac{1}{t}$. Since Linda can clean the house by herself in 7 hours, her rate is $\frac{1}{7}$ of the job per hour. In the table below, we use the fact that together they can clean the house in 4 hours.

Worker	Rate of Work	Time	Part of Task
Linda	$\frac{1}{7}$	4	$\frac{4}{7}$
John	$\frac{1}{t}$	4	$\frac{4}{t}$

$$\begin{pmatrix} \text{part of house} \\ \text{cleaned by Linda} \end{pmatrix} + \begin{pmatrix} \text{part of house} \\ \text{cleaned by John} \end{pmatrix} = 1$$

$$\frac{4}{7} \qquad + \qquad \frac{4}{t} \qquad = 1$$

Carry Out
$$7t\left(\frac{4}{7} + \frac{4}{t}\right) = 7t \cdot 1 \qquad \text{Multiply both sides by the LCD, } 7t.$$

$$\cancel{7}t\left(\frac{4}{\cancel{7}}\right) + 7\cancel{t}\left(\frac{4}{\cancel{t}}\right) = 7t \qquad \text{Distributive property was used.}$$

$$4t + 28 = 7t$$

$$28 = 3t$$

$$\frac{28}{3} = t$$

$$9\frac{1}{3} = t$$

Understanding Algebra

In Example 8, notice that if two people were to work at Linda's rate, they would clean the house in $\frac{1}{2} \times 7 = \frac{7}{2}$, or $3\frac{1}{2}$, hours.

Since Linda and John together clean the house in 4 hours, we know that John cleans at a slower rate than Linda!

This is one way to determine that our answer makes sense.

Check and Answer   Thus, it takes John $9\frac{1}{3}$ hours, or 9 hours 20 minutes, to clean the house by himself. This answer is reasonable because we expect it to take longer for John to clean the house by himself than it would for Linda and John working together.

Now Try Exercise 39

EXAMPLE 9 **Thank-You Notes** Peter and Kaitlyn Kewin are handwriting thank-you notes to guests who attended their 20th wedding anniversary party. Kaitlyn by herself could write all the notes in 6 hours and Peter could write all the notes by himself in 10 hours. After Kaitlyn has been writing thank-you notes for 4 hours by herself, she must leave town on business. Peter then continues the task of writing the thank-you notes. How long will it take Peter to finish writing the remaining notes?

Solution   Understand and Translate   Let $t =$ time it will take Peter to finish writing the notes.

Person	Rate of Work	Time	Part of Task
Kaitlyn	$\dfrac{1}{6}$	4	$\dfrac{4}{6} = \dfrac{2}{3}$
Peter	$\dfrac{1}{10}$	t	$\dfrac{t}{10}$

$$\left(\begin{array}{c} \text{part of notes written} \\ \text{by Kaitlyn} \end{array} \right) + \left(\begin{array}{c} \text{part of notes written} \\ \text{by Peter} \end{array} \right) = 1$$

$$\frac{2}{3} \qquad + \qquad \frac{t}{10} \qquad = 1$$

Carry Out

$$30\left(\frac{2}{3} + \frac{t}{10}\right) = 30 \cdot 1 \qquad \text{Multiply both sides by the LCD, 30.}$$

$$\overset{10}{\cancel{30}}\left(\frac{2}{\cancel{3}_{1}}\right) + \overset{3}{\cancel{30}}\left(\frac{t}{\cancel{10}_{1}}\right) = 30 \qquad \text{Distributive property}$$

$$20 + 3t = 30$$

$$3t = 10$$

$$t = \frac{10}{3} \quad \text{or} \quad 3\frac{1}{3}$$

Answer   Thus, it will take Peter $3\frac{1}{3}$ hours to complete the notes.

Now Try Exercise 37

EXERCISE SET 6.7   *MathXL* MathXL®   *MyMathLab* MyMathLab

Warm-Up Exercises

Fill in the blanks with the appropriate word, phrase, or symbol(s) from the following list.

1 hour	$\dfrac{1}{5}$	$\dfrac{1}{3}$	$\dfrac{\text{distance}}{\text{rate}}$	$\dfrac{\text{rate}}{\text{distance}}$	3	1 complete task

1. In most work problems, one side of the equation is 1. The 1 represents _____ .

2. If Harlan Bricker can paint a room in 3 hours by himself, then his rate of work is _____ of the task per hour.

3. If Michelle Slocum can complete a task in 5 hours, then _____ represents the part of the task completed by her in one hour.

4. If we solve the equation distance = rate · time for time, we get, time = _____ .

Practice the Skills/Problem Solving

In Exercises 5–36, solve the problem and answer the question.

Geometry Problems; see Example 1.

5. **Packaging Computers** The Phillips Paper Company makes rectangular pieces of cardboard for packing computers. The sheets of cardboard are to have an area of 99 square inches, and the length of a sheet is to be 5 inches more than $\frac{2}{3}$ its width. Determine the length and width of the cardboard to be manufactured. Use $A = l \cdot w$.

6. **Carry-on Luggage** On most airlines carry-on luggage can have a maximum width of 10 inches with a maximum volume of 3840 cubic inches (see the figure). If the height of the luggage is $\frac{2}{3}$ the length, determine the dimensions of the largest piece of carry-on luggage. Use $V = lwh$.

7. **Triangles of Dough** Pillsbury Crescent Rolls are packaged in tubes that contain perforated triangles of dough. The base of the triangular piece of dough is about 5 centimeters more than its height. Determine the base and height of a piece of dough if the area is about 42 square centimeters. Use $A = \frac{1}{2}bh$.

© Nikola Spasenoski\Shutterstock

8. **Yield Sign** Yield right of way signs used in the United States are triangles. The area of the sign is about 558 square inches. The height of the sign is about 5 inches less than its base. Determine the length of the base of a yield right of way sign.

9. **Triangular Garden** A triangular area is 20 square feet. Find the base of the triangular area if the height is 1 foot more than $\frac{1}{2}$ the base. Use $A = \frac{1}{2}bh$.

10. **Roofing** One side of the roof of Shelby Kaylor's house is in the shape of a trapezoid and has an area of 200 square feet. If the height of the trapezoid is $\frac{1}{4}$ the sum of the 2 bases, determine the height of the trapezoid. Use $A = \frac{1}{2}h(b + d)$.

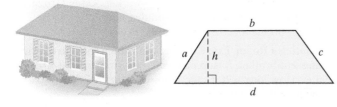

Number Problems; see Example 2.

11. **Difference of Numbers** One number is 9 times larger than another. The difference of their reciprocals is 1. Determine the two numbers.

12. **Sum of Numbers** One number is 3 times larger than another. The sum of their reciprocals is $\frac{4}{3}$. Determine the two numbers.

13. **Increased Numerator** The numerator of the fraction $\frac{3}{4}$ is increased by an amount so that the value of the resulting fraction is $\frac{5}{2}$. Determine the amount by which the numerator was increased.

14. **Decreased Denominator** The denominator of the fraction $\frac{8}{21}$ is decreased by an amount so that the value of the resulting fraction is $\frac{1}{2}$. Determine the amount by which the denominator was decreased.

Motion Problems; see Examples 3–5.

15. **Paddleboat Ride** In the Mississippi River near New Orleans, the Creole Queen paddleboat travels 6 miles upstream (against the current) in the same amount of time it travels 12 miles downstream (with the current). If the current of the river is 3 miles per hour, determine the speed of the Creole Queen in still water.

16. **Kayak Ride** Kathy Boothby-Sestak can paddle her kayak 6 miles per hour in still water. It takes her as long to paddle 5 miles upstream as 10 miles downstream in the Wabash River near Lafayette, Indiana. Determine the river's current.

© Jozef Sedmak\Shutterstock

17. **Trolley Ride** A trolley travels in one direction at an average of 12 miles per hour, then turns around and travels on the same track in the opposite direction at 12 miles per hour. If the total time traveling on the trolley is $2\frac{1}{2}$ hours, how far did the trolley travel in one direction?

18. **Motorcycle Trip** Brandy Dawson and Jason Dodge start a motorcycle trip at the same point north of Fort Worth, Texas. Both are traveling to San Antonio, Texas, a distance of about 400 kilometers. Brandy rides 30 kilometers per hour faster than Jason does. When Brandy reaches her destination, Jason has only traveled to Austin, Texas, a distance of about 250 kilometers. Determine the approximate speed of each motorcycle.

19. **Jet Flight** Elenore Morales traveled 1600 miles by commercial jet from Kansas City, Missouri, to Spokane, Washington. She then traveled an additional 500 miles on a private

propeller plane from Spokane to Billings, Montana. If the speed of the jet was 4 times the speed of the propeller plane and the total time in the air was 6 hours, determine the speed of each plane.

20. **Exercise Regimen** Chris Barker walks a distance of 2 miles on an indoor track and then jogs at twice his walking speed for another 2 miles. If the total time spent on the track was one hour, determine the speeds at which he walks and jogs.

21. **No Wake Zone** Alisha is traveling by motorboat from her dock to Paradise Island. While she is in a no wake zone, her average speed is 4 miles per hour. Once she leaves the no wake zone, her average speed is 28 miles per hour. If the total distance traveled from her dock to the island is 36.6 miles and the total time of the trip is 1.7 hours, determine the distance from her dock to the end of the no wake zone and the distance from the end of the no wake zone to Paradise Island.

22. **The Tail of the Dragon** US 129 in Tennessee is a very popular road for motorcyclists because one stretch of that road has 318 curves and is called The Tail of the Dragon. Larry Gilligan rode his motorcycle in one direction and averaged 22 miles per hour. On the return trip it was raining and he only averaged 11 miles per hour. If the round trip took 1.5 hours, what is the length of The Tail of the Dragon?

23. **Headwind and Tailwind** A Boeing 747 flew from San Francisco to Honolulu, a distance of 2900 miles. Flying with the wind, it averaged 600 miles per hour. When the wind changed from a tailwind to a headwind, the plane's speed dropped to 550 miles per hour. If the total time of the trip was 5 hours, determine the length of time it flew at each speed.

24. **Thalys Train** The Thalys train in Europe has been known to travel an average 240 kilometers per hour (kph). Prior to using the Thalys trains in Europe, trains traveled an average speed of 120 kph. If a Thalys train traveling from Brussels to Amsterdam can complete its trip in 0.88 hour less time than an older train, determine the distance from Brussels to Amsterdam.

Thalys train

25. **Water Skiers** At a water show a boat pulls a water skier at a speed of 30 feet per second. When it reaches the end of the lake, more skiers are added to be pulled by the boat, so the boat's speed drops to 25 feet per second. If the boat traveled the same distance on both trips and the trip back with the additional skiers took 8 seconds longer than the trip with the single skier, how far, in feet, in one direction, had the boat traveled?

26. **Cross-Country Skiing** Alana Bradley and her father Tim begin skiing the same cross-country ski trail in Elmwood Park in Sioux Falls, South Dakota, at the same time. If Alana, who averages 9 miles per hour, finishes the trail 0.25 hours sooner than her father, who averages 6 miles per hour, determine the length of the trail.

Work Problems; see Examples 6–9.

27. **Wallpaper** Reynaldo and Felicia Fernandez decide to wallpaper their family room. Felicia, who has wallpapering experience, can wallpaper the room in 6 hours. Reynaldo can wallpaper the same room in 8 hours. How long will it take them to wallpaper the family room if they work together?

28. **Conveyor Belt** At a salt mine, one conveyor belt requires 20 minutes to fill a large truck with ore. A second conveyor belt requires 30 minutes to fill the same truck with ore. How long would it take if both conveyor belts were working together to fill the truck with ore?

29. **Picking Peaches** In a peach orchard in Williamson, New York, Gary Rominger can load his truck with peaches in 6 hours. His friend, Alex Taurke, takes twice as long to load Gary's truck with peaches. How long will it take them working together to load the truck with peaches?

30. **Watering Plants** In a small nursery, Becky Hailey can water all the plants in 30 minutes. Her co-worker, Karen Grizzaffi, can water all the plants in 20 minutes. How long will it take them working together to water the plants?

31. **Painting a Room** Eric Kweeder can paint a room in 60 minutes. His brother, Jessup, can paint the same room in 40 minutes. How long will it take them working together to paint the room?

32. Tree Chipping The ClearCut Tree Service has two models of chippers, the "Pirate" and the "Ninja." The Pirate can chip a 20-ton load of trees in 2 hours while the Ninja can chip a 20-ton load of trees in 4 hours. How long will it take the two chippers working simultaneously to chip the 20-ton load of trees?

33. Hot Tub Pam and Loren Fornieri know that their hot tub can be filled in 40 minutes and drained completely in 60 minutes. If the water is turned on and the drain is left open, how long would it take the tub to fill completely?

34. Filling a Tank During a rainstorm, the rain is flowing into a large holding tank. At the rate the rain is falling, the empty tank would fill in 8 hours. At the bottom of the tank is a spigot to dispense water. Typically, it takes about 12 hours with the spigot wide open to empty the water in a full tank. If the tank is empty and the spigot has been accidentally left open, and the rain falls at the constant rate, how long would it take for the tank to fill completely?

35. Payroll Checks At the Community Savings Bank, it takes a computer 40 minutes to process and print payroll checks. When a second computer is used and the two computers work together, the checks can be processed and printed in 24 minutes. How long would it take the second computer by itself to process and print the payroll checks?

36. Flowing Water When the water is turned on and passes through a small hose, a pool can be filled in 6 hours. When the water is turned on at two spigots and passes through both the small hose and a large hose, the pool can be filled in 2 hours. How long would it take to fill the pool using only the large hose?

37. Digging a Trench A construction company with two backhoes has contracted to dig a long trench for drainage pipes. The larger backhoe can dig the entire trench by itself in 12 days. The smaller backhoe can dig the entire trench by itself in 15 days. The large backhoe begins working on the trench by itself, but after 5 days it is transferred to a different job and the smaller backhoe begins working on the trench. How long will it take for the smaller backhoe to complete the job?

38. Delivery of Food Ian and Nicole Murphy deliver food to various restaurants. If Ian drove the entire trip, the trip would take about 10 hours. If Nicole drove the entire trip, the trip would take about 8 hours. After Nicole had been driving for 4 hours, Ian takes over the driving. About how much longer will Ian drive before they reach their final destination?

39. Snowstorm Following a snowstorm, Ken and Bettina Reeves must clear their driveway and sidewalk. Ken can clear the snow by himself in 4 hours, and Bettina can clear the snow by herself in 6 hours. After Bettina has been working for 3 hours, Ken is able to join her. How much longer will it take them working together to remove the rest of the snow?

40. Photocopying The College of Applied Science just added two new photocopier machines to its business office and retained one older machine. The older machine, working alone, can copy a full set of diplomas in 3 hours. Each of the two new machines, working alone, can copy a full set of diplomas in 2 hours.

a) How long would it take the three copiers working together to copy a full set of diplomas?

b) How long would it take the three copiers working together to copy 100 full sets of diplomas?

41. Skimming Oil A boat designed to skim oil off the surface of the water has two skimmers. One skimmer can fill the boat's holding tank in 60 hours while the second skimmer can fill the boat's holding tank in 50 hours. There is also a valve in the holding tank that is used to transfer the oil to a larger vessel. If no new oil is coming into the holding tank, a full holding tank of skimmed oil can be transferred to a larger tank in 30 hours. If both skimmers begin skimming and the valve on the holding tank is opened, how long will it take for the empty holding tank on the boat to fill?

42. Flower Garden Bob can plant a flower garden by himself in 8 hours. Mary can plant the same garden by herself in 10 hours, and Gloria can plant the same garden by herself in 12 hours. How long would it take them working together to plant the garden?

Challenge Problems

43. Reciprocal of a Number If 2 times a number is added to 3 times the reciprocal of the number, the answer is 7. Determine the number(s).

44. Determine a Number The reciprocal of the difference of a certain number and 5 is twice the reciprocal of the difference of twice the number and 10. Determine the number(s).

45. Picking Blueberries Ed and Samantha Weisman, whose parents own a fruit farm, must each pick the same number of pints of blueberries each day during the season. Ed picks an average of 8 pints per hour, while Samantha picks an average of 4 pints per hour. If Ed and Samantha begin picking blueberries at the same time, and Samantha finishes 1 hour after Ed, how many pints of blueberries must each pick?

46. Sorting Mail A mail processing machine can sort a large bin of mail in 1 hour. A newer model can sort the same quantity of mail in 30 minutes. If they operate together, how long will it take them to sort the bin of mail?

Cumulative Review Exercises

[2.1] **47.** Simplify $\frac{1}{2}(x + 3) - (2x + 15)$.

[5.2] **48.** Factor $y^2 + 6y - y - 6$ by grouping.

[6.2] **49.** Divide $\dfrac{x^2 - 14x + 48}{x^2 - 5x - 24} \div \dfrac{2x^2 - 13x + 6}{2x^2 + 5x - 3}$.

[6.4] **50.** Subtract $\dfrac{x}{6x^2 - x - 15} - \dfrac{5}{9x^2 - 12x - 5}$.

6.8 Variation

1. Set up and solve direct variation problems.

2. Set up and solve inverse variation problems.

Variation equations show how one quantity changes in relation to another quantity or quantities. In this section we will discuss two types of variation: *direct* and *inverse*. In the exercises, we will address two additional types of variation: *joint* and *combined*.

1 Set Up and Solve Direct Variation Problems

Direct variation involves two variables that increase together or decrease together. For example, consider a car traveling 80 miles per hour on an interstate highway. The car travels

- 80 miles in 1 hour,
- 160 miles in 2 hours,
- 240 miles in 3 hours, and so on.

As the *time* increases, the *distance* also increases.

The formula used to calculate distance traveled is

$$\text{distance} = \text{rate} \cdot \text{time}$$
$$d = rt$$

Since the rate in the example above is constant, the formula can be written

$$d = 80t$$

We say distance *varies directly* as time or that distance is *directly proportional* to time.

> ### Understanding Algebra
>
> *Direct variation* involves two variables that increase together or decrease together. The phrases
>
> - "y varies directly as x" and
> - "y is directly proportional to x"
>
> are both represented by the direct variation equation
>
> $$y = kx.$$

> ### Direct Variation
>
> If a variable y varies directly as a variable x, then
>
> $$y = kx$$
>
> where k is the **constant of proportionality** or the **variation constant**.

EXAMPLE 1 **Heating Up a Hot Tub** When the heater is turned on to warm the water in a hot tub, the temperature of the water, w, increases directly with the length of time in minutes, t, the heater is on.

a) Write the variation equation.

b) If the constant of proportionality, k, is 0.8, find the increase in temperature of the water after 40 minutes.

Solution

a) We are told that the water temperature varies directly with the time. Thus we set up the direct variation equation as follows.

$$w = kt$$

b) To find the increase in water temperature, we will substitute 0.8 for k and 40 for t.

$$w = kt$$
$$w = 0.8(40) = 32$$

Thus, after 40 minutes the water temperature has increased by 32°.

NowTry Exercise 35

In many variation problems you will first have to solve for the constant of proportionality before you can solve for the variable you are asked to find. To determine the constant of proportionality, substitute the values given for the variables, and solve for k.

EXAMPLE 2 **Direct Variation Problem** s varies directly as the square of m. If $s = 125$ when $m = 5$, find s when $m = 12$.

Solution Understand and Translate We begin by setting up the variation equation. Notice that we are told that s varies directly as the square of m. The square of m is written m^2. Therefore, the equation is $s = km^2$. Since we are not given the constant of proportionality, we find it by substituting the values we are given for the variables.

$$s = km^2$$
$$125 = k(5^2) \quad \text{Substituted values.}$$
$$125 = k(25)$$
$$125 = 25k$$
$$5 = k$$

Now that we have determined k, we can answer the question by substituting 5 for k, and 12 for m.

Carry Out
$$s = km^2$$
$$s = 5(12)^2$$
$$s = 5(144)$$
$$s = 720$$

Answer Thus, when $m = 12$, $s = 720$.

NowTry Exercise 27

EXAMPLE 3 **Drug Dosage** The amount of a drug, d, given to a person is directly proportional to the person's weight, w. If an adult who weighs 75 kilograms is given 300 milligrams (mg) of the drug, determine how many milligrams of the drug are given to an adult who weighs 96 kg.

Solution Understand and Translate We are told that the amount of the drug is directly proportional to the person's weight. Thus we set up the equation

$$d = kw$$

Now we determine k by substituting the values given for d and w.

Carry Out

$$d = kw$$
$$300 = k(75)$$
$$\frac{300}{75} = k$$
$$4 = k$$

Now we proceed to find the number of milligrams of the drug to be given by substituting 4 for k and 96 for w.

$$d = kw$$
$$d = 4(96) = 384$$

Check and Answer   Since we expect the amount of the drug to be greater than 300 milligrams, our answer is reasonable. A 96-kg adult should be given 384 milligrams of the drug.

Now Try Exercise 39

2 Set Up and Solve Inverse Variation Problems

Inverse variation involves two variables in which one variable increases as the other decreases and vice versa. For example, consider traveling 120 miles in a car. If the car is traveling

- 30 miles per hour, the trip takes 4 hours,
- 40 miles per hour, the trip takes 3 hours,
- 60 miles per hour, the trip takes 2 hours, and so on.

As the *rate* increases, the time to travel 120 miles decreases.

The formula used to calculate time, given the distance and the rate is

$$\text{time} = \frac{\text{distance}}{\text{rate}}$$

Since the distance in the example above is constant, the formula can be rewritten

$$\text{time} = \frac{120}{\text{rate}}$$

We say time *varies inversely* as rate or that time is *inversely proportional* to rate.

EXAMPLE 4   **Chartering a Sailboat** The cost per person for chartering a sailboat, c, is inversely proportional to the number of people chartering the boat, n. If 8 friends decide to charter the boat, the cost per person is $60. Determine the cost per person if 15 friends decide to charter the boat.

Solution   Understand and Translate   We are told this is an example of inverse variation. Therefore, we will set up an equation to represent the inverse proportion.

$$c = \frac{k}{n}$$

Since we are not given the constant of proportionality, we determine k by substituting the values given for c and n.

$$60 = \frac{k}{8}$$
$$480 = k$$

Now we can determine the answer to the question by using $k = 480$ and $n = 15$.

Carry Out

$$c = \frac{k}{n}$$
$$c = \frac{480}{15}$$
$$c = 32$$

Check and Answer   The cost to each person would be $32 if 15 friends decided to charter the sailboat.

Now Try Exercise 41

EXAMPLE 5 **Speaker Loudness** The loudness, l, of a stereo speaker, measured in decibels (dB), varies inversely as the square of the distance, d, of the listener from the speaker. Assume that for a particular speaker the loudness is 20 dB when the listener is 6 feet from the speaker.

a) Determine an equation that expresses the relationship between the loudness and the distance.

b) Using the equation obtained in part **a)**, determine the loudness when a person is 3 feet from the speaker.

Solution   This problem is broken down into two parts. The first part asks us to find a general formula, while the second part asks us to use the formula.

a) Understand and Translate   We are told that the loudness varies inversely as the *square* of the distance. Thus we write the following equation and solve for k.

Carry Out

$$l = \frac{k}{d^2}$$

$$20 = \frac{k}{6^2}$$

$$20 = \frac{k}{36}$$

$$720 = k$$

Check and Answer   The constant of proportionality, k, is 720. Since for this speaker $k = 720$, the equation we are seeking is

$$l = \frac{720}{d^2}$$

b) Understand and Translate   In part **a)** we determined the equation used to find the loudness. We substitute 3 for d in the formula and solve for l.

$$l = \frac{720}{d^2}$$

$$l = \frac{720}{3^2}$$

Carry Out

$$l = \frac{720}{9}$$

$$l = 80$$

Check and Answer   Thus at 3 feet the loudness is 80 decibels. This is reasonable because at a shorter distance (3 feet versus 6 feet) the sound will be louder.

Now Try Exercise 49

© Roman Barelko\Shutterstock

Understanding Algebra

Direct variation:

As x increases so does y and as x decreases, so does y; we write $y = kx$.

Inverse variation:

As x increases, y decreases and as x decreases, y increases; we write $y = \dfrac{k}{x}$.

k is called the *constant of proportionality* in each case.

EXERCISE SET 6.8   Math XL   MyMathLab
MathXL®   MyMathLab

Warm-Up Exercises

Fill in the blanks with the appropriate word, phrase, or symbol(s) from the following list.

directly   inversely $y = kx$ $y = \dfrac{k}{x}$ uniformly $x = ky$

1. "The variable y varies inversely as x" can be expressed as _____ .

2. "The variable y varies directly as x" can be expressed as _____ .

3. "The speed of a car and the amount of time it takes to travel a specific distance" is an example of speed varying _____ with respect to time.

4. The formula for the surface area (A) of a cube with sides of measure s is $A = 6s^2$. Thus, A varies _____ with respect to the square of the side.

Practice the Skills

Determine if the following are examples of direct variation or inverse variation.

5. The radius of a hose and the amount of water coming out of the hose.

6. The lens opening on a camera and the amount of light reaching the film.

7. The speed of a turtle and the length of time it takes the turtle to cross a road.

8. The age of a car, up to 8 years old, and the value of a car.

9. The temperature of water and the time it takes for an ice cube placed in the water to melt.

10. The number of people in line at the rock concert and the time it takes for all people in line to purchase tickets.

11. The length of a roll of Scotch tape and the number of 2-inch strips that can be obtained from the roll.

12. A person's reading speed and the time it takes to read a novel.

13. The cubic-inch displacement, in liters, and the horsepower of the engine.

14. The speed of a riding lawn mower and the time it takes to cut the lawn.

In Exercises 15–22, find the quantity indicated.

15. x varies directly as z. Find x when $z = 11$ and $k = 40$.

16. x varies directly as y. Find x when $y = 9$ and $k = 6$.

17. x varies inversely as y. Find x when $y = 25$ and $k = 5$.

18. R varies inversely as W. Find R when $W = 80$ and $k = 120$.

19. C varies directly as the square of Z. Find C when $Z = 5$ and $k = 3$.

20. L varies directly as the square of R. Find L when $R = 9$ and $k = 2$.

21. y varies inversely as the square of x. Find y when $x = 10$ and $k = 250$.

22. y varies inversely as the square of w. Find y when $w = 8$ and $k = 288$.

For Exercises 23–30, find the quantity indicated.

23. x varies directly as y. If $x = 9$ when $y = 27$, find x when $y = 60$.

24. Z varies directly as W. If $Z = 7$ when $W = 21$, find Z when $W = 51$.

25. C varies inversely as J. If $C = 7$ when $J = 1$, find C when $J = 2$.

26. H varies inversely as L. If $H = 15$ when $L = 60$, find H when $L = 10$.

27. y varies directly as the square of R. If $y = 4$ when $R = 4$, find y when $R = 12$.

28. A varies directly as the square of B. If $A = 245$ when $B = 7$, find A when $B = 9$.

29. L varies inversely as the square of P. If L is 320 when $P = 20$, find L when $P = 40$.

30. x varies inversely as the square of P. If $x = 10$ when $P = 6$, find x when $P = 20$.

Problem Solving

31. Assume a varies directly as b. If b is doubled, how will it affect a? Explain.

32. Assume a varies directly as b^2. If b is doubled, how will it affect a? Explain.

33. Assume y varies inversely as x. If x is doubled, how will it affect y? Explain.

34. Assume y varies inversely as a^2. If a is doubled, how will it affect y? Explain.

In Exercises 35–54, determine the quantity you are asked to find.

35. **Distance and Speed** The distance, d, a car travels is directly proportional to the speed, s, the car is traveling. Determine the distance traveled if the constant of proportionality, k, is 2 and the speed is 55 miles per hour.

36. **Swimming Pool** The time, t, it takes to fill an inground pool is directly proportional to the amount of water coming out of the hose, w. Determine the time it takes a hose to fill the pool if the constant of proportionality is 0.3 and the amount of water coming out of the hose is 200 gallons per hour.

37. **College Tuition** The amount of tuition a part-time college student is billed, A, varies directly as the number of credits, c, the student is taking. If a student is billed \$1520 for 8 credits, how much would a student be billed for taking 10 credits?

38. **Light through Water** The percent of light that filters through water, l, is inversely proportional to the depth of the water, d. Determine the percent of light that filters down to a depth of 10 feet if the constant of proportionality is 200.

39. **Kiddie Train** The income, I, for a kiddie train at an amusement park is directly proportional to the number of tickets sold, n. If the income, I, is \$33 when 22 tickets are sold, determine the income when 38 tickets are sold.

40. Lawn Mowing The time it takes Sue to mow her lawn, t, is directly proportional to the area of the lawn, A. If it takes Sue 1 hour to cut an area of 2400 square feet, how long will it take her to cut an area of 1800 square feet?

41. Roofing The time, t, it takes to nail in shingles on a roof is inversely proportional to the number of people nailing in the shingles, n. When three people are nailing in the shingles it takes 7 hours to complete the job. How long will it take to complete the job if five people are nailing in the shingles?

42. Baking a Turkey The time, t, it takes to bake a turkey is inversely proportional to the oven temperature, T. If it takes 3 hours to bake a turkey at 300°F, how long will it take to bake the turkey at 250°F?

43. Baseball Gate Receipts The receipts r, at an International League baseball park are directly proportional to the number of people attending the game, n. If the receipts for a game are $37,200 when 1200 people attend, determine how many people attend if the receipts for a game are $31,000.

44. Daily Newspaper The time, t, it takes to print a specific number of copies of a daily newspaper is inversely proportional to the number of presses it has working, n. When 6 presses are working, the newspapers are printed in 8 hours. Determine the number of presses working if the newspapers are printed in 3 hours.

45. Powerboats The horsepower it takes to propel a speedboat, P, is directly proportional to the square of the velocity, v, of the boat. If it takes 900 horsepower for the boat to travel at 45 mph, what horsepower is needed to propel the speedboat at 54 mph?

46. Cleaning Windows The time, t, it takes to clean all the windows in a large office building is inversely proportional to the number of teams, n, of window workers used. If 6 teams can clean all the windows in 20 days, how many teams are used if the windows are cleaned in 12 days?

47. Area of a Circle The area of a circle, A, is directly proportional to the square of the radius of a circle, r. If the area of a circle is about 78.5 square inches when the radius is 5 inches, determine the area when the radius is 12 inches.

48. Falling Object The velocity, v, of a falling object is directly proportional to the square of the time, t, it has been in free fall. An object that has been in free fall for 2 seconds has a velocity of 64 feet per second. Determine the velocity of an object that has been falling for 8 seconds.

49. Electrical Circuit In an electrical circuit the resistance, r, of an appliance is inversely proportional to the square of the current, c. If the resistance is 100 ohms when the current is 0.4 amps, determine the resistance if the current is 0.6 amps.

50. Volume of a Cylinder For a cylinder of a specific volume, the height, h, of the cylinder is inversely proportional to the square of the radius of the cylinder, r. When the radius is 6 inches, the height is 10 inches. Determine the height when the radius is 5 inches.

51. Finding Interest The amount of interest earned on an investment, I, varies directly as the interest rate, r. If the interest earned is $40 when the interest rate is 4%, find the amount of interest earned when the interest rate is 5%.

52. Brick Wall The time, t, required to build a brick wall varies inversely as the number of people, n, working on the wall. If it takes 9 hours for six bricklayers to build a wall, how long will it take two bricklayers to build a wall?

53. Volume of Gas The volume of a gas, V, varies inversely as its pressure, P. If the volume, V, is 800 cubic centimeters when the pressure is 200 millimeters (mm) of

mercury, find the volume when the pressure is 25 mm of mercury.

54. Hooke's Law Hooke's law states that the length a spring will stretch, S, varies directly with the force (or weight), F, attached to the spring. If a spring stretches 1.4 inches when 20 pounds is attached, how far will it stretch when 10 pounds is attached?

Concept/Writing Exercises

55. In variation problems, the constant of proportionality often has a unit attached to it. In Hooke's Law (Exercise 54) for example, where $F = kS$, F is measured in pounds, and S is measured in inches, what is the unit of k?

56. Consider the relationship between the resistance, r, and current, c, in Exercise 49, $r = \dfrac{k}{c^2}$. If r is measured in ohms and c is measured in amperes, what is the unit of k?

Challenge Problems

*In addition to direct variation and inverse variation, there is also joint variation and combined variation. In **joint variation**, one quantity may vary directly (as the product of) two or more quantities. In **combined variation**, one quantity may vary directly with some variables and inversely with other variables. Exercise 57 is a joint variation problem, and Exercise 58 is a combined variation problem. For Exercises 57 and 58, **a)** write the variation equation, and **b)** find the quantity indicated.*

57. x varies jointly as y and z. If x is 72 when $y = 18$ and $z = 2$, find x when $y = 36$ and $z = 3$.

58. T varies directly as the square of D and inversely as F. If $T = 18$ when $D = 6$ and $F = 4$, find T when $D = 8$ and $F = 8$.

Cumulative Review Exercises

[4.6] **59.** Divide $\dfrac{8x^2 + 6x - 21}{4x + 9}$.

[5.1] **60.** Factor $y(z - 2) + 8(z - 2)$.

[5.6] **61.** Solve $3x^2 - 24 = -6x$.

[6.2] **62.** Multiply $\dfrac{x + 8}{x - 3} \cdot \dfrac{x^3 - 27}{x^2 + 3x + 9}$.

Chapter 6 Summary

IMPORTANT FACTS AND CONCEPTS	EXAMPLES
Section 6.1	
A **rational expression** is an expression of the form $\dfrac{p}{q}$, where p and q are polynomials and $q \neq 0$.	$\dfrac{x + 2}{x}$ and $\dfrac{x^2 + x}{x - 1}$ are rational expressions.
Whenever we have a rational expression containing a variable in the denominator, we always assume that the value or values of the variable that make the denominator 0 are excluded.	The rational expression $\dfrac{x - 5}{x - 3}$ is defined for all real numbers except 3.
A rational expression is simplified or reduced to its lowest terms when the numerator and denominator have no common factors other than 1.	$\dfrac{1}{8}$ and $\dfrac{x^2 + x + 1}{2x^2 + 3x + 7}$ are expressions reduced to lowest terms.
To Simplify Rational Expressions 1. Factor both the numerator and denominator completely. 2. Divide out common factors.	$\dfrac{12x^2 - 11x - 5}{9x^2 + 6x + 1} = \dfrac{\cancel{(3x + 1)}(4x - 5)}{\cancel{(3x + 1)}(3x + 1)} = \dfrac{4x - 5}{3x + 1}$

IMPORTANT FACTS AND CONCEPTS	EXAMPLES

Section 6.2

To Multiply Two Fractions

$$\frac{a}{b} \cdot \frac{c}{d} = \frac{a \cdot c}{b \cdot d}, \quad b \neq 0 \quad \text{and} \quad d \neq 0$$

$$\frac{1}{3} \cdot \frac{4}{5} = \frac{1 \cdot 4}{3 \cdot 5} = \frac{4}{15}$$

To Multiply Rational Expressions

1. Factor all numerators and denominators completely.
2. Divide out common factors.
3. Multiply numerators together and multiply denominators together.

$$\frac{4x^3}{7y^2} \cdot \frac{14y^3}{6x} = \frac{\overset{2}{\cancel{4}}\overset{x^2}{\cancel{x^3}} \cdot \overset{2}{\cancel{14}}\overset{y^3}{\cancel{y^3}}}{\cancel{7}y^2 \cdot \underset{3}{\cancel{6}}\,\cancel{x}} = \frac{4x^2y}{3}$$

To Divide Two Fractions

$$\frac{a}{b} \div \frac{c}{d} = \frac{a}{b} \cdot \frac{d}{c} = \frac{ad}{bc}, \quad b \neq 0, \quad d \neq 0, \quad \text{and} \quad c \neq 0$$

$$\frac{3}{5} \div \frac{6}{7} = \frac{\overset{1}{\cancel{3}}}{5} \cdot \frac{7}{\underset{2}{\cancel{6}}} = \frac{7}{10}$$

To Divide Rational Expressions

Multiply the first fraction by the reciprocal of the second fraction.

$$\frac{x+4}{x+3} \div \frac{3x+12}{x+3} = \frac{\cancel{x+4}}{\cancel{x+3}} \cdot \frac{\cancel{x+3}}{3\cancel{(x+4)}} = \frac{1}{3}$$

Section 6.3

To Add or Subtract Two Fractions

$$\frac{a}{c} + \frac{b}{c} = \frac{a+b}{c}, c \neq 0 \qquad \frac{a}{c} - \frac{b}{c} = \frac{a-b}{c}, c \neq 0$$

$$\frac{3}{11} + \frac{4}{11} = \frac{7}{11}, \qquad \frac{18}{19} - \frac{5}{19} = \frac{13}{19}$$

To Add or Subtract Rational Expressions with a Common Denominator

1. Add or subtract the numerators.
2. Place the sum or difference of the numerators over the common denominator.
3. Simplify the fraction if possible.

$$\frac{2}{x-3} + \frac{x+5}{x-3} = \frac{2+x+5}{x-3} = \frac{x+7}{x-3}$$

To Find the Least Common Denominator of Rational Expressions

1. Factor each denominator completely.
2. List all different factors of each denominator. When the same factor appears in more than one denominator, write that factor with the highest power that appears on it.
3. The least common denominator is the product of all the factors listed in step 2.

Find the least common denominator.

$$\frac{1}{9x^3y^4} + \frac{1}{6x^5y^3}$$

$$9x^3y^4 = 3 \cdot 3x^3y^4$$

$$6x^5y^3 = 3 \cdot 2x^5y^3$$

LCD is $2 \cdot 3^2 x^5 y^4 = 18x^5y^4$.

Section 6.4

To Add or Subtract Two Rational Expressions with Unlike Denominators

1. Determine the LCD.
2. Rewrite each fraction as an equivalent fraction with the LCD.
3. Add or subtract the numerators while maintaining the LCD.
4. When possible, factor the remaining numerator and simplify the fraction.

$$\frac{9}{m} + \frac{5}{m-1} = \frac{m-1}{m-1} \cdot \frac{9}{m} + \frac{5}{m-1} \cdot \frac{m}{m}$$

$$= \frac{9(m-1)}{m(m-1)} + \frac{5m}{m(m-1)}$$

$$= \frac{9m-9+5m}{m(m-1)}$$

$$= \frac{14m-9}{m(m-1)}$$

Section 6.5

A **complex fraction** is one that has a fraction in its numerator or its denominator or in both its numerator and denominator.

$$\frac{\dfrac{2}{3}}{\dfrac{4}{7}}, \qquad \frac{\dfrac{1}{x} + \dfrac{1}{y}}{\dfrac{1}{a} + \dfrac{1}{b}}$$

IMPORTANT FACTS AND CONCEPTS	EXAMPLES

Section 6.5 (cont.)

Method 1—To Simplify a Complex Fraction by Combining Terms

1. Add or subtract the fractions in both the numerator and denominator of the complex fraction to obtain single fractions in both.
2. Multiply the fraction in the numerator by the reciprocal of the fraction in the denominator.
3. Simplify further if possible.

$$\frac{1 + \dfrac{1}{x}}{x} = \frac{\dfrac{x}{x} + \dfrac{1}{x}}{x} = \frac{\dfrac{x+1}{x}}{x}$$

$$= \frac{x+1}{x} \cdot \frac{1}{x} = \frac{x+1}{x^2}$$

Method 2—To Simplify a Complex Fraction Using Multiplication First

1. Find the LCD of *all* the denominators appearing in the complex fraction.
2. Multiply both the numerator and denominator of the complex fraction by the LCD found in step 1.
3. Simplify when possible.

$$\frac{1 + \dfrac{1}{x}}{x} = \frac{x}{x} \cdot \frac{1 + \dfrac{1}{x}}{x} = \frac{x(1) + x\left(\dfrac{1}{x}\right)}{x(x)} = \frac{x+1}{x^2}$$

Note: LCD = x.

Section 6.6

A **rational equation** is an equation that contains one or more rational expressions.

$$\frac{1}{3}x - \frac{1}{7}x = 10, \qquad x + \frac{9}{x} = \frac{1}{3}$$

To Solve Rational Equations

1. Determine the LCD of all fractions in the equation.
2. Multiply *both* sides of the equation by the LCD.
3. Remove any parentheses and combine like terms on each side of the equation.
4. Solve the equation using the properties discussed in earlier chapters.
5. Check your solution in the *original* equation.

$$\frac{x}{5} - \frac{x}{8} = 1$$

$$40\left(\frac{x}{5} - \frac{x}{8}\right) = 40\,(1)$$

$$8x - 5x = 40$$

$$3x = 40$$

$$x = \frac{40}{3}$$

A check shows that $\frac{40}{3}$ is the solution.

Section 6.7

Applications

A **geometry problem** involves geometric figures and formulas.

A rectangle has an area of 70 square meters. Find the dimensions if the width is 3 meters shorter than the length.

The answer is 7 meters by 10 meters.

A **motion problem** involves distance, rate, and time and uses the formula

$$\text{distance} = \text{rate} \cdot \text{time}$$

or

$$\text{time} = \frac{\text{distance}}{\text{rate}}$$

or

$$\text{rate} = \frac{\text{distance}}{\text{time}}$$

A cyclist can travel 20 miles with the wind to his back in the same time he can travel 12 miles going into the wind. If the wind is blowing at 2 miles per hour, find the speed of the cyclist without any wind.

The answer is 8 miles per hour.

A **work problem** involves two or more machines or people working together to complete a specific task.

Tom can paint a room in 6 hours and Bill can paint the same room in 4 hours. How long will it take them working together to paint this room?

The answer is 2.4 hours.

Section 6.8

A **variation equation** is an equation that relates one variable to one or more other variables using the operations of multiplication or division.

IMPORTANT FACTS AND CONCEPTS	EXAMPLES

Section 6.8 (cont.)

Direct Variation

In direct variation, as one variable increases, so does the other, and as one variable decreases, so does the other.

If a variable y varies directly as a variable x, then

$$y = kx$$

where k is the *constant of proportionality* (or the variation constant).

m varies directly as the square of n. Find m when $n = 5$ and $k = 4$.

$$
\begin{aligned}
m &= kn^2 \\
&= 4(5)^2 \\
&= 4(25) \\
&= 100
\end{aligned}
$$

Inverse Variation

In inverse variation, as one variable increases, the other quantity decreases, and vice versa.

If a variable y varies inversely as a variable x, then

$$y = \frac{k}{x} \,(\text{or } xy = k)$$

where k is the constant of proportionality.

y varies inversely as the square root of x. Find y when $x = 4$ and $k = 30$.

$$
\begin{aligned}
y &= \frac{k}{\sqrt{x}} \\
&= \frac{30}{\sqrt{4}} \\
&= \frac{30}{2} \\
&= 15
\end{aligned}
$$

Chapter 6 Review Exercises

[6.1]   *Determine the values of the variable for which the following expressions are defined.*

1. $\dfrac{5}{2x - 38}$

2. $\dfrac{2x + 1}{x^2 - 8x + 15}$

3. $\dfrac{7x - 1}{5x^2 + 4x - 1}$

Simplify.

4. $\dfrac{y}{xy - 8y}$

5. $\dfrac{x^3 + 5x^2 + 12x}{x}$

6. $\dfrac{9x^2 + 3xy}{3x}$

7. $\dfrac{x^2 + 2x - 8}{x - 2}$

8. $\dfrac{a^2 - 81}{a - 9}$

9. $\dfrac{-2x^2 + 7x + 4}{x - 4}$

10. $\dfrac{b^2 - 7b + 10}{b^2 - 3b - 10}$

11. $\dfrac{4x^2 - 11x - 3}{4x^2 - 7x - 2}$

12. $\dfrac{2x^2 - 21x + 40}{4x^2 - 4x - 15}$

[6.2]   *Multiply.*

13. $\dfrac{5a^2}{6b} \cdot \dfrac{2}{4a^2 b}$

14. $\dfrac{30x^2 y^3}{3z} \cdot \dfrac{6z^3}{5xy^3}$

15. $\dfrac{20a^3 b^4}{7c^3} \cdot \dfrac{14c^7}{5a^5 b}$

16. $\dfrac{2}{x - 4} \cdot \dfrac{4 - x}{9}$

17. $\dfrac{-m + 4}{15m} \cdot \dfrac{10m}{m - 4}$

18. $\dfrac{a - 2}{a + 3} \cdot \dfrac{a^2 + 4a + 3}{a^2 - a - 2}$

Divide.

19. $\dfrac{9x^6}{y^2} \div \dfrac{x^4}{4y}$

20. $\dfrac{5xy^2}{z} \div \dfrac{x^4 y^2}{4z^2}$

21. $\dfrac{6a + 6b}{a^2} \div \dfrac{a^2 - b^2}{a^2}$

22. $\dfrac{1}{a^2 + 8a + 15} \div \dfrac{8}{a + 5}$

23. $(t + 8) \div \dfrac{t^2 + 5t - 24}{t - 3}$

24. $\dfrac{x^2 + xy - 2y^2}{2y} \div \dfrac{x + 2y}{12y^2}$

[6.3]   *Add or subtract.*

25. $\dfrac{n}{n + 5} - \dfrac{2}{n + 5}$

26. $\dfrac{4x}{x + 7} + \dfrac{28}{x + 7}$

27. $\dfrac{5x - 4}{x + 8} + \dfrac{44}{x + 8}$

28. $\dfrac{7x - 3}{x^2 + 7x - 30} - \dfrac{3x + 9}{x^2 + 7x - 30}$

29. $\dfrac{5h^2 + 12h - 1}{h + 5} - \dfrac{h^2 - 5h + 14}{h + 5}$

30. $\dfrac{6x^2 - 4x}{2x - 3} - \dfrac{-3x + 12}{2x - 3}$

Find the least common denominator for each expression.

31. $\dfrac{a}{8} + \dfrac{5a}{3}$

32. $\dfrac{10}{x + 3} + \dfrac{2x}{x + 3}$

33. $\dfrac{10}{4xy^3} - \dfrac{11}{10x^2 y}$

34. $\dfrac{6}{x-3} - \dfrac{2}{x}$

35. $\dfrac{8}{n+5} + \dfrac{2n-3}{n-4}$

36. $\dfrac{5x-12}{x^2+2x} - \dfrac{4}{x+2}$

37. $\dfrac{2r+1}{r-s} - \dfrac{6}{r^2-s^2}$

38. $\dfrac{3x^2}{x-9} + 10x^3$

39. $\dfrac{19x-5}{x^2+2x-35} + \dfrac{-10x+1}{x^2+9x+14}$

[6.4]   *Add or subtract.*

40. $\dfrac{5}{3y^2} + \dfrac{y}{2y}$

41. $\dfrac{3x}{xy} + \dfrac{1}{4x}$

42. $\dfrac{5x}{3xy} - \dfrac{6}{x^2}$

43. $7 - \dfrac{2}{x+2}$

44. $\dfrac{x-y}{y} - \dfrac{x+y}{x}$

45. $\dfrac{7}{x+4} + \dfrac{2}{x}$

46. $\dfrac{2}{3x} - \dfrac{3}{3x-6}$

47. $\dfrac{1}{(z+5)} + \dfrac{9}{(z+5)^2}$

48. $\dfrac{x+2}{x^2-x-6} + \dfrac{x-3}{x^2-8x+15}$

[6.2–6.4]   *Perform each indicated operation.*

49. $\dfrac{x+4}{x+6} - \dfrac{x-5}{x+2}$

50. $2 + \dfrac{x}{x-4}$

51. $\dfrac{a+2}{b} \div \dfrac{a-2}{5b^2}$

52. $\dfrac{x+5}{x^2-9} + \dfrac{2}{x+3}$

53. $\dfrac{6p+12q}{p^2q} \cdot \dfrac{p^5}{p+2q}$

54. $\dfrac{8}{(x+2)(x-3)} - \dfrac{6}{(x-2)(x+2)}$

55. $\dfrac{x+7}{x^2+9x+14} - \dfrac{x-10}{x^2-49}$

56. $\dfrac{x-y}{x+y} \cdot \dfrac{xy+x^2}{x^2-y^2}$

57. $\dfrac{3x^2-27y^2}{30} \div \dfrac{(x-3y)^2}{6}$

58. $\dfrac{a^2-11a+30}{a-6} \cdot \dfrac{a^2-8a+15}{a^2-10a+25}$

59. $\dfrac{a}{a^2-1} - \dfrac{3}{3a^2-2a-5}$

60. $\dfrac{2x^2+6x-20}{x^2-2x} \div \dfrac{x^2+7x+10}{2x^2-8}$

[6.5]   *Simplify each complex fraction.*

61. $\dfrac{5+\dfrac{1}{3}}{\dfrac{3}{4}}$

62. $\dfrac{1+\dfrac{5}{8}}{3-\dfrac{9}{16}}$

63. $\dfrac{\dfrac{12ab}{9c}}{\dfrac{4a}{c^2}}$

64. $\dfrac{\dfrac{18x^4y^2}{9xy^5}}{4z^2}$

65. $\dfrac{a-\dfrac{a}{b}}{\dfrac{1+a}{b}}$

66. $\dfrac{r^2+\dfrac{7}{s}}{s^2}$

67. $\dfrac{\dfrac{3}{x}+\dfrac{2}{x^2}}{5-\dfrac{1}{x}}$

68. $\dfrac{\dfrac{x}{x+y}}{\dfrac{x^2}{4x+4y}}$

69. $\dfrac{\dfrac{9}{x}}{\dfrac{9}{x^2}}$

70. $\dfrac{\dfrac{1}{a}+3}{\dfrac{1}{a}+\dfrac{3}{a}}$

71. $\dfrac{\dfrac{1}{x^2}-\dfrac{1}{x}}{\dfrac{1}{x^2}+\dfrac{1}{x}}$

72. $\dfrac{\dfrac{8x}{y}-x}{\dfrac{y}{x}-1}$

[6.6]   *Solve.*

73. $\dfrac{5}{8} = \dfrac{10}{x+3}$

74. $\dfrac{x}{4} = \dfrac{x-3}{2}$

75. $\dfrac{12}{n} + 2 = \dfrac{n}{4}$

76. $\dfrac{10}{m} + \dfrac{3}{2} = \dfrac{m}{10}$

77. $\dfrac{-4}{d} = \dfrac{3}{2} + \dfrac{4-d}{d}$

78. $\dfrac{1}{x-7} + \dfrac{1}{x+7} = \dfrac{1}{x^2-49}$

79. $\dfrac{x-3}{x-2} + \dfrac{x+1}{x+3} = \dfrac{2x^2+x+1}{x^2+x-6}$

80. $\dfrac{a}{a^2-64} + \dfrac{4}{a+8} = \dfrac{3}{a-8}$

81. $\dfrac{d}{d-4} - 4 = \dfrac{4}{d-4}$

[6.7]   *Solve.*

82. Sandcastles It takes John and Amy Brogan 6 hours to build a sandcastle. It takes Paul and Cindy Carter 4 hours to make the same sandcastle. How long will it take all four people together to build the sandcastle?

83. Filling a Pool One hose can fill a swimming pool in 7 hours. A second hose can siphon all the water out of a full pool in

12 hours. How long will it take to fill the pool if, while one hose is filling the pool, the other hose is siphoning water from the pool?

84. Sum of Numbers One number is six times as large as another. The sum of their reciprocals is 7. Determine the numbers.

85. Rollerblading and Bicycling Robert Johnston can travel 3 miles on his rollerblades in the same time Tran Lee can travel 8 miles on his mountain bike. If Tran's speed on his bike is 3.5 miles per hour faster than that of Robert on his rollerblades, determine Robert's and Tran's speeds.

© Jupiter Unlimited

[6.8]

86. Drug Dosage The recommended dosage, d, of the antibiotic drug vancomycin is directly proportional to a person's weight, w. If Carmen Brown, who is 132 pounds, is given 182 milligrams, find the recommended dosage for Bill Glenn, who is 198 pounds.

87. Boyle's Law When a gas is kept at a constant temperature, its volume, V, is inversely proportional to the pressure on the gas. If the pressure on 18 cubic inches of argon gas is 4 pounds per square inch, determine the volume of the gas when the pressure is 6 pounds per square inch.

Chapter 6 Practice Test

CHAPTER Test Prep VIDEOS — *Chapter Test Prep Videos provide fully worked-out solutions to any of the exercises you want to review. Chapter Test Prep Videos are available via **MyMathLab**, or on **YouTube** (search "Angel Elementary Algebra" and click on "Channels").*

Simplify.

1. $\dfrac{-8 + x}{x - 8}$

2. $\dfrac{x^3 - 1}{x^2 - 1}$

Perform each indicated operation.

3. $\dfrac{20x^2y^3}{4z^2} \cdot \dfrac{8xz^3}{5xy^4}$

4. $\dfrac{a^2 - 9a + 14}{a - 2} \cdot \dfrac{a^2 - 4a - 21}{(a - 7)^2}$

5. $\dfrac{x^2 - x - 6}{x^2 - 9} \cdot \dfrac{x^2 - 6x + 9}{x^2 + 4x + 4}$

6. $\dfrac{x^2 - 1}{x + 2} \cdot \dfrac{x + 2}{1 - x^2}$

7. $\dfrac{x^2 - 4y^2}{5x + 20y} \div \dfrac{x + 2y}{x + 4y}$

8. $\dfrac{15}{y^2 + 2y - 15} \div \dfrac{5}{y - 3}$

9. $\dfrac{m^2 + 3m - 18}{m - 3} \div \dfrac{m^2 - 8m + 15}{3 - m}$

10. $\dfrac{4x + 3}{8y} + \dfrac{2x - 5}{8y}$

11. $\dfrac{7x^2 - 4}{x + 3} - \dfrac{6x + 9}{x + 3}$

12. $\dfrac{2}{xy} - \dfrac{8}{xy^3}$

13. $3 - \dfrac{5z}{z - 5}$

14. $\dfrac{x - 5}{x^2 - 16} - \dfrac{x - 2}{x^2 + 2x - 8}$

Simplify.

15. $\dfrac{2 + \dfrac{1}{2}}{3 - \dfrac{1}{5}}$

16. $\dfrac{x + \dfrac{x}{y}}{\dfrac{7}{x}}$

17. $\dfrac{4 + \dfrac{3}{x}}{\dfrac{9}{x} - 5}$

Solve.

18. $2 + \dfrac{8}{x} = 6$

19. $\dfrac{2x}{3} - \dfrac{x}{4} = x + 1$

20. $\dfrac{x}{x - 8} + \dfrac{6}{x - 2} = \dfrac{x^2}{x^2 - 10x + 16}$

Solve.

21. Working Together Mr. Jackson, on his tractor, can clear a 1-acre field in 10 hours. Mr. Hackett, on his tractor, can clear a 1-acre field in 15 hours. If they work together, how long will it take them to clear a 1-acre field?

22. Determine a Number The sum of a positive number and its reciprocal is 2. Determine the number.

23. Area of Triangle The area of a triangle is 30 square inches. If the height is 2 inches less than 2 times the base, determine the height and base of the triangle.

24. Exercising LaConya Bertrell exercises for $1\frac{1}{2}$ hours each day. During the first part of her routine, she rides a bicycle and averages 10 miles per hour. For the remainder of the time, she rollerblades and averages 4 miles per hour. If the total distance she travels is 12 miles, how far did she travel on the rollerblades?

25. Making Music The wavelength of sound waves, w, is inversely proportional to the frequency, f (or pitch). If a frequency of 263 cycles per second (middle C on a piano) produces a wavelength of about 4.3 feet, determine the length of a wavelength of a frequency of 1000 cycles per second.

© Losevsky Pavel\Shutterstock

Cumulative Review Test

Take the following test and check your answers with those given in the back of the book. Review any questions that you answered incorrectly. The section where the material was covered is indicated after the answer.

1. Evaluate $3x^2 - 5xy^2 - 7$, when $x = -4$ and $y = -2$.

2. Solve $5z + 4 = -3(z - 7)$.

3. Simplify $\left(\dfrac{10x^6y^3}{2x^5y^5}\right)^3$.

4. The cost of a 2009 Ford Mustang increased by 1.8% over the cost of the 2008 Mustang. Write an expression for the sum of the costs of a 2009 and a 2008 Mustang.

5. Simplify $(6x^2 - 3x - 5) - (-2x^2 - 8x - 19)$.

6. Multiply $(3n^2 - 4n + 3)(2n - 5)$.

7. Factor $8a^2 - 8a - 5a + 5$.

8. Factor $13x^2 + 26x - 39$.

9. Evaluate $\{6 - [3(8 \div 4)]^2 + 9 \cdot 4\}^2$

10. Solve $2(x + 4) \le -(x + 3) - 1$ and graph the solution on a real number line.

11. Divide $\dfrac{4x - 38}{8}$.

12. Solve $2x^2 = 11x - 12$.

13. Multiply $\dfrac{x^2 + x - 12}{x^2 - x - 6} \cdot \dfrac{x^2 - 2x - 8}{2x^2 - 7x - 4}$.

14. Subtract $\dfrac{r}{r + 2} - \dfrac{3}{r - 5}$.

15. Add $\dfrac{4}{x^2 - 3x - 10} + \dfrac{6}{x^2 + 5x + 6}$.

16. Solve the equation $\dfrac{x}{9} - \dfrac{x}{6} = \dfrac{1}{12}$.

17. Solve the equation $\dfrac{7}{x + 3} + \dfrac{5}{x + 2} = \dfrac{5}{x^2 + 5x + 6}$.

18. Medical Plans A school district allows its employees to choose from two medical plans. With plan 1, the employee pays 10% of all medical bills (the school district pays the balance). With plan 2, the employee pays the school district a one-time payment of $150, then the employee pays 5% of all medical bills. What total medical bills would result in the employee paying the same amount with the two plans?

19. Bird Seed A feed store owner wishes to make his own store-brand mixture of bird seed by mixing sunflower seed that costs $0.50 per pound with a premixed assorted seed that costs $0.20 per pound. How many pounds of each will he have to use to make a 50-pound mixture that will cost $16.00?

20. Sailing During the first leg of a race, the sailboat *Thumper* sailed at an average speed of 6.5 miles per hour. During the second leg of the race, the winds increased and *Thumper* sailed at an average speed of 9.5 miles per hour. If the total distance sailed by *Thumper* was 12.75 miles, and the total time spent racing was 1.5 hours, determine the distance traveled by *Thumper* on each leg of the race.

© Allen R. Angel

7

Graphing Linear Equations

7.1 The Cartesian Coordinate System and Linear Equations in Two Variables

7.2 Graphing Linear Equations

7.3 Slope of a Line

Mid-Chapter Test: Sections 7.1–7.3

7.4 Slope-Intercept and Point-Slope Forms of a Linear Equation

7.5 Graphing Linear Inequalities

7.6 Functions

Chapter 7 Summary

Chapter 7 Review Exercises

Chapter 7 Practice Test

Cumulative Review Test

Goals of This Chapter

In this chapter you will learn how to graph linear equations. The graphs of linear equations are straight lines. Graphing is one of the most important topics in mathematics.

The two most important concepts we will discuss in this chapter are slopes and functions. Functions are a unifying concept in mathematics.

This chapter contains concepts that are central to mathematics. If you plan to take more mathematics courses, graphs and functions will probably be a significant part of those courses.

We see graphs daily. They are very important in both mathematics and in everyday living. Graphs are used to display information. For example, in Exercise 75 on page 419, we use a graph to illustrate the total monthly cost for telephone calls.

7.1 The Cartesian Coordinate System and Linear Equations in Two Variables

1 Plot points in the Cartesian coordinate system.

2 Determine whether an ordered pair is a solution to a linear equation.

© Library of Congress

René Descartes

1 Plot Points in the Cartesian Coordinate System

Many algebraic relationships are easier to understand if we can see a picture of them. A **graph** shows the relationship between two variables in an equation. In this chapter we discuss several procedures that can be used to draw graphs using the **Cartesian (or rectangular) coordinate system**. The Cartesian coordinate system is named for its developer, the French mathematician and philosopher René Descartes (1596–1650).

The Cartesian coordinate system provides a means of locating and identifying points just as the coordinates on a map help us find cities and other locations. Consider the map of the Great Smoky Mountains (see **Fig. 7.1**). Can you find Cades Cove on the map? If we tell you that it is in grid A3, you can probably find it much more quickly and easily.

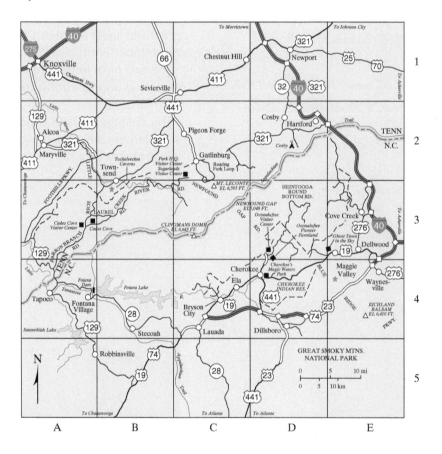

FIGURE 7.1

The Cartesian coordinate system is a grid system, like that of a map, except that it is formed by two axes (or number lines) drawn perpendicular to each other. The two intersecting axes form four **quadrants**, numbered I through IV in **Figure 7.2**.

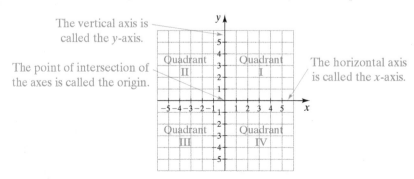

The vertical axis is called the y-axis.

The point of intersection of the axes is called the origin.

The horizontal axis is called the x-axis.

FIGURE 7.2

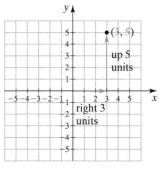

FIGURE 7.3

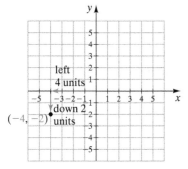

FIGURE 7.4

Understanding Algebra

Remember that the order of the numbers in an *ordered pair* is very important. For example, (3, 5) is a different point than (5, 3). The *x*-coordinate is always listed first in an ordered pair.

To locate a point in the Cartesian coordinate system, we will use an **ordered pair** of the form (x, y). The first number, x, is called the **x-coordinate** and the second number, y, is called the **y-coordinate.**

To plot the point $(3, 5)$, start at the origin,

$$(3, 5)$$
$$\begin{cases} x\text{-coordinate is } 3 \xrightarrow{\quad} & y\text{-coordinate is } 5 \\ \text{means} & \text{means} \\ \text{go } right \ 3 \text{ units} & \text{then go } up \ 5 \text{ units} \end{cases}$$

To plot the point, $(-4, -2)$, start at the origin,

$$(-4, -2)$$
$$\text{go } left \ 4 \text{ units} \xrightarrow{\quad} \text{then go } down \ 2 \text{ units}$$

EXAMPLE 1 Plot each point on the same axes.

a) $A(5, 3)$ **b)** $B(2, 4)$ **c)** $C(-3, 1)$

d) $D(4, 0)$ **e)** $E(-2, -5)$ **f)** $F(0, -3)$

g) $G(0, 2)$ **h)** $H\left(6, -\dfrac{9}{2}\right)$ **i)** $I\left(-\dfrac{3}{2}, -\dfrac{5}{2}\right)$

Solution   The first number in each ordered pair is the *x*-coordinate and the second number is the *y*-coordinate. The points are plotted in **Figure 7.5**.

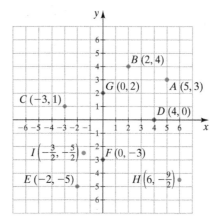

FIGURE 7.5

Note that when the *x*-coordinate is 0, as in Example 1 **f)** and 1 **g)**, the point is on the *y*-axis. When the *y*-coordinate is 0, as in Example 1 **d)**, the point is on the *x*-axis.

Now Try Exercise 23

EXAMPLE 2 List the ordered pairs for each point shown in **Figure 7.6**.

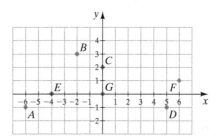

FIGURE 7.6

Solution   Remember to give the *x*-value first in the ordered pair.

Point	Ordered Pair
A	$(-6, -1)$
B	$(-2, 3)$
C	$(0, 2)$
D	$(5, -1)$
E	$(-4, 0)$
F	$(6, 1)$
G	$(0, 0)$

Now Try Exercise 21

2   Determine Whether an Ordered Pair Is a Solution to a Linear Equation

Linear Equations in Two Variables

A **linear equation in two variables** is an equation that can be put in the form

$$ax + by = c$$

where $a, b,$ and c are real numbers.

The graphs of equations of the form $ax + by = c$ are straight lines. For this reason such equations are called linear. A linear equation in the form $ax + by = c$ is said to be in **standard form**.

Examples of Linear Equations
$$4x - 3y = 12$$
$$y = 5x + 3$$
$$x - 3y + 4 = 0$$

Note in the examples that only the equation $4x - 3y = 12$ is in standard form. However, the bottom two equations can be written in standard form, as follows:

$$y = 5x + 3 \qquad\qquad x - 3y + 4 = 0$$
$$-5x + y = 3 \qquad\qquad x - 3y = -4$$

Most of the equations we have discussed thus far have contained only one variable. Consider the linear equation in *one* variable, $2x + 3 = 5$. What is its solution?

$$2x + 3 = 5$$
$$2x = 2$$
$$x = 1$$

This equation has only one solution, 1.

Check
$$2x + 3 = 5$$
$$2(1) + 3 \stackrel{?}{=} 5$$
$$5 = 5 \quad \text{True}$$

Now consider the linear equation in *two* variables, $y = x + 1$. Since the equation contains two variables, its solutions must contain two numbers, one for each variable. One pair of numbers that satisfies this equation is $x = 1$ and $y = 2$. To see that this is true, we substitute both values into the equation.

Check
$$y = x + 1$$
$$2 \stackrel{?}{=} 1 + 1$$
$$2 = 2 \qquad \text{True}$$

We write this answer as an ordered pair by writing the x- and y-values within parentheses separated by a comma. Therefore, one solution to this equation is the ordered pair $(1, 2)$. The equation $y = x + 1$ has other solutions.

Solution	Solution	Solution
$x = 2, y = 3$	$x = -3, y = -2$	$x = -\dfrac{1}{3}, y = \dfrac{2}{3}$

Check	$y = x + 1$	$y = x + 1$	$y = x + 1$
	$3 \overset{?}{=} 2 + 1$	$-2 \overset{?}{=} -3 + 1$	$\dfrac{2}{3} \overset{?}{=} -\dfrac{1}{3} + 1$
	$3 = 3$ True	$-2 = -2$ True	$\dfrac{2}{3} = \dfrac{2}{3}$ True

Solution Written as an Ordered Pair

$(2, 3)$	$(-3, -2)$	$\left(-\dfrac{1}{3}, \dfrac{2}{3}\right)$

How many possible solutions does the equation $y = x + 1$ have? The equation $y = x + 1$ has an unlimited or *infinite number* of possible solutions. Since it is not possible to list all the specific solutions, the solutions are illustrated with a graph.

> **Graph of an Equation**
>
> A **graph** of an equation in two variables is an illustration of the set of points whose coordinates satisfy the equation.

Figure 7.7a shows the points $(2, 3)$, $(-3, -2)$, and $\left(-\dfrac{1}{3}, \dfrac{2}{3}\right)$ plotted in the Cartesian coordinate system. **Figure 7.7b** shows a straight line drawn through the three points. Arrowheads are placed at the ends of the line to show that the line continues in both directions. Every point on this line will satisfy the equation $y = x + 1$, so this graph illustrates all the solutions of $y = x + 1$. The ordered pair $(1, 2)$, which is on the line, also satisfies the equation.

In **Figure 7.7b**, what do you notice about the points $(2, 3)$, $(1, 2)$, $\left(-\dfrac{1}{3}, \dfrac{2}{3}\right)$, and $(-3, -2)$? You probably noticed that they are in a straight line. A set of points that are on a line are said to be **collinear**.

Understanding Algebra

The equation $y = x + 1$ has an infinite number of solutions. Each solution is represented by a point on the line in **Figure 7.7b**. Also, each point on the line represents a solution to the equation $y = x + 1$.

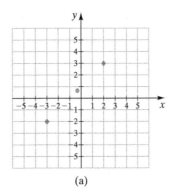

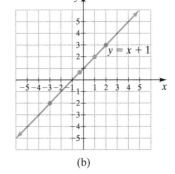

FIGURE 7.7   (a)   (b)

EXAMPLE 3 Determine whether the three points appear to be collinear.

a) $(2, 7), (0, 3),$ and $(-2, -1)$

b) $(0, 5), \left(\dfrac{5}{2}, 0\right),$ and $(5, -5)$

c) $(-2, -5), (0, 1),$ and $(6, 8)$

Solution We plot the points to determine whether they appear to be collinear. The solution is shown in **Figure 7.8**.

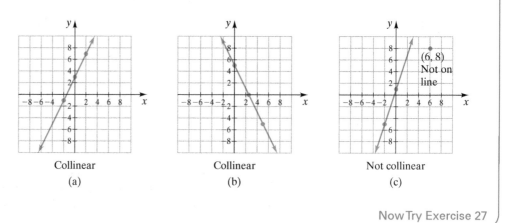

FIGURE 7.8

Collinear
(a)

Collinear
(b)

Not collinear
(c)

Now Try Exercise 27

To graph an equation, you will need to determine ordered pairs that satisfy the equation and then plot the points.

> **Helpful Hint**
>
> Only two points are needed to graph a linear equation because the graph of every linear equation is a straight line. However, if you graph a linear equation using only two points and you have made an error in determining or plotting one of those points, your graph will be wrong and you will not know it. In **Figures 7.9a** and **b** we plot only two points to show that if only one of the two points plotted is incorrect, the graph will be wrong. In both **Figures 7.9a** and **b** we use the ordered pair $(-2, -2)$. However, in **Figure 7.9a** the second point is $(1, 2)$, while in **Figure 7.9b** the second point is $(2, 1)$. Notice how the two graphs differ.
>
> If you use at least three points to plot your graph, as in Figure 7.7b on page 407, and they appear to be collinear, you probably have not made a mistake.
>
>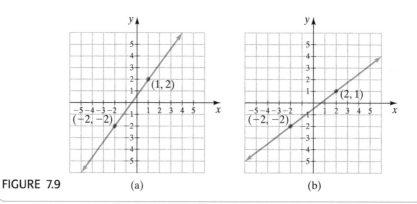
>
> FIGURE 7.9 (a) (b)

EXAMPLE 4

a) Determine which of the following ordered pairs satisfy the equation $2x + y = 4$.

$$(2, 0), (0, 4), (3, 1), (-1, 6)$$

b) Plot all the points that satisfy the equation on the same axes and draw a straight line through the points.

c) What does this line represent?

Solution

a) We substitute values for x and y into the equation $2x + y = 4$ and determine whether they check.

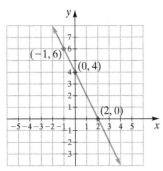

FIGURE 7.10

Check

$$(2, 0)$$
$$2x + y = 4$$
$$2(2) + 0 \stackrel{?}{=} 4$$
$$4 = 4 \quad \text{True}$$

$$(0, 4)$$
$$2x + y = 4$$
$$2(0) + 4 \stackrel{?}{=} 4$$
$$4 = 4 \quad \text{True}$$

$$(3, 1)$$
$$2x + y = 4$$
$$2(3) + 1 \stackrel{?}{=} 4$$
$$7 = 4 \quad \text{False}$$

$$(-1, 6)$$
$$2x + y = 4$$
$$2(-1) + 6 \stackrel{?}{=} 4$$
$$4 = 4 \quad \text{True}$$

The ordered pairs (2, 0), (0, 4), and (−1, 6) satisfy the equation. The ordered pair (3, 1) does not satisfy the equation.

b) **Figure 7.10** shows the three points that satisfy the equation. A line drawn through the three points shows that they appear to be collinear. Note that the ordered pair (3, 1), which is not a solution to the equation, is not a point on this line.

c) The line represents all solutions of $2x + y = 4$. The coordinates of every point on this line satisfy the equation $2x + y = 4$.

Now Try Exercise 31

EXERCISE SET 7.1

Math XP MyMathLab
MathXL®   MyMathLab

Warm-Up Exercises

Fill in the blanks with the appropriate word, phrase, or symbol(s) from the following list.

line	solution	Roman numerals	*y*-axis	linear
collinear	*x*-axis	Cartesian	*x*-coordinate	*y*-coordinate

1. In an ordered pair the _____ is listed first and the _____ is listed second.

2. The _____ is the horizontal axis.

3. The _____ is the vertical axis.

4. A _____ equation can be put into the form $ax + by = c$.

5. The graph of a linear equation is a _____ .

6. A _____ to an equation with two variables is an ordered pair that makes the equation true.

7. The quadrants of the Cartesian coordinate system are labeled using _____ .

8. Three or more points that are on the same line are called _____ .

Practice the Skills

Indicate the quadrant in which each of the points belongs.

9. (−2, 5)
10. (−4, 4)
11. (5, −6)
12. (2, −3)
13. (3, 6)
14. (4, 30)
15. (−17, −87)
16. (63, 47)
17. (−124, −132)
18. (75, 200)
19. (−8, 42)
20. (76, −92)

21. List the ordered pairs corresponding to each point.

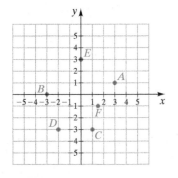

22. List the ordered pairs corresponding to each point.

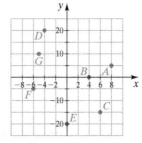

Plot each point on the same axes.

23. $A(3, 2), B(-4, 1), C(0, -3), D(-2, 0), E(-3, -4), F\left(-4, -\dfrac{5}{2}\right)$

24. $A(-3, -1), B(2, 0), C(3, 2), D\left(\dfrac{1}{2}, -4\right), E(-4, 2), F(0, 5)$

25. $A(4, 0), B(-1, 3), C(2, 4), D(0, -2), E(-3, -3), F(2, -3)$

26. $A(-3, 4), B(2, 3), C(0, 3), D(-1, 0), E(-2, -2), F(2, -4)$

Plot the following points. Then determine whether they appear to be collinear.

27. $A(1, -1), B(5, 3), C(-3, -5), D(0, -2), E(2, 0)$ 28. $A(1, -1), B(3, 5), C(0, -3), D(-2, -7), E(2, 1)$

29. $A(1, 5), B\left(-\dfrac{1}{2}, \dfrac{1}{2}\right), C(0, 2), D(-5, -3), E(-2, -4)$ 30. $A(1, -2), B(0, -5), C(4, 1), D(-1, -8), E\left(\dfrac{1}{2}, -\dfrac{7}{2}\right)$

*In Exercises 31–36, **a)** determine which of the four ordered pairs does not satisfy the given equation. **b)** Plot all the points that satisfy the equation on the same axes and draw a straight line through the points.*

31. $y = x + 2$,   **a)** $(2, 4)$ **b)** $(-2, 0)$ **c)** $(-1, 5)$ **d)** $(0, 2)$

32. $2x + y = -4$,   **a)** $(-2, 0)$ **b)** $(2, 3)$ **c)** $(0, -4)$ **d)** $(-1, -2)$

33. $3x - 2y = 6$,   **a)** $(4, 0)$ **b)** $(2, 0)$ **c)** $\left(\dfrac{2}{3}, -2\right)$ **d)** $\left(\dfrac{4}{3}, -1\right)$

34. $4x - 3y = 0$,   **a)** $(3, 4)$ **b)** $(-3, -4)$ **c)** $(0, 0)$ **d)** $(2, 5)$

35. $\dfrac{1}{2}x + 4y = 4$,   **a)** $(-2, 3)$ **b)** $\left(2, \dfrac{3}{4}\right)$ **c)** $(0, 1)$ **d)** $\left(-4, \dfrac{3}{2}\right)$

36. $y = \dfrac{1}{2}x + 2$,   **a)** $(0, 2)$ **b)** $(-4, 3)$ **c)** $(-2, 1)$ **d)** $(4, 4)$

Problem Solving

Consider the linear equation $y = 3x - 4$. In Exercises 37–40, find the value of y that makes the given ordered pair a solution to the equation.

37. $(2, y)$ 38. $(-1, y)$ 39. $(0, y)$ 40. $(3, y)$

Consider the linear equation $2x + 3y = 12$. In Exercises 41–44, find the value of x that makes the given ordered pair a solution to the equation.

41. $(x, 0)$ 42. $(x, -2)$ 43. $\left(x, \dfrac{11}{3}\right)$ 44. $\left(x, \dfrac{22}{3}\right)$

45. **Longitude and Latitude** Another type of coordinate system that is used to identify a location or position on earth's surface involves *latitude* and *longitude*. On a globe, the longitudinal lines are lines that go from top to bottom; on a world map they go up and down. The latitudinal lines go around the globe, or left to right on a world map. The locations of Hurricane Georges and Tropical Storm Hermine are indicated on the map on the right.

a) Estimate the latitude and longitude of Hurricane Georges.

b) Estimate the latitude and longitude of Tropical Storm Hermine.

c) Estimate the latitude and longitude of the city of Miami.

d) Use either a map or a globe to estimate the latitude and longitude of your college.

Source: National Weather Service

Concept/Writing Exercises

46. What is the value of y at the point where a straight line crosses the x-axis? Explain.

47. What is the value of x at the point where a straight line crosses the y-axis? Explain.

48. What does the graph of a linear equation illustrate?

49. Why are arrowheads added to the ends of graphs of linear equations?

50. How many solutions does a linear equation in two variables have?

Group Activity

In Section 7.2 we discuss how to find ordered pairs to plot when graphing linear equations. Let's see if you can draw some graphs now. Individually work parts **a)** *through* **c)** *in Exercises 51–54.*

a) *Select any three values for x and find the corresponding values of y.*

b) *Plot the points (they should appear to be collinear).*

c) *Draw the graph.*

d) *As a group, compare your answers. You should all have the same lines.*

51. $y = 2x$

53. $y = 2x + 1$

52. $y = x$

54. $y = -2x$

Cumulative Review Exercises

[2.5] **55.** Solve the equation $\frac{1}{2}(x - 3) = \frac{1}{3}x + 2$.

[2.6] **56.** Solve the equation $3x - 2y = 4$ for y.

[4.1] **57.** Simplify $(2x^3)^4$

[5.3] **58.** Factor $x^2 - 6x - 27$.

[5.6] **59.** Solve $y(y - 7) = 0$.

[6.4] **60.** Add $\frac{6}{x^2} + \frac{5}{3x}$.

7.2 Graphing Linear Equations

1. Graph linear equations by plotting points.

2. Graph linear equations of the form $ax + by = 0$.

3. Graph linear equations using the x- and y-intercepts.

4. Graph horizontal and vertical lines.

5. Study applications of graphs.

Now we are ready to graph linear equations.

1 Graph Linear Equations by Plotting Points

Graphing by plotting points is the most versatile method of graphing because we can also use it to graph other types of equations.

To Graph Linear Equations by Plotting Points

1. **Solve for y:** Solve the equation for the variable y. That is, get y by itself on the left side of the equation.

2. **Substitute a number in for x:** Select a number and substitute it into the equation for x and find the corresponding value for y. Record the ordered pair (x, y).

3. **Repeat step 2:** Select two different values for x. This will give you two additional ordered pairs.

4. **Plot the points:** Plot the three ordered pairs. The three points should be collinear. If they are not, recheck your work.

5. **Draw the line:** With a straightedge, draw a straight line through the three points. Draw an arrowhead on each end of the line.

Helpful Hints

- If you have forgotten how to solve an equation for y, review Section 2.6.
- When selecting numbers for x, you should select numbers that result in integer values for y.
- Select numbers for x that are small enough so that the ordered pairs obtained can be plotted easily on the axes.
- A good number to select for x is always 0.

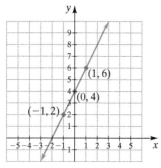

FIGURE 7.11

EXAMPLE 1 Graph $y = 2x + 4$.

Solution   The equation is already solved for y. We will arbitrarily select the numbers -1, 0, and 1 and substitute them into the equation for x and find the corresponding values for y. The calculations that follow show that when $x = -1$, $y = 2$, when $x = 0$, $y = 4$, and when $x = 1$, $y = 6$.

x	$y = 2x + 4$	Ordered Pair
-1	$y = 2(-1) + 4 = 2$	$(-1, 2)$
0	$y = 2(0) + 4 = 4$	$(0, 4)$
1	$y = 2(1) + 4 = 6$	$(1, 6)$

x	y
-1	2
0	4
1	6

We then plot the three ordered pairs on the same axes **(Fig. 7.11).** Connect the points with a straight line and place the arrowheads at the ends of the line.

Now Try Exercise 25

If we select any point on this line, the ordered pair represented by that point will be a solution to the equation $y = 2x + 4$. Similarly, any solution to the equation will be represented by a point on the line. Notice that $(-2, 0)$ and $(2, 8)$ are points on the line (see **Figure 7.12**). Let's verify that they are solutions to the equation

Check $(-2, 0)$

$y = 2x + 4$
$0 = 2(-2) + 4$
$0 = -4 + 4$
$0 = 0$ True

Check $(2, 8)$

$y = 2x + 4$
$8 = 2(2) + 4$
$8 = 4 + 4$
$8 = 8$ True

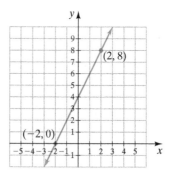

FIGURE 7.12

EXAMPLE 2 Graph $3y = 5x - 6$.

Solution   We begin by solving the equation for y.

$$3y = 5x - 6$$

$$y = \frac{5x - 6}{3} \qquad \text{Divided both sides by 3.}$$

$$y = \frac{5x}{3} - \frac{6}{3} \qquad \text{Wrote as two fractions.}$$

$$y = \frac{5}{3}x - 2$$

Now we can see that if we select values for x that are multiples of the denominator, 3, the values we obtain for y will be integers. Let's select the values -3, 0, and 3 for x.

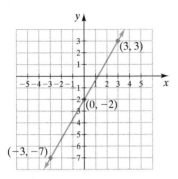

FIGURE 7.13

$$y = \frac{5}{3}x - 2$$

Let $x = -3$. $y = \frac{5}{3}(-3) - 2 = -5 - 2 = -7$

Let $x = 0$. $y = \frac{5}{3}(0) - 2 = 0 - 2 = -2$

Let $x = 3$. $y = \frac{5}{3}(3) - 2 = 5 - 2 = 3$

x	y
-3	-7
0	-2
3	3

Finally, we plot the points and draw the straight line (**Figure 7.13**).

Now Try Exercise 31

2 Graph Linear Equations of the Form $ax + by = 0$

EXAMPLE 3   Graph $2x + 5y = 0$.

Solution   We begin by solving the equation for y.

$$2x + 5y = 0$$
$$5y = -2x$$
$$y = -\frac{2x}{5} \quad \text{or} \quad y = -\frac{2}{5}x$$

If we select values for x that are multiples of 5, we will get integer values for y. We will arbitrarily select the values $x = -5$, $x = 0$, and $x = 5$.

$$y = -\frac{2}{5}x$$

Let $x = -5$. $y = \left(-\frac{2}{5}\right)(-5) = 2$

Let $x = 0$. $y = \left(-\frac{2}{5}\right)(0) = 0$

Let $x = 5$. $y = -\frac{2}{5}(5) = -2$

x	y
-5	2
0	0
5	-2

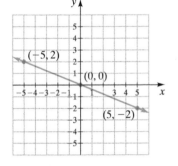

FIGURE 7.14

Now we plot the points and draw the graph (**Fig. 7.14**).

Now Try Exercise 37

Note that the graph in Example 3 passes through the origin.

Understanding Algebra

The graph of every linear equation with a constant of 0 (equations of the form, $ax + by = 0$) will pass through the origin.

3 Graph Linear Equations Using the x- and y-Intercepts

> **x- and y-intercepts**
> - The **x-intercept** is the point at which a graph crosses the x-axis.
> - The **y-intercept** is the point at which a graph crosses the y-axis.

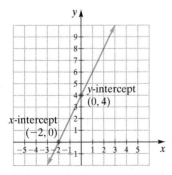

FIGURE 7.15

Consider the graph in **Figure 7.15**, which is the graph we drew in Example 1. Note that the line crosses the x-axis at -2. Therefore, the x-intercept is $(-2, 0)$. Also note that the line crosses the y-axis at 4. Therefore, the y-intercept is $(0, 4)$.

Understanding Algebra

In general terms, the *x*-intercept is (*x*, 0) and the *y*-intercept is (0, *y*).

It is often convenient to graph linear equations by finding the *x*- and *y*-intercepts.

To Graph Linear Equations Using the *x*- and *y*-intercepts

1. **Find the *y*-intercept.** Set *x* equal to 0 and find the corresponding value for *y*.
2. **Find the *x*-intercept.** Set *y* equal to 0 and find the corresponding value for *x*.
3. **Determine a checkpoint.** Select a nonzero value for *x* and find the corresponding value for *y*.
4. **Plot the intercepts and checkpoint.** The three points should be collinear. If not, check your work.
5. **Draw the line.** Using a straightedge, draw a straight line through the three points. Draw an arrowhead on each end of the line.

EXAMPLE 4   Graph $3y = 6x + 12$ using the *x*- and *y*-intercepts.

Solution   To find the *y*-intercept, set $x = 0$ and find the corresponding value of *y*.

$$3y = 6x + 12$$
$$3y = 6(0) + 12$$
$$3y = 0 + 12$$
$$3y = 12$$
$$y = \frac{12}{3} = 4$$

Therefore, the *y*-intercept is $(0, 4)$. To find the *x*-intercept, set $y = 0$ and find the corresponding value of *x*.

$$3y = 6x + 12$$
$$3(0) = 6x + 12$$
$$0 = 6x + 12$$
$$-12 = 6x$$
$$\frac{-12}{6} = x$$
$$-2 = x$$

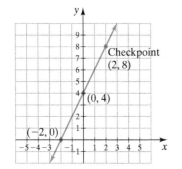

FIGURE 7.16

Therefore, the *x*-intercept is $(-2, 0)$.

Next, to find a checkpoint, we will select a nonzero value for *x* and find the corresponding value for *y*. We will select $x = 2$.

$$x = 2$$
$$3y = 6x + 12$$
$$3y = 6(2) + 12$$
$$3y = 12 + 12$$
$$3y = 24$$
$$y = \frac{24}{3} = 8$$

Therefore, the checkpoint is $(2, 8)$. Now plot the *y*-intercept, $(0, 4)$, the *x*-intercept, $(-2, 0)$, and the checkpoint $(2, 8)$ (**Fig. 7.16**). Since the three points appear to be collinear, draw the straight line through all three points.

Now try Exercise 55

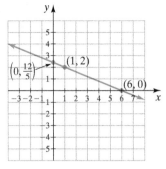

FIGURE 7.17

EXAMPLE 5 Graph $2x + 5y = 12$ using the x- and y-intercepts.

Solution

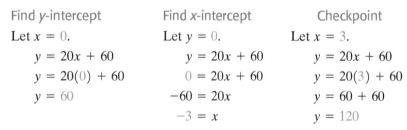

Find y-intercept	Find x-intercept	Checkpoint
Let $x = 0$.	Let $y = 0$.	Let $x = 1$.
$2x + 5y = 12$	$2x + 5y = 12$	$2x + 5y = 12$
$2(0) + 5y = 12$	$2x + 5(0) = 12$	$2(1) + 5y = 12$
$0 + 5y = 12$	$2x + 0 = 12$	$2 + 5y = 12$
$5y = 12$	$2x = 12$	$5y = 10$
$y = \dfrac{12}{5}$	$x = 6$	$y = 2$

The three ordered pairs are $\left(0, \dfrac{12}{5}\right)$, $(6, 0)$, and $(1, 2)$.

The three points appear to be collinear. Draw a straight line through all three points (**Fig. 7.17**).

Now Try Exercise 45

EXAMPLE 6 Graph $y = 20x + 60$ using the x- and y-intercepts.

Solution

Find y-intercept	Find x-intercept	Checkpoint
Let $x = 0$.	Let $y = 0$.	Let $x = 3$.
$y = 20x + 60$	$y = 20x + 60$	$y = 20x + 60$
$y = 20(0) + 60$	$0 = 20x + 60$	$y = 20(3) + 60$
$y = 60$	$-60 = 20x$	$y = 60 + 60$
	$-3 = x$	$y = 120$

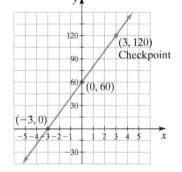

FIGURE 7.18

The three ordered pairs are $(0, 60)$, $(\quad, 0)$, and $(3, 120)$. Since the values of y are large, we let each interval on the y-axis be 15 units rather than 1 (**Fig. 7.18**). Now we plot the points and draw the graph.

Now Try Exercise 59

When selecting the scales for your axes, you should realize that different scales will result in the same equation having a different appearance. Consider the graphs shown in **Figure 7.19**. Both graphs represent the same equation, $y = x$. In **Figure 7.19a** both the x- and y-axes have the same scale. In **Figure 7.19b**, the x- and y-axes do not have the same scale. Both graphs are correct in that each represents the graph of $y = x$. The difference in appearance is due to the difference in scales on the x-axis.

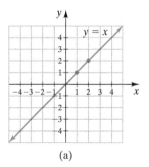

(a)

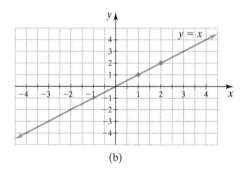

(b)

FIGURE 7.19

4 Graph Horizontal and Vertical Lines

When a linear equation contains only one variable, its graph will be either a horizontal or a vertical line, as is explained in Examples 7 and 8.

EXAMPLE 7 Graph $y = 3$.

Solution   This equation can be written as $y = 3 + 0x$. Thus, for any value of x selected, y will be 3. The graph of $y = 3$ is illustrated in **Figure 7.20**.

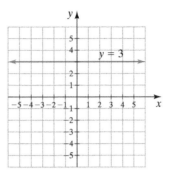

FIGURE 7.20

Now Try Exercise 23

Horizontal Line

The graph of an equation of the form $y = b$ is a **horizontal line** whose y-intercept is $(0, b)$.

EXAMPLE 8 Graph $x = -2$.

Solution   This equation can be written as $x = -2 + 0y$. Thus, for any value of y selected, x will have a value of -2. The graph of $x = -2$ is illustrated in **Figure 7.21**.

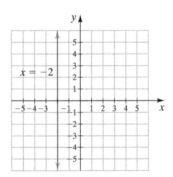

FIGURE 7.21

Now Try Exercise 21

Vertical Line

The graph of an equation of the form $x = a$ is a **vertical line** whose x-intercept is $(a, 0)$.

5 Study Applications of Graphs

Let's look at an application of graphing a linear equation.

EXAMPLE 9 **Weekly Salary** Carol Waters accepted a position as a sales representative at a furniture store where she is paid a weekly salary plus a commission on her sales. She will receive a salary of $300 per week plus a 7% commission on all her sales, s.

a) Write an equation for the salary Carol will receive, R, in terms of the sales, s.

b) Graph the salary for sales of $0 up to and including $20,000.

c) From the graph, estimate Carol's salary if her weekly sales are $15,000.

d) From the graph, estimate the sales needed for Carol to earn a weekly salary of $900.

Solution

a) Since *s* is the amount of sales, a 7% commission on *s* dollars in sales is 0.07s.

$$\text{salary received} = \$300 + \text{commission}$$
$$R = 300 + 0.07s$$

b) We select three values for *s* and find the corresponding values of *R*.

$R = 300 + 0.07s$		*s*	*R*
Let *s* = 0.	$R = 300 + 0.07(0) = 300$	0	300
Let *s* = 10,000.	$R = 300 + 0.07(10,000) = 1000$	10,000	1000
Let *s* = 20,000.	$R = 300 + 0.07(20,000) = 1700$	20,000	1700

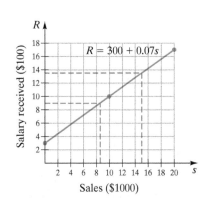

FIGURE 7.22

The graph is illustrated in **Figure 7.22**. Notice that since we only graph the equation for values of *s* from $0 to $20,000, we do not place arrowheads on the ends of the graph.

c) To determine Carol's weekly salary on sales of $15,000, locate $15,000 on the sales axis. Then draw a vertical line up to where it intersects the graph, the *purple* line in **Figure 7.22**. Now draw a horizontal line across to the salary axis. Since the horizontal line crosses the salary axis at about $1350, weekly sales of $15,000 would result in a weekly salary of about $1350. We can find the exact salary by substituting 15,000 for *s* in the equation $R = 300 + 0.07s$ and finding the value of *R*. Do this now.

d) To find the sales needed for Carol to earn a weekly salary of $900, we find $900 on the salary axis. We then draw a horizontal line from that point to the graph, as shown with the *green* line in **Figure 7.22**. We then draw a vertical line from the point of intersection of the graph to the sales axis. Thus, sales of about $8600 per week would result in a salary of $900. We can find an exact answer by substituting 900 for *R* in the equation $R = 300 + 0.07s$ and solving the equation for *s*. Do this now.

Now Try Exercise 75

EXERCISE SET 7.2

Math XL
MathXL®

MyMathLab
MyMathLab

Warm-Up Exercises

Fill in the blanks with the appropriate word, phrase, or symbol(s) from the following list.

$(x, 0)$	horizontal	*y*-intercept	*x*-axis	diagonal
$(0, y)$	*x*-intercept	vertical	*y*-axis	

1. The point at which a graph crosses the _____ is called the *x*-intercept.

2. The point at which a graph crosses the _____ is called the *y*-intercept.

3. To find the _____ of a graph of a linear equation, set *x* equal to 0 and find the corresponding value for *y*.

4. To find the _____ of a graph of a linear equation, set *y* equal to 0 and find the corresponding value for *x*.

5. The *x*-intercept of a graph will have coordinates _____ .

6. The *y*-intercept of a graph will have coordinates _____ .

7. The graph of an equation of the form $y = b$ is a _____ line.

8. The graph of an equation of the form $x = a$ is a _____ line.

Practice the Skills

Find the missing coordinate if the ordered pair is to be a solution to the equation $3x + y = 9$.

9. $(2, ?)$ **10.** $(-2, ?)$ **11.** $(?, -6)$

12. $(?, -9)$ **13.** $(?, 0)$ **14.** $\left(\dfrac{3}{2}, ?\right)$

Find the missing coordinate in the given solutions for $3x - 2y = 8$.

15. $(4, ?)$ **16.** $(0, ?)$ **17.** $(?, 0)$

18. $\left(?, -\dfrac{5}{2}\right)$ **19.** $(-4, ?)$ **20.** $(?, -3)$

Graph each equation.

21. $x = -3$ **22.** $x = \dfrac{3}{2}$ **23.** $y = 4$ **24.** $y = -\dfrac{5}{3}$

Graph by plotting points. Plot at least three points for each graph.

25. $y = 3x - 1$ **26.** $y = -x + 3$ **27.** $y = 4x - 2$ **28.** $y = x - 4$

29. $x + 2y = 6$ **30.** $-3x + 3y = 6$ **31.** $3x - 2y = 4$ **32.** $3x - 2y = 6$

33. $4x + 3y = -9$ **34.** $6y - 12x = 18$ **35.** $6x + 5y = 30$ **36.** $2x + 3y = -6$

37. $-4x + 5y = 0$ **38.** $3x + 2y = 0$ **39.** $y = -20x + 60$ **40.** $2y - 100x = 50$

41. $y = \dfrac{4}{3}x$ **42.** $y = -\dfrac{3}{5}x$ **43.** $y = \dfrac{1}{2}x + 4$ **44.** $y = -\dfrac{2}{5}x + 2$

Graph using the x- and y-intercepts.

45. $y = 3x + 3$ **46.** $y = -3x + 6$ **47.** $y = -4x + 2$ **48.** $y = -2x + 5$

49. $y = 4x + 16$ **50.** $y = -5x + 4$ **51.** $4y + 6x = 24$ **52.** $4x = 3y - 9$

53. $\dfrac{1}{2}x + 2y = 4$ **54.** $x + \dfrac{1}{2}y = 2$ **55.** $12x - 24y = 48$ **56.** $25x + 50y = 100$

57. $8y = 6x - 12$ **58.** $6y = -4x + 12$ **59.** $y = 15x + 45$ **60.** $y = -10x + 30$

61. $\dfrac{1}{3}x + \dfrac{1}{4}y = 12$ **62.** $\dfrac{1}{4}x - \dfrac{2}{3}y = 60$ **63.** $\dfrac{1}{2}x = \dfrac{2}{5}y - 80$ **64.** $\dfrac{2}{3}y = \dfrac{5}{4}x + 120$

Write the equation represented by the given graph.

65.
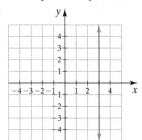

66.
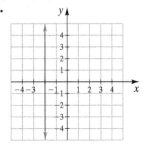

67.
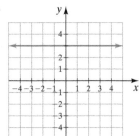

68.
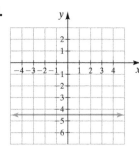

Problem Solving

69. What is the value of a if the graph of $ax + 2y = 15$ is to have an x-intercept of $(3, 0)$?

70. What is the value of a if the graph of $ax - 4y = 8$ is to have an x-intercept of $(4, 0)$?

71. What is the value of b if the graph of $3x + by = 14$ is to have a y-intercept of $(0, 7)$?

72. What is the value of b if the graph of $4x + by = 15$ is to have a y-intercept of $(0, -3)$?

The bar graphs in Exercises 73 and 74 display information. State whether the graph displays a linear relationship. Explain your answer.

73.

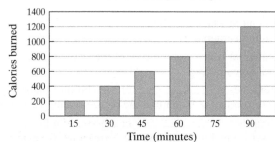
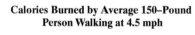

74.

Average Price of a Gallon of Gasoline

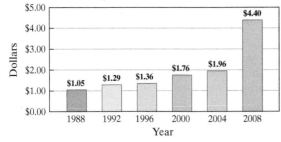

Source: American Petroleum Institute

Review Example 9 before working Exercises 75–80.

75. Telephone Calls Alexus Judd's telephone plan consists of a monthly fee of $15 plus 10 cents per minute for long-distance calls made.

a) Write an equation for the total monthly cost, C, when n minutes are used for long-distance calls.

b) Graph the equation for up to and including 100 minutes of long-distance calls made.

c) Estimate the total monthly cost if 40 minutes of long-distance calls are made.

d) If the total monthly bill is $25, estimate the number of minutes used for long-distance calls.

76. Distance Traveled Distance traveled is calculated using the formula,

$$\text{distance} = \text{rate} \cdot \text{time or } d = rt.$$

Assume the rate of a car is a constant 30 miles per hour.

a) Write an equation for the distance, d, in terms of time, t.

b) Graph the equation for times of 0 to 20 hours inclusive.

c) Estimate the distance traveled in 12 hours.

d) If the distance traveled is 150 miles, estimate the time traveled.

77. Truck Rental Lynn Brown needs a large truck to move some furniture. She found that the cost, C, of renting a truck is $40 per day plus $1 per mile, m.

a) Write an equation for the cost in terms of the miles driven.

b) Graph the equation for values up to and including 100 miles.

c) Estimate the cost of driving 60 miles in one day.

d) Estimate the miles driven if the cost for one day is $70.

78. Simple Interest Simple interest is calculated by the simple interest formula,

$$\text{interest} = \text{principal} \cdot \text{rate} \cdot \text{time or } I = prt.$$

Suppose the principal is $10,000 and the rate is 5%.

a) Write an equation for simple interest in terms of time.

b) Graph the equation for times of 0 to 20 years inclusive.

c) What is the simple interest for 10 years?

d) If the simple interest is $500, find the length of time.

79. Video Store Profit The weekly profit, P, of a video rental store can be approximated by the formula $P = 1.5n - 200$, where n is the number of videos rented weekly.

a) Draw a graph of profit in terms of video rentals for up to and including 1000 videos.

b) Estimate the weekly profit if 500 videos are rented.

c) Estimate the number of videos rented if the week's profit is $1000.

80. Playing Tennis The cost, C, of playing tennis in the Downtown Tennis Club includes an annual $200 membership fee plus $10 per hour, h, of court time.

a) Write an equation for the annual cost of playing tennis at the Downtown Tennis Club in terms of hours played.

b) Graph the equation for up to and including 300 hours.

c) Estimate the cost for playing 50 hours in a year.

d) If the annual cost for playing tennis was $1700, estimate how many hours of tennis were played.

© Jupiter Unlimited

Determine the coefficients to be placed in the shaded areas so that the graph of the equation will be a line with the x- and y-intercepts specified. Explain how you determined your answer.

81. ▨x + ▨y = 6; x-intercept at 2; y-intercept at 3

82. ▨x + ▨y = 18; x-intercept at −3, y-intercept at 6

83. ▨x − ▨y = −12; x-intercept at −2, y-intercept at 3

84. ▨x − ▨y = 30; x-intercept at −10, y-intercept at −15

Challenge Problems

85. Consider the following equations: $y = 2x - 1$, $y = -x + 5$.

a) Carefully graph both equations on the same axes.

b) Determine the point of intersection of the two graphs.

c) Substitute the values for x and y at the point of intersection into each of the two equations and determine whether the point of intersection satisfies each equation.

d) Do you believe there are any other ordered pairs that satisfy both equations? Explain your answer. (We will

86. The graphs of quadratic equations are *not* straight lines. Graph the quadratic equation $y = x^2 - 4$ by selecting values for x and find the corresponding values of y, then plot the points. Make sure you plot a sufficient number of points to get an accurate graph.

Group Activity

Discuss and answer Exercise 87 as a group.

87. Let's study the graphs of the equations $y = 2x + 4$, $y = 2x + 2$, and $y = 2x - 2$ to see how they are similar and how they differ. Each group member should start with the same axes.

    a) Group member 1: Graph $y = 2x + 4$.

    b) Group member 2: Graph $y = 2x + 2$.

    c) Group member 3: Graph $y = 2x - 2$.

    d) Now transfer all three graphs onto the same axes. (You can use one of the group members' graphs or you can construct new axes.)

    e) Explain what you notice about the three graphs.

    f) Explain what you notice about the *y*-intercepts.

Cumulative Review Exercises

[1.9] **88.** Evaluate $2[6 - (4 - 5)] \div 2 - 8^2$.

[2.7] **89. House Cleaning** According to the instructions on a bottle of concentrated household cleaner, 8 ounces of the cleaner should be mixed with 3 gallons of water. If your bucket holds only 2.5 gallons of water, how much cleaner should you use?

[3.2] **90. Refrigerator Purchase** Kristin Runde purchased a new refrigerator. The cost of the refrigerator, including a 6.5% sales tax, was $1491. What was the price of the refrigerator before tax?

[6.2] **91.** Divide $\dfrac{3xy^3}{z} \div \dfrac{x^2y^2}{5z^3}$.

See Exercise 90.

[6.4] **92.** Add $\dfrac{3}{x - 2} + \dfrac{4}{x - 3} + 2$

[6.6] **93.** Solve $\dfrac{3}{x - 2} + \dfrac{4}{x - 3} = 3$

7.3 Slope of a Line

1 Find the slope of a line.

2 Recognize positive and negative slopes.

3 Examine the slopes of horizontal and vertical lines.

4 Examine the slopes of parallel and perpendicular lines.

1 Find the Slope of a Line

The *slope of a line* is a measure of the *steepness* of the line. The slope of a line is an important concept in many areas of mathematics. A knowledge of slope is helpful in understanding linear equations.

> **Slope of a Line**
>
> - The **slope of a line,** m, is the ratio of the vertical change, or *rise*, to the horizontal change, or *run*, between any two selected points on the line.
>
> - $m = \text{slope} = \dfrac{\text{vertical change}}{\text{horizontal change}} = \dfrac{\text{rise}}{\text{run}}$

Understanding Algebra

Slope is often described with the phrase *"rise over run."*

> **Helpful Hint**
>
> *Slope*
>
> We often come across slope in everyday life. A road may have a slope (called the *grade*) of 8%. A roof may have a slope (called the *pitch*) of $\dfrac{6}{15}$. Suppose a road has an 8% grade. Since $8\% = \dfrac{8}{100}$, this means the road rises 8 feet for each 100 feet of horizontal length. A roof pitch of $\dfrac{6}{15}$ means the roof rises 6 feet for each 15 feet of horizontal length.
>
>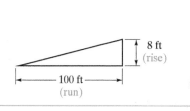
>
>

As an example of slope, consider the line that goes through the two points $(1, 2)$ and $(3, 6)$ (see **Fig. 7.23a**). From **Figure 7.23b**, we can see that the vertical change is $6 - 2$, or 4 units. The horizontal change is $3 - 1$, or 2 units.

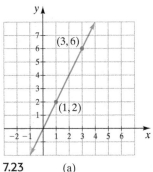 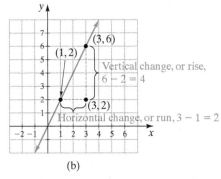

FIGURE 7.23   (a)   (b)

$$m = \text{slope} = \frac{\text{vertical change}}{\text{horizontal change}} = \frac{\text{rise}}{\text{run}} = \frac{4}{2} = 2$$

Thus, the slope of the line through these two points is 2. By examining the line connecting these two points, we can see that as the graph moves up 2 units it moves to the right 1 unit (**Fig. 7.24**).

Now we present the formula to find the slope of a line given any two points (x_1, y_1) and (x_2, y_2) on the line. Look at **Figure 7.25**. The *rise* is the difference between y_2 and y_1 and the *run* is the difference between x_2 and x_1.

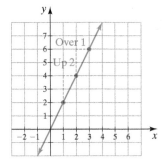

FIGURE 7.24

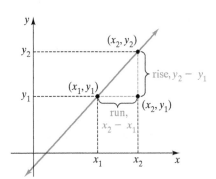

FIGURE 7.25

Understanding Algebra

The Greek letter delta, Δ, is often used to represent the phrase "the change in." So, Δy represents "the change in y" and Δx represents "the change in x" and the formula for slope can be given as

$$m = \frac{\Delta y}{\Delta x} = \frac{y_2 - y_1}{x_2 - x_1}$$

Slope of a Line Through the Points (x_1, y_1) and (x_2, y_2)

$$m = \text{slope} = \frac{\text{vertical change}}{\text{horizontal change}} = \frac{\text{rise}}{\text{run}} = \frac{y_2 - y_1}{x_2 - x_1}$$

Helpful Hint

It makes no difference which two points on a line are selected when finding the slope of the line. It also makes no difference which point you choose as (x_1, y_1) or (x_2, y_2).

EXAMPLE 1   Find the slope of the line through the points $(-6, 1)$ and $(3, 5)$.

Solution   We will designate $(-6, 1)$ as (x_1, y_1) and $(3, 5)$ as (x_2, y_2).

$$m = \frac{y_2 - y_1}{x_2 - x_1}$$

$$= \frac{5 - 1}{3 - (-6)}$$

$$= \frac{5 - 1}{3 + 6} = \frac{4}{9}$$

Thus, the slope is $\frac{4}{9}$.

If we had designated $(3, 5)$ as (x_1, y_1) and $(-6, 1)$ as (x_2, y_2), we would have obtained the same results.

$$m = \frac{y_2 - y_1}{x_2 - x_1}$$

$$= \frac{1 - 5}{-6 - 3} = \frac{-4}{-9} = \frac{4}{9}$$

Now Try Exercise 13

Avoiding Common Errors

Students sometimes subtract the x's and y's in the slope formula in the wrong order. For instance, using the problem in Example 1:

$$m = \frac{y_2 - y_1}{x_1 - x_2} = \frac{5 - 1}{-6 - 3} = \frac{4}{-9} = -\frac{4}{9}$$

Notice that subtracting in this incorrect order results in a negative slope, when the actual slope of the line is positive. The same sign error will occur each time subtraction is done incorrectly in this manner.

---

2 Recognize Positive and Negative Slopes

The slope of a line that is neither horizontal nor vertical is either positive or negative. See the lines in **Figure 7.26**.

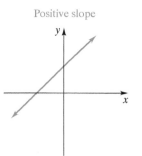

Positive slope

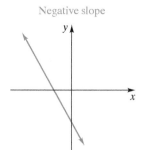

Negative slope

• Line rises from left to right
• As x increases, y increases

• Line falls from left to right
• As x increases, y decreases

FIGURE 7.26   (a)   (b)

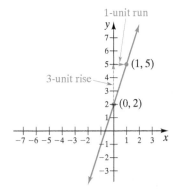

FIGURE 7.27

EXAMPLE 2 Consider the line in **Figure 7.27**.

a) Determine the slope of the line by observing the rise and the run between the points $(1, 5)$ and $(0, 2)$ on the graph.

b) Calculate the slope of the line using the two given points.

Solution

a) Notice that the slope is positive since the line rises from left to right. From **Figure 7.27** we see that the rise is $+3$ units and the run is $+1$ unit. Thus, the slope of the line is $\frac{3}{1}$ or 3.

b) We will use the ordered pairs $(1, 5)$ and $(0, 2)$.

Let (x_2, y_2) be $(1, 5)$. Let (x_1, y_1) be $(0, 2)$.

$$m = \frac{y_2 - y_1}{x_2 - x_1} = \frac{5 - 2}{1 - 0} = \frac{3}{1} = 3$$

Note that the slope obtained in part **b)** agrees with the slope obtained in part **a)**. If we had designated $(1, 5)$ as (x_1, y_1) and $(0, 2)$ as (x_2, y_2), the slope would not have changed. Try it and see that you will still obtain a slope of 3.

Now Try Exercise 25

EXAMPLE 3 Find the slope of the line in **Figure 7.28** using the vertical change and horizontal change between the two points shown.

Solution   Since the graph falls from left to right, the line has a negative slope. From **Figure 7.28** we see that the vertical change between the two given points is -3 units and the horizontal change between the two given points is 4 units. Thus, the slope is $\dfrac{-3}{4}$ or $-\dfrac{3}{4}$.

Now Try Exercise 29

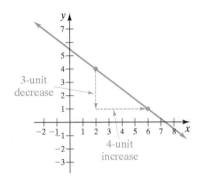

FIGURE 7.28

Using the two points shown in **Figure 7.28** and the definition of slope, calculate the slope of the line in Example 3. You should obtain the same answer.

EXAMPLE 4 **Driving to a Concert** Boyd Williamson is driving to see an AC/DC concert. The graph shown in **Figure 7.29** shows the time in hours along the horizontal axis and the distance in miles along the vertical axis.

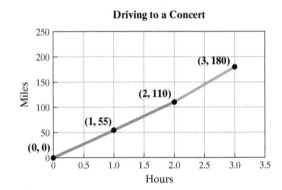

FIGURE 7.29

a) Determine the slope of the red line segment.

b) Determine the slope of the blue line segment.

Solution

a) We can choose any two points on the red line segment. We will use the points $(0, 0)$ as (x_1, y_1) and $(1, 55)$ as (x_2, y_2).

$$m = \frac{y_2 - y_1}{x_2 - x_1} = \frac{55 - 0}{1 - 0} = \frac{55}{1} = 55$$

Thus, the slope of the red line segment is 55.

b) We will use the points $(2, 110)$ as (x_1, y_1) and $(3, 180)$ as (x_2, y_2).

$$m = \frac{y_2 - y_1}{x_2 - x_1} = \frac{180 - 110}{3 - 2} = \frac{70}{1} = 70$$

Thus, the slope of the blue line segment is 70.

Now Try Exercise 71

3 Examine the Slopes of Horizontal and Vertical Lines

Consider the graph of $y = 5$ (**Fig. 7.30**). What is its slope?

The graph is parallel to the x-axis and goes through the points $(2, 5)$ and $(6, 5)$. Select $(6, 5)$ as (x_2, y_2) and $(2, 5)$ as (x_1, y_1). Then the slope of the line is

$$m = \frac{y_2 - y_1}{x_2 - x_1} = \frac{5 - 5}{6 - 2} = \frac{0}{4} = 0$$

Since there is no change in y, this line has a slope of 0. Note that *any* two points on the line would yield the same slope, 0.

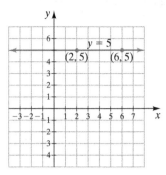

FIGURE 7.30

> **Slope of a Horizontal Line**
>
> Every horizontal line has a slope of 0.

Consider the graph of $x = 2$ (**Fig. 7.31**). What is its slope?

The graph is parallel to the y-axis and goes through the points $(2, 1)$ and $(2, 4)$. Select $(2, 4)$ as, (x_2, y_2) and $(2, 1)$ as (x_1, y_1). Then the slope of the line is

$$m = \frac{y_2 - y_1}{x_2 - x_1} = \frac{4 - 1}{2 - 2} = \frac{3}{0}$$

We learned in Section 1.8 that $\frac{3}{0}$ is undefined. Thus, we say that the slope of this line is undefined.

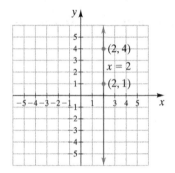

FIGURE 7.31

> **Slope of a Vertical Line**
>
> The slope of any vertical line is undefined.

4 Examine the Slopes of Parallel and Perpendicular Lines

> **Parallel Lines**
>
> Two lines are **parallel** when they lie in the same plane but do not intersect.

Figure 7.32 illustrates two parallel lines.

If we compute the slope of line 1 using the given points, we obtain a slope of 3. If we compute the slope of line 2, we obtain a slope of 3. Notice both lines have the same slope. Any two nonvertical lines that have the same slope are parallel lines.

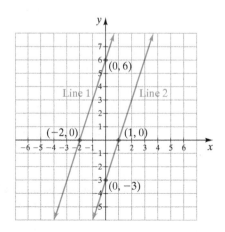

FIGURE 7.32

Slopes of Parallel Lines

Two lines are parallel when they have the same slope and different y-intercepts. Any two vertical lines are parallel to each other.

EXAMPLE 5

a) Draw a line with a slope of $\frac{1}{2}$ through the point $(2, 3)$.

b) On the same set of axes, draw a line with a slope of $\frac{1}{2}$ through the point $(-1, -3)$.

c) Are the two lines in parts **a)** and **b)** parallel? Explain.

Solution

a) Place a dot at $(2, 3)$. Because the slope is a positive $\frac{1}{2}$, from the point $(2, 3)$ move *up* 1 unit and to the *right* 2 units to get a second point. Draw a line through the two points; see the blue line in **Figure 7.33**.

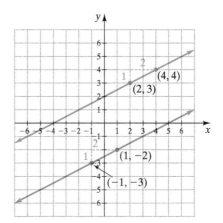

FIGURE 7.33

b) Place a dot at $(-1, -3)$. From the point $(-1, -3)$ move up 1 unit and to the right 2 units to get a second point. Draw a line through the two points; see the red line in **Figure 7.33**.

c) The lines appear to be parallel on the graph. Since both lines have the same slope, $\frac{1}{2}$, they are parallel lines.

Now Try Exercise 73

Perpendicular Lines

Two lines are **perpendicular** when they intersect and form right ($90°$) angles.

Figure 7.34 illustrates two perpendicular lines.

If we compute the slope of line 1 using the given points, we obtain a slope of $\frac{1}{2}$. If we compute the slope of line 2 using the given points, we obtain a slope of -2.

Notice the product of their slopes, $\frac{1}{2}(-2)$, is -1. Any two numbers whose product is -1 are said to be **negative reciprocals** of each other.

Slopes of Perpendicular Lines

Two lines are perpendicular when their slopes are negative reciprocals. Any vertical line is perpendicular to any horizontal line.

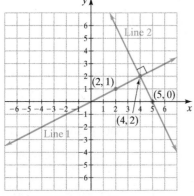

FIGURE 7.34

EXAMPLE 6

a) Draw a line with a slope of -3 through the point $(2, 3)$.

b) On the same set of axes, draw a line with a slope of $\frac{1}{3}$ through the point $(-1, -3)$.

c) Are the two lines in parts **a)** and **b)** perpendicular? Explain.

Solution

a) Place a dot at $(2, 3)$. A slope of -3 means $\frac{-3}{1}$. So, from the point $(2, 3)$ move *down* 3 units and to the *right* 1 unit to get a second point. Draw a line through the two points; see the blue line in **Figure 7.35**.

b) Place a dot at $(-1, -3)$. The slope is $\frac{1}{3}$, so from this point move *up* 1 unit and to the *right* 3 units. Draw a line through the two points; see the red line in **Figure 7.35**.

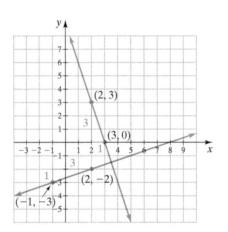

FIGURE 7.35

c) The lines appear to be perpendicular on the graph. To determine if they are perpendicular, multiply the slopes of the two lines together.

$$(-3)\left(\frac{1}{3}\right) = -1$$

Since the slopes are negative reciprocals, the two lines are perpendicular.

Now Try Exercise 75

EXAMPLE 7   If m_1 represents the slope of line 1 and m_2 represents the slope of line 2, determine if line 1 and line 2 are parallel, perpendicular or neither.

a) $m_1 = \frac{5}{6}, m_2 = \frac{5}{6}$ b) $m_1 = \frac{2}{5}, m_2 = 4$ c) $m_1 = \frac{3}{5}, m_2 = -\frac{5}{3}$

Solution

a) Since the slopes are the same, both $\frac{5}{6}$, the lines are parallel.

b) Since the slopes are not the same, the lines are not parallel. Since $m_1 \cdot m_2 = \left(\frac{2}{5}\right)(4) \neq -1$, the slopes are not negative reciprocals and the lines are not perpendicular. Thus the answer is neither.

c) Since the slopes are not the same, the lines are not parallel. Since $m_1 \cdot m_2 = \frac{3}{5}\left(-\frac{5}{3}\right) = -1$, the slopes are negative reciprocals and the lines are perpendicular.

Now Try Exercise 53

EXERCISE SET 7.3

Math **XL**   **MyMathLab**
MathXL®   MyMathLab

Warm-Up Exercises

Fill in the blanks with the appropriate word, phrase, or symbol(s) from the following list.

horizontal	over	vertical	equal
perpendicular	run	opposites	ratio
rise	parallel	product	negative reciprocals

1. The vertical change between two points on a line is known as the _____ .

2. The horizontal change between two points on a line is known as the _____ .

3. Slope is the _____ of the vertical change to the horizontal change.

4. Slope is often described with the phrase rise _____ run.

5. Every _____ line has a slope of 0.

6. Every _____ line has an undefined slope.

7. Two lines are _____ when they lie in same plane but do not intersect.

8. Two line are _____ when they intersect and form right angles.

9. The slopes of parallel lines are _____ .

10. The slopes of perpendicular lines are _____ .

Practice the Skills

Using the slope formula, find the slope of the line through the given points.

11. $(2,1)$ and $(5,7)$

12. $(-2,3)$ and $(3,8)$

13. $(8,0)$ and $(4,-2)$

14. $(-3,2)$ and $(-6,1)$

15. $(3,5)$ and $(-1,5)$

16. $\left(-4,\dfrac{1}{2}\right)$ and $\left(2,\dfrac{1}{2}\right)$

17. $(5,-6)$ and $(8,-3)$

18. $(9,3)$ and $(5,-6)$

19. $(6,4)$ and $(6,2)$

20. $(-7,8)$ and $(3,-1)$

21. $(6,0)$ and $(-2,3)$

22. $(-2,3)$ and $(-2,-5)$

23. $\left(0,\dfrac{5}{2}\right)$ and $\left(-\dfrac{3}{4},2\right)$

24. $(-1,8)$ and $\left(\dfrac{1}{3},-1\right)$

By observing the vertical and horizontal change of the line between the two points indicated, determine the slope of each line.

25.
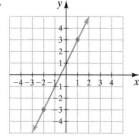

26.
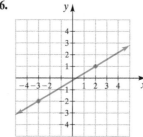

27.
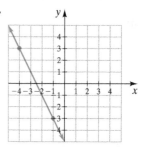

28.
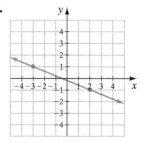

29.
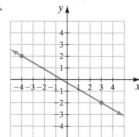

30.
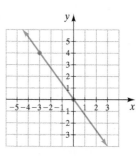

31.
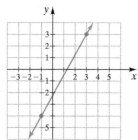

32.
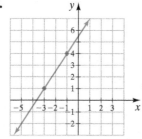

33.
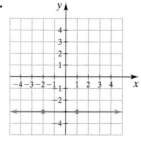

34.
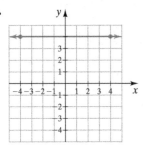

35.
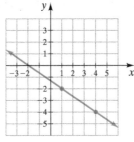

36.
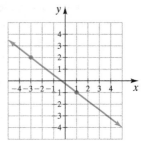

37.
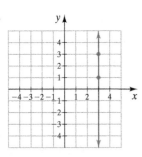

38.
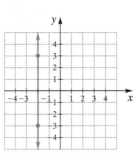

In Exercises 39–48, graph the line with the given slope that goes through the given point.

39. Through $(3, -1)$ with $m = 2$.

40. Through $(-1, -2)$ with $m = -2$

41. Through $(0, -2)$ with $m = \dfrac{1}{2}$

42. Through $(0, 2)$ with $m = -\dfrac{1}{2}$

43. Through $(0, 0)$ with $m = -\dfrac{1}{3}$

44. Through $(-3, 4)$ with $m = -\dfrac{2}{3}$

45. Through $(-3, 2)$ with $m = 0$

46. Through $(-1, 3)$ with $m = 0$

47. Through $(2, -2)$ with slope undefined

48. Through $(-1, 5)$ with slope undefined

In Exercises 49–64, m_1 represents the slope of line 1, and m_2 represents the slope of the distinct line, line 2. Indicate whether line 1 and line 2 are parallel, perpendicular, or neither.

49. $m_1 = 5, m_2 = 5$

50. $m_1 = -1, m_2 = -1$

51. $m_1 = 7, m_2 = -7$

52. $m_1 = \dfrac{3}{2}, m_2 = -4$

53. $m_1 = \dfrac{2}{3}, m_2 = -\dfrac{3}{2}$

54. $m_1 = \dfrac{1}{4}, m_2 = -4$

55. $m_1 = 6, m_2 = \dfrac{2}{3}$

56. $m_1 = -\dfrac{1}{3}, m_2 = -3$

57. $m_1 = \dfrac{1}{4}, m_2 = 4$

58. $m_1 = 6, m_2 = -\dfrac{1}{6}$

59. $m_1 = 0, m_2 = 0$

60. $m_1 = 0, m_2 = -\dfrac{2}{5}$

61. m_1 is undefined, m_2 is undefined

62. $m_1 = 0, m_2$ is undefined

63. m_1 is undefined, $m_2 = 0$

64. $m_1 = 5, m_2 = -5$

65. The slope of a given line is 3. If a line is to be drawn parallel to the given line, what will be its slope?

66. The slope of a given line is -2. If a line is to be drawn parallel to the given line, what will be its slope?

67. The slope of a given line is -4. If a line is to be drawn perpendicular to the given line, what will be its slope?

68. The slope of a given line is 5. If a line is to be drawn perpendicular to the given line, what will be its slope?

Problem Solving

In Exercises 69 and 70, determine which line (the first or second) has the greater slope. Explain your answer. Notice that the scales on the x- and y-axes are different.

69.
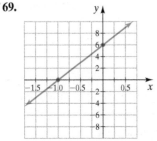

70.
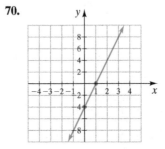

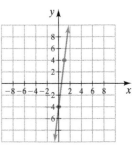

In Exercises 71 and 72, find the slope of the line segments indicated in **a)** *red and* **b)** *blue.*

71.

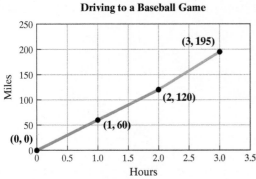

Driving to a Baseball Game

72.

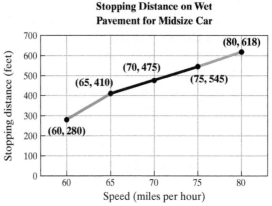

Stopping Distance on Wet Pavement for Midsize Car

Source: Automobile Association of America

73. A given line goes through the points $(2, 6)$ and $(4, -2)$. If a line is to be drawn parallel to the given line, what will be its slope?

74. A given line goes through the points $(-2, 5)$ and $(4, 7)$. If a line is to be drawn parallel to the given line, what will be its slope?

75. A given line goes through the points $(1, -7)$ and $(2, 1)$. If a line is to be drawn perpendicular to the given line, what will be its slope?

76. A given line goes through the points $(-3, 0)$ and $(-2, 3)$. If a line is to be drawn perpendicular to the given line, what will be its slope?

Challenge Problems

77. A line contains the points $(1, b)$ and $(4, 9)$. If the line has slope $m = 2$, what is the value of b?

78. A line contains the points $(1, 2)$ and $(a, -4)$. If the line has slope $m = 3$, what is the value of a?

79. A quadrilateral (a four-sided figure) has four vertices (the points where the sides meet). Vertex A is at $(0, 1)$, vertex B is at $(6, 2)$, vertex C is at $(5, 4)$, and vertex D is at $(1, -1)$.

a) Graph the quadrilateral in the Cartesian coordinate system.

b) Find the slopes of sides AC, CB, DB, and AD.

c) Do you think this figure is a parallelogram? Explain.

80. Population The following graph shows the world's population estimated to the year 2016.

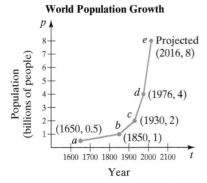

World Population Growth

Year

a) Find the slope of the line segment between each pair of points, that is, ab, bc, and so on. Remember, the second coordinate is in billions. Thus, for example, 0.5 billion is actually 500,000,000.

b) Would you say that this graph represents a linear equation? Explain.

81. Consider the graph below.

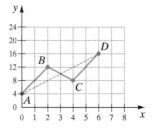

a) Determine the slope of each of the three solid blue lines.

b) Determine the average of the three slopes found in part **a)**.

c) Determine the slope of the red dashed line from A to D.

d) Determine whether the slope of the red dashed line from A to D is the same as the (mean) average of the slopes of the three solid blue lines.

e) Explain what this example illustrates.

Group Activity

Discuss and answer Exercise 82 as a group, according to the instructions.

82. The slope of a hill and the slope of a line both measure steepness. However, there are several important differences.

   a) As a group, explain how you think the slope of a hill is determined.

   b) Is the slope of a line, graphed in the Cartesian coordinate system, measured in any specific unit?

   c) Is the slope of a hill measured in any specific unit?

© Ija Masik\Shutterstock

Cumulative Review Exercises

[1.9]   **83.** Evaluate $-5x^2 + 3x + 4$ when $x = 1$.

[2.3]   **84. a)** If $-x = 3$, what is the value of x?

   b) If $-4x = 0$, what is the value of x?

[4.4]   **85.** Subtract $(2x - 9)$ from $(4x + 7)$.

[6.6]   **86.** Solve the equation $\dfrac{2x}{x - 3} = 2 + \dfrac{3}{x}$

[7.2]   **87.** Find the x- and y-intercepts for the line whose equation is $5x - 3y = 30$.

Mid-Chapter Test: 7.1–7.3

To find out how well you understand the chapter material to this point, take this brief test. The answers, and the section where the material was initially discussed, are given in the back of the book. Review any questions that you answered incorrectly.

1. In which quadrant does the point $(3, -4)$ belong?

2. Plot the points $A(2, 6)$, $B(-3, 1)$, $C(-5, -2)$, $D(0, -4)$, $E(4, -7)$ on the same axes.

3. Determine which of the three ordered pairs does not satisfy the equation $\frac{1}{3}x + y = -2$.

   a) $(3, -3)$ **b)** $(0, 2)$ **c)** $(-6, 0)$

4. Find the value of y that makes the ordered pair $(-1, y)$ a solution to the linear equation $y = 5x + 1$.

5. Find the value of x that makes the ordered pair $(x, 2)$ a solution to the equation $3x - 4y = 1$.

6. What does the graph of an equation illustrate?

Graph each equation.

7. $x = \dfrac{5}{2}$

8. $y = -2$

Graph by plotting points.

9. $y = 3x + 1$

10. $y = -\dfrac{1}{2}x + 4$

Graph using the x- and y-intercepts.

11. $3x - 4y = 12$

12. $\dfrac{1}{2}x + \dfrac{1}{5}y = 10$

Find the slope of the line through each pair of points.

13. $(-1, 5)$ and $(6, 3)$ **14.** $(4, 2)$ and $(7, 2)$

15. $(-3, 0)$ and $(-3, 5)$

Graph the line with the given slope that goes through the given point.

16. Through $(-2, 3)$ with $m = -\dfrac{1}{2}$

17. Through $(4, 1)$ with $m = \dfrac{3}{5}$.

Indicate whether the lines with the following slopes are parallel, perpendicular, or neither.

18. $m_1 = 5$ and $m_2 = \dfrac{1}{5}$

19. $m_1 = \dfrac{6}{7}$ and $m_2 = -\dfrac{7}{6}$

20. Interest The following graph illustrates the interest obtained when $1000 is invested for 1 year at various interest rates from 0% to 10%. Determine the slope of the line in the graph.

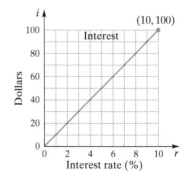

7.4 Slope-Intercept and Point-Slope Forms of a Linear Equation

1. Write a linear equation in slope-intercept form.

2. Graph a linear equation using the slope and y-intercept.

3. Use the slope-intercept form to determine the equation of a line.

4. Use the point-slope form to determine the equation of a line.

5. Compare the three methods of graphing linear equations.

In Section 7.1 we introduced the *standard form* of a linear equation, $ax + by = c$. In this section we introduce two more forms, the slope-intercept form and the point-slope form.

1 Write a Linear Equation in Slope-Intercept Form

A very important form of a linear equation is the **slope-intercept form, $y = mx + b$**. The graph of an equation of the form $y = mx + b$ will always be a straight line with a **slope of m** and a **y-intercept $(0, b)$**.

Slope-Intercept Form of a Linear Equation

$$y = mx + b$$

where m is the slope, and $(0, b)$ is the y-intercept of the line.

Slope y-intercept is $(0, b)$

$$y = mx + b$$

Equations in Slope-Intercept Form	Slope, m	y-Intercept $(0, b)$
$y = 4x - 6$	4	$(0, -6)$
$y = \dfrac{1}{2}x + \dfrac{3}{2}$	$\dfrac{1}{2}$	$\left(0, \dfrac{3}{2}\right)$
$y = -5x + 3$	-5	$(0, 3)$

Writing an Equation in Slope-Intercept Form

To write a linear equation in slope-intercept form, solve the equation for y.

Once the equation is solved for y, the numerical coefficient of the x-term will be the slope, and the constant term will give the y-intercept.

EXAMPLE 1 Write the equation $-3x + 4y = 8$ in slope-intercept form. State the slope and y-intercept.

Solution   To write this equation in slope-intercept form, we solve the equation for y.

$$-3x + 4y = 8$$
$$4y = 3x + 8 \qquad \text{Added } 3x \text{ to both sides.}$$
$$y = \frac{3x + 8}{4} \qquad \text{Divided both sides by 4.}$$
$$y = \frac{3}{4}x + \frac{8}{4} \qquad \text{Wrote as two fractions.}$$
$$y = \frac{3}{4}x + 2 \qquad \text{Equation in slope-intercept form.}$$

$$y = \frac{3}{4}x + 2$$

$$m = \frac{3}{4} \qquad b = 2$$

Thus, the slope is $\dfrac{3}{4}$, and the y-intercept is $(0, 2)$.

Now Try Exercise 11

EXAMPLE 2 Determine whether the two equations represent lines that are parallel, perpendicular, or neither.

a) $2x + y = 9$

$2y = -4x + 5$

b) $3x - 2y = 7$

$6y + 4x = -6$

Solution   Two lines that have the same slope are parallel lines, and two lines whose slopes are negative reciprocals are perpendicular lines. We can determine the slope of each line by solving each equation for y. The coefficient of the x term will be the slope.

a) $2x + y = 9$

$$y = \boxed{-2}x + 9$$

$$m = -2$$

$$2y = -4x + 5$$

$$y = \frac{-4x + 5}{2}$$

$$y = \boxed{-2}x + \frac{5}{2}$$

$$m = -2$$

Since both equations have the same slope, -2, the equations represent lines that are parallel. Notice the equations represent two different lines because their y-intercepts are different.

b) $3x - 2y = 7$

$$-2y = -3x + 7$$

$$y = \frac{-3x + 7}{-2}$$

$$y = \boxed{\frac{3}{2}}x - \frac{7}{2}$$

$$m = \frac{3}{2}$$

$$6y + 4x = -6$$

$$6y = -4x - 6$$

$$y = \frac{-4x - 6}{6}$$

$$y = \boxed{-\frac{2}{3}}x - 1$$

$$m = -\frac{2}{3}$$

The slope of one line is $\frac{3}{2}$ and the slope of the other line is $-\frac{2}{3}$. Since the slopes are negative reciprocals, the lines are perpendicular.

Now Try Exercise 39

Understanding Algebra

When graphing using the slope-intercept form, our starting point is always the y-intercept.

2 Graph a Linear Equation Using the Slope and y-Intercept

In Section 7.2 we discussed graphing a linear equation by (1) plotting points and by (2) using the x- and y-intercepts. Now we present a third method. This method makes use of the slope and the y-intercept. We graph equations using the slope and y-intercept in a manner very similar to the way we worked Examples 5 and 6 in Section 7.3.

To Graph Linear Equations Using the Slope and y-intercept

1. If necessary, solve the equation for y.
2. Plot the y-intercept.
3. Use the slope to find two more points on the line.
4. Using a straightedge, draw a straight line through the three points. Draw an arrowhead on each end of the line.

EXAMPLE 3 Graph $-3x + 4y = 8$ by using the slope and y-intercept.

Solution   In Example 1 we solved $-3x + 4y = 8$ for y. We found that

$$y = \frac{3}{4}x + 2$$

The slope of the line is $\frac{3}{4}$ and the y-intercept is $(0, 2)$. We plot the y-intercept at 2 on the y-axis (**Fig. 7.36**). Now we use the slope $\frac{3}{4}$, to find a second point. Since the slope is positive, we move 3 units up and 4 units to the right to find a second point at $(4, 5)$. We continue this process to obtain a third point at $(8, 8)$. Now we draw a straight line through the three points.

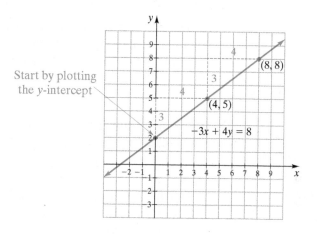

FIGURE 7.36

Now Try Exercise 19

EXAMPLE 4   Graph $5x + 3y = 12$ by using the slope and y-intercept.

Solution   First, solve the equation for y.

$$5x + 3y = 12$$
$$3y = -5x + 12$$
$$y = \frac{-5x + 12}{3}$$
$$= -\frac{5}{3}x + 4$$

Thus, the slope is $-\frac{5}{3}$ and the y-intercept is $(0, 4)$. Plot the y-intercept at 4 on the y-axis (**Fig. 7.37**). Then, since $-\frac{5}{3} = \frac{-5}{3}$, move 5 units down and 3 units to the right to determine the next point. You can follow this procedure again to obtain a third point. Finally, draw the straight line between the plotted points.

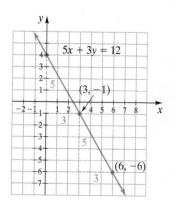

FIGURE 7.37

Now Try Exercise 21

3 Use the Slope-Intercept Form to Determine the Equation of a Line

We can also use the slope-intercept form to write the equation of a given line. To do so, we need to determine the slope, m, and the y-intercept, $(0, b)$. We then can substitute m and b into $y = mx + b$ to get the equation of the given line.

EXAMPLE 5 Determine the equation of the line shown in **Figure 7.38**

Solution   The graph shows that the y-intercept is at -5 so $b = -5$. Since the line falls from left to right it has a negative slope. Looking at the point $(0, -5)$ and $(-2, 1)$, we can see that the rise is 6 and the run is -2. So,

$$m = \frac{\text{rise}}{\text{run}} = \frac{6}{-2} = -3$$

Substituting -3 for m and -5 for b into the slope-intercept form gives us the equation $y = -3x - 5$, which is the equation of the line shown.

Now Try Exercise 29

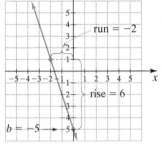

FIGURE 7.38

EXAMPLE 6 **Artistic Vases** Kris, a pottery artist, makes ceramic vases that he sells at art shows. His business has a fixed monthly cost (booth rental, advertising, cell phone, etc.) and a variable cost per vase made (cost of materials, cost of labor, cost for kiln use, etc.). The total monthly cost for making x vases is illustrated in the graph in **Figure 7.39**.

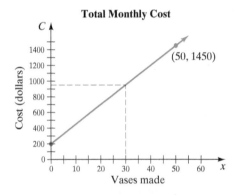

FIGURE 7.39

a) Find the equation of the total monthly cost when x vases are made.

b) Use the equation found in part **a)** to find the total monthly cost if 30 vases are made.

c) Use the graph in **Figure 7.39** to see whether your answer in part **b)** appears correct.

Solution

a) Understand and Translate   Notice that the vertical axis is cost, C, and not y. Since y is replaced by C, we will use $C = mx + b$, in which b is where the graph crosses the vertical or C-axis. Note that the graph crosses the vertical axis at 200. Thus, b is 200. Now use the points $(0, 200)$ and $(50, 1450)$ to find the slope.

Carry Out
$$m = \frac{y_2 - y_1}{x_2 - x_1}$$

$$= \frac{1450 - 200}{50 - 0} = \frac{1250}{50} = 25$$

Answer   The slope is 25. So $m = 25$ and $b = 200$ and the equation in slope-intercept form is

$$C = mx + b$$
$$= 25x + 200$$

b) To find the monthly cost when 30 vases are made, we substitute 30 for x.

$$C = 25x + 200$$
$$= 25(30) + 200$$
$$= 750 + 200 = 950$$

The monthly cost when 30 vases are made is $950.

c) If we draw a vertical line up from 30 on the x-axis (the red line), we see that the corresponding cost is about $950. Thus, our answer in part **b)** appears correct.

Now Try Exercise 65

4 Use the Point-Slope Form to Determine the Equation of a Line

When the slope of a line and a point on the line are known, we can use the point-slope form to determine the equation of the line. The **point-slope form** can be obtained by beginning with the slope between any selected point (x, y) and a fixed point (x_1, y_1) on a line.

$$m = \frac{y - y_1}{x - x_1} \quad \text{or} \quad \frac{m}{1} = \frac{y - y_1}{x - x_1}$$

Now cross-multiply to obtain

$$m(x - x_1) = y - y_1 \quad \text{or} \quad y - y_1 = m(x - x_1)$$

> **Point-Slope Form of a Linear Equation**
>
> $$y - y_1 = m(x - x_1)$$
>
> where m is the slope of the line and (x_1, y_1) is a point on the line.

EXAMPLE 7 Write an equation, in slope-intercept form, of the line that goes through the point $(1, 3)$ and has a slope of 2.

Solution   Since we are given a point on the line and the slope of the line, we begin by writing the equation in point-slope form. Since the slope is 2 and the point on the line is $(1, 3)$, we have $m = 2$, $x_1 = 1$, and $y_1 = 3$. We substitute into the point-slope form and solve for y as follows.

$$y - y_1 = m(x - x_1)$$
$$y - 3 = 2(x - 1) \qquad \text{Equation in point-slope form}$$
$$y - 3 = 2x - 2 \qquad \text{Distributive property}$$
$$y = 2x + 1 \qquad \text{Equation in slope-intercept form}$$

Now Try Exercise 51

EXAMPLE 8 Write an equation, in slope-intercept form, of the line that goes through the point $(1, -2)$ and has a slope of $\frac{3}{4}$.

Solution   We will begin with the point-slope form of a line, where $m = \frac{3}{4}$, $x_1 = 1$, and $y_1 = -2$.

$$y - y_1 = m(x - x_1)$$

$$y - (-2) = \frac{3}{4}(x - 1) \qquad \text{Equation in point-slope form}$$

$$4(y + 2) = 4 \cdot \frac{3}{4}(x - 1) \quad \text{Multiply both sides by 4.}$$

$$4y + 8 = 3(x - 1) \qquad \text{Distributive property (left side of equation)}$$

$$4y + 8 = 3x - 3 \qquad \text{Distributive property (right side of equation)}$$

$$4y = 3x - 11 \qquad \text{Subtracted 8 from both sides.}$$

$$y = \frac{3x - 11}{4} \qquad \text{Divided both sides by 4.}$$

$$y = \frac{3}{4}x - \frac{11}{4} \qquad \text{Equation in slope-intercept form}$$

Now Try Exercise 53

Helpful Hints

We have discussed three forms of a linear equation. We summarize the three forms below. It is important that you memorize these forms.

Standard Form	Examples
$ax + by = c$	$2x - 3y = 8$
	$-5x + y = -2$

Slope-Intercept Form	Examples
$y = mx + b$	$y = 2x - 5$
m is the slope, $(0, b)$ is the y-intercept	$y = -\frac{3}{2}x + 2$

Point-Slope Form	Examples
$y - y_1 = m(x - x_1)$	$y - 3 = 2(x + 4)$
m is the slope, (x_1, y_1) is a point on the line	$y + 5 = -4(x - 1)$

We now discuss how to use the point-slope form to determine the equation of a line when two points on the line are known.

EXAMPLE 9 Find an equation of the line through the points $(-1, 3)$ and $(-5, 1)$. Write the equation in slope-intercept form.

Solution   To use the point-slope form, we must first find the slope of the line through the two points.

$$m = \frac{y_2 - y_1}{x_2 - x_1} = \frac{1 - 3}{-5 - (-1)} = \frac{1 - 3}{-5 + 1} = \frac{-2}{-4} = \frac{1}{2}$$

Thus $m = \frac{1}{2}$. We can use either point in determining the equation of the line.

This example will be worked out using each of the points to show that the solutions obtained are identical.

Using the point $(-1, 3)$ as (x_1, y_1),

$$y - y_1 = m(x - x_1)$$

$$y - 3 = \frac{1}{2}[x - (-1)]$$

$$y - 3 = \frac{1}{2}(x + 1)$$

$$2 \cdot (y - 3) = 2 \cdot \frac{1}{2}(x + 1) \quad \text{Multiply both sides by the LCD, 2.}$$

$$2y - 6 = x + 1$$

$$2y = x + 7$$

$$y = \frac{x + 7}{2} \quad \text{or} \quad y = \frac{1}{2}x + \frac{7}{2}$$

Using the point $(-5, 1)$ as (x_1, y_1),

$$y - y_1 = m(x - x_1)$$

$$y - 1 = \frac{1}{2}[x - (-5)]$$

$$y - 1 = \frac{1}{2}(x + 5)$$

$$2 \cdot (y - 1) = 2 \cdot \frac{1}{2}(x + 5) \quad \text{Multiply both sides by the LCD, 2.}$$

$$2y - 2 = x + 5$$

$$2y = x + 7$$

$$y = \frac{x + 7}{2} \quad \text{or} \quad y = \frac{1}{2}x + \frac{7}{2}$$

Note that the equations are identical.

Now Try Exercise 57

Helpful Hints

In the Exercises, you will be asked to write a linear equation in slope-intercept form. Even though you will eventually write the equation in slope-intercept form, you may need to start your work with the point-slope form. Below we indicate the initial form to use to solve the problem.

1. Begin with the **slope-intercept form** if you know
   • The slope of the line and the y-intercept
2. Begin with the **point-slope form** if you know
   a) The slope of the line and a point on the line other than the y-intercept or
   b) Two points on the line (first find the slope, then use the point-slope form)

5 Compare the Three Methods of Graphing Linear Equations

We have discussed three methods to graph a linear equation: (1) plotting points, (2) using the x- and y-intercepts, and (3) using the slope and y-intercept. No single method is always the easiest to use. If the equation is given in slope-intercept form, $y = mx + b$, then graphing by plotting points or by using the slope and y-intercept might be easier. If the equation is given in standard form, $ax + by = c$, then graphing using the intercepts might be easier.

EXAMPLE 10 Graph $3x - 2y = 8$

a) by plotting points;

b) using the x- and y-intercepts;

c) using the slope and y-intercept.

Solution For parts **a)** and **c)** we will write the equation in slope-intercept form by solving for y.

$$3x - 2y = 8$$

$$-2y = -3x + 8$$

$$y = \frac{-3x + 8}{-2} = \frac{3}{2}x - 4$$

a) Plotting Points We substitute values for x and find the corresponding values of y. Three ordered pairs are indicated in the following table. Next we plot the ordered pairs and draw the graph (**Fig. 7.40**).

$$y = \frac{3}{2}x - 4$$

x	y
0	-4
2	-1
4	2

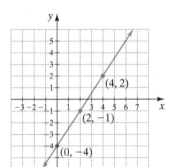

FIGURE 7.40

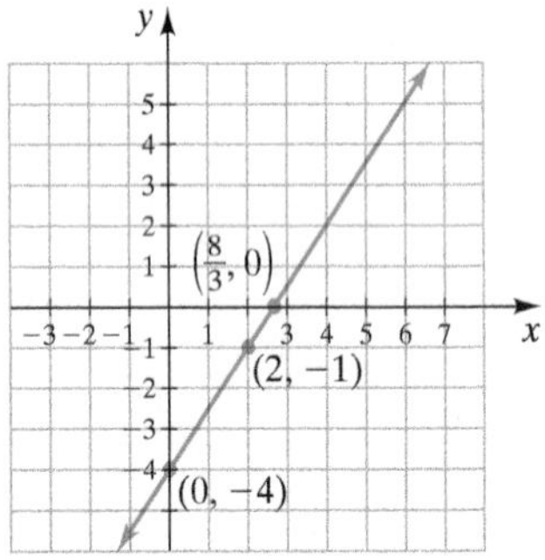

b) Intercepts We find the x- and y-intercepts and a checkpoint. Then we plot the points and draw the graph (**Fig. 7.41**).

$$3x - 2y = 8$$

x-Intercept	y-Intercept	Checkpoint
Let $y = 0$.	Let $x = 0$.	Let $x = 2$.
$3x - 2y = 8$	$3x - 2y = 8$	$3x - 2y = 8$
$3x - 2(0) = 8$	$3(0) - 2y = 8$	$3(2) - 2y = 8$
$3x = 8$	$-2y = 8$	$6 - 2y = 8$
$x = \dfrac{8}{3}$	$y = -4$	$-2y = 2$
		$y = -1$

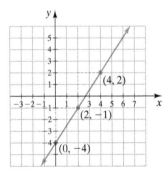

FIGURE 7.41

The three ordered pairs are $\left(\dfrac{8}{3}, 0\right)$, $(0, -4)$, and $(2, -1)$.

c) Slope and y-intercept The y-intercept is $(0, -4)$; therefore, we place a point at -4 on the y-axis. Since the slope is $\dfrac{3}{2}$, we obtain a second point by moving 3 units up and 2 units to the right. The graph is illustrated in **Figure 7.42**. Notice that we get the same line by all three methods.

Now Try Exercise 27

FIGURE 7.42

EXERCISE SET 7.4   Math XL   MyMathLab
MathXL®   MyMathLab

Warm-Up Exercises

Fill in the blanks with the appropriate word, phrase, or symbol(s) from the following list.

numerator	y-intercept	standard	point-slope	slope
slope-intercept	denominator	point	y	

1. The _____ form of a linear equation is $y - y_1 = m(x - x_1)$.

2. The _____ form of a linear equation is $ax + by = c$.

3. The _____ form of a linear equation is $y = mx + b$.

4. To write a linear equation in slope-intercept form, solve the equation for _____ .

5. When graphing a linear equation using the slope and y-intercept, you first plot the _____ .

6. To simplify an equation that contains a fraction, multiply both sides of the equation by the _____ of the fraction.

7. If you are asked to find the equation of a line and if you know the _____ and the *y*-intercept, you should use the slope-intercept form.

8. If you are asked to find the equation of a line and if you know the _____ and the slope, you should use the point-slope form.

Practice the Skills

Determine the slope and y-intercept of the line represented by the given equation.

9. $y = 3x + 1$

10. $y = -3x + 17$

11. $4x - 3y = 21$

12. $7x = 5y + 25$

Determine the slope and y-intercept of the line represented by each equation. Graph the line using the slope and y-intercept.

13. $y = x - 3$

14. $y = -x + 5$

 15. $y = 3x + 2$

16. $3x + y = 4$

17. $y = 2x$

18. $y = -4x$

19. $-2x + y = -3$

20. $3x + 3y = 9$

21. $5x - 2y = 10$

22. $-x + 2y = 8$

23. $6x + 12y = 18$

24. $16y = 8x + 32$

25. $-6x + 2y - 8 = 0$

26. $4x = 6y + 9$

27. $3x = 2y - 4$

28. $20x = 80y + 40$

Determine the equation of each line.

29.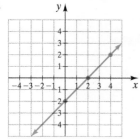

30.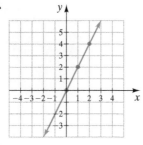

31.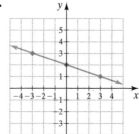

32.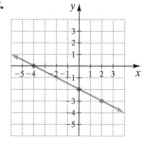

33.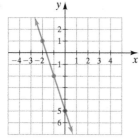

34.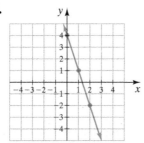

35.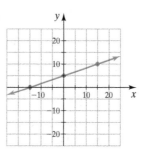

36.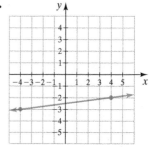

Determine whether each pair of lines are parallel, perpendicular, or neither.

37. $y = 3x - 2$
$y = 3x + 2$

38. $2x + 3y = 1$
$y = -\dfrac{2}{3}x + 3$

39. $4x + 2y = 7$
$4x = 8y + 12$

40. $3x - 5y = 7$
$5y + 3x = 4$

41. $3x + 5y = 9$
$6x = -10y + 9$

42. $8x + 2y = 10$
$x - 7 = 4y$

43. $y = \dfrac{1}{2}x - 2$
$2y = 6x + 9$

44. $3y - 4 = -5x$
$y = -\dfrac{5}{3}x - 3$

45. $5y = 2x + 9$
$-10x = 4y + 11$

46. $3x - 9y = 21$
$-3x + 9y = 27$

47. $3x + 7y = 21$
$7x + 3y = 21$

48. $5x - 6y = 18$
$-6x + 5y = 10$

Problem Solving

Write the equation of each line, with the given properties, in slope-intercept form.

49. Slope $= 3$, through $(0, 2)$

50. Slope $= 2$, through $(4, 3)$

51. Slope $= -3$, through $(-4, 5)$

52. Slope $= -3$, through $(2, 0)$

53. Slope $= \frac{1}{2}$, through $(-1, -3)$

54. Slope $= -\frac{2}{3}$, through $(4, -5)$

55. Slope $= \frac{2}{3}$, y-intercept is $(0, 6)$

56. Slope $= \frac{1}{9}$, y-intercept is $\left(0, -\frac{2}{5}\right)$

57. Through $(-4, -2)$ and $(-2, 4)$

58. Through $(7, 4)$ and $(6, 3)$

59. Through $(-6, 9)$ and $(8, -12)$

60. Through $(3, 0)$ and $(-3, 5)$

61. Through $(10, 3)$ and $(0, -2)$

62. Through $(-6, -2)$ and $(5, -3)$

63. Slope $= 7.4$, y-intercept is $(0, -4.5)$

64. Slope $= -\frac{7}{8}$, y-intercept is $\left(0, -\frac{3}{10}\right)$

65. Weight Loss Clinic Stacy Best owns a weight loss clinic. She charges her clients a one-time membership fee. She also charges per pound of weight lost. Therefore, the more successful she is at helping clients lose weight, the more income she will receive. The following graph shows a client's cost of losing weight.

a) Find the equation that represents the cost for a client who loses x pounds.

b) Use the equation found in part **a)** to determine the cost for a client who loses 30 pounds.

66. Submarine Submerges A submarine is submerged below sea level. Tom Johnson, the captain, orders the ship to dive slowly. The following graph illustrates the submarine's depth at a time t minutes after the submarine begins to dive.

See Exercise 66.

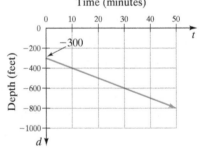

a) Find the equation that represents the depth at time t.

b) Use the equation found in part **a)** to find the submarine's depth after 30 minutes.

Concept/Writing Exercises

67. Suppose that you were asked to write the equation of a line with the properties given below. Which form of a linear equation—standard form, slope-intercept form, or point-slope form—would you start with? Explain your answer.

a) The slope of the line and the y-intercept of the line

b) The slope and a point on the line

c) Two points on the line

68. Consider the two equations $20x - 30y = 50$ and $-20x + 30y = 40$.

a) When these equations are graphed, will the two lines have the same slope? Explain how you determined your answer.

b) When these two equations are graphed, will they be parallel lines?

69. Assume the slope of a line is 2 and two points on the line are $(-5, -4)$ and $(3, 12)$.

a) If you use $(-5, -4)$ as (x_1, y_1) and then $(3, 12)$ as (x_1, y_1) will the appearance of the two equations be the same in point-slope form? Explain.

b) Find the equation, in point-slope form, using $(-5, -4)$ as (x_1, y_1).

c) Find the equation, in point-slope form, using $(3, 12)$ as (x_1, y_1).

d) Write the equation obtained in part **b)** in slope-intercept form.

e) Write the equation obtained in part **c)** in slope-intercept form.

f) Are the equations obtained in parts **d)** and **e)** the same? If not, explain why.

70. Assume the slope of a line is -3 and two points on the line are $(-1,8)$ and $(2, -1)$.

a) If you use $(-1, 8)$ as (x_1, y_1) and then $(2, -1)$ as (x_1, y_1) will the appearance of the two equations be the same in point-slope form? Explain.

b) Find the equation, in point-slope form, using $(-1, 8)$ as (x_1, y_1).

c) Find the equation, in point-slope form, using $(2, -1)$ as (x_1, y_1).

d) Write the equation obtained in part **b)** in slope-intercept form.

e) Write the equation obtained in part **c)** in slope-intercept form.

f) Are the equations obtained in parts **d)** and **e)** the same? If not, explain why.

Challenge Problems

71. Unit Conversions The following graph shows the approximate relationship between speed in miles per hour and feet per second.

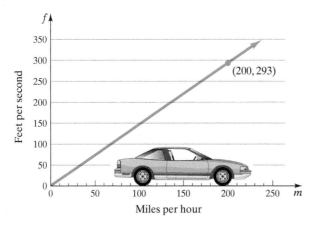

a) Determine the slope of the line.

b) Determine the equation of the line.

c) At the 2008 Daytona 500, Ryan Newman, the winner, had an average speed of 152.7 miles per hour. Use the equation you obtained in part **b)** to determine the speed in feet per second.

d) Use the graph to estimate a speed of 100 miles per hour in feet per second.

e) Use the graph to estimate a speed of 80 feet per second in miles per hour.

72. Temperature The following graph shows the relationship between Fahrenheit temperature and Celsius temperature.

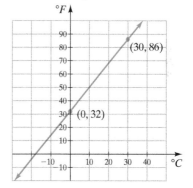

a) Determine the slope of the line.

b) Determine the equation of the line in slope-intercept form.

c) Use the equation (or formula) you obtained in part **b)** to find the Fahrenheit temperature when the Celsius temperature is $20°$.

d) Use the graph to estimate the Celsius temperature when the Fahrenheit temperature is $100°$.

e) Estimate the Celsius temperature that corresponds to a Fahrenheit temperature of $0°$.

73. Determine the equation of the line with y-intercept at 5 that is parallel to the line whose equation is $2x + y = 6$. Explain how you determined your answer.

74. Will a line through the points $(60, 30)$ and $(20, 90)$ be parallel to the line with x-intercept at 2 and y-intercept at 3? Explain how you determined your answer.

75. Write an equation of the line parallel to the graph of $3x - 4y = 6$ that passes through the point $(-8, -1)$.

76. Determine the equation of the straight line that intersects the greatest number of shaded points on the following graph.

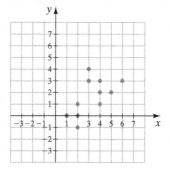

Group Activity

Discuss and answer Exercise 77 as a group, according to the instructions.

77. Consider the equation $-3x + 2y = 4$.

   a) Group member 1: Explain how to graph this equation by plotting points. Then graph the equation by plotting points.

   b) Group member 2: Explain how to graph this equation using the intercepts. Then graph the equation using the intercepts.

   c) Group member 3: Explain how to graph this equation using the slope and *y*-intercept. Then graph the equation using the slope and *y*-intercept.

   d) As a group, compare your graphs. Did you all obtain the same graph? If not, determine why.

Cumulative Review Exercises

[1.5]   **78.** Insert either $>$, $<$, or $=$ in the shaded area to make the statement true: $|-4|$ $|-9|$.

[2.6]   **79.** Solve $i = prt$ for r.

[2.8]   **80.** Solve $2(x - 3) \geq 5x + 6$ and graph the solution on a number line.

[5.2]   **81.** Factor $x^2 - 4xy + 3xy - 12y^2$ by grouping.

[6.6]   **82.** Solve $\dfrac{x}{3} - \dfrac{3x + 2}{6} = \dfrac{1}{2}$.

7.5 Graphing Linear Inequalities

1   Graph linear inequalities in two variables.

1 Graph Linear Inequalities in Two Variables

A **linear inequality** occurs when the equals sign in a linear equation is replaced with an inequality sign.

Examples of Linear Inequalities in Two Variables

$3x + 2y > 4$ $-x + 3y < -2$

$-x + 4y \geq 3$ $4x - y \leq 4$

Understanding Algebra

When graphing inequalities:

- If the symbol is $\leq$ or $\geq$ use a solid line.
- If the symbol is $<$ or $>$ use a dashed line.

To Graph a Linear Inequality in Two Variables

1. Replace the inequality symbol with an equals sign.

2. Draw the graph of the equation in step 1. If the original inequality contained the symbol $\geq$ or $\leq$, draw the graph using a solid line. If the original inequality contained the symbol $>$ or $<$, draw the graph using a dashed line.

3. Select any point not on the line and determine whether this point is a solution to the original inequality. If the selected point is a solution, shade the region on the side of the line containing this point. If the selected point does not satisfy the inequality, shade the region on the side of the line not containing this point.

EXAMPLE 1 Graph the inequality $y < 2x - 4$.

Solution   First we graph the equation $y = 2x - 4$ (**Fig. 7.43**). Since the original inequality contains the symbol $<$, we use a dashed line when drawing the graph. The dashed line indicates that the points on this line are not solutions to the inequality $y < 2x - 4$.

Next we select a point not on the line and determine whether this point satisfies the inequality. Often the easiest point to use is the origin, $(0, 0)$. In the check we will use the symbol $\overset{?}{<}$ until we determine whether the statement is true or false.

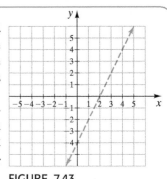

FIGURE 7.43

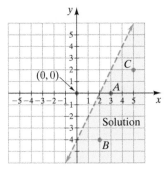

FIGURE 7.44

Checkpoint

$$y < 2x - 4$$
$$0 \overset{?}{<} 2(0) - 4$$
$$0 \overset{?}{<} 0 - 4$$
$$0 < -4 \qquad \text{False}$$

Since 0 is not less than −4, the point $(0, 0)$ does not satisfy the inequality. The solution will therefore be all the points on the opposite side of the line from the point $(0, 0)$. We shade this region (**Fig. 7.44**).

Every point in the shaded region satisfies the given inequality. Let's check a few selected points A, B, and C.

Point A	Point B	Point C
$(3, 0)$	$(2, -4)$	$(5, 2)$
$y < 2x - 4$	$y < 2x - 4$	$y < 2x - 4$
$0 \overset{?}{<} 2(3) - 4$	$-4 \overset{?}{<} 2(2) - 4$	$2 \overset{?}{<} 2(5) - 4$
$0 < 2$ True	$-4 < 0$ True	$2 < 6$ True

All points in the shaded region in **Figure 7.44** satisfy the inequality $y < 2x - 4$. The points in the unshaded region as well as the points on the line itself do not satisfy the inequality $y < 2x - 4$.

Now Try Exercise 11

EXAMPLE 2 Graph the inequality $y \geq -\dfrac{1}{2}x$.

Solution Graph the equation $y = -\dfrac{1}{2}x$. Since the inequality symbol is $\geq$, we will use a solid line (**Fig. 7.45**). Since the point $(0, 0)$ is on the line, we cannot select it as our test point. Let's select the point $(3, 1)$.

$$y \geq -\frac{1}{2}x$$

Checkpoint

$$1 \overset{?}{\geq} -\frac{1}{2}(3)$$
$$1 \geq -\frac{3}{2} \qquad \text{True}$$

Since the ordered pair $(3, 1)$ satisfies the inequality, every point on the same side of the line as $(3, 1)$ will also satisfy the inequality $y \geq -\dfrac{1}{2}x$. We shade this region (**Fig. 7.46**). Every point in the shaded region as well as every point on the line satisfies the inequality $y \geq -\dfrac{1}{2}x$. The points in the unshaded region do not satisfy the inequality.

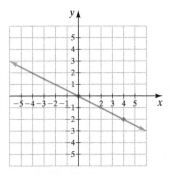

FIGURE 7.45

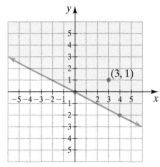

FIGURE 7.46

Now Try Exercise 9

> **Helpful Hint**
>
> Earlier in this chapter we discussed three methods of graphing linear equations: (1) plotting points, (2) using x-intercepts and y-intercepts, and (3) using the slope and y-intercept. You may use any of these methods to graph the corresponding equations when graphing inequalities. Example 10 on pages 437–438 provides a review of each of the methods.

EXERCISE SET 7.5

Math XL   MathXL®   MyMathLab   MyMathLab

Warm-Up Exercises

Fill in the blanks with the appropriate word, phrase, or symbol(s) from the following list.

contains   does not contain   dashed   solid   solutions

1. When graphing an inequality with the symbol $\leq$ or $\geq$, use a _____ line.

2. When graphing an inequality with the symbol $<$ or $>$, use a _____ line.

3. The points in the shaded region of the graph of an inequality represent _____ to the inequality.

4. If the checkpoint satisfies the inequality, shade the region that _____ the point.

Practice the Skills

Graph each inequality.

5. $y > -3$

6. $y \leq \dfrac{7}{2}$

7. $x \geq \dfrac{3}{2}$

8. $x < -1$

9. $y \leq 3x$

10. $y > -2x$

11. $y < x - 4$

12. $y < 2x + 1$

13. $y < -3x + 4$

14. $y \geq 2x - 3$

15. $y \geq \dfrac{1}{2}x - 4$

16. $y > -\dfrac{x}{2} + 2$

17. $y > \dfrac{1}{2}x - 2$

18. $y > \dfrac{1}{3}x + 1$

19. $3x - 2 < y$

20. $y - 5 \leq -3x$

21. $2x + y \leq 3$

22. $x + y > -2$

23. $3y > 2x - 3$

24. $4x - 2y \leq 6$

Problem Solving

25. Determine whether $(4, 2)$ is a solution to each inequality.
  - **a)** $2x + 4y < 16$
  - **b)** $2x + 4y > 16$
  - **c)** $2x + 4y \geq 16$
  - **d)** $2x + 4y \leq 16$

26. Determine whether $(-3, 7)$ is a solution to each inequality.
  - **a)** $-2x + 3y < 9$
  - **b)** $-2x + 3y > 9$
  - **c)** $-2x + 3y \geq 9$
  - **d)** $-2x + 3y \leq 9$

27. Determine whether the given phrase means: less than, less than or equal to, greater than, or greater than or equal to.
  - **a)** no more than
  - **b)** no less than
  - **c)** at most
  - **d)** at least

28. Consider the two inequalities $2x + 1 > 5$ and $2x + y > 5$.
  - **a)** How many variables does the inequality $2x + 1 > 5$ contain?
  - **b)** How many variables does the inequality $2x + y > 5$ contain?
  - **c)** What is the solution to $2x + 1 > 5$? Indicate the solution on a number line.
  - **d)** Graph $2x + y > 5$.

Concept/Writing Exercises

29. When graphing inequalities that contain either $\leq$ or $\geq$, explain why the points on the line will be solutions to the inequality.

30. When graphing inequalities that contain either $<$ or $>$, explain why the points on the line will not be solutions to the inequality.

31. If an ordered pair is not a solution to the inequality $ax + by < c$, must the ordered pair be a solution to $ax + by > c$? Explain.

32. If an ordered pair is not a solution to the inequality $ax + by \leq c$, must the ordered pair be a solution to $ax + by > c$? Explain.

33. If an ordered pair is a solution to $ax + by > c$, is it possible for the ordered pair to be a solution to $ax + by \leq c$? Explain.

34. Is it possible for an ordered pair to be a solution to both $ax + by < c$ and $ax + by > c$? Explain.

35. How do the graphs of $2x + 3y > 6$ and $2x + 3y < 6$ differ?

36. Which of the following inequalities have the same graphs? Explain how you determined your answer.

a) $2x - y > 4$ **b)** $-2x + y < -4$

c) $y < 2x - 4$ **d)** $-2y + 4x < -8$

Cumulative Review Exercises

[1.4] **37.** Consider the set of numbers

$$\left\{ 2, -5, 0, \sqrt{7}, \frac{2}{5}, -6.3, \sqrt{3}, -\frac{23}{34} \right\}$$

List those that are

a) natural numbers;

b) whole numbers;

c) rational numbers;

d) irrational numbers;

e) real numbers.

[2.5] **38.** Solve $3(x - 2) + 4x = 5x - 2$.

[4.6] **39.** Divide $\dfrac{10x^2 - 15x + 25}{5x}$.

[6.1] **40.** Simplify $\dfrac{3x}{3x^2 + 6xy}$.

7.6 Functions

1 Find the domain and range of a relation.

2 Recognize functions.

3 Evaluate functions.

4 Graph linear functions.

In this section we introduce relations and functions. A function is a special type of relation. Functions are a common thread in mathematics courses from algebra through calculus. In this section we give an informal introduction to relations and functions.

1 Find the Domain and Range of a Relation

First we will discuss **relations**.

> **Relation**
>
> A **relation** is any set of ordered pairs.

Since a relation is *any* set of points, *every graph will represent a relation*.

Examples of Relations

$\{(2, 5), (4, 6), (5, 9), (7, 12)\}$

$\{(1, 2), (2, 2), (3, 2), (4, 2)\}$

$\{(3, 2), (3, 3), (3, 4), (3, 5), (3, 6)\}$

In the ordered pair (x, y), the x and y are called the **components of the ordered pair**. The **domain** of a relation is the set of *first components* in the set of ordered pairs. For example,

Relation	Domain
$\{(2, 5), (4, 6), (5, 9), (7, 12)\}$	$\{2, 4, 5, 7\}$
$\{(1, 2), (2, 2), (3, 2), (4, 2)\}$	$\{1, 2, 3, 4\}$
$\{(3, 2), (3, 3), (3, 4), (3, 5), (3, 6)\}$	$\{3\}$

The **range** of a relation is the set of *second components* in the set of ordered pairs. For example,

Relation	Range
$\{(2, 5), (4, 6), (5, 9), (7, 12)\}$	$\{5, 6, 9, 12\}$
$\{(1, 2), (2, 2), (3, 2), (4, 2)\}$	$\{2\}$
$\{(3, 2), (3, 3), (3, 4), (3, 5), (3, 6)\}$	$\{2, 3, 4, 5, 6\}$

Domain   Range

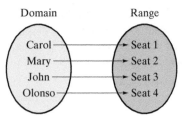

FIGURE 7.47

In relations, the sets can contain elements other than numbers. For example,

Relation

{(Carol, Seat 1), (Mary, Seat 2), (John, Seat 3), (Olonso, Seat 4)}

Domain

{Carol, Mary, John, Olonso}

Range

{Seat 1, Seat 2, Seat 3, Seat 4}

Figure 7.47 illustrates the relation between the person and the seat number.

2 Recognize Functions

Consider the relation shown in **Figure 7.47**. Notice that each member in the domain corresponds with exactly one member of the range. That is, each person is assigned to exactly one seat. This is an example of a **function**.

> **Function**
>
> A **function** is a set of ordered pairs in which each first component corresponds to exactly one second component.

Since a function is a special type of relation, our discussion of domain and range applies to functions. In the definition of a function, *the set of first components represents the domain of the function and the set of second components represents the range of the function.*

EXAMPLE 1   Consider the relations in **Figures 7.48a** through **d**. Which relations are functions?

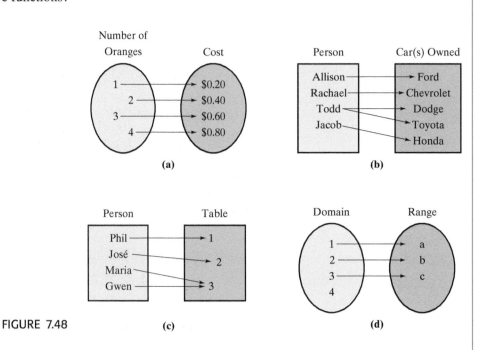

FIGURE 7.48

Solution

a) If we wished, we could represent the information given in the figure as the following set of ordered pairs: {(1, $0.20), (2, $0.40), (3, $0.60), (4, $0.80)}. Notice that each first component corresponds to exactly one second component. Therefore, this relation is a function.

b) If we look at **Figure 7.48b**, we can see that Todd does *not* correspond to exactly one car. If we were to list the set of ordered pairs to represent this relation, the set would contain the ordered pairs (Todd, Dodge) and (Todd, Toyota). Therefore, each first component does not correspond to exactly one second component and this relation is not a function.

c) Although both Maria and Gwen share a table, each person corresponds to exactly one table. If we listed the ordered pairs we would have (Phil, 1), (José, 2), (Maria, 3), (Gwen, 3). Note that each *first* component corresponds to exactly one second component. Therefore, this relation is a function.

d) Since the number 4 in the domain does not correspond to any component in the range, this relation is not a function. *Every* component in the domain must correspond to exactly one component in the range for the relation to be a function.

Now Try Exercise 19

The functions given in Example 1a) and 1c) were determined by looking at correspondences in figures. Most functions have an infinite number of ordered pairs and are usually defined with an equation (or rule) that tells how to obtain the second component when you are given the first component. In Example 2, we determine a function from the information provided.

EXAMPLE 2 **Cost of Matchbox Cars** At a toy store, matchbox cars cost $0.99 each. Write a function to determine the cost, c, when n matchbox cars are purchased.

Solution When one car is purchased, the cost is $0.99. When two cars are purchased, the cost is 2($0.99), and when n cars are purchased, the cost is n($0.99) or $0.99n. The function $c = 0.99n$ will give the cost, c, in dollars, when n cars are purchased. Note that for any value of n, there is exactly one value of c.

Now Try Exercise 51

EXAMPLE 3 Determine whether the following sets of ordered pairs are functions.

a) $\{(4, 5), (3, 2), (-2, -3), (2, 5), (1, 6)\}$

b) $\{(4, 5), (3, 2), (-2, -3), (4, 1), (5, -2)\}$

Solution

a) Since each first component corresponds with exactly one second component, this set of ordered pairs is a function.

b) The ordered pairs (4, 5) and (4, 1) contain the same first component. Therefore, each first component does not correspond to exactly one second component, and this set of ordered pairs is not a function.

Now Try Exercise 13

In **Figures 7.49a** and **7.49b** we plot the ordered pairs from Example 3a) and 3b), respectively.

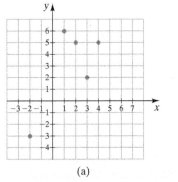

(a)

First set of ordered pairs,
Function

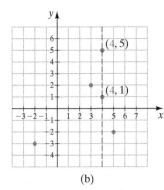

(b)

Second set of ordered pairs,
Not a function

FIGURE 7.49

Consider **Figure 7.49a** on page 447. If a vertical line is drawn through each point, no vertical line intersects more than one point. This indicates that each value of x in the domain corresponds to exactly one value of y in the range. Therefore, this set of points represents a function.

Now look at **Figure 7.49b** on page 447. The dashed red vertical line intersects both $(4, 5)$ and $(4, 1)$. Each element in the domain *does not* correspond to exactly one element in the range. Therefore, this set of ordered pairs does *not* represent a function.

To determine whether a graph represents a function, we can use the **vertical line test.**

Vertical Line Test

If a vertical line can be drawn so that it intersects a graph at more than one point, then the graph does not represent a function.

EXAMPLE 4 Use the vertical line test to determine which graphs represent functions.

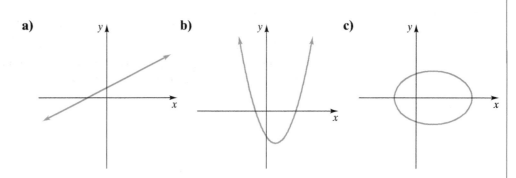

Solution

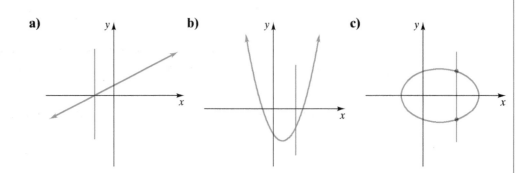

The graphs in parts **a)** and **b)** represent functions since it is not possible to draw a vertical line that intersects the graph at more than one point. The graph in part **c)** does not represent a function since a vertical line can be drawn to intersect the graph at more than one point.

Now Try Exercise 31

Consider the information provided in **Table 7.1**. This table of values is a function because each amount of sales corresponds to exactly one income.

Consider the graph shown in **Figure 7.50** on page 449. This graph represents a function. Notice that each year corresponds to exactly one value of exports to China. Both graphs in **Figure 7.51** on page 449, represent functions. Each graph passes the vertical line test.

TABLE 7.1 Monthly Income

Sales (dollars)	Income (dollars)
0	$1500
$5000	$1800
$10,000	$2100
$15,000	$2400
$20,000	$2700
$25,000	$3000

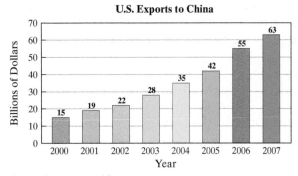

U.S. Exports to China

Source: U.S. Department of Commerce

FIGURE 7.50

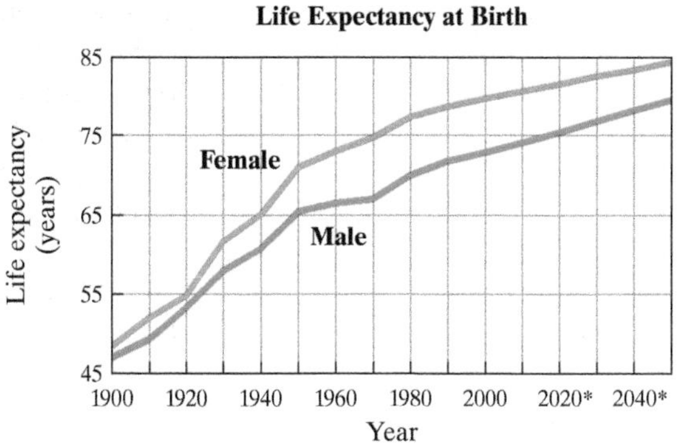

Life Expectancy at Birth

Source: U.S. Bureau of the Census   * Projections

FIGURE 7.51

3 Evaluate Functions

When a function is represented by an equation, it is often convenient to use **function notation**, $f(x)$. If we were to graph $y = x + 2$, we would see that it is a function because its graph passes the vertical line test. The value of y *depends on* the value of x. Therefore, we say that y *is a function of* x, and we can write $y = f(x)$. We can write

$$y = f(x) = x + 2 \quad \text{or simply} \quad f(x) = x + 2$$

To evaluate a function for a specific value of x, we substitute that value for x everywhere the x appears in the function. For example, to evaluate the function $f(x) = x + 2$ at $x = 1$, we do the following:

$$f(x) = x + 2$$
$$f(1) = 1 + 2 = 3$$

Thus, when x is 1, $f(x)$ or y is 3.

When $x = 4$, $f(x)$ or $y = 6$, as illustrated below.

$$y = f(x) = x + 2$$
$$y = f(4) = 4 + 2 = 6$$

The notation $f(1)$ is read "f of 1" and $f(4)$ is read "f of 4."

EXAMPLE 5 For the function $f(x) = x^2 + 4x - 9$, find **a)** $f(3)$ and **b)** $f(-6)$. **c)** If $x = -1$, determine the value of y.

Solution

a) Substitute 3 for each x in the function, and then evaluate.

$$f(x) = x^2 + 4x - 9$$
$$f(3) = 3^2 + 4(3) - 9$$
$$= 9 + 12 - 9 = 12$$

b)
$$f(x) = x^2 + 4x - 9$$
$$f(-6) = (-6)^2 + 4(-6) - 9$$
$$= 36 - 24 - 9 = 3$$

c) Since $y = f(x)$, we evaluate $f(x)$ at -1.

$$f(x) = x^2 + 4x - 9$$
$$f(-1) = (-1)^2 + 4(-1) - 9$$
$$= 1 - 4 - 9 = -12$$

Thus, when $x = -1$, $y = -12$.

Now Try Exercise 39

4 Graph Linear Functions

The graphs of all equations of the form $y = ax + b$ will be straight lines that are functions. Therefore, we may refer to equations of the form $y = f(x) = ax + b$ as **linear functions**.

EXAMPLE 6 Graph $f(x) = 2x + 4$. ————————————

Solution   Since $f(x)$ is the same as y, write $y = f(x) = 2x + 4$. Select values for x and find the corresponding values for y or $f(x)$.

$$y = f(x) = 2x + 4$$

		x	y
Let $x = -3$.	$y = f(-3) = 2(-3) + 4 = -2$	-3	-2
Let $x = 0$.	$y = f(0) = 2(0) + 4 = 4$	0	4
Let $x = 1$.	$y = f(1) = 2(1) + 4 = 6$	1	6

Now plot the points and draw the graph of the function (**Fig. 7.52**).

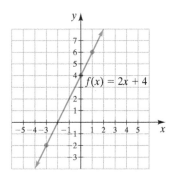

FIGURE 7.52

Now Try Exercise 45

EXAMPLE 7 **Ice Skating Rink** The weekly profit, p, of an ice skating rink is a function of the number of skaters per week, n. The function approximating the profit is $p = f(n) = 8n - 600$, where $0 \leq n \leq 400$.

a) Construct a graph showing the relationship between the number of skaters and the weekly profit.

b) Estimate the profit if there are 200 skaters in a given week.

Rockefeller Plaza, New York City

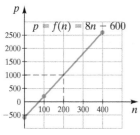

FIGURE 7.53

Solution

a) Select values for n, and find the corresponding values for p. Then draw the graph (**Fig. 7.53**). Notice there are no arrowheads on the line because the function is defined only for values of n between 0 and 400 inclusive.

$$p = f(n) = 8n - 600$$

Let $n = 0$. $p = f(0) = 8(0) - 600 = -600$
Let $n = 100$. $p = f(100) = 8(100) - 600 = 200$
Let $n = 400$. $p = f(400) = 8(400) - 600 = 2600$

n	p
0	−600
100	200
400	2600

b) Using the red dashed line on the graph, we can see that if there are 200 skaters the weekly profit is $1000.

Now Try Exercise 57

EXERCISE SET 7.6

MathXL®   MyMathLab

Warm-Up Exercises

Fill in the blanks with the appropriate word, phrase, or symbol(s) from the following list.

relation	function	x-component	domain	vertical line test
range	$f(x)$	vertical line	y-components	

1. The _____ consists of the x-components in a set of ordered pairs.

2. The range consists of the _____ in a set of ordered pairs.

3. A _____ is any set of ordered pairs.

4. A _____ is a relation in which each first component corresponds to exactly one second component.

5. If a _____ intersects a graph in more than one point, then this graph does not represent a function.

6. The notation _____ is pronounced "f of x."

7. In a function, every _____ corresponds to exactly one y-component.

8. In a function, every element in the domain must correspond to exactly one element in the _____ .

Practice the Skills

Determine which of the relations are also functions. Give the domain and range of each relation or function.

9. $\{(5, 4), (2, 2), (3, 5), (1, 3), (4, 1)\}$

10. $\{(1, 1), (-3, 2), (5, 3), (-3, 0), (4, 6)\}$

11. $\{(5, 5), (3, 0), (3, 2), (1, 4), (2, 4), (7, -2)\}$

12. $\{(-2, 1), (1, -3), (3, 4), (4, 5), (-2, 0)\}$

13. $\{(5, 0), (4, -4), (0, -1), (3, 2), (1, 1)\}$

14. $\{(-6, 3), (-3, 4), (0, 3), (5, 2), (3, 5), (2, 3)\}$

15. $\{(3, 0), (0, -3), (1, 5), (1, 0), (1, 2)\}$

16. $\{(4, 5), (3, -7), (4, -9), (3, -3)\}$

17. $\{(0, 3), (1, 3), (2, 3), (3, 3), (4, 3)\}$

18. $\{(3, 5), (2, 4), (1, 0), (0, 1), (-1, 4)\}$

In the figures in Exercises 19–22, the domain and range of a relation are illustrated. **a)** *Construct a set of ordered pairs that represent the relation.* **b)** *Determine whether the relation is a function.*

19.

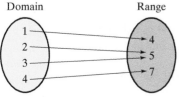

20.

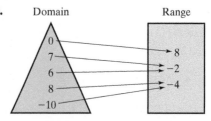

21.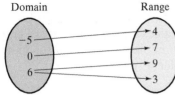

22.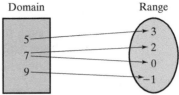

Use the vertical line test to determine whether each relation is also a function.

23.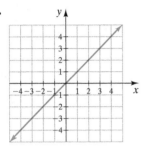

24.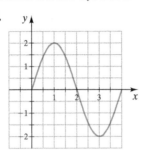

25.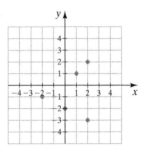

26.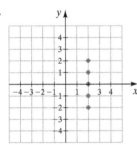

27.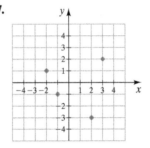

28.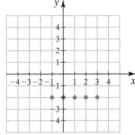

29.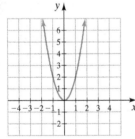

30.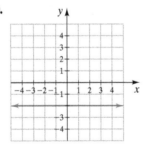

31.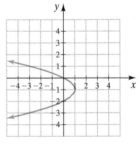

32.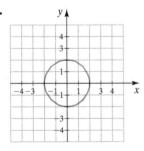

33.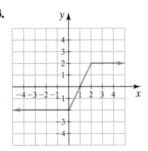

34.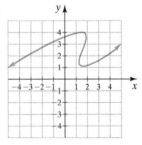

Evaluate each function at the indicated values.

35. $f(x) = 4x + 2$; find **a)** $f(3)$, **b)** $f(-1)$

36. $f(x) = -4x + 7$; find **a)** $f(0)$, **b)** $f(4)$,

37. $f(x) = x^2 + 4$; find **a)** $f(2)$, **b)** $f(-2)$

38. $f(x) = 2x^2 + 3x - 4$; find **a)** $f(2)$, **b)** $f(-3)$

39. $f(x) = 3x^2 - x + 4$; find **a)** $f(0)$, **b)** $f(1)$

40. $f(x) = \frac{1}{2}x - 4$; find **a)** $f(10)$, **b)** $f(-8)$

41. $f(x) = \frac{x + 4}{2}$; find **a)** $f(2)$, **b)** $f(12)$

42. $f(x) = \frac{1}{2}x^2 + 6$; find **a)** $f(4)$, **b)** $f(-6)$

Graph each function.

43. $f(x) = x + 3$

44. $f(x) = -x + 4$

45. $f(x) = 2x - 1$

46. $f(x) = 4x + 2$

47. $f(x) = -2x + 4$

48. $f(x) = -x + 5$

49. $f(x) = -\dfrac{1}{2}x + 2$

50. $f(x) = -4x$

Problem Solving

51. Cost of Oranges Oranges cost $0.35 each. Write a function to determine the cost, c, when n oranges are purchased.

52. Cost of Shirts Shirts cost $19.95 each. Write a function to determine the cost, c, when n shirts are purchased.

In Exercises 53–54, are the graphs functions? Explain.

53.

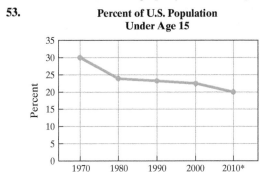

Percent of U.S. Population Under Age 15

Source: U.S. Bureau of the Census   * Projection

54.

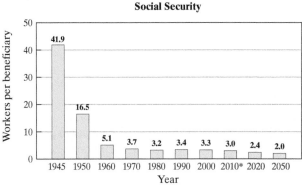

Social Security

Source: Social Security Administration   * Projections for 2010 and beyond

55. Babysitting Jacci Cavanaugh gets paid $8 per hour for babysitting. Her weekly income, I, from babysitting can be represented using the function $I = 8h$, where h is the number of hours she babysits.

a) Draw a graph of the function for times up to and including 60 hours.

b) Estimate her weekly income from babysitting if she babysits for 20 hours per week.

56. Bike Riding Rachel Falk and Tony Mathias go bike riding together. If they ride at a constant rate of 8 miles per hour, the distance they travel, d, can be found by the function $d = 8t$, where t is time in hours.

a) Draw a graph of the function for times up to and including 6 hours.

b) Estimate the distance they will travel if they ride for 4 hours.

57. Selling a House The Ferreras are selling their house. The cost they will pay to the realtor is 6% of the selling price of the house, p. They expect to have $2000 in other selling costs. Therefore, the total cost, C, to the Ferreras for selling their house can be represented by the function

$$C = 2000 + 0.06p$$

a) Draw a graph of the function for selling prices from $0 up to and including $200,000.

b) Estimate the total cost if the selling price is $150,000.

58. Vacationing Frank Duomo plans to take a vacation in the San Diego/Los Angeles area. He determines that the cost, C, of the vacation can be estimated using the function $C = 350n + 400$, where n is the number of days spent in the area.

a) Draw a graph of the function for up to and including 10 days.

b) Estimate the cost of a 5-day vacation in the area.

Grauman's Chinese Theater, Hollywood

59. Photo Printer A photo printer costs $120. The cost per picture printed, n, is 40 cents each. Therefore, the total cost, C, of the printer plus the photos printed is $C = 120 + 0.40n$.

a) Draw a graph showing the total cost for up to and including 500 photos.

b) If 300 photos are printed, estimate the total cost.

60. Auto Registration A state's auto registration fee, f, is $20 plus $15 per 1000 pounds of the vehicle's gross weight. The registration fee is a function of the vehicle's weight, $f = 20 + 0.015w$, where w is the weight of the vehicle in pounds.

a) Draw a graph of the function for vehicle weights up to and including 10,000 pounds.

b) Estimate the registration fee of a vehicle whose gross weight is 6000 pounds.

61. Singing Sensation A new singing group, Three Forks and a Spoon, signs a recording contract with the Smash Record label. The contract provides a signing bonus of $10,000, plus an 8% royalty on the sales, s, of the group's new record, *There's Mud in Your Eye!* The group's income, i, is a function of its sales, $i = 10,000 + 0.08s$.

a) Draw a graph of the function for sales of up to and including $100,000.

b) Estimate the group's income if its sales are $20,000.

62. Electric Bill A monthly electric bill, m, in dollars, consists of a $20 monthly fee plus $0.07 per kilowatt-hour, k, of electricity used. The amount of the bill is a function of the kilowatt-hours used, $m = 20 + 0.07k$.

a) Draw a graph for up to and including 3000 kilowatt-hours of electricity used in a month.

b) Estimate the bill if 2100 kilowatt-hours of electricity are used.

Concept/Writing Exercises

63. a) If two distinct ordered pairs in a relation have the same first coordinate, can the relation be a function? Explain.

b) In a function is it necessary for each value of y in the range to correspond to exactly one value of x in the domain? Explain.

64. a) If a relation consists of six ordered pairs and the domain of the relation consists of five values of x, can the relation be a function? Explain.

b) If a relation consists of six ordered pairs and the range of the relation consists of five values of y, can the relation be a function? Explain.

Consider the following graphs. Recall from Section 2.8 that an open circle at the end of a line segment means that the endpoint is not included in the answer. A solid circle at the end of a line segment indicates that the endpoint is included in the answer. Determine whether the following graphs are functions. Explain your answer.

65.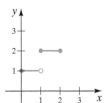

66.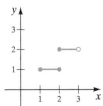

67.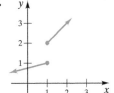

68.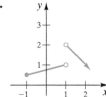

Challenge Problems

69. $f(x) = \dfrac{1}{2}x^2 - 3x + 5$; find

a) $f\left(\dfrac{1}{2}\right)$,

b) $f\left(\dfrac{2}{3}\right)$,

c) $f(0.4)$

70. $f(x) = x^2 + 2x - 4$; find

a) $f(1)$,

b) $f(2)$,

c) $f(a)$.

Explain how you determined your answer to part **c)**.

Group Activity

Discuss and answer Exercises 71 and 72 as a group.

71. Submit three real-life examples (different from those already given) of a quantity that is a function of another. Write each as a function, and indicate what each variable represents.

72. Postage In July 2009 the cost of mailing a first class letter was 44 cents for the first ounce and 17 cents for each additional ounce. A graph showing the cost of mailing a letter first class is pictured below.

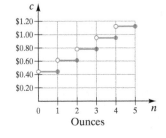

a) Does this graph represent a function? Explain your answer.

b) From the graph, estimate the cost of mailing a 4-ounce package first class.

c) Determine the exact cost of mailing a 4-ounce package first class.

d) From the graph, estimate the cost of mailing a 3.6-ounce package first class.

e) Determine the exact cost of mailing a 3.6-ounce package first class.

Cumulative Review Exercises

[1.3] **73.** Evaluate $\dfrac{4}{9} - \dfrac{3}{7}$.

[2.5] **74.** Solve $2x - 3(x + 2) = 8$.

[3.2] **75. Taxi Ride** The cost of a taxi ride is $2.00 for the first mile and $1.50 for each additional mile or part thereof. Find the maximum distance Andrew Collins can ride in the taxi if he has only $20.

[5.5] **76.** Factor $25x^2 - 49y^2$.

[6.5] **77.** Simplify $\dfrac{\frac{28x}{y^2}}{\frac{7}{xy}}$.

[7.1] **78.** What is a graph?

Chapter 7 Summary

IMPORTANT FACTS AND CONCEPTS	EXAMPLES

Section 7.1

The **Cartesian coordinate system** is formed by two axes drawn perpendicular to each other. The point of intersection is called the **origin**. The horizontal axis is called the **x-axis**. The vertical axis is called the **y-axis**. **Ordered pairs** are of the form (x, y).	**Cartesian coordinate system** 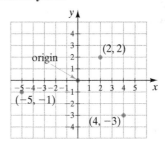
A **linear equation in two variables** is an equation that can be put in the form $$ax + by = c$$ where a, b, and c are real numbers. This form is also called the **standard form** for a linear equation.	$3x + 7y = 2$, $-2x - y = 9$
A **graph** of an equation in two variables is an illustration of a set of points whose coordinates satisfy the equation. Points that lie in a straight line are **collinear**.	Every point on the graph satisfies the equation $y = 2x - 1$. The points on the graph are collinear and the graph is a straight line. 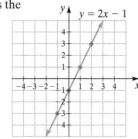

Section 7.2

To Graph Linear Equations by Plotting Points **1.** Solve the linear equation for the variable y. **2.** Select a value for the variable x. Substitute this value in the equation for x and find the corresponding value of y. Record the ordered pair (x, y). **3.** Repeat step 2 with two different values of x. **4.** Plot the three ordered pairs. **5.** Draw a straight line through the three points. Draw an arrowhead on each end of the line.	Graph $y = -x + 2$. **Table** | x	y
-1	3
0	2
2	0 | 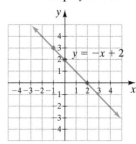
The **x-intercept** is the point where the graph crosses the x-axis. The **y-intercept** is the point where the graph crosses the y-axis.	On the graph above, the x-intercept is $(2, 0)$ and the y-intercept is $(0, 2)$.

IMPORTANT FACTS AND CONCEPTS	EXAMPLES

Section 7.2 (cont.)

To Graph Linear Equations using the *x*- and *y*-Intercepts

1. Find the *y*-intercept by setting *x* in the given equation equal to 0 and finding the corresponding value of *y*.
2. Find the *x*-intercept by setting *y* in the given equation equal to 0 and finding the corresponding value of *x*.
3. Determine a checkpoint by selecting a nonzero value for *x* and finding the corresponding value of *y*.
4. Plot the *y*-intercept, the *x*-intercept, and the checkpoint.
5. Draw a straight line through the three points. Draw an arrowhead on each end of the line.

Graph $4x + 2y = 8$ using the *x*- and *y*-intercepts.
Let $x = 0$:
$$4(0) + 2y = 8$$
$$2y = 8$$
$$y = 4.$$
y-intercept: $(0, 4)$
Let $y = 0$:
$$4x + 2(0) = 8$$
$$4x = 8$$
$$x = 2$$
x-intercept: $(2, 0)$

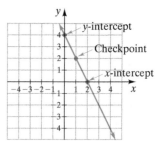

Checkpoint: $(1, 2)$

Horizontal Line

The graph of an equation of the form $y = b$ is a horizontal line whose *y*-intercept is $(0, b)$.

Vertical Line

The graph of an equation of the form $x = a$ is a vertical line whose *x*-intercept is $(a, 0)$.

Graph $y = 2$.   Graph $x = -4$.

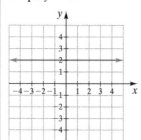 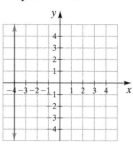

Section 7.3

The **slope of a line** is a ratio of the vertical change to the horizontal change between any two selected points on the line. The slope of a line through the points (x_1, y_1) and (x_2, y_2) is

$$m = \text{slope} = \frac{\text{change in } y \text{ (vertical change)}}{\text{change in } x \text{ (horizontal change)}} = \frac{\text{rise}}{\text{run}} = \frac{y_2 - y_1}{x_2 - x_1}$$

The slope of the line through $(-1, 3)$ and $(5, 7)$ is

$$m = \frac{7 - 3}{5 - (-1)} = \frac{4}{6} = \frac{2}{3}$$

A line where the value of *y* increases as *x* increases has a **positive slope**.

A line where the value of *y* decreases as *x* increases has a **negative slope**.

A horizontal line has a **slope of 0**.

The slope of a vertical line is **undefined**.

Positive slope
(rises to right)

Negative slope
(falls to right)

Slope is 0.
(horizontal line)

Slope is undefined.
(vertical line)

Two nonvertical lines with the same slope and different *y*-intercepts are **parallel lines**. Any two vertical lines are parallel to each other.

The graphs of the equations $y = 2x + 3$ and $y = 2x + 4$ are parallel lines since the graphs have the same slope, 2, and different *y*-intercepts.

Two lines whose slopes are negative reciprocals of each other are **perpendicular lines**. Any vertical line is perpendicular to any horizontal line.

The graphs of the equations $y = 2x + 4$ and $y = -\frac{1}{2}x + 3$

are perpendicular lines since the slopes of the graphs are negative reciprocals of each other.

IMPORTANT FACTS AND CONCEPTS	EXAMPLES

Section 7.4

Slope-Intercept Form of a Linear Equation

$$y = mx + b$$

where m is the slope, and $(0, b)$ is the y-intercept of the line.

The graph of $y = 3x - 4$ has a slope of 3 and a y-intercept of $(0, -4)$.

The equation of a line with a slope of $-\frac{1}{2}$ and a y-intercept of $(0, 6)$ is $y = -\frac{1}{2}x + 6$.

To Graph Linear Equations Using the Slope and y-intercept

1. If necessary, solve the equation for y.
2. Plot the y-intercept.
3. Use the slope to find two more points on the line.
4. Using a straightedge, draw a straight line through the three points. Draw an arrowhead on each end of the line.

$2x + 4y = 8$ written in slope-intercept form is $y = -\frac{1}{2}x + 2$.

The slope is $-\frac{1}{2}$ and the y-intercept is $(0, 2)$.

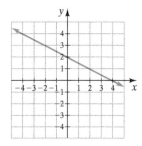

Point-Slope Form of a Linear Equation

$$y - y_1 = m(x - x_1)$$

where m is the slope of the line and (x_1, y_1) is a point on the line.

The graph of $y - 7 = \frac{5}{6}(x - 3)$ has a slope of $\frac{5}{6}$ and contains the point $(3, 7)$.

Section 7.5

A **linear inequality** occurs when the equals sign in a linear equation is replaced with an inequality sign.

$$4x - 3y > 1, \quad -x + 2y \le 7$$

To Graph a Linear Inequality in Two Variables

1. Replace the inequality symbol with an equals sign.
2. Draw the graph of the equation in step 1. If the original inequality symbol is $\ge$ or $\le$, draw a solid line. If the original inequality symbol is $>$ or $<$, draw a dashed line.
3. Select any point not on the line and determine whether this point is a solution to the original inequality. If the selected point is a solution, shade the region on the side of the line containing this point. If the selected point does not satisfy the inequality, shade the region on the side of the line not containing this point.

Graph $y \le x + 3$.

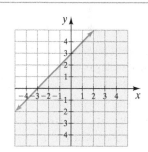

Section 7.6

A **relation** is any set of ordered pairs.

A **function** is a set of ordered pairs in which each first component corresponds to exactly one second component. The **domain** of a relation or function is the set of first components in the set of ordered pairs. The **range** of a relation or function is the set of second components in the set of ordered pairs.

Relation

$$\{(-1, 1), (3, 2), (3, 5), (0, 4)\}$$

Function

$$\{(1, 2), (2, -1), (6, 5), (0, 3)\}$$
Domain: $\{0, 1, 2, 6\}$, Range: $\{-1, 2, 3, 5\}$

Vertical Line Test

If a vertical line intersects a graph at more than one point, then the graph does not represent a function.

Function

Not a Function

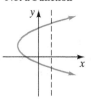

IMPORTANT FACTS AND CONCEPTS	EXAMPLES

Section 7.6 (cont.)

When a function is represented by an equation, we can use function notation, $f(x)$.

Given the function $f(x)$, to compute $f(a)$, replace x by a.

$y = ax + b$ is a linear equation.

$f(x) = ax + b$ is a linear function.

The function $y = 3x^2 - x + 7$ can be written as
$$f(x) = 3x^2 - x + 7.$$
If $f(x) = 3x^2 - x + 7$, then
$$f(-1) = 3(-1)^2 - (-1) + 7 = 11.$$

Earlier we graphed the equation $y = -\dfrac{1}{2}x + 2$.

Both $y = -\dfrac{1}{2}x + 2$ and $f(x) = -\dfrac{1}{2}x + 2$ have the same graph since y can be replaced by $f(x)$.

Chapter 7 Review Exercises

[7.1]

1. Plot each ordered pair on the same axes.
   a) $A(5, 3)$ b) $B(0, 6)$ c) $C\left(5, \dfrac{1}{2}\right)$
   d) $D(-4, 3)$ e) $E(-6, -1)$ f) $F(-2, 0)$

2. Determine whether the following points are collinear.
   $$(7, 1), (6, 8), (-2, 0), (4, 5)$$

3. Which of the following ordered pairs satisfy the equation $2x + 3y = 9$?
   a) $(3, 1)$ b) $\left(5, -\dfrac{1}{3}\right)$
   c) $(-2, 4)$ d) $\left(2, \dfrac{5}{3}\right)$

[7.2]

4. Find the missing coordinate in the following solutions to $3x - 2y = 8$.
   a) $(-2, ?)$ b) $(0, ?)$
   c) $(?, 5)$ d) $(?, 0)$

Graph each equation using the method of your choice.

5. $y = 4$
6. $x = 2$
7. $y = 3x$
8. $y = 2x - 1$
9. $y = -2x + 5$
10. $2y + x = 8$
11. $-2x + 3y = 6$
12. $5x + 2y + 10 = 0$
13. $5x + 10y = 20$
14. $\dfrac{2}{3}x = \dfrac{1}{4}y + 20$

[7.3] *Find the slope of the line through the given points.*

15. $(6, -4)$ and $(1, 5)$
16. $(-4, -6)$ and $(8, -7)$
17. $(-2, -3)$ and $(-4, 1)$

18. What is the slope of a horizontal line?
19. What is the slope of a vertical line?

20. Define the slope of a straight line.

Find the slope of each line.

21.

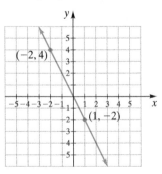

22.

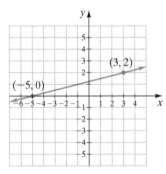

Assume that line 1 and line 2 are distinct lines. If m_1 represents the slope of line 1 and m_2 represents the slope of line 2, determine if line 1 and line 2 are parallel, perpendicular, or neither.

23. $m_1 = \dfrac{7}{8}, m_2 = -\dfrac{7}{8}$

24. $m_1 = -3, m_2 = \dfrac{1}{3}$

25. David Nezelek is riding his bicycle in a charity fund raiser. The graph below shows the time in hours along the horizontal axis and the distance in miles along the vertical axis.

Find the slope of the line segment in

a) red   **b)** blue

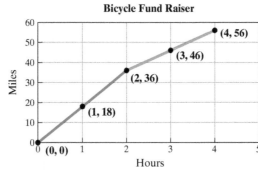

Bicycle Fund Raiser

[7.4] *Determine the slope and y-intercept of the graph of each equation.*

26. $6x + 7y = 21$ **27.** $2x + 7 = 0$ **28.** $4y + 12 = 0$

Write the equation of each line.

29.

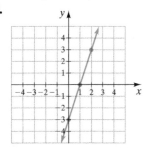

30.

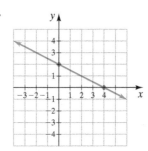

Determine whether each pair of lines is parallel, perpendicular, or neither.

31. $y = 2x - 7$
    $3y = 6x + 18$

32. $2x - 3y = 15$
    $3x + 2y = 12$

Find the equation of each line with the given properties.

33. Slope $= 3$ through $(2, 7)$

34. Slope $= -\dfrac{2}{3}$, through $(3, 2)$

35. Slope $= 0$, through $(6, 2)$

36. Slope is undefined, through $(4, 1)$

37. Through $(-2, 4)$ and $(0, -3)$

38. Through $(-5, -2)$ and $(-5, 3)$

[7.5] *Graph each inequality.*

39. $y \geq 1$ **40.** $x < 4$ **41.** $y < 3x$

42. $y > 2x + 1$ **43.** $-6x + y \geq 5$ **44.** $3y + 6 \leq x$

[7.6] *Determine which of the following relations are also functions. Give the domain and range of each.*

45. $\{(3, 2), (4, -3), (1, 5), (2, -1), (6, 4)\}$

46. $\{(3, 1), (4, 2), (4, 5), (6, 1), (7, 0)\}$

47. $\{(3, 1), (4, 1), (5, 1), (6, 2), (3, -3)\}$

48. $\{(5, -2), (3, -2), (4, -2), (9, -2), (-2, -2)\}$

In Exercises 49 and 50, the domain and range of a relation are illustrated. **a)** *Construct a set of ordered pairs that represent the relation.* **b)** *Determine whether the relation is a function. Explain your answer.*

49.

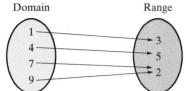

50.

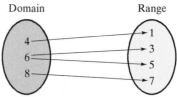

In Exercises 51–54, **a)** *indicate the domain and range of the relation, and* **b)** *indicate if the relation is a function. If it is not a function, explain why.*

51.

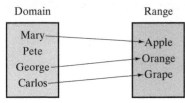

52.

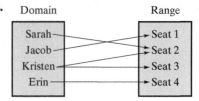

53.

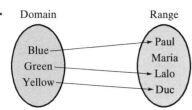

54.

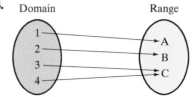

Use the vertical line test to determine whether the relation is also a function.

55.

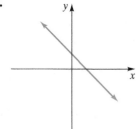

56.

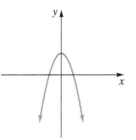

57.

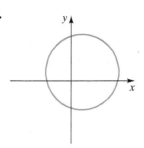

58.

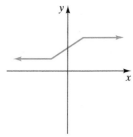

Evaluate each function at the indicated values.

59. $f(x) = 6x - 1$; find
a) $f(1)$,
b) $f(-5)$

60. $f(x) = -4x - 7$; find
a) $f(-4)$,
b) $f(8)$

61. $f(x) = \frac{1}{3}x - 5$; find
a) $f(3)$,
b) $f(-9)$

62. $f(x) = 2x^2 - 4x + 6$; find
a) $f(3)$,
b) $f(-5)$

Determine whether the following graphs are functions. Explain your answer.

63.

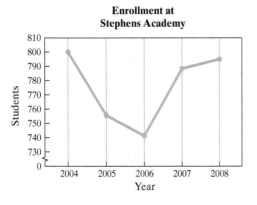

64.

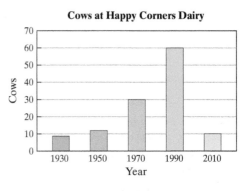

Graph the following functions.

65. $f(x) = 3x - 5$

66. $f(x) = -2x + 3$

67. Stock Purchase A discount stock broker charges $25 plus 3 cents per share of stock bought or sold. A customer's cost, c, in dollars, is a function of the number of shares, n, bought or sold, $c = 25 + 0.03n$.

  a) Draw a graph illustrating a customer's cost for up to and including 10,000 shares of stock.

  b) Estimate the cost if 4000 shares of a stock are purchased.

68. Dollar Store The monthly profit, p, of an Everything for a Dollar store can be estimated by the function $p = 4x - 1600$, where x represents the number of items sold.

  a) Draw a graph of the function for up to and including 1000 items sold.

  b) Estimate the profit if 500 items are sold.

Chapter 7 Practice Test

Chapter Test Prep Videos provide fully worked-out solutions to any of the exercises you want to review. Chapter Test Prep Videos are available via MyMathLab, or on YouTube (search "Angel Elementary Algebra" and click on "Channels").

1. What is a graph?

2. In which quadrants do the following points lie?

  a) $(3, -5)$

  b) $\left(-2, \frac{1}{2}\right)$

3. a) What is the standard form of a linear equation?

  b) What is the slope-intercept form of a linear equation?

  c) What is the point-slope form of a linear equation?

4. Which of the following ordered pairs satisfy the equation $3y = 5x - 9$?

  a) $(4, 2)$ **b)** $\left(\frac{9}{5}, 0\right)$

  c) $(-1, -10)$ **d)** $(0, -3)$

5. Find the slope of the line through the points $(-2, 5)$ and $(4, -3)$.

6. Find the slope and y-intercept of $4x - 9y = 15$

7. Write an equation of the graph in the accompanying figure.

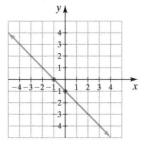

8. Graph $x = -4$.

9. Graph $y = 2$.

10. Graph $y = 3x - 2$ by plotting points.

11. a) Solve the equation $3x - 6y = 12$ for y.

  b) Graph the equation by plotting points.

12. Graph $3x + 5y = 15$ using the intercepts.

13. Write, in slope-intercept form, an equation of the line with a slope of 4 passing through the point $(2, -5)$

14. Write, in slope-intercept form, an equation of the line passing through the points $(3, -1)$ and $(-4, 2)$.

15. Determine whether the following equations represent parallel lines. Explain how you determined your answer.

$$2y = 3x - 6 \quad \text{and} \quad y - \frac{3}{2}x = -5$$

16. Graph $y = 3x - 4$ using the slope and y-intercept.

17. Graph $4x - 2y = 6$ using the slope and y-intercept.

18. Define a function.

19. a) Determine whether the following relation is a function. Explain your answer.

$$\{(1, 2), (3, -4), (5, 3), (3, 0), (6, 5)\}$$

  b) Give the domain and range of the relation or function.

20. Determine whether the following graphs are functions. Explain how you determined your answer.

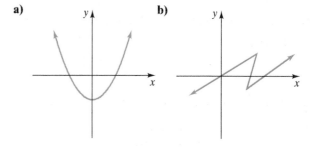

21. If $f(x) = 2x^2 + 3x + 1$ find **a)** $f(2)$ and **b)** $f(-3)$.

22. Graph the function $f(x) = 2x - 4$.

23. Graph $y \geq -3x + 5$.

24. Graph $y < 4x - 2$.

25. Weekly Income Kate Moore, a salesperson, has a weekly income, i, that can be determined by the function $i = 200 + 0.05s$, where s is her weekly sales.

  a) Draw a graph of her weekly income for sales from $0 to $10,000.

  b) Estimate her weekly income if her sales are $5000.

Cumulative Review Test

Take the following test and check your answers with those given in the back of the book. Review any questions that you answered incorrectly. The section where the material was covered is indicated after the answer.

1. Write the set of
   a) natural numbers.
   b) whole numbers.

2. Name each indicated property.
   a) $3(x + 2) = 3x + 3 \cdot 2$
   b) $a + b = b + a$

3. Solve $2x + 5 = 3(x - 5)$.

4. Solve $3(x - 1) - (x + 4) = 2x - 7$

5. Solve the inequality $2x - 14 > 5x + 1$. Graph the solution on a number line.

6. **Chicken Soup** At Tsong Hsu's Grocery Store, 3 cans of chicken soup sell for $1.50. Find the cost of 8 cans.

7. **Rectangle** The length of a rectangle is 3 more than twice the width. Find the length and width of the rectangle if its perimeter is 36 feet.

8. **Running** Two runners start at the same point and run in opposite directions. One runs at 6 mph and the other runs at 8 mph. In how many hours will they be 28 miles apart?

9. Simplify $\dfrac{x^{-4}}{x^{11}}$.

10. Express 652.3 in scientific notation.

11. Factor $2x^2 - 12x + 10$.

12. Factor $4a^2 + 4a - 35$

13. Solve $3x^2 = 21x$.

14. Simplify $\dfrac{2r - 7}{14 - 4r}$.

15. Multiply $\dfrac{x - 2}{3x + 7} \cdot \dfrac{8x}{x - 2}$.

16. Solve $\dfrac{y^2}{y - 6} = \dfrac{36}{y - 6}$.

17. Graph $6x - 3y = -12$ using the intercepts.

18. Graph $y = \dfrac{2}{3}x - 3$ using the slope and y-intercept.

19. Write the equation, in point-slope form, of the line with a slope of 3 passing through the point $(5, 2)$.

20. Determine whether the following relations are functions. Explain your answer.

   a)

   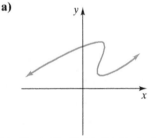

   b) $\{(-4, 1), (5, 3), (7, 3), (-2, 0)\}$

Appendices

A Review of Decimals and Percent

B Finding the Greatest Common Factor and Least Common Denominator

C Geometry

Appendix A Review of Decimals and Percent

Decimals

> **To Add or Subtract Numbers Containing Decimal Points**
>
> 1. Align the numbers by the decimal points.
> 2. Add or subtract the numbers as if they were whole numbers.
> 3. Place the decimal point in the sum or difference directly below the decimal points in the numbers being added or subtracted.

EXAMPLE 1 Add $4.6 + 13.813 + 9.02$.

Solution

$$
\begin{array}{r}
4.600 \\
13.813 \\
+\ 9.020 \\
\hline
27.433
\end{array}
$$

EXAMPLE 2 Subtract 3.062 from 34.9.

Solution

$$
\begin{array}{r}
34.900 \\
-\ 3.062 \\
\hline
31.838
\end{array}
$$

> **To Multiply Numbers Containing Decimal Points**
>
> 1. Multiply as if the factors were whole numbers.
> 2. Determine the total number of digits to the right of the decimal points in the factors.
> 3. Place the decimal point in the product so that the product contains the same number of digits to the right of the decimal as the total found in step 2. For example, if there are a total of three digits to the right of the decimal points in the factors, there must be three digits to the right of the decimal point in the product.

EXAMPLE 3 Multiply 2.34×1.9.

Solution

$$
\begin{array}{r}
2.34 \quad \longleftarrow \text{ two digits to the right of the decimal point} \\
\times \quad 1.9 \quad \longleftarrow \text{ one digit to the right of the decimal point} \\
\hline
2106 \\
234 \quad\quad \\
\hline
4.446 \quad \longleftarrow \text{ three digits to the right of the decimal point in the product}
\end{array}
$$

EXAMPLE 4 Multiply 2.13 × 0.02.

Solution
$$
\begin{array}{ll}
2.13 & \longleftarrow \quad \text{two digits to the right of the decimal point} \\
\underline{\times\ 0.02} & \longleftarrow \quad \text{two digits to the right of the decimal point} \\
0.0426 & \longleftarrow \quad \text{four digits to the right of the decimal point in the product}
\end{array}
$$

Note that it was necessary to add a zero preceding the digit 4 in the answer in order to have four digits to the right of the decimal point.

To Divide Numbers Containing Decimal Points

1. Multiply both the dividend and divisor by a power of 10 that will make the divisor a whole number.
2. Divide as if working with whole numbers.
3. Place the decimal point in the quotient directly above the decimal point in the dividend.

To make the divisor a whole number, multiply *both* the dividend and divisor by 10 if the divisor is given in tenths, by 100 if the divisor is given in hundredths, by 1000 if the divisor is given in thousandths, and so on. Multiplying both the numerator and denominator by the same nonzero number is the same as multiplying the fraction by 1. Therefore, the value of the fraction is unchanged.

EXAMPLE 5 Divide $\dfrac{1.956}{0.12}$.

Solution   Since the divisor, 0.12, is twelve-hundredths, we multiply both the divisor and dividend by 100.

$$
\frac{1.956}{0.12} \times \frac{100}{100} = \frac{195.6}{12.}
$$

Now we divide.

$$
\begin{array}{r}
16.3 \\
12\overline{)195.6} \\
\underline{12} \\
75 \\
\underline{72} \\
3\,6 \\
\underline{3\,6} \\
0
\end{array}
$$

The decimal point in the answer is placed directly above the decimal point in the dividend. Thus, $\dfrac{1.956}{0.12} = 16.3$.

EXAMPLE 6 Divide 0.26 by 10.4.

Solution   First, multiply both the dividend and divisor by 10.

$$
\frac{0.26}{10.4} \times \frac{10}{10} = \frac{2.6}{104.}
$$

Now divide.

$$
\begin{array}{r}
0.025 \\
104\overline{)2.600} \\
\underline{2\,08} \\
520 \\
\underline{520} \\
0
\end{array}
$$

Note that a zero had to be placed before the digit 2 in the quotient.

$$\frac{0.26}{10.4} = 0.025$$

Rounding Decimal Numbers

Now we will explain how to round decimal numbers. The explanation of the procedure will refer to the positional values to the right of the decimal point, as illustrated here:

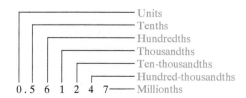

To Round a Decimal Number

1. Identify the number in the problem to the right of the positional value to which the number is to be rounded. For example, if you wish to round to tenths, you identify the number in the hundredths position. If you wish to round to hundredths, you identify the number in the thousandths position, and so on.

2. **a)** If the number you identified in step 1 is greater than or equal to 5, the number in the preceding position is increased by 1 unit, and all numbers to the right of the number that has been increased by 1 unit are eliminated.

   b) If the number you identified in step 1 is less than 5, the number you identified in step 1 and all numbers to its right are eliminated.

EXAMPLE 7   Round 4.863 to tenths.

Solution   Since we are rounding to tenths, we identify the number in the hundredths position as 6. Because the number 6 is greater than or equal to 5, we increase the number in the preceding position by 1 unit and drop the remaining digits. Therefore, 4.863 when rounded to tenths is 4.9.

EXAMPLE 8   Round 5.4738 to hundredths.

Solution   Since we are rounding to hundredths, we identify the number in the thousandths position as 3. Because the number 3 is less than 5, we drop the 3 and all numbers to the right of 3. Therefore, 5.4738 when rounded to hundredths is 5.47.

Percent

The word *percent* means "per hundred." The symbol % means percent. One percent means "one per hundred."

One Percent

$$1\% = \frac{1}{100} \quad \text{or} \quad 1\% = 0.01$$

EXAMPLE 9   Convert 16% to a decimal.

Solution   Since 1% = 0.01,

$$16\% = 16(0.01) = 0.16$$

EXAMPLE 10 Convert 4.7% to a decimal.

Solution   4.7% = 4.7(0.01) = 0.047

EXAMPLE 11 Convert 1.14 to a percent.

Solution   To change a decimal number to a percent, we multiply the number by 100%.

$$1.14 = 1.14 \times 100\% = 114\%$$

Often, you will need to find an amount that is a certain percent of a number. For example, when you purchase an item in a state or county that has a sales tax you must often pay a percent of the item's price as the sales tax. Examples 12 and 13 show how to find a certain percent of a number.

EXAMPLE 12 Find 32% of 300.

Solution   To find a percent of a number, use multiplication. Change 32% to a decimal number, then multiply by 300.

$$(0.32)(300) = 96$$

Thus, 32% of 300 is 96.

EXAMPLE 13 Johnson County charges an 8% sales tax.

a) Find the sales tax on a stereo system that cost $580.

b) Find the total cost of the system, including tax.

Solution

a) The sales tax is 8% of 580.

$$(0.08)(580) = 46.40$$

The sales tax is $46.40.

b) The total cost is the purchase price plus the sales tax:

$$\text{total cost} = \$580 + \$46.40 = \$626.40$$

Appendix B Finding the Greatest Common Factor and Least Common Denominator

Prime Factorization

In Section 1.3, we mentioned that to simplify fractions you can divide both the numerator and denominator by the *greatest common factor* (GCF). One method to find the GCF is to use *prime factorization*. **Prime factorization** is the process of writing a given number as a product of prime numbers. **Prime numbers** are natural numbers, excluding 1, that can be divided by only themselves and 1. The first ten prime numbers are 2, 3, 5, 7, 11, 13, 17, 19, 23, and 29. Can you find the next prime number? If you answered 31, you answered correctly.

To write a number as a product of primes, we can use a *tree diagram*. Begin by selecting any two numbers whose product is the given number. Then continue factoring each of these numbers into prime numbers, as shown in Example 1.

EXAMPLE 1 Determine the prime factorization of the number 120.

Solution   We will use three different tree diagrams to illustrate the prime factorization of 120.

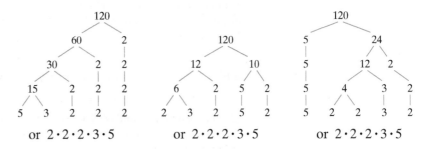

or $2 \cdot 2 \cdot 2 \cdot 3 \cdot 5$ or $2 \cdot 2 \cdot 2 \cdot 3 \cdot 5$ or $2 \cdot 2 \cdot 2 \cdot 3 \cdot 5$

Note that no matter how you start, if you do not make a mistake, you find that the prime factorization of 120 is $2 \cdot 2 \cdot 2 \cdot 3 \cdot 5$. There are other ways 120 can be factored but all will lead to the prime factorization $2 \cdot 2 \cdot 2 \cdot 3 \cdot 5$.

Greatest Common Factor

The **greatest common factor (GCF)** of two natural numbers is the greatest integer that is a factor of both numbers. We use the GCF when simplifying fractions.

> **To Find the Greatest Common Factor of a Given Numerator and Denominator**
>
> 1. Write both the numerator and the denominator as a product of primes.
> 2. Determine all the prime factors that are common to both prime factorizations.
> 3. Multiply the prime factors found in step 2 to obtain the GCF.

EXAMPLE 2 Consider the fraction $\dfrac{108}{156}$.

a) Find the GCF of 108 and 156.   **b)** Simplify $\dfrac{108}{156}$.

Solution

a) First determine the prime factorizations of both 108 and 156.

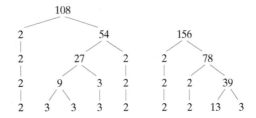

There are two 2s and one 3 common to both prime factorizations; thus

$$GCF = 2 \cdot 2 \cdot 3 = 12$$

The greatest common factor of 108 and 156 is 12. Twelve is the greatest integer that divides into both 108 and 156.

b) To simplify $\dfrac{108}{156}$, we divide both the numerator and denominator by the GCF, 12.

$$\frac{108 \div 12}{156 \div 12} = \frac{9}{13}$$

Thus, $\dfrac{108}{156}$ simplifies to $\dfrac{9}{13}$.

Least Common Denominator

When adding two or more fractions, you must write each fraction with a common denominator. The best denominator to use is the *least common denominator*. The **least common denominator (LCD)** is the smallest number that each denominator divides into. Sometimes the least common denominator is referred to as the **least common multiple** of the denominators.

To Find the Least Common Denominator of Two or More Fractions

1. Write each denominator as a product of prime numbers.
2. For each prime number, determine the maximum number of times that prime number appears in any of the prime factorizations.
3. Multiply all the prime numbers found in step 2. Include each prime number the maximum number of times it appears in any of the prime factorizations. The product of all these prime numbers will be the LCD.

Example 3 illustrates the procedure to determine the LCD.

EXAMPLE 3 Consider $\dfrac{7}{108} + \dfrac{5}{156}$.

a) Determine the least common denominator.

b) Add the fractions.

Solution

a) We found in Example 2 that

$$108 = \boxed{2} \cdot \boxed{2} \cdot \boxed{3} \cdot \boxed{3} \cdot \boxed{3} \quad \text{and} \quad 156 = 2 \cdot 2 \cdot 3 \cdot \boxed{13}$$

We can see that the maximum number of 2s that appear in either prime factorization is two (there are two 2s in both factorizations), the maximum number of 3s is three, and the maximum number of 13s is one. Multiply as follows:

$$2 \cdot 2 \cdot 3 \cdot 3 \cdot 3 \cdot 13 = 1404$$

Thus, the least common denominator is 1404. This is the smallest number that both 108 and 156 divide into.

b) To add the fractions, we need to write both fractions with a common denominator. The best common denominator to use is the LCD. Since $1404 \div 108 = 13$, we will multiply $\dfrac{7}{108}$ by $\dfrac{13}{13}$. Since $1404 \div 156 = 9$, we will multiply $\dfrac{5}{156}$ by $\dfrac{9}{9}$.

$$\frac{7}{108} \cdot \frac{13}{13} + \frac{5}{156} \cdot \frac{9}{9} = \frac{91}{1404} + \frac{45}{1404} = \frac{136}{1404} = \frac{34}{351}$$

Thus, $\dfrac{7}{108} + \dfrac{5}{156} = \dfrac{34}{351}$.

Appendix C Geometry

This appendix introduces or reviews important geometric concepts. **Table C.1** gives the names and descriptions of various types of angles.

Angles

TABLE C.1	
Angle	**Sketch of Angle**
An **acute angle** is an angle whose measure is between 0° and 90°.	
A **right angle** is an angle whose measure is 90°.	
An **obtuse angle** is an angle whose measure is between 90° and 180°.	
A **straight angle** is an angle whose measure is 180°.	
Two angles are **complementary angles** when the sum of their measures is 90°. Each angle is the complement of the other. Angles *A* and *B* are complementary angles.	60° *A* *B* 30°
Two angles are **supplementary angles** when the sum of their measures is 180°. Each angle is the supplement of the other. Angles *A* and *B* are supplementary angles.	130° *A* *B* 50°

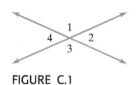

FIGURE C.1

When two lines intersect, four angles are formed as shown in **Figure C.1**. The pair of opposite angles formed by the intersecting lines are called **vertical angles**.

Angles 1 and 3 are vertical angles. Angles 2 and 4 are also vertical angles. *Vertical angles have equal measures.* Thus, angle 1, symbolized by ∠1, is equal to angle 3, symbolized by ∠3. We can write ∠1 = ∠3. Similarly, ∠2 = ∠4.

Parallel and Perpendicular Lines

Parallel lines are two lines in the same plane that do not intersect (**Fig. C.2**). **Perpendicular lines** are lines that intersect at right angles (**Fig. C.3**).

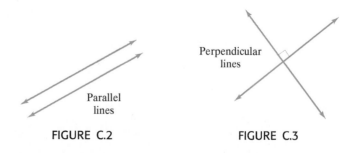

Parallel lines

Perpendicular lines

FIGURE C.2   **FIGURE C.3**

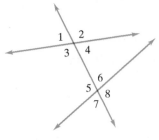

FIGURE C.4

A **transversal** is a line that intersects two or more lines at different points. When a transversal line intersects two other lines, eight angles are formed, as illustrated in **Figure C.4**. Some of these angles are given special names.

Interior angles: 3, 4, 5, 6

Exterior angles: 1, 2, 7, 8

Pairs of corresponding angles: 1 and 5; 2 and 6; 3 and 7; 4 and 8

Pairs of alternate interior angles: 3 and 6; 4 and 5

Pairs of alternate exterior angles: 1 and 8; 2 and 7

Parallel Lines Cut by a Transversal

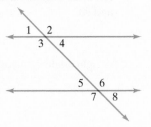

When two parallel lines are cut by a transversal,

1. Corresponding angles are equal ($\angle 1 = \angle 5$, $\angle 2 = \angle 6$, $\angle 3 = \angle 7$, $\angle 4 = \angle 8$).
2. Alternate interior angles are equal ($\angle 3 = \angle 6$, $\angle 4 = \angle 5$).
3. Alternate exterior angles are equal ($\angle 1 = \angle 8$, $\angle 2 = \angle 7$).

EXAMPLE 1 If line 1 and line 2 are parallel lines and the measure of angle 1 is 112° ($m\angle 1 = 112°$), find the measure of angles 2 through 8.

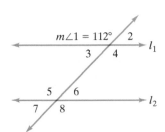

Solution   Angles 1 and 2 are supplementary, so $m\angle 2$ is $180° - 112° = 68°$. The measures of angles 1 and 4 are equal since they are vertical angles. Thus, $m\angle 4 = 112°$. Angles 1 and 5 are corresponding angles. Thus, $m\angle 5 = 112°$. It is equal to its vertical angle, $\angle 8$, so $m\angle 8 = 112°$. The measures of angles 2, 3, 6, and 7 are all equal and measure 68°.

Polygons

A **polygon** is a closed figure in a plane determined by three or more line segments. Some polygons are illustrated in **Figure C.5**.

A **regular polygon** has sides that are all the same length, and interior angles that all have the same measure. In **Figure C.5**, (b) and (d) are regular polygons.

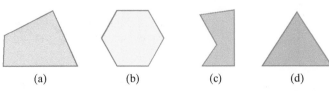

(a)   (b)   (c)   (d)

FIGURE C.5

Sum of the Interior Angles of a Polygon

The sum of the interior angles of a polygon can be found by the formula

$$\text{Sum} = (n - 2)180°$$

where n is the number of sides of the polygon.

EXAMPLE 2   Find the sum of the measures of the interior angles of **a)** a triangle; **b)** a quadrilateral (4 sides); **c)** an octagon (8 sides).

Solution

a) Since $n = 3$, we write

$$\text{Sum} = (n - 2)180°$$
$$= (3 - 2)180° = 1(180°) = 180°$$

The sum of the measures of the interior angles in a triangle is 180°.

b)
$$\text{Sum} = (n - 2)180°$$
$$= (4 - 2)180° = 2(180°) = 360°$$

The sum of the measures of the interior angles in a quadrilateral is 360°.

c)
$$\text{Sum} = (n - 2)(180°) = (8 - 2)180° = 6(180°) = 1080°$$

The sum of the measures of the interior angles in an octagon is 1080°.

Now we will briefly define several types of triangles in **Table C.2**.

Triangles

TABLE C.2

Triangle	Sketch of Triangle
An **acute triangle** is one that has three acute angles (angles of less than 90°).	
An **obtuse triangle** has one obtuse angle (an angle greater than 90°).	
A **right triangle** has one right angle (an angle equal to 90°). The longest side of a right triangle is opposite the right angle and is called the **hypotenuse**. The other two sides are called the **legs**.	
An **isosceles triangle** has two sides of equal length. The angles opposite the equal sides have the same measure.	
An **equilateral triangle** has three sides of equal length. It also has three equal angles that measure 60° each.	

When two sides of a *right triangle* are known, the third side can be found using the **Pythagorean Theorem**, $a^2 + b^2 = c^2$, where a and b are the legs and c is the hypotenuse of the triangle. (See Section 5.7 for examples.)

Congruent and Similar Figures

If two triangles are **congruent**, it means that the two triangles are identical in size and shape. Two congruent triangles would match up exactly if one were placed on the other.

Two Triangles Are Congruent If Any One of the Following Statements Is True

1. Two angles of one triangle are equal to two corresponding angles of the other triangle, and the lengths of the sides between each pair of angles are equal. This method of showing that triangles are congruent is called the *angle, side, angle* method.

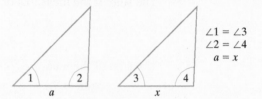

2. Corresponding sides of both triangles are equal. This is called the *side, side, side* method.

3. Two corresponding pairs of sides are equal, and the angle between them is equal. This is referred to as the *side, angle, side* method.

EXAMPLE 3 Determine whether the two triangles are congruent.

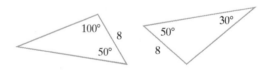

Solution   The unknown angle in the figure on the right must measure 100° since the sum of the angles of a triangle is 180°. Both triangles have the same two angles (100° and 50°), with the same length side between them, 8 units. Thus, these two triangles are congruent by the angle, side, angle method.

Two triangles are **similar** if all three pairs of corresponding angles are equal and corresponding sides are in proportion. Similar figures do not have to be the same size but must have the same general shape.

Two Triangles Are Similar If Any One of the Following Statements Is True

1. Two angles of one triangle equal two angles of the other triangle.

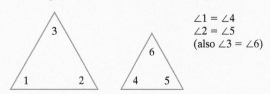

$\angle 1 = \angle 4$
$\angle 2 = \angle 5$
(also $\angle 3 = \angle 6$)

2. Corresponding sides of the two triangles are proportional.

$\dfrac{a}{x} = \dfrac{b}{y} = \dfrac{c}{z}$

3. Two pairs of corresponding sides are proportional, and the angles between them are equal.

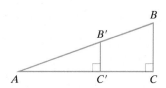

$\dfrac{a}{x} = \dfrac{b}{y}$
and $\angle 1 = \angle 2$

EXAMPLE 4 Are the triangles ABC and $AB'C'$ similar?

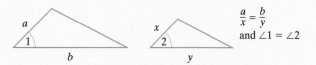

Solution   Angle A is common to both triangles. Since angle C and angle C' are equal (both 90°), then $\angle B$ and $\angle B'$ must be equal. Since the three angles of triangle ABC equal the three angles of triangle $AB'C'$, the two triangles are similar.

Answers

Chapter 1

Exercises Set 1.1 1. Answers will vary. **3.** Answers will vary. **5.** Answers will vary. **7.** Answers will vary. **9.** Answers will vary. **11.** Do all the homework carefully and completely and preview the new material that is to be covered in class. **13.** At least 2 hours of study and homework time for each hour of class time in generally recommended. **15. a)** You need to do the homework in order to practice what was presented in class. **b)** When you miss class, you miss important information; therefore, it is important that you attend class regularly **17.** Answers will vary.

Exercise Set 1.2 1. Median **3.** Approximately equal to **5.** Checking **7.** Circle graphs **9.** Problem solving **11. a)** 76.4 **b)** 74 **13. a)** $87.32 **b)** $86.57 **15. a)** 11.593 **b)** 11.68 **17.** $470 **19. a)** $1336 **b)** $18,036 **21.** 1,610,000,000 operations **23. a)** 19.375 minutes **b)** 88 minutes **c)** 10 minutes **25.** ≈18.49 miles per gallon **27.** $153 **29.** On the 3 on the right **31. a)** 4106.25 gallons **b)** ≈ $21.35 **33. a)** $193 **b)** $172 **35. a)** Finland; 550 **b)** Mexico; 405 **c)** 145 **37. a)** 0.275 million or 275,000; 1.05 million or 1,050,000 **b)** 0.775 million or 775,000 **c)** ≈3.96 times greater **39. a)** 1.394 million **b)** 0.255 million **c)** 0.051 million **41. a)** 48 **b)** He cannot get a C. **43.** Bachelor's degree **45.** One example is 50, 60, 70, 80, 90. **47.** Mean

Exercise Set 1.3 1. Added or subtracted **3.** Variables **5.** $\frac{2}{3}$ **7.** Denominator **9.** $\frac{3}{2}$ **11.** $\frac{2}{3}$ **13.** $\frac{1}{4}$ **15.** $\frac{9}{19}$ **17.** $\frac{3}{7}$

19. Simplified **21.** Simplified **23.** $\frac{43}{15}$ **25.** $\frac{23}{3}$ **27.** $\frac{59}{18}$ **29.** $\frac{159}{17}$ **31.** $1\frac{3}{4}$ **33.** $3\frac{1}{4}$ **35.** $4\frac{4}{7}$ **37.** $6\frac{1}{7}$ **39.** $\frac{4}{15}$ **41.** $\frac{1}{9}$

43. $\frac{3}{2}$ or $1\frac{1}{2}$ **45.** $\frac{1}{2}$ **47.** 6 **49.** $\frac{5}{2}$ or $2\frac{1}{2}$ **51.** $\frac{43}{10}$ or $4\frac{3}{10}$ **53.** $\frac{8}{13}$ **55.** $\frac{5}{8}$ **57.** $\frac{1}{7}$ **59.** $\frac{6}{5}$ or $1\frac{1}{5}$ **61.** $\frac{10}{17}$ **63.** $\frac{7}{12}$ **65.** $\frac{13}{36}$

67. $\frac{65}{24}$ or $2\frac{17}{24}$ **69.** $\frac{17}{6}$ or $2\frac{5}{6}$ **71.** $\frac{29}{10}$ or $2\frac{9}{10}$ **73.** $\frac{277}{30}$ or $9\frac{7}{30}$ **75.** $\frac{11}{24}$ mile **77.** $8\frac{15}{16}$ inches **79.** $\frac{9}{55}$ **81.** $\frac{63}{100}$

83. 11 feet, $11\frac{1}{4}$ inches or $143\frac{1}{4}$ inches or ≈11.94 feet **85.** $2\frac{3}{10}$ minutes **87.** $1\frac{9}{16}$ inches **89.** 5 mg **91.** 40 times **93.** $1\frac{1}{2}$ inches

95. 6 strips **97. a)** Yes **b)** $82\frac{3}{8}$ in. **99.** Answers will vary **101. a)** $\frac{*+?}{a}$ **b)** $\frac{\odot - \square}{?}$ **c)** $\frac{\triangle + 4}{\square}$ **d)** $\frac{x-2}{3}$ **e)** $\frac{8}{x}$

103. 270 pills **105.** Answers will vary. **106.** 16 **107.** 15 **108.** Variables are letters used to represent numbers.

Exercise Set 1.4 1. Irrational numbers **3.** Counting numbers **5.** Real number line **7.** Whole numbers **9.** π
11. $\{\ldots, -3, -2, -1, 0, 1, 2, 3, \ldots\}$ **13.** $\{0, 1, 2, 3, \ldots\}$ **15.** $\{\ldots, -3, -2, -1\}$ **17.** True **19.** True **21.** False **23.** False **25.** True
27. True **29.** False **31.** True **33.** True **35.** False **37.** True **39.** True **41.** False **43.** True **45.** False **47.** True **49. a)** 13
b) $-2, 13$ **c)** $-2, 13$ **d)** 13 **51. a)** $3, 77$ **b)** $0, 3, 77$ **c)** $0, -2, 3, 77$ **d)** $-\frac{5}{7}, 0, -2, 3, 6\frac{1}{4}, 1.63, 77$ **e)** $\sqrt{7}, -\sqrt{3}$ **f)** $-\frac{5}{7}, 0, -2,$
$3, 6\frac{1}{4}, \sqrt{7}, -\sqrt{3}, 1.63, 77$ **53.** Answers will vary; three examples are 0, 1, and 2. **55.** Answers will vary; three examples are $-\sqrt{2}$,
$-\sqrt{3}$, and $-\sqrt{7}$. **57.** Answers will vary; three examples are $-\frac{2}{3}, \frac{1}{2}$, and 6.3. **59.** Answers will vary; three examples are $-13, -5$,
and -1. **61.** Answers will vary; three examples are $\sqrt{2}, \sqrt{3}$, and $-\sqrt{5}$. **63.** Answers will vary; three examples are $-7, 1$, and 5.
65. 87 **67. a)** $\{1, 3, 4, 5, 8\}$ **b)** $\{2, 5, 6, 7, 8\}$ **c)** $\{5, 8\}$ **d)** $\{1, 2, 3, 4, 5, 6, 7, 8\}$ **69. a)** Set B continues beyond 4. **b)** 4
c) An infinite number of elements **d)** An infinite set **71. a)** An infinite number **b)** An infinite number

73. $\frac{29}{5}$ **74.** $5\frac{1}{3}$ **75.** $\frac{13}{24}$ **76.** $\frac{4}{45}$

Exercise Set 1.5 1. 0 **3.** $|a|$ **5.** True **7.** $|6 - (-4)|$ **9.** Negative number **11.** 7 **13.** 15 **15.** 0 **17.** -5 **19.** -26
21. > **23.** < **25.** > **27.** < **29.** > **31.** > **33.** < **35.** > **37.** < **39.** > **41.** > **43.** < **45.** >
47. < **49.** < **51.** < **53.** > **55.** > **57.** > **59.** < **61.** < **63.** < **65.** < **67.** = **69.** = **71.** <

73. < **75.** $-|-1|, \frac{3}{7}, \frac{4}{9}, 0.46, |-5|$ **77.** $\frac{5}{12}, 0.6, \frac{2}{3}, \frac{19}{25}, |-2.6|$ **79.** $4, -4$ **81.** Not possible **83.** Answers will vary: one example
is $-3, -4$ and -5. **85.** Answers will vary: one example is 4, 5, and 6. **87.** Answers will vary: one example is 3, 4, and 5.

89. a) Does not include the endpoints **b)** Answers will vary: one example is $4.1, 5$, and $5\frac{1}{2}$. **c)** No **d)** Yes **e)** True

91. a) Dietary fiber and thiamin **b)** Vitamin E, niacin, and riboflavin **93.** Yes **95.** No, $|-4| > |-3|$ but $-4 < -3$.

97. Greater than **99.** No **102.** $\frac{89}{15}$ or $5\frac{14}{15}$ **103.** $\{\ldots, -3, -2, -1, 0, 1, 2, 3, \ldots\}$ **104.** $\{0, 1, 2, 3, \ldots\}$ **105. a)** 5 **b)** $5, 0$

c) $5, -2, 0$ **d)** $5, -2, 0, \frac{1}{3}, -\frac{5}{9}, 2.3$ **e)** $\sqrt{3}, \pi$ **f)** $5, -2, 0, \frac{1}{3}, \sqrt{3}, -\frac{5}{9}, 2.3, \pi$

Mid-Chapter Test: Sections 1.1–1.5[*]   **1.** At least two hours of study and homework for each hour of class time is generally recommended. [1.1]   **2. a)** \$80.63   **b)** \$83.81 [1.2]   **3.** \$824.59 [1.2]   **4. a)** Natwora's   **b)** \$24 [1.2]   **5.** \$62.35 [1.2]
6. $\frac{1}{6}$ [1.3]   **7.** $\frac{39}{80}$ [1.3]   **8.** $\frac{49}{40}$ or $1\frac{9}{40}$ [1.3]   **9.** $\frac{61}{20}$ or $3\frac{1}{20}$ [1.3]   **10.** $54\frac{1}{3}$ feet [1.3]   **11.** False [1.4]   **12.** True [1.4]   **13.** False [1.4]
14. True [1.4]   **15.** False [1.4]   **16.** $-\frac{7}{10}$ [1.5]   **17.** $>$ [1.5]   **18.** $>$ [1.5]   **19.** $<$ [1.5]   **20.** $=$ [1.5]

Exercise Set 1.6   **1.** Negative   **3.** Absolute Value   **5.** Sum   **7.** -8 **9.** Common Denominator   **11.** Correct   **13.** -19
15. 28   **17.** 0   **19.** $-\frac{5}{3}$ **21.** $-2\frac{3}{5}$ **23.** -3.72 **25.** 21   **27.** 1   **29.** -6 **31.** 0   **33.** 0   **35.** -10 **37.** -4 **39.** -13 **41.** 0   **43.** -8
45. -27 **47.** -64 **49.** 16   **51.** -12 **53.** 3   **55.** -6 **57.** -40 **59.** -31 **61.** -39 **63.** 91   **65.** -9.9 **67.** -144.0 **69.** -141.91
71. -53.65 **73.** $\frac{26}{35}$ **75.** $\frac{107}{84}$ or $1\frac{23}{84}$ **77.** $\frac{4}{55}$ **79.** $-\frac{26}{45}$ **81.** $-\frac{31}{30}$ or $-1\frac{1}{30}$ **83.** $\frac{3}{10}$ **85.** $-\frac{13}{15}$ **87.** $\frac{19}{56}$ **89.** $-\frac{43}{60}$ **91.** $-\frac{23}{21}$ or
$-1\frac{2}{21}$ **93. a)** Positive   **b)** 390   **95. a)** Negative   **b)** -373 **97. a)** Negative   **b)** -452 **99. a)** Negative   **b)** -1300
101. a) Negative   **b)** -112 **103. a)** Negative   **b)** -3880 **105. a)** Positive   **b)** 1111   **107. a)** Negative   **b)** -2050 **109.** True
111. True   **113.** False   **115.** \$277   **117.** 21 yards   **119.** 61 feet   **121.** 13,796 feet   **123. a)** $-$ \$12 thousand   **b)** 2006–2008 surplus,
\$91 thousand   **125.** -26 **127.** 20   **129.** 0   **131.** $\frac{11}{30}$ **133.** 55   **135.** $\frac{19}{14}$ or $1\frac{5}{14}$ **136.** $\frac{43}{16}$ or $2\frac{11}{16}$ **137.** False   **138.** $>$ **139.** $<$

Exercise Set 1.7   **1.** Minuend   **3.** Difference   **5.** Opposite   **7.** Left to right   **9.** $-a+b$ **11.** Correct   **13.** 6   **15.** 7   **17.** -1
19. 12   **21.** -16 **23.** -9 **25.** 0   **27.** -4 **29.** -3 **31.** 9   **33.** -20 **35.** 9.8   **37.** 0.3   **39.** 37   **41.** 4   **43.** 22   **45.** -11
47. -131.0 **49.** -84 **51.** 140   **53.** -7.4 **55.** -3.93 **57.** -11 **59.** 0   **61.** 6.1   **63.** 18.2   **65.** -11 **67.** -18.1
69. $\frac{31}{72}$ **71.** $\frac{17}{45}$ **73.** $-\frac{67}{60}$ or $-1\frac{7}{60}$ **75.** $-\frac{5}{12}$ **77.** $-\frac{17}{24}$ **79.** $\frac{1}{2}$ **81.** $\frac{7}{45}$ **83.** $\frac{13}{16}$ **85.** $-\frac{13}{63}$ **87.** $-\frac{7}{60}$ **89. a)** Positive   **b)** 99
c) Yes   **91. a)** Negative   **b)** -619 **c)** Yes   **93. a)** Positive   **b)** 1588   **c)** Yes   **95. a)** Positive   **b)** 196   **c)** Yes
97. a) Negative   **b)** -448 **c)** Yes   **99. a)** Positive   **b)** 116.1   **c)** Yes   **101. a)** Negative   **b)** -69 **c)** Yes   **103. a)** Negative
b) -1670 **c)** Yes   **105. a)** Zero   **b)** 0   **c)** Yes   **107.** 4   **109.** 4   **111.** -15 **113.** -2 **115.** 13   **117.** -5 **119.** -32 **121.** -14
123. 9   **125.** -12 **127.** 12   **129.** -18 **131. a)** 43   **b)** 143   **133.** $1\frac{7}{8}$ inches   **135.** Dropped $100°F$ **137. a)** 280   **b)** 14 strokes more
139. $x-y=-5, y-x=5,$ and $x-(-y)=11$ **141.** -5 **143. a)** 8   **b)** $-3-(-11)$ **145. a)** 9ft   **b)** -3ft   **146.** $\{1,2,3,\dots\}$
147. The set of rational numbers together with the set of irrational numbers form the set of real numbers.   **148.** $>$ **149.** $<$
150. $-\frac{1}{24}$

Exercise Set 1.8   **1.** Negative   **3.** Zero   **5.** $\frac{a}{b}$ **7.** Positive   **9.** 63   **11.** Negative   **13.** Positive   **15.** Negative   **17.** 20
19. -15 **21.** 160   **23.** -12.6 **25.** 42   **27.** -81 **29.** 30   **31.** 0   **33.** -84 **35.** -72 **37.** 1400   **39.** 0   **41.** $-\frac{3}{10}$ **43.** $\frac{7}{27}$ **45.** 4
47. $-\frac{1}{10}$ **49.** -7 **51.** 4   **53.** 4   **55.** -18 **57.** 9.9   **59.** -10 **61.** -33 **63.** -4 **65.** 16.2   **67.** 0   **69.** -5.5 **71.** 6   **73.** $-\frac{2}{5}$
75. $\frac{5}{36}$ **77.** 1   **79.** $-\frac{144}{5}$ or $-28\frac{4}{5}$ **81.** -32 **83.** 20   **85.** -14 **87.** -9.3 **89.** -20 **91.** 1   **93.** 0   **95.** Undefined   **97.** 0
99. Undefined   **101. a)** Negative   **b)** -3496 **c)** Yes   **103. a)** Negative   **b)** -16 **c)** Yes   **105. a)** Negative   **b)** -9 **c)** Yes
107. a) Positive   **b)** 6174   **c)** Yes   **109. a)** Zero   **b)** 0   **c)** Yes   **111. a)** Undefined   **b)** Undefined   **c)** Yes   **113. a)** Positive
b) 3.2   **c)** Yes   **115. a)** Positive   **b)** 226.8   **c)** Yes   **117.** False   **119.** False   **121.** True   **123.** True   **125.** False   **127.** True
129. 45 yard loss or -45 yards   **131. a)** \$104   **b)** $-$ \$416   **133.** \$143.85   **135. a)** 20 point loss or -20 points   **b)** 80   **137. a)** 102 to
128 beats per minute   **b)** Answers will vary.   **139.** -125 **141.** 1   **143.** Positive   **146.** $>$ **147.** $-\frac{41}{60}$ **148.** -2 **149.** -3 **150.** 3

Exercise Set 1.9   **1.** Left to right   **3.** Grouping symbols   **5.** Exponent   **7.** 25   **9.** 1   **11.** -64 **13.** 9   **15.** -1 **17.** -100
19. 81   **21.** 27   **23.** 256   **25.** -16 **27.** $\frac{9}{16}$ **29.** $-\frac{1}{32}$ **31.** 225   **33.** 576   **35. a)** Positive   **b)** 343   **c)** Yes   **37. a)** Positive
b) 1296   **c)** Yes   **39. a)** Negative   **b)** -243 **c)** Yes   **41. a)** Positive   **b)** 625   **c)** Yes   **43. a)** Negative   **b)** -81 **c)** Yes
45. a) Negative   **b)** -0.140625 **c)** Yes   **47.** 21   **49.** 8   **51.** 57   **53.** 0   **55.** -16 **57.** 29   **59.** -19 **61.** -77 **63.** $\frac{83}{100}$ **65.** 2
67. 10   **69.** -34 **71.** 103   **73.** 169   **75.** -23 **77.** 36.75   **79.** $\frac{5}{8}$ **81.** $\frac{1}{4}$ **83.** $\frac{49}{30}$ or $1\frac{19}{30}$ **85.** $\frac{5}{27}$ **87.** $\frac{32}{53}$ **89.** 9   **91.** -4 **93.** 1
95. a) 25   **b)** -25 **c)** 25   **97. a)** 4   **b)** -4 **c)** 4   **99. a)** 36   **b)** -36 **c)** 36   **101. a)** $\frac{1}{9}$ **b)** $-\frac{1}{9}$ **c)** $\frac{1}{9}$ **103.** 4   **105.** -45

---

*Numbers in blue brackets after the answer indicates the section where the material was discussed.

107. 3   **109.** −4   **111.** −1   **113.** $\frac{15}{4}$ or $3\frac{3}{4}$ **115.** 994   **117.** −5   **119.** 193   **121.** −25   **123.** $[(6 \cdot 3) - 4] - 2; 12$

125. $\{[(10 \cdot 4) + 9] - 6\} \div 7; \frac{43}{7}$ or $6\frac{1}{7}$ **127.** $\left(\frac{4}{5} + \frac{3}{7}\right) \cdot \frac{2}{3}; \frac{86}{105}$ **129.** All real numbers   **131.** 162.5 miles   **133.** 102 feet

135. 50 ft³   **137.** 1.71 inches   **139.** $12 - (4 - 6) + 10 = 24$ **145. a)** 3   **b) Dogs   Number of Houses   c)** 18

d) ≈ 1.29 dogs per house   **146.** $6.40   **147.** $-\frac{5}{36}$ **148.** $\frac{10}{3}$ or $3\frac{1}{3}$

Dogs	Number of Houses
0	4
1	5
2	3
3	1
4	1

Exercise Set 1.10   1. Associative property of addition   **3.** Zero   **5.** Additive inverse   **7.** Distributive property of multiplication over addition   **9.** Multiplicative identity   **11. a)** −6   **b)** $\frac{1}{6}$ **13. a)** 3   **b)** $-\frac{1}{3}$ **15. a)** $-x$ **b)** $\frac{1}{x}$ **17. a)** −1.6   **b)** $\frac{1}{1.6}$ or 0.625

19. a) $-\frac{1}{5}$ **b)** 5   **21. a)** $\frac{5}{6}$ **b)** $-\frac{6}{5}$ **23.** Distributive property   **25.** Associative property of addition   **27.** Commutative property of multiplication   **29.** Associative property of multiplication   **31.** Distributive property   **33.** Identity property of multiplication   **35.** Inverse property of multiplication   **37.** $1 + (-4)$ **39.** $(-6 \cdot 4) \cdot 2$ **41.** $-2 \cdot x + -2 \cdot y$ or $-2x - 2y$ **43.** $y \cdot x$

45. $3y + 4x$ **47.** $a + (b + 3)$ **49.** $3x + (4 + 6)$ **51.** $(m + n)3$ **53.** $4x + 4y + 12$ **55.** 0   **57.** $\frac{5}{2}n$ **59.** Yes   **61.** Yes   **63.** No

65. Yes   **67.** No   **69.** No   **71.** The $(3 + 4)$ is treated as one value.   **73.** Commutative property of addition

75. No; Associative property of addition   **77.** $\frac{49}{15}$ or $3\frac{4}{15}$ **78.** $\frac{23}{16}$ or $1\frac{7}{16}$ **79.** −11.2   **80.** $-\frac{7}{8}$

Chapter 1 Review Exercises   1. 28   **2.** $572.45   **3. a)** $74.25   **b)** $974.24   **4.** $100   **5. a)** 78.4   **b)** 79   **6. a)** 11   **b)** 9.5
7. a) 30 minutes   **b)** 27 minutes   **8. a)** 225   **b)** 165   **9.** $\frac{1}{2}$ **10.** $\frac{127}{21}$ or $6\frac{1}{21}$ **11.** $\frac{25}{36}$ **12.** $\frac{7}{6}$ or $1\frac{1}{6}$ **13.** $\frac{23}{12}$ or $1\frac{11}{12}$ **14.** $\frac{177}{10}$ or $17\frac{7}{10}$
15. $\{1, 2, 3, ...\}$ **16.** $\{0, 1, 2, 3, ...\}$ **17.** $\{..., -3, -2, -1, 0, 1, 2, 3, ...\}$ **18.** The set of all numbers which can be expressed as the quotient of two integers, denominator not zero   **19. a)** $3, 426$ **b)** $3, 0, 426$ **c)** $3, -5, -12, 0, 426$ **d)** $3, -5, -12, 0, \frac{1}{2}, -0.62, 426, -3\frac{1}{4}$

e) $\sqrt{7}$ **f)** $3, -5, -12, 0, \frac{1}{2}, -0.62, \sqrt{7}, 426, -3\frac{1}{4}$ **20. a)** 1   **b)** 1   **c)** $-8, -9$ **d)** $-8, -9, 1$ **e)** $-2.3, -8, -9, 1\frac{1}{2}, 1, -\frac{3}{17}$

f) $\sqrt{2}, -\sqrt{2}$ **g)** $-2.3, -8, -9, 1\frac{1}{2}, \sqrt{2}, -\sqrt{2}, 1, -\frac{3}{17}$ **21.** <   **22.** >   **23.** <   **24.** >   **25.** <   **26.** >
27. =   **28.** >   **29.** −14   **30.** 0   **31.** −3   **32.** −6   **33.** −6   **34.** 2   **35.** 8   **36.** 0   **37.** −5   **38.** 14   **39.** 4   **40.** −12
41. $\frac{7}{12}$ **42.** $\frac{11}{10}$ or $1\frac{1}{10}$ **43.** $-\frac{7}{36}$ **44.** $-\frac{19}{56}$ **45.** $-\frac{5}{4}$ or $-1\frac{1}{4}$ **46.** $-\frac{37}{84}$ **47.** $-\frac{7}{90}$ **48.** $\frac{61}{60}$ or $1\frac{1}{60}$ **49.** 14   **50.** −3   **51.** −12
52. −7   **53.** 16   **54.** 11   **55.** −63   **56.** 25.42   **57.** −120   **58.** $-\frac{6}{35}$ **59.** $-\frac{6}{11}$ **60.** $\frac{15}{56}$ **61.** 0   **62.** 144   **63.** −15   **64.** −6
65. −3.2   **66.** 4.3   **67.** 8   **68.** 9   **69.** $\frac{56}{27}$ or $2\frac{2}{27}$ **70.** $-\frac{35}{9}$ or $-3\frac{8}{9}$ **71.** 0   **72.** 0   **73.** Undefined   **74.** Undefined
75. Undefined   **76.** 0   **77.** 25   **78.** −8   **79.** 1   **80.** 3   **81.** −6   **82.** −32   **83.** 6   **84.** −4   **85.** 10   **86.** 1   **87.** 15   **88.** −4   **89.** −36
90. 36   **91.** 16   **92.** −27   **93.** −1   **94.** −32   **95.** $\frac{16}{25}$ **96.** $\frac{8}{125}$ **97.** 500   **98.** 4   **99.** 12   **100.** −256   **101.** 7   **102.** 32   **103.** 6.36
104. −17   **105.** −39   **106.** −2.3   **107.** 0   **108.** $\frac{9}{7}$ or $1\frac{2}{7}$ **109.** −60   **110.** 10   **111.** 20   **112.** 20   **113.** 14   **114.** 9   **115.** −4
116. 50   **117.** 5   **118.** 26   **119.** 45   **120.** 0   **121.** −11   **122.** −3   **123.** −3   **124.** 39   **125.** −215   **126.** 353.6   **127.** −2.88
128. 117.8   **129.** 65,536   **130.** −74.088   **131.** Associative property of addition   **132.** Distributive property   **133.** Commutative property of addition   **134.** Commutative property of multiplication   **135.** Distributive property   **136.** Associative property of addition   **137.** Identity property of multiplication   **138.** Inverse property of addition

Chapter 1 Practice Test   1. a) $10.65   **b)** $0.23   **c)** $10.88   **d)** $39.12 [1.2]   **2.** ≈2.5 times greater [1.2]   **3. a)** ≈13 thousand
b) During this specific time, half the time KFUN had more than 8.8 thousand listeners and half the time KFUN had less than 8.8 thousand listeners. [1.2]   **4. a)** 42   **b)** 42, 0   **c)** $-6, 42, 0, -7, -1$ **d)** $-6, 42, -3\frac{1}{2}, 0, 6.52, \frac{5}{9}, -7, -1$ **e)** $\sqrt{5}$ **f)** $-6, 42, -3\frac{1}{2}, 0,$
$6.52, \sqrt{5}, \frac{5}{9}, -7, -1 [1.4]$ **5.** < [1.5]   **6.** > [1.5]   **7.** −15 [1.6]   **8.** −11 [1.7]   **9.** −14 [1.7]   **10.** 8 [1.9]   **11.** −24 [1.8]   **12.** $\frac{16}{63}$ [1.8]
13. −3 [1.9]   **14.** $-\frac{53}{56}$ [1.7]   **15.** 12 [1.9]   **16.** $-\frac{32}{243}$ [1.9]   **17.** 100 [1.9]   **18.** $-x^2$ means $-(x^2)$ and x^2 will always be positive for any nonzero value of x. Therefore, $-x^2$ will always be negative. [1.9]   **19.** 37 [1.9]   **20.** 11 [1.9]   **21.** 10 [1.9]   **22.** 1 [1.9]
23. Commutative property of addition [1.10]   **24.** Distributive property [1.10]   **25.** Associative property of addition [1.10]

Chapter 2

Exercise Set 2.1 **1.** Constant **3.** Like terms **5.** Unlike terms **7.** Terms **9.** $14x$ **11.** $3x + 6$ **13.** $5y + 3$ **15.** $\frac{9}{44}a$

17. $-6x + 7t$ **19.** $-5w + 5$ **21.** $-2x$ **23.** 0 **25.** $-2t + 21$ **27.** $-12p - 8$ **29.** $10x^2 - 10y^2 - 7$ **31.** $2x - 8$ **33.** $b + \frac{23}{5}$

35. $0.8n + 6.42$ **37.** $\frac{1}{2}a + 3b + 1$ **39.** $14.6x + 8.3$ **41.** $x^2 + y$ **43.** $-3x - 5y$ **45.** $-3n^2 - 2n + 13$ **47.** $21.72x - 7.11$

49. $-\frac{23}{20}x - 5$ **51.** $5w^3 + 2w^2 + w + 3$ **53.** $-7z^3 - z^2 + 2z$ **55.** $6x^2 - 6xy + 3y^2$ **57.** $4a^2 + 3ab + b^2$ **59.** $5x + 10$

61. $5x + 20$ **63.** $3x - 18$ **65.** $-x + 2$ **67.** $x - 4$ **69.** $\frac{4}{5}s - 4$ **71.** $-0.9x^2 - 1.5$ **73.** $-r + 4$ **75.** $1.4x + 0.35$ **77.** $x - y$

79. $-2x - 4y + 8$ **81.** $3.41x - 5.72y + 3.08$ **83.** $10x - 45y$ **85.** $r + 3s - 19$ **87.** $3x - 6y - 12$ **89.** $-3x + 1$ **91.** $2x + 1$

93. $14x + 18$ **95.** $4x - 2y + 3$ **97.** $5c$ **99.** $7x + 3$ **101.** $\frac{5}{4}x + \frac{1}{3}$ **103.** $\frac{19}{6}x - 2$ **105.** $-4s - 6$ **107.** $2x - 2$ **109.** 0

111. $-y - 6$ **113.** $3x - 5$ **115.** $x + 15$ **117.** $0.2x - 4y - 2.8$ **119.** $-6x + 7y$ **121.** $\frac{3}{2}x + \frac{7}{2}$ **123.** $2\square + 3\ominus$

125. $2x + 3y + 2\triangle$ **127.** $1, 2, 3, 6, 9, 18$ **129. a)** The signs of all terms inside the parentheses change when the parentheses are removed. **b)** $-x + 8$ **131.** $22x^2 - 25y^2 - 4x + 3$ **133.** $9x - 39$ **135.** 7 **136.** -16 **137.** -11 **138.** Answers will vary. **139.** -12

Exercise Set 2.2 **1.** 2 **3.** Isolate **5.** Linear **7.** Equation **9.** Additive inverse **11.** Yes **13.** No **15.** Yes **17.** Yes
19. No **21.** Yes **23.** 5 **25.** -7 **27.** -4 **29.** 43 **31.** 15 **33.** 11 **35.** -4 **37.** -5 **39.** -12 **41.** -30 **43.** 0 **45.** -57
47. -4 **49.** -65 **51.** 0 **53.** 17 **55.** -26 **57.** 28 **59.** -46.1 **61.** 46.5 **63.** -8.23 **65.** 5.57 **67.** No, the equation is
equivalent to $1 = 2$, a false statement. **69.** Use properties that allow us to get the variable by itself on one side of the equation.
71. $x = \square + \triangle$ **73.** $\square = \odot - \triangle$ **76.** $\frac{11}{30}$ **77.** $-\frac{31}{24}$ **78.** $2x - 13$ **79.** $7t - 25$

Exercise Set 2.3 **1.** $\frac{x}{3}$ **3.** 3 **5.** Check **7.** $-\frac{7}{x}$ **9.** 4 **11.** 21 **13.** -3 **15.** -80 **17.** 20 **19.** -3 **21.** $-\frac{7}{3}$ **23.** -13

25. 8 **27.** 30 **29.** $-\frac{1}{3}$ **31.** 6 **33.** $\frac{26}{43}$ **35.** 2 **37.** $\frac{1}{5}$ **39.** $-\frac{3}{40}$ **41.** -64 **43.** 240 **45.** -45 **47.** 20 **49.** -50 **51.** 0 **53.** 0

55. 22.5 **57.** 6 **59.** -20.2 **61.** 7 **63.** 9 **65. a)** In $5 + x = 10$, 5 is added to the variable, whereas in $5x = 10$, 5 is multiplied by the

variable. **b)** $x = 5$ **c)** $x = 2$ **67.** Multiply by $\frac{3}{2}$; 6 **69.** Multiply by $\frac{7}{3}$; $\frac{28}{15}$ **71. a)** $\square$ **b)** Divide both sides of the equation by $\triangle$.

c) $\square = \frac{\odot}{\triangle}$ **73.** -4 **74.** -30 **75.** 6 **76.** Associative property of addition **77.** -57

Exercise Set 2.4 **1.** Multiplication property of equality **3.** A power of ten **5.** Expression **7.** 5 **9.** -5 **11.** 2 **13.** $\frac{12}{5}$

15. 2 **17.** 7 **19.** $\frac{11}{3}$ **21.** $-\frac{19}{16}$ **23.** -12 **25.** 2 **27.** $-\frac{51}{5}$ **29.** 3 **31.** 6.8 **33.** 4 **35.** 12 **37.** 22 **39.** 60 **41.** -14 **43.** -11

45. -2 **47.** $\frac{19}{8}$ **49.** 0 **51.** -10 **53.** -3 **55.** 6 **57.** -21 **59.** $-\frac{19}{7}$ **61.** -9 **63.** 4 **65.** 5 **67.** 0.8 **69.** -1 **71.** $\frac{2}{7}$ **73.** -3.1

75. $-\frac{14}{5}$ **77.** 18 **79.** $-\frac{1}{15}$ **81.** $\frac{18}{7}$ **83.** $-\frac{16}{21}$ **85.** 10 **87.** 5 **89.** $-\frac{39}{4}$ **91.** 2 **93.** $\frac{25}{3}$ **95.** $\frac{26}{45}$ **97. a)** You will not have to

work with fractions. **b)** $x = 3$ **99.** $\frac{35}{6}$ **101.** -4 **105.** False **106.** 64 **107.** Isolate the variable on one side of the equation.

108. Divide both sides of the equation by -4 to isolate the variable.

Mid-Chapter Test: Sections 2.1–2.4 **1.** $-2x - 5y - 6$ [2.1] **2.** $-\frac{7}{20}x - \frac{15}{2}$ [2.1] **3.** $-8a + 12b - 64$ [2.1]

4. $3.36x - 5.44y - 8.32$ [2.1] **5.** $2t - 38$ [2.1] **6.** Yes [2.2] **7.** No [2.2] **8.** -4 [2.2] **9.** -160 [2.2] **10.** -23 [2.2]

11. Multiply both sides by 4. [2.3] **12.** $\frac{1}{3}$ [2.3] **13.** 24 [2.3] **14.** 10 [2.3] **15.** $-\frac{3}{7}$ [2.3] **16.** $\frac{5}{2}$ [2.4] **17.** $-\frac{3}{2}$ [2.4] **18.** $\frac{13}{16}$ [2.4]

19. -6 [2.4] **20.** $-\frac{20}{9}$ [2.4]

Exercise Set 2.5 **1.** Identity **3.** Least common denominator **5.** Specific value(s) of the variable **7.** No real numbers

9. False **11.** 2 **13.** 1 **15.** $\frac{3}{5}$ **17.** 3 **19.** -2 **21.** No Solution **23.** 6.5 **25.** 3.2 **27.** 3 **29.** -2 **31.** No solution **33.** $\frac{13}{5}$

35. $\frac{7}{9}$ **37.** 5 **39.** 30 **41.** $\frac{3}{2}$ **43.** $\frac{5}{2}$ **45.** 25 **47.** All real numbers **49.** 23 **51.** 0 **53.** All real numbers **55.** $\frac{21}{20}$ **57.** 14

59. $-\frac{15}{4}$ **61.** 5 **63.** 4 **65.** 0 **67.** 16 **69.** $-\frac{24}{5}$ **71.** $-\frac{4}{21}$ **73.** 5 **75.** 30 **77.** 4 **79. a)** One example is $x + x + 1 = x + 2$.

b) It has a single solution. **c)** For the example given in part **a)**, $x = 1$. **81. a)** One example is $x + x + 1 = 2x + 1$.
b) Both sides simplify to the same expression. **c)** All real numbers **83. a)** One example is $x + x + 1 = 2x + 2$.

b) It simplifies to a false statement. **c)** No solution **85.** $* = -\frac{1}{4}$ **87.** All real numbers **89.** $x = -4$ **91. a)** 4 **b)** 7

c) 0 **92.** x^{a-b} **93.** Factors are expressions that are multiplied. Terms are expressions that are added. **94.** $7x - 10$

95. $\frac{10}{7}$ **96.** -3

Exercise Set 2.6
1. Quadrilateral **3.** Formula **5.** Cubic feet **7.** π **9.** Evaluating **11.** 480 **13.** 96 **15.** 360 **17.** 36
19. 314.16 **21.** 82 **23.** 2 **25.** 8 **27.** 6.00 **29.** 127.03 **31.** ≈ 50.27 square feet **33.** 16.5 square feet **35.** ≈ 452.39 cubic centimeters
37. $C = 10°$ **39.** $F = 77°$ **41.** $P = 40$ **43.** $V = 5$ **45.** $l = A/w$ **47.** $t = d/r$ **49.** $t = i/(pr)$ **51.** $b = 2A/h$
53. $w = (P - 2l)/2$ **55.** $r = (-n + 3)/2$ **57.** $b = y - mx$ **59.** $b = d - a - c$ **61.** $y = (-ax - c)/b$ **63.** $h = 3V/(\pi r^2)$
65. $m = 2A - d$ **67.** $y = -2x + 8$ **69.** $y = x - 6$ **71.** $y = \frac{2}{3}x + \frac{4}{3}$ **73.** $y = \frac{3}{5}x - 2$ **75.** $y = \frac{1}{2}x - \frac{5}{2}$ **77.** $y = -\frac{1}{2}x + 5$
79. $y = -\frac{1}{3}x - \frac{5}{3}$ **81.** $y = 2x + \frac{13}{15}$ **83.** \$1440 **85.** \$5000 **87.** 60 mph **89.** 7.632 miles **91.** 48 square inches
93. 558 square inches **95.** ≈ 75.40 feet **97.** 3 square feet **99.** 7 square feet **101.** ≈ 124.1 feet **103.** ≈ 381.7 cubic inches
105. a) $B = \frac{703w}{h^2}$ **b)** ≈ 23.91 **107. a)** $V = 18x^3 - 3x^2$ **b)** 6027 cubic centimeters **c)** $S = 54x^2 - 8x$
d) 2590 square centimeters **109.** doubles **111.** 8 times as large **113.** circle **115.** $\frac{1}{3}$ **116.** -6 **117.** 0 **118.** 8

Exercise Set 2.7
1. Proportion **3.** Means **5.** Similar **7.** Units **9.** yes **11.** No **13.** 2:3 **15.** 1:2 **17.** 8:1 **19.** 7:4
21. 1:3 **23.** 6:1 **25.** 7:30 **27.** 8:1 **29. a)** 50:23 **b)** $\approx 2.17:1$ **31.** 7.25:4.75 or about 1.53 to 1 **33. a)** 35.7:2.4 or 11.9:0.8
b) 5.3:7.1 **35. a)** 40:32 or 5:4 **b)** 15:11 **37.** 12 **39.** 45 **41.** -9 **43.** -2 **45.** -54 **47.** 6 **49.** 32 inches **51.** 15.75 inches
53. 19.5 inches **55.** 25 loads **57.** 403 miles **59.** 1.5 feet **61.** 24 teaspoons **63.** ≈ 0.43 feet **65.** 3.75 cups **67.** ≈ 9.49 feet
69. 0.55 milliliter **71.** 570 minutes or 9 hours 30 minutes **73.** ≈ 360 children **75.** 6.5 feet **77.** 2.9 square yards **79.** 20 inches
81. ≈ 22 **83.** \$307 **85.** 2020 pesos **87.** Less. It is 2.12:1. **89.** It must increase. **91.** $\approx 41{,}667$ miles **93.** 0.625 cubic centimeters
96. Commutative property of addition **97.** Associative property of multiplication **98.** Distributive property
99. All real numbers. **100.** $m = (y - b)/x$

Exercise Set 2.8
1. All real numbers **3.** No solution **5.** $<$ **7.** $5 > -6$ **9. a)** $28 > -12$ **b)** $\frac{7}{4} > -\frac{3}{4}$

11. $x > 4$; **13.** $x > 4$; **15.** $x > -5$; **17.** $r \le -6$;

19. $x > -\frac{3}{2}$; **21.** $t \le 1$; **23.** $x < -2$; **25.** $x < \frac{3}{2}$;

27. $x > \frac{35}{9}$; **29.** $x < -\frac{3}{2}$; **31.** No solution; **33.** $x \ge -6$;

35. $x < 1$; **37.** All real numbers; **39.** All real numbers; **41.** $x > \frac{3}{8}$;

43. No solution; **45.** $x \ge -\frac{7}{11}$; **47.** $x > 3$; **49.** $m \ge 2.5$;

51. $x \ge 30$; **53.** $t > -\frac{1}{2}$; **55.** $r \ge 2$; **57.** $t \le -17$;

59. a) May, September, June, August, and July **b)** January, February, December, March, November, and April **c)** January,
February, and December **d)** June, August, and July **61.** $\ne$ **63.** We do not know that y is positive. If y is negative, we must
reverse the sign of the inequality. **65.** $x > 4$ **66.** -9 **67.** -25 **68.** $\frac{14}{5}$ **69.** 500 kilowatt-hours

Chapter 2 Review Exercises
1. $3x + 24$ **2.** $5x - 10$ **3.** $-2x - 8$ **4.** $-x - 2$ **5.** $-m - 8$ **6.** $-16 + 4x$ **7.** $25 - 5p$
8. $24x - 30$ **9.** $-25t + 25$ **10.** $-4x + 12$ **11.** $x + 2$ **12.** $-1 - 2y$ **13.** $-x - 2y + z$ **14.** $-6a + 15b - 21$ **15.** $4q$
16. $-3y + 8$ **17.** $5x + 1$ **18.** $-3x + 3y$ **19.** $8m + 8n$ **20.** $9x + 3y + 2$ **21.** $4x + 3y + 6$ **22.** 3 **23.** $-12x^2 + 3$ **24.** 0
25. $5x + 7$ **26.** $-3b + 2$ **27.** 0 **28.** $4x - 4$ **29.** $22x - 42$ **30.** $6x^2 - 3x + y$ **31.** $-\frac{7}{20}d + 7$ **32.** 3 **33.** $\frac{1}{6}x + 2$
34. $-\frac{7}{12}n$ **35.** 1 **36.** -13 **37.** 11 **38.** -27 **39.** $\frac{11}{5}$ **40.** $\frac{11}{2}$ **41.** -8 **42.** -3 **43.** 12 **44.** 4 **45.** 2 **46.** -3 **47.** $\frac{3}{2}$ **48.** -3
49. $-\frac{1}{2}$ **50.** -1 **51.** All real numbers **52.** 2 **53.** -5 **54.** -35.5 **55.** -1.125 **56.** 0.6 **57.** $-\frac{21}{4}$ **58.** $\frac{78}{7}$ **59.** $-\frac{3}{2}$ **60.** $-\frac{2}{3}$
61. 2 **62.** $\frac{10}{7}$ **63.** 0 **64.** -1 **65.** 10 **66.** No solution **67.** All real numbers **68.** -4 **69.** No solution **70.** All real numbers

71. $\frac{17}{3}$ **72.** $-\frac{20}{7}$ **73.** No solution **74.** 7 **75.** 52 **76.** 32 **77.** 7 **78.** -18 **79.** 3 **80.** 48 **81.** 12 square centimeters

82. ≈ 33.51 cubic inches **83.** $l = (P - 2w)/2$ **84.** $m = \dfrac{y - y_1}{x - x_1}$ **85.** $y = \dfrac{1}{3}x + \dfrac{2}{3}$ **86.** 308.5 miles **87.** 240 square feet

88. ≈ 25.13 cubic inches **89.** $3:4$ **90.** $5:12$ **91.** $6:1$ **92.** 2 **93.** 20 **94.** 9 **95.** $\dfrac{135}{4}$ **96.** -10 **97.** -16 **98.** $\dfrac{108}{7}$ **99.** 90

100. 40 inches **101.** 1 foot **102.** $x \geq 2$; **103.** $a < 3$; **104.** $r \geq -2$;

105. No solution; **106.** All real numbers; **107.** $x < -3$; **108.** $x \leq \dfrac{19}{4}$;

109. $y > \dfrac{8}{5}$; **110.** $x > -12$; **111.** $t \geq -3$; **112.** 6.3 hours **113.** 72 dishes

114. 440 pages **115.** $6\dfrac{1}{3}$ inches **116.** 15.75 feet **117.** $\approx\$0.109$ **118.** 192 bottles

Chapter 2 Practice Test

1. $6x - 12$ [2.1] **2.** $-x - 3y + 4$ [2.1] **3.** $-3x + 4$ [2.1] **4.** $-x + 10$ [2.1] **5.** $-5x - y - 6$ [2.1]

6. $7a - 8b - 3$ [2.1] **7.** $2x^2 + 6x - 1$ [2.1] **8.** $x = 4$ [2.4] **9.** $x = 8$ [2.5] **10.** $x = -\dfrac{1}{7}$ [2.5] **11.** No solution [2.5]

12. All real numbers [2.5] **13.** $x = \dfrac{-by - c}{a}$ [2.6] **14.** $y = \dfrac{6}{5}x - \dfrac{2}{5}$ [2.6] **15.** $x = 0$ [2.5] **16.** $x = -45$ [2.7]

17. a) Conditional equation **b)** Contradiction **c)** Identity [2.5] **18.** $x > -7$; [2.8] **19.** $x \leq 12$; [2.8]

20. No solution; [2.8] **21.** All real numbers; [2.5] **22.** $x = \dfrac{32}{3}$ feet or $10\dfrac{2}{3}$ feet [2.7] **23.** 4% [2.6]

24. ≈ 28.27 inches [2.6] **25.** 175 minutes or 2 hours 55 minutes [2.6]

Cumulative Review Test

1. $\dfrac{8}{3}$ [1.3] **2.** $\dfrac{15}{16}$ [1.3] **3.** $>$ [1.5] **4.** 3 [1.7] **5.** -1 [1.7] **6.** 16 [1.9] **7.** 168 [1.9] **8.** 12 [1.9]

9. Distributive property [1.10] **10.** $12x + y$ [2.1] **11.** $\dfrac{1}{12}x + 25$ [2.1] **12.** -1 [2.4] **13.** $-\dfrac{5}{4}$ [2.5] **14.** $\dfrac{12}{5}$ [2.5]

15. $b = 3A - a - c$ [2.6] **16.** $\dfrac{9}{4}$ or 2.25 [2.7] **17.** $x > 10$, [2.8] **18.** $x \geq -12$, [2.8]

19. ≈ 380.13 square feet [2.6] **20.** \$42 [2.7]

Chapter 3

Exercise Set 3.1

1. $0.07c$ **3.** $7 - c$ **5.** $c + 0.07$ **7.** $2c + 7$ **9.** Equals **11.** $h + 4$ **13.** $a - 5$ **15.** $5h$ **17.** $2d$ **19.** $\dfrac{1}{2}a$

21. $r - 5$ **23.** $12 - m$ **25.** $2w + 8$ **27.** $5a - 4$ **29.** $\dfrac{1}{3}w - 9$ **31.** $x =$ Sonya's height **33.** $x =$ length of Jones Beach

35. $x =$ number of medals Finland won **37.** $x =$ cost of the Chevy **39.** $x =$ Teri's grade **41.** $x =$ amount Kristen receives or $x =$ amount Yvonne receives **43.** $x =$ Don's weight or $x =$ Angela's weight **45.** Let $c =$ cost of chair, then $5c =$ cost of table.

47. Let $a =$ area of the kitchen, then $2a + 20 =$ area of the living room. **49.** Let $w =$ width of rectangle, then $6w - 2 =$ length of rectangle. **51.** Let $w =$ number of medals won by Sweden, then $20 - w =$ number of medals won by Brazil, or let $w =$ number of medals won by Brazil, then $20 - w =$ number of medals won by Sweden. **53.** Let $g =$ George's age, then $\dfrac{1}{2}g + 2 =$ Mike's age.

55. Let $m =$ number of miles Jan walked, then $6.4 - m =$ number of miles Edward walked, or let $m =$ number of miles Edward walked, then $6.4 - m =$ number of miles Jan walked. **57.** $n + 8$ **59.** $\dfrac{1}{2}x$ **61.** $2a - 1$ **63.** $2t - 30$ **65.** $2p - 2.3$

67. $80,000 - m$ **69.** $2r - 673$ **71.** $10x$ **73.** $100d$ **75.** $45 + 0.40x$ **77.** $s + 0.20s$ **79.** $e - 0.12e$ **81.** $c + 0.07c$
83. $m - 0.307m$ **85.** $f + (f + 15)$ **87.** $(2l - 1) - l$ **89.** $x - (3x - 40)$ **91.** $w + (2w - 3)$ **93.** $r + (479r + 462)$
95. $r + (r + 0.394r)$ **97.** $a - (a + 0.112a)$ **99.** $x + 4x = 20$ **101.** $x + (x + 1) = 41$ **103.** $2x - 8 = 12$

105. $\dfrac{1}{5}(x + 10) = 150$ **107.** $x + 2(x + 2) = 22$ **109.** $12.50h = 150$ **111.** $2.99x = 17.94$ **113.** $25q = 175$

115. $a + (2a + 1) = 52$ **117.** $(2s + 300) - s = 420$ **119.** $s + (2s - 4) = 890$ **121.** $m + (3m - 2) = 12.6$
123. $c + 0.002c = 86,460$ **125.** $p - 0.019p = 12,087$ **127.** $c + 0.07c = 32,600$ **129.** $c + 0.15c = 42.50$

131. a) $86,400d + 3600h + 60m + s$ **b)** 368,125 seconds **134.** 4 **135.** 15 **136.** $y = \dfrac{3x - 6}{2}$ or $y = \dfrac{3}{2}x - 3$ **137.** 2.52

138. $x > \dfrac{7}{2}$,

Exercise Set 3.2

1. $x + (2x + 2) = 20$ **3.** $x + (x + 2) = 20$ **5.** $(2x + 2) - x = 20$ **7.** 5 **9.** 43, 44 **11.** 47, 49
13. 8, 19 **15.** 2, 6 **17.** 25, 42 **19.** 65 cards **21.** 22.2 hours **23.** 13 weeks **25.** 9.6 years **27.** December: 22, June: 226

29. $14.74   **31.** Japan: $2.17, U.S.: $0.77   **33.** 12.5 gallons   **35.** 18,100 copies   **37.** 6 movies   **39.** 150 miles   **41.** 6 years
43. 4000 pages   **45.** 2000 newsletters   **47.** $276.02   **49.** $23,230.77   **51.** $\approx$1.21 million   **53.** $25,000   **55.** $39,387.76   **57.** $49,867.37
59. $7500   **61.** 500 pages   **63.** $1071.43   **65.** $24.59   **67.** $77,777.78   **69.** 15.3 million gallons   **71.** Answers will vary
73. a) $80 = \dfrac{74 + 88 + 76 + x}{4}$ **b)** 82   **75.** 4   **76.** Commutative property of addition   **77.** $h = \dfrac{2A}{b}$ **78.** 12

Mid-Chapter Test: Sections 3.1–3.2

1. $6w$ [3.1]   **2.** $3h + 5$ [3.1]   **3.** $c + 0.20c$ [3.1]   **4.** $60 + 0.95m$ [3.1]   **5.** $50n$ [3.1]
6. $25 - x$ [3.1]   **7.** $c - 0.25c$ [3.1]   **8.** $x =$ length of Poison Dart Frog [3.1]   **9.** Let $p =$ distance Pedro traveled, then
$4p + 6 =$ distance Mary traveled. [3.1]   **10.** $v - (v - 0.18v)$ [3.1]   **11.** $p + 0.12p = 38,619$ [3.1]   **12.** $x + 3(x + 2) = 26$ [3.1]
13. 46, 47 [3.2]   **14.** 4, 11 [3.2]   **15.** 18 days [3.2]   **16.** 15 hours [3.2]   **17.** $700 [3.2]   **18.** Betty: 196 clients, Anita: 404 clients [3.2]
19. 52 miles [3.2]   **20.** $5000 [3.2]

Exercise Set 3.3

1. 10   **3.** 360°   **5.** Isosceles   **7.** $l \cdot w$ **9.** 45°   **11.** 46°, 46°, 88°   **13.** 11.5 inches   **15.** $A = 67°, B = 23°$
17. $A = 47°, B = 133°$ **19.** 88°   **21.** 50°, 60°, 70°   **23.** Length is 14 feet, width is 8 feet   **25.** Length is 78 feet, width is 36 feet
27. Smaller angles are 50°, larger angles are 130°   **29.** 30°, 30°, 150°, 150°   **31.** 63°, 73°, 140°, 84°   **33.** Width is 4 feet, height is 7
feet   **35. a)** Length: 100 inches, width: 190 inches   **b)** 7.69 inches   **c)** 76 inches   **d)** 53.85 inches   **e)** 19,000 square inches
37. Width is 11 feet, length is 16 feet   **39.** $ac + ad + bc + bd$ **41.** $<$ **42.** $>$ **43.** -10 **44.** $-2x - 5y + 6$ **45.** $y = -2x + 3$

Exercise Set 3.4

1. Subtracting   **3.** $d = r \cdot t$ **5.** Adding   **7.** 1 hour   **9.** 6 mph   **11.** $\approx$0.72 hour   **13.** 2.4 hours   **15.** 70 mph
17. $\approx$44.4 seconds   **19.** 35 mph, 40 mph   **21.** $\approx$0.61 hour   **23.** 1.5 miles/day, 2.25 miles/day   **25.** *Apollo*: 5 mph, *Pythagoras*: 9 mph
27. 1.5 hours   **29. a)** 2.4 miles   **b)** 112.0 miles   **c)** 26.2 miles   **d)** 140.6 miles   **e)** 9.23 hours   **31.** Dom: 21 km/hr, Sue: 11 km/hr
33. $10,000 at 7%, $2000 at 5%   **35.** $2400 at 6%, $3600 at 4%   **37.** $2000 at 4%, $8000 at 5%   **39.** November   **41.** 8 hours at
Home Depot, 10 hours at clinic   **43.** 1200 adult admissions   **45. a)** 41 shares of Nike, 205 shares of Kellogg   **b)** $37   **47.** 11.25
pounds almonds, 18.75 pounds walnuts   **49.** $160: 6 cubic yards, $120: 2 cubic yards   **51.** $2.74 per pound   **53.** $\approx$11.1%
55. $1\dfrac{2}{3}$ liters   **57.** 18.96%   **59.** $\approx$11.1%   **61.** 40% pure juice   **63.** $\approx$3.77 cups Clorox, $\approx$2.23 cups shock treatment   **65.** 11.25 pints
67. $\approx$5.74 hours   **70. a)** $\dfrac{22}{13}$ or $1\dfrac{9}{13}$ **b)** $\dfrac{35}{8}$ or $4\dfrac{3}{8}$ **71.** All real numbers   **72.** $\dfrac{3}{4}$ or 0.75   **73.** $x \leq \dfrac{1}{4}$

Chapter 3 Review Exercises

1. $3n + 7$ **2.** $1.2g$ **3.** $d - 0.25d$ **4.** $16y$ **5.** $200 - x$ **6.** Let $d =$ Dino's age, then
$7d + 6 =$ Mario's age.   **7.** $c - (c - 0.12c)$ **8.** $n - (3n - 24) = 8$ **9.** 33 and 41   **10.** 118 and 119   **11.** 38 and 7   **12.** $21,738.32
13. 19 months   **14.** $2000   **15.** $618.75   **16.** 10 hours   **17.** $\approx$ $171,000   **18.** $684   **19.** 45°, 55°, 80°   **20.** 30°, 40°, 150°, 140°
21. Width is 15.5 feet, length is 19.5 feet   **22.** Width is 50 feet, length is 80 feet   **23.** 45°, 45°, 135°, 135°   **24.** Height is 2 feet, length
is 4 feet   **25.** 2 hours   **26.** 4 hours   **27.** $\approx$8.8 feet per second   **28.** $4000 at 8%, $8000 at $7\dfrac{1}{4}$%   **29.** $700 at 3%, $3300 at 3.5%
30. $\approx$0.67 gallon   **31.** 9 smaller and 21 larger   **32.** 1.2 liters of 10%, 0.8 liters of 5%   **33.** 103 and 105   **34.** $450   **35.** $12,000
36. 42°, 50°, 88°   **37.** 8 years   **38.** 70°, 70°, 110°, 110°   **39.** 500 copies   **40.** 0.6 mph   **41.** 60 pounds of $3.50, 20 pounds of $4.10
42. Older brother: 55 mph, younger brother: 60 mph   **43.** 0.4 liters   **44.** Width is 16 feet, length is 24 feet   **45.** 1.5 liters

Chapter 3 Practice Test

1. $500 - n$ [3.1]   **2.** $2w + 6000$ [3.1]   **3.** $60t$ [3.1]   **4.** $c + 0.06c$ [3.1]   **5.** Let $n =$ number of packages of orange, then $7n - 105 =$ number of packages of peppermint. [3.1]   **6.** Let $x =$ number of men, then $600 - x =$ number of
women, or let $x =$ number of women, then $600 - x =$ number of men. [3.1]   **7.** $(2n - 1) - n$ [3.1]   **8.** $n + (n + 18)$ [3.1]
9. $(c + 0.84c) - c$ [3.1]   **10.** 56 and 102 [3.2]   **11.** 5 and 7 [3.2]   **12.** 9 and 33 [3.2]   **13.** $2500 [3.2]   **14.** $34.78 [3.2]   **15.** Peter:
$40,000, Julie: $80,000 [3.2]   **16.** 6 times [3.2]   **17.** 7450 pages [3.2]   **18.** 15 inches, 30 inches, 30 inches [3.3]   **19.** Width is 6 feet,
length is 8 feet [3.3]   **20.** 59°, 59°, 121°, 121° [3.3]   **21.** Harlene: 0.3 feet per minute, Ellis: 0.5 feet per minute [3.4]   **22.** 6 mph [3.4]
23. Jelly Belly: $\approx$1.91 pounds, Kits: $\approx$1.09 pounds [3.4]   **24.** 20 liters [3.4]   **25.** 1 liter of 8%, 2 liters of 5% [3.4]

Cumulative Review Test

1. $16,000 [1.2]   **2. a)** 11.6%   **b)** 36 [1.2]   **3. a)** 7.2 parts per million   **b)** 6 parts per million [1.2]
4. $\dfrac{5}{9}$ [1.3]   **5.** $\dfrac{13}{24}$ inch [1.3]   **6. a)** $\{1, 2, 3, 4, \ldots\}$ **b)** $\{0, 1, 2, 3, \ldots\}$ **c)** A rational number is a quotient of two integers where the
denominator is not 0. [1.4]   **7. a)** 4   **b)** $|-5|$ [1.5]   **8.** -34 [1.9]   **9.** $2x - 28$ [2.1]   **10.** 5 [2.5]   **11.** $\dfrac{1}{5}$ [2.5]   **12.** No solution [2.5]
13. $\approx$113.10 [2.6]   **14. a)** $y = -\dfrac{1}{2}x + 2$ **b)** 4 [2.6]   **15.** $w = \dfrac{P - 2l}{2}$ [2.6]   **16.** 9 gallons [2.7]   **17.** $x \leq 1$, $\longleftarrow\!\!\!\bullet\!\!\longrightarrow$ [2.8]
18. 40 minutes [3.2]   **19.** 6, 23 [3.2]   **20.** 40°, 45°, 90°, 185° [3.3]

Chapter 4

Exercise Set 4.1

1. 0   **3.** Base   **5.** Expanded power rule for exponents   **7.** Product rule for exponents   **9.** $p^3 q^4 r^5$ **11.** x^{10}
13. $-z^5$ **15.** y^5 **17.** $3^5 = 243$ **19.** z^8 **21.** 6   **23.** x^7 **25.** $3^4 = 81$ **27.** $\dfrac{1}{y^2}$ **29.** 1   **31.** $\dfrac{1}{q^6}$ **33.** 1   **35.** 3   **37.** 4   **39.** -9
41. $6x^3 y^2$ **43.** $-8r$ **45.** x^8 **47.** x^{25} **49.** x^3 **51.** x^{12} **53.** n^{18} **55.** $-8w^6$ **57.** $-27t^9$ **59.** $64x^9 y^6$ **61.** $\dfrac{x^2}{9}$ **63.** $\dfrac{y^4}{x^4}$ **65.** $-\dfrac{216}{x^3}$

67. $\dfrac{8x^3}{y^3}$ **69.** $\dfrac{16p^2}{25}$ **71.** $\dfrac{27x^{12}}{y^3}$ **73.** $\dfrac{a^7}{b^3}$ **75.** $\dfrac{x^{11}}{2y^7}$ **77.** $\dfrac{6y^4}{z^3}$ **79.** $\dfrac{7}{3x^5y^3}$ **81.** $-\dfrac{3y^2}{x^3}$ **83.** $-\dfrac{2}{x^3y^2z^5}$ **85.** $\dfrac{8}{x^6}$ **87.** $27y^9$ **89.** 1   **91.** $\dfrac{x^4}{y^4}$

93. $\dfrac{z^{24}}{16y^{28}}$ **95.** $\dfrac{125}{s^6t^9}$ **97.** $9x^2y^8$ **99.** $5ab^4$ **101.** $-6x^2y^2$ **103.** $15x^3y^6$ **105.** $-9p^6q^3$ **107.** $49r^6s^4$ **109.** x^2 **111.** x^{12} **113.** $6.25x^6$

115. $\dfrac{x^7}{y^4}$ **117.** $-\dfrac{m^{12}}{n^9}$ **119.** $-216x^9y^6$ **121.** $-8x^{12}y^6z^3$ **123.** $729r^{12}s^{15}$ **125.** $108x^5y^7$ **127.** $1.69x^4y^8$ **129.** $x^{11}y^{13}$ **131.** x^8z^8

133. Cannot be simplified   **135.** Cannot be simplified   **137.** $6z^2$ **139.** Cannot be simplified   **141.** 40   **143.** 1   **145.** The sign will be positive because a negative number with an even exponent will be positive. This is because $(-1)^m = 1$ when m is even.   **147.** $8x^2$ **149.** $ab + a^2 + b^2$ **151.** product rule: $x^m \cdot x^n = x^{m+n}$; power rule: $(x^m)^n = x^{m \cdot n}$ **153.** $576y^8z^{13}$ **156.** 13   **157.** $x + 10$

158. All real numbers   **159. a)** 4 inches, 4 inches, 9 inches, 9 inches   **b)** $w = \dfrac{P - 2l}{2}$

Exercise Set 4.2   1. $\dfrac{1}{x^2}$ **3.** $(-2)^4$ **5.** x^4 **7.** $\dfrac{1}{x^4}$ **9.** $4x^4$ **11.** $\dfrac{1}{x^6}$ **13.** $\dfrac{1}{5}$ **15.** t^3 **17.** a **19.** 36   **21.** $\dfrac{1}{x^{20}}$ **23.** $\dfrac{1}{y^{20}}$ **25.** $\dfrac{1}{x^8}$

27. 9   **29.** y^2 **31.** x^2 **33.** 9   **35.** $\dfrac{1}{r}$ **37.** p^3 **39.** $\dfrac{1}{x^4}$ **41.** 27   **43.** $\dfrac{1}{125}$ **45.** z^9 **47.** p^{24} **49.** y^6 **51.** $\dfrac{1}{x^4}$ **53.** $\dfrac{1}{x^{15}}$ **55.** $-\dfrac{1}{16}$

57. $-\dfrac{1}{16}$ **59.** $-\dfrac{1}{8}$ **61.** $\dfrac{1}{36}$ **63.** $\dfrac{1}{x^{10}}$ **65.** n^2 **67.** 1   **69.** 1   **71.** 64   **73.** x^8 **75.** 1   **77.** $\dfrac{1}{4}$ **79.** $\dfrac{1}{49}$ **81.** x^3 **83.** $\dfrac{1}{16}$ **85.** 125

87. $\dfrac{1}{9}$ **89.** 1   **91.** $\dfrac{1}{36x^4}$ **93.** $\dfrac{3y^2}{x^2}$ **95.** 4   **97.** $\dfrac{64}{125}$ **99.** $\dfrac{d^4}{c^8}$ **101.** $-\dfrac{s^4}{r^{16}}$ **103.** $-\dfrac{7}{a^3b^4}$ **105.** $\dfrac{y^9}{64x^{15}}$ **107.** $\dfrac{18}{z^9}$ **109.** -8 **111.** $12x^5$

113. $-\dfrac{20z^5}{y}$ **115.** $8d^4$ **117.** $\dfrac{4}{x^2}$ **119.** $\dfrac{x^4}{2y^5}$ **121.** $\dfrac{8x^6}{y^2}$ **123.** $\dfrac{y^{14}z^6}{25x^8}$ **125.** $\dfrac{r^{20}t^{48}}{16s^{36}}$ **127.** $\dfrac{y^{12}}{x^{18}z^6}$ **129.** $\dfrac{1}{16p^4q^6}$ **131. a)** Yes   **b)** No

133. $16\dfrac{1}{16}$ **135.** $125\dfrac{1}{125}$ **137.** $\dfrac{2}{3}$ **139.** $-\dfrac{7}{8}$ **141.** $-\dfrac{5}{6}$ **143.** $\dfrac{22}{9}$ **145.** -2 **147.** -3 **149.** Answers will vary.   **151.** -2 **153.** $2, -3$

155. The product rule is $(xy)^m = x^m y^m$, not $(x + y)^m = x^m + y^m$.   **157.** 186 miles   **158.** 94, 96   **159.** 12 feet by 16 feet
160. $3400 at 4%, $5600 at 3%

Exercise Set 4.3   1. 5.12×10^{-5} **3.** Integer   **5.** 5.12×10^{-6} **7.** 11   **9.** 2.0×10^4 **11.** 4.5×10^2 **13.** 3.5×10^5
15. 7.950×10^3 **17.** 5.3×10^{-2} **19.** 7.26×10^{-4} **21.** 5.26×10^9 **23.** 9.14×10^{-6} **25.** 2.203×10^5 **27.** 5.104×10^{-3}
29. 43,000   **31.** 0.00000932   **33.** 0.0000213   **35.** 625,000   **37.** 9,000,000   **39.** 535   **41.** 0.000000773   **43.** 10,000   **45.** 0.000008 meter
47. 125,000,000,000 watts   **49.** 15,300 meters   **51.** 0.0482 meter   **53.** 90,000,000   **55.** 0.243   **57.** 0.000064   **59.** 0.0013   **61.** 2500
63. 250,000   **65.** 5.6×10^{12} **67.** 1.28×10^{-1} **69.** 7.0×10^2 **71.** 1.75×10^2 **73.** $3.3 \times 10^{-4}, 5.3, 7.3 \times 10^2, 1.75 \times 10^6$
75. a) $\approx 6.415 \times 10^9$ **b)** ≈ 22 **77.** 8,640,000,000 cubic feet   **79.** 1.6×10^7 seconds   **81. a)** 1.66×10^8 **b)** ≈ 1.38
83. a) 5.25×10^{10} **b)** ≈ 6.5 **85. a)** Earth: 5.794×10^{24} metric tons; Moon: 7.34×10^{19} metric tons; Jupiter: 1.899×10^{27} metric tons
b) $\approx 7.89 \times 10^4$ **c)** $\approx 3.28 \times 10^2$ **87.** 1.36×10^9 **89. a)** 2.0×10^7;   **b)** 7.6×10^7 **c)** 2.2×10^7 **91.** 17   **93.** A number greater than or equal to 1 and less than 10 multiplied by some power of 10.   **95. a)** Less   **b)** 1.5×10^{78} **97.** Answers will vary.

99. 1,000,000 times greater   **102.** 0   **103. a)** $\dfrac{3}{2}$ **b)** 0   **104.** 2   **105.** $-\dfrac{y^{12}}{64x^9}$

Mid-Chapter Test: Sections 4.1–4.3   1. y^{31} [4.1]   **2.** x^3 [4.1]   **3.** $6x^6y^{13}$ [4.1]   **4.** $\dfrac{2a^5b^6}{3}$ [4.1]   **5.** $-64x^6y^{12}$ [4.1]   **6.** $\dfrac{t^6}{4s^4}$ [4.1]

7. $63x^{11}y^{13}$ [4.1]   **8.** $\dfrac{1}{p^8}$ [4.2]   **9.** $\dfrac{1}{x^{10}}$ [4.2]   **10.** 1 [4.2]   **11.** $\dfrac{49}{9}$ [4.2]   **12.** $\dfrac{32x}{y}$ [4.2]   **13.** $\dfrac{3}{m^4n^6}$ [4.2]   **14.** $\dfrac{x^{12}y^{10}}{4z^4}$ [4.2]   **15. a)** and
b) Answers will vary. [4.3]   **16.** 6.54×10^9 [4.3]   **17.** 0.0000327 [4.3]   **18.** 18,900 meters [4.3]   **19.** 0.0238 [4.3]   **20.** 3.0×10^{-7} [4.3]

Exercise Set 4.4   1. $-5x^3 + 3x + 4$ **3.** $3x + 4$ **5.** 1   **7.** 5   **9.** True   **11.** 3   **13.** 1   **15.** 4   **17.** 5   **19.** 8   **21.** 3   **23.** 10
25. 9   **27.** Trinomial   **29.** Monomial   **31.** Binomial   **33.** Monomial   **35.** Not a polynomial   **37.** Polynomial   **39.** Trinomial
41. Not a polynomial   **43.** Already in descending order, 0   **45.** $x^2 - 2x - 4, 2$ **47.** $3x^2 + x - 8, 2$ **49.** Already in descending order, 1   **51.** Already in descending order, 2   **53.** $4x^3 - 3x^2 + x - 4, 3$ **55.** $-2x^4 + 3x^2 + 5x - 6, 4$ **57.** $13x - 9$

59. $-x + 11$ **61.** $-2t - 1$ **63.** $x^2 + 6.6x + 0.8$ **65.** $5m^2 + 4$ **67.** $x^2 + 3x - 3$ **69.** $-3x^2 + x + \dfrac{17}{2}$ **71.** $8.2n^2 - 4.8n - 0.6$

73. $-2x^3 - 3x^2 + 4x - 3$ **75.** $11x^2 - 7x - y + 5$ **77.** $5x^2y - 3x + 2$ **79.** $11x - 3$ **81.** $7y^2 - 2y + 5$ **83.** $4x^2 + 2x - 4$
85. $2x^3 - x^2 + 6x - 2$ **87.** $3n^3 - 11n^2 - n + 2$ **89.** $2x - 6$ **91.** $3x + 4$ **93.** $-3r$ **95.** $-6y^2 + 1.9y - 12.7$ **97.** $8x^2 + x + 4$

99. $-6.4n^2 + 6n - 7.6$ **101.** $8x^3 - 7x^2 - 4x - 3$ **103.** $2x^3 - \dfrac{23}{5}x^2 + 2x - 2$ **105.** $x - 2$ **107.** $2x^2 - 9x + 14$

109. $-5c^3 - 4c^2 - 7c + 14$ **111.** $3x + 8$ **113.** $3a^2 - 16a + 28$ **115.** $x^2 - 3x - 3$ **117.** $-4x^2$ **119.** $4x^3 - 7x^2 + x - 2$
121. Answers will vary.   **123.** Answers will vary.   **125.** Sometimes   **127.** Sometimes   **129.** Answers will vary; one example is: $x^4 - 2x^3 + x$.   **131.** $a^2 + 2ab + b^2$ **133.** $4x^2 + 3xy$ **135.** No, all three terms would have to be degree 4 or 1. Therefore at least two of the terms would be like terms.   **137.** $-12x + 18$ **139.** $8x^2 + 28x - 24$ **141.** $>$ **142.** True   **143.** True   **144.** False   **145.** False

146. $\dfrac{4c^8}{b^8}$

Exercise Set 4.5   1. Trinomial   **3.** False   **5.** Align   **7.** Difference of two squares   **9.** $15x^5$ **11.** $-30t^{10}$ **13.** $-20x^6$

15. $-24x^6$ 17. $20x^5y^6$ 19. $-28x^3y^{15}$ 21. $54x^6y^{14}$ 23. $3x^6y$ 25. $5.94x^8y^3$ 27. $9x - 54$ 29. $-6x^2 + 6x$ 31. $-16y - 10$
33. $-2x^3 + 4x^2 - 10x$ 35. $-20x^3 + 30x^2 - 20x$ 37. $0.5x^5 - 3x^4 - 0.5x^2$ 39. $0.6x^2y + 1.5x^2 - 1.8xy$ 41. $x^2y^4 - 4y^7 - 3y^4$
43. $5x^2 + 18x - 8$ 45. $6t^2 + 3t - 30$ 47. $4x^2 - 16$ 49. $-5x^2 - 22x + 48$ 51. $-12x^2 + 32x - 5$ 53. $4x^2 - 10x + 4$
55. $12k^2 - 30k + 12$ 57. $x^2 - 4$ 59. $4x^2 - 12x + 9$ 61. $-6z^2 + 46z - 28$ 63. $8x^2 - 50x + 63$ 65. $xy - 3x + 7y - 21$

67. $6x^2 - 5xy - 6y^2$ 69. $-27x^2 - 3xy + 36x + 4y$ 71. $x^2 + 0.9x + 0.18$ 73. $x^2 + \frac{7}{2}x - 2$ 75. $x^2 - 64$ 77. $9x^2 - 64$

79. $x^2 + 2xy + y^2$ 81. $x^2 - 0.4x + 0.04$ 83. $16x^2 + 40x + 25$ 85. $0.16x^2 + 0.8xy + y^2$ 87. $16c^2 - 25d^2$ 89. $4x^2 - 36$
91. $49s^2 - 42st + 9t^2$ 93. $16m^3 - 8m^2 + 9m + 18$ 95. $12x^3 + 5x^2 + 13x + 10$ 97. $-14x^3 - 22x^2 + 19x - 3$ 99. $a^3 + b^3$
101. $6t^4 + 5t^3 + 5t^2 + 10t + 4$ 103. $x^4 - 3x^3 + 5x^2 - 6x$ 105. $2x^5 + 2x^4 - 23x^3 + x^2 - 12x$ 107. $b^3 - 3b^2 + 3b - 1$
109. $27a^3 - 135a^2 + 225a - 125$ 111. Yes   113. No   115. 6, 3, 1   117. a) $(x + 2)(2x + 1)$ or $2x^2 + 5x + 2$ b) 54 square feet
c) 1 foot   119. a) $3x^2 + 19x + 20$ b) $6x^3 + 32x^2 + 2x - 40$ c) 864 cubic feet   d) 864 cubic feet   e) Yes

121. $\frac{1}{3}x^2 + \frac{11}{45}x - \frac{4}{15}$ 123. No solution   124. $C = 53°, D = 37°$ 125. $\frac{x^4}{16y^8}$ 126. a) -216 b) $\frac{1}{216}$ 127. $-5x^2 - 2x + 14$

Exercise Set 4.6   1. $\frac{6x^2 - 7x - 20}{(2x - 5)} = (3x + 4)$ 3. Divisor   5. Remainder   7. $6x^3 + 8x^2 + 0x + 16$ 9. False

11. $\frac{x^2 - x - 42}{x - 7} = x + 6$ or $\frac{x^2 - x - 42}{x + 6} = x - 7$ 13. $\frac{2x^2 + 5x + 3}{2x + 3} = x + 1$ or $\frac{2x^2 + 5x + 3}{x + 1} = 2x + 3$

15. $\frac{4x^2 - 9}{2x + 3} = 2x - 3$ or $\frac{4x^2 - 9}{2x - 3} = 2x + 3$ 17. $t + 2$ 19. $n + \frac{5}{2}$ 21. $\frac{7}{3}x + 2$ 23. $-3x + 2$ 25. $3x + 1$ 27. $\frac{1}{2}x + 4$

29. $-1 + \frac{5}{2}w$ 31. $1 + \frac{2}{x} - \frac{3}{x^2}$ 33. $-2x^3 + \frac{3}{x} + \frac{4}{x^2}$ 35. $x^2 + 3x - \frac{3}{x^3}$ 37. $3x^2 - 2x + 6 - \frac{5}{2x}$ 39. $-2k^2 - \frac{3}{2}k + \frac{2}{k}$

41. $-4x^3 - x^2 + \frac{10}{3} + \frac{3}{x^2}$ 43. $x + 3$ 45. $5y + 1$ 47. $2x + 4$ 49. $x + 4$ 51. $x + 5 - \frac{3}{2x - 3}$ 53. $x + 6$

55. $3x^2 + 4x + 5 + \frac{4}{3x - 4}$ 57. $4x - 3 - \frac{3}{2x + 3}$ 59. $7x^2 - 5$ 61. $2t^2 + \frac{12}{t - 2}$ 63. $w^2 + 3w + 9 + \frac{19}{w - 3}$ 65. $x^2 + 3x + 9$

67. $2x^2 + x - 2 - \frac{2}{2x - 1}$ 69. $-m^2 - 7m - 5 - \frac{8}{m - 1}$ 71. $4t^2 - 8t + 15 - \frac{26}{t + 2}$ 73. No; for example $\frac{x + 2}{x} = 1 + \frac{2}{x}$ which
is not a binomial.   75. $2x^2 + 11x + 16$ 77. 3   79. 4x   81. Since the shaded areas minus 2 must equal 3, 1, 0, and -1, respectively,
the shaded areas are 5, 3, 2, and 1, respectively.   83. $x^2 + \frac{2}{3}x + \frac{4}{9} - \frac{37}{9(3x - 2)}$ 85. $-3x + 3 + \frac{1}{x + 3}$ 88. a) 2   b) 2, 0

c) $2, -5, 0, \frac{2}{5}, -6.3, -\frac{23}{34}$ d) $\sqrt{7}, \sqrt{3}$ e) $2, -5, 0, \sqrt{7}, \frac{2}{5}, -6.3, \sqrt{3}, -\frac{23}{34}$ 89. a) 0   b) Undefined   90. Parentheses,
exponents, multiplication or division from left to right, addition or subtraction from left to right   91. $-\frac{2}{3}$ 92. \$39.50   93. x^{13}

Chapter 4 Review Exercises   1. x^8 2. x^6 3. 243   4. 32   5. x^3 6. 1   7. 25   8. 64   9. $\frac{1}{x^2}$ 10. y^3 11. 1   12. 7   13. 1

14. 1   15. $25x^2$ 16. $27a^3$ 17. $-27x^3$ 18. $216s^3$ 19. $16x^8$ 20. t^{24} 21. p^{32} 22. $\frac{4x^6}{y^2}$ 23. $\frac{25y^4}{4b^2}$ 24. $24x^5$ 25. $\frac{4x}{y}$ 26. $54x^4y^9$

27. $9x^2$ 28. $24x^7y^7$ 29. $16x^8y^{11}$ 30. $6c^6d^3$ 31. $\frac{27a^6}{b^{15}}$ 32. $27x^{12}y^3$ 33. $\frac{1}{b^9}$ 34. $\frac{1}{27}$ 35. $\frac{1}{25}$ 36. z^2 37. x^7 38. 16   39. $\frac{1}{y^3}$

40. $\frac{1}{x^5}$ 41. $\frac{1}{p^2}$ 42. $\frac{1}{a^5}$ 43. m^{10} 44. x^7 45. $\frac{1}{x^6}$ 46. $\frac{1}{9x^8}$ 47. $\frac{x^9}{64y^3}$ 48. $\frac{4n^2}{m^6}$ 49. $12y^2$ 50. $-\frac{125z^3}{y^9}$ 51. $\frac{x^4}{16y^6}$ 52. $\frac{6}{x}$

53. $10x^2y^2$ 54. $\frac{12x^2}{y}$ 55. $\frac{24y^2}{x^2}$ 56. $3y^5$ 57. $\frac{4y}{x^3}$ 58. $\frac{7x^5}{y^4}$ 59. $\frac{x}{2y^5}$ 60. $\frac{4y^{10}}{x}$ 61. 1.72×10^6 62. 1.53×10^{-1} 63. 7.63×10^{-3}
64. 4.7×10^4 65. 5.76×10^3 66. 3.14×10^{-4} 67. 0.0075   68. 0.000652   69. 8,900,000   70. 51,200   71. 0.0000314
72. 11,030,000   73. 0.092 liter, 9.2×10^{-2} liter   74. 6,000,000,000 meters, 6.0×10^9 meters   75. 0.0000128 gram, 1.28×10^{-5} gram
76. 19,200 grams, 1.92×10^4 grams   77. 0.085   78. 1260   79. 245   80. 397,000,000   81. 0.00003   82. 0.0325   83. 3.64×10^9
84. 2.12×10^1 85. 5.0×10^9 86. 5.0×10^{-4} 87. 3.4×10^{-3} 88. 3.4×10^7 89. 50,000 gallons   90. a) \$4,300,000,000,000
b) 1.075×10^{11} dollars   91. Not a polynomial   92. Monomial, 0   93. $x^2 + 3x - 4$, trinomial, 2   94. $4x^2 - x - 3$, trinomial, 2
95. Not a polynomial   96. Binomial, 3   97. $-4x^2 + x$, binomial, 2   98. Not a polynomial   99. $2x^3 + 4x^2 - 3x - 7$, polynomial, 3
100. $5x - 3$ 101. $7d + 4$ 102. $-3x - 5$ 103. $-4x^2 + 11x - 7$ 104. $5m^2 - 10$ 105. $8.1p + 2.8$ 106. $-3y - 15$
107. $4x^2 - 12x - 15$ 108. $3a^2 - 5a - 21$ 109. $4x + 2$ 110. $-5x^2 + 8x - 19$ 111. $3x^2 + 3x$ 112. $-15x^2 - 12x$
113. $6x^3 - 12x^2 + 21x$ 114. $-2c^3 + 3c^2 - 5c$ 115. $28b^3 + 21b^2 + 35b$ 116. $x^2 + 9x + 20$ 117. $-12x^2 - 21x + 6$
118. $25x^2 - 30x + 9$ 119. $-6x^2 + 14x + 12$ 120. $r^2 - 25$ 121. $3x^3 + x^2 - 10x + 6$ 122. $3x^3 + 7x^2 + 14x + 4$

123. $-12x^3 + 10x^2 - 30x + 14$ 124. $x + 2$ 125. $4y + 6$ 126. $8x + 4$ 127. $2x^2 + 3x - \frac{4}{3}$ 128. $2w - \frac{5}{3} + \frac{1}{w}$

129. $4x^5 - 2x^4 - \frac{3}{4}x^2 + \frac{1}{4x}$ 130. $-4m + 2$ 131. $\frac{5}{2}x + \frac{5}{x} + \frac{1}{x^2}$ 132. $\frac{5}{3}x - 2 + \frac{5}{x}$ 133. $x + 4$ 134. $5x - 2 + \frac{2}{x + 6}$
135. $n + 3$ 136. $2x^2 + 3x - 4$ 137. $2x - 3$

Chapter 4 Practice Test   1. $15x^6$ [4.1]   2. $27x^3y^6$ [4.1]   3. $8p^5$ [4.1]   4. $\frac{x^3}{8y^6}$ [4.1]   5. $\frac{y^4}{4x^6}$ [4.2]   6. 4 [4.1]   7. $\frac{2x^7y}{3}$ [4.2]

8. 1.425×10^{10} [4.3]   **9.** 2.0×10^{-7} [4.3]   **10.** Monomial [4.4]   **11.** Binomial [4.4]   **12.** Not a polynomial [4.4]
13. $6x^3 - 2x^2 + 5x - 5, 3$ [4.4]   **14.** $2x^2 + x - 7$ [4.4]   **15.** $-3y^2 - 2y + 5$ [4.4]   **16.** $3x^2 - x + 3$ [4.4]   **17.** $15d^2 - 40d$ [4.5]
18. $15x^2 + 4x - 32$ [4.5]   **19.** $-12c^2 + 7c + 45$ [4.5]   **20.** $6x^3 + 2x^2 - 35x + 25$ [4.5]   **21.** $4x^2 + 2x - 1$ [4.6]
22. $4x + 2 - \dfrac{5}{3x}$ [4.6]   **23.** $4x + 5$ [4.6]   **24.** $3x - 2 - \dfrac{2}{4x + 5}$ [4.6]   **25. a)** 5.73×10^3 **b)** $\approx 7.78 \times 10^5$ [4.3]

Cumulative Review Test   **1.** 17 [1.9]   **2.** $8x + 2$ [2.1]   **3.** -25 [1.9]   **4. a)** Associative property of addition

b) Commutative property of multiplication   **c)** Commutative property of multiplication [1.10]   **5.** $-\dfrac{13}{3}$ [2.5]   **6.** 0 [2.5]

7. $x > -\dfrac{9}{2}$, [2.8]   **8.** $y = 3x + 5$ [2.6]   **9.** $y = \dfrac{7x - 21}{3}, 7$ [2.6]   **10.** $\dfrac{25x^6}{y^{16}}$ [4.1]   **11.** $-7x^2 - 5x + 2, 2$ [4.4]

12. $3x^2 + 9x - 2$ [4.4]   **13.** $5a^2 + 6a + 5$ [4.4]   **14.** $10t^2 - 11t + 3$ [4.5]   **15.** $6x^3 - 13x^2 + 9x - 2$ [4.5]   **16.** $\dfrac{5}{2}d + 3 - \dfrac{2}{d}$ [4.6]
17. $2x + 5$ [4.6]   **18.** $\$3.33$ [2.7]   **19.** Bob: 56.5 mph, Nick: 63.5 mph [3.4]   **20.** $l = 10$ feet, $w = 4$ feet [3.3]

Chapter 5

Exercise Set 5.1   **1.** 6   **3.** $2x^2y^3$ **5.** 2   **7.** 12   **9.** $2^2 \cdot 5$ **11.** $2 \cdot 3^2 \cdot 5$ **13.** $2^3 \cdot 31$ **15.** 8   **17.** 14   **19.** 2   **21.** x^2 **23.** $3x$
25. a **27.** qr **29.** x^3y^5 **31.** 1   **33.** x^2y^2 **35.** x **37.** $x - 4$ **39.** $2x - 3$ **41.** $3w + 5$ **43.** $x - 4$ **45.** $x - 1$ **47.** $x - 9$
49. $4(x - 20)$ **51.** $5(3x - 1)$ **53.** $7(q + 4)$ **55.** $3x(3x - 4)$ **57.** $x^4(7x - 9)$ **59.** $3x^2(x^3 - 4)$ **61.** $12x^8(3x^4 + 2)$
63. $9y^3(3y^{12} - 1)$ **65.** $y(1 + 6x^3)$ **67.** $a^2(7a^2 + 3)$ **69.** $4xy(4yz + x^2)$ **71.** $4x^2yz^3(20x^3y^2z - 9)$ **73.** $25x^2yz(z^2 + x)$
75. $x^4y^3z^9(19y^9z^4 - 8x)$ **77.** $4(2c^2 - c - 8)$ **79.** $3(3x^2 + 6x + 1)$ **81.** $4x(x^2 - 2x + 3)$ **83.** $8(5b^2 - 6c + 3)$
85. $3(5p^2 - 2p + 3)$ **87.** $3a(3a^3 - 2a^2 + b)$ **89.** $xy(8x + 12y + 5)$ **91.** $(x - 7)(x + 6)$ **93.** $(a - 2)(3b - 4)$
95. $(2x + 1)(4x + 1)$ **97.** $(2x + 1)(5x + 1)$ **99.** $(6c + 7)(3c - 2)$ **101.** $6\triangledown(2 - \triangledown)$ **103.** $4\square(3\square^2 - \square + 1)$ **105.** Multiply
to obtain the original expression and be sure all common factors have been factored out.   **107.** $2x^2(2x + 7)(3x^3 + 2x - 1)$

109. $(x + 2)(x + 3)$ **110.** $-3x + 17$ **111.** 2   **112.** $y = \dfrac{4x - 20}{5}$ or $y = \dfrac{4}{5}x - 4$ **113.** ≈ 201.06 cubic inches   **114.** 14, 27

115. $\dfrac{9y^2}{4x^6}$

Exercise Set 5.2   **1.** Factoring by grouping   **3.** $(2x - 1)(x + 3)$ **5.** FOIL   **7.** $(x + 3)(x + 2)$ **9.** $(t + 5)(t + 4)$
11. $(x + 2)(x + 5)$ **13.** $(c - 4)(c + 7)$ **15.** $(2x - 3)(2x + 3)$ **17.** $(x + 3)(3x + 1)$ **19.** $(2x + 1)(3x - 1)$
21. $(x + 4)(8x + 1)$ **23.** $(3t - 2)(4t - 1)$ **25.** $(x + 9)(x - 1)$ **27.** $(2p + 5)(3p - 2)$ **29.** $(x + 2y)(x - 3y)$
31. $(3x + 2y)(x - 3y)$ **33.** $(5x - 6y)(2x - 5y)$ **35.** $(x - b)(x - a)$ **37.** $(y + 9)(x - 5)$ **39.** $(a + 3)(a + b)$
41. $(y - 1)(x + 5)$ **43.** $(3 + 2y)(4 - x)$ **45.** $(z + 5)(z^2 + 1)$ **47.** $(x - 5)(x^2 + 8)$ **49.** $2(x - 6)(x + 4)$
51. $4(x + 2)(x + 2) = 4(x + 2)^2$ **53.** $x(2x + 3)(3x - 1)$ **55.** $p(p - 6q)(p + 2q)$ **57.** $(y + 5)(x + 5)$ **59.** $(x + 5)(y + 6)$
61. $(a + b)(x + y)$ **63.** $(r + 6)(s - 7)$ **65.** $(c - a)(d + 3)$ **67.** No; $xy + 2x + 5y + 10$ is factorable; $xy + 10 + 2x + 5y$ is
not factorable in this arrangement.   **69.** $(\odot + 3)(\odot - 5)$ **71.** $x^2 - 2xy - 3x + 6y$ or $x^2 - 3x - 2xy + 6y$
73. a) $2x^2 - 5x - 6x + 15$ **b)** $(2x - 5)(x - 3)$ **75. a)** $2x^2 - 6x - 5x + 15$ **b)** $(x - 3)(2x - 5)$

77. a) $4x^2 + 3x - 20x - 15$ **b)** $(4x + 3)(x - 5)$ **79.** $(\odot + 3)(\star + 2)$ **81.** $\dfrac{6}{5}$ **82.** 30 pounds of jelly beans, 20 pounds of
gumdrops   **83.** $5x^2 - 2x - 3 + \dfrac{5}{3x}$ **84.** $a - 4$

Exercise Set 5.3   **1.** Both negative   **3.** $2(x - 2)(x - 3)$ **5.** $2(x - 5)(x - 1)$ **7.** Both positive   **9.** $y(x - 1)(x - 5)$
11. $(x + 3)(x + 8)$ **13.** $(y - 8)(y - 2)$ **15.** $(x - 5)(x - 2)$ **17.** $(x + 2)(x + 4)$ **19.** $(x + 8)(x - 3)$ **21.** Prime
23. $(y - 12)(y - 1)$ **25.** $(a - 4)(a + 2)$ **27.** $(r - 5)(r + 3)$ **29.** $(b - 9)(b - 2)$ **31.** Prime   **33.** $(q + 9)(q - 5)$
35. $(x - 10)(x + 3)$ **37.** $(x + 2)^2$ **39.** $(s - 4)^2$ **41.** $(p - 6)^2$ **43.** $(w - 15)(w - 3)$ **45.** $(x + 13)(x - 3)$
47. $(x - 5)(x + 4)$ **49.** $(y + 5)(y + 8)$ **51.** $(x + 16)(x - 4)$ **53.** Prime   **55.** $(x - 16)(x - 4)$ **57.** $(a - 9)(a - 11)$
59. $(x + 2)(x + 1)$ **61.** $(w + 9)(w - 2)$ **63.** $(x - 3y)(x - 5y)$ **65.** $(m - 3n)^2$ **67.** $(x + 6y)(x + 2y)$
69. $(m + 3n)(m - 8n)$ **71.** $6(x - 4)(x - 1)$ **73.** $5(x + 3)(x + 1)$ **75.** $2(x - 4)(x - 5)$ **77.** $b(b - 5)(b - 2)$
79. $3z(z - 9)(z + 2)$ **81.** $x(x + 4)^2$ **83.** $7(a - 2b)(a - 3b)$ **85.** $3r(r + 4t)(r - 2t)$ **87.** $x^2(x - 7)(x + 3)$ **89.** Both
negative; one positive and one negative; one positive and one negative; both positive   **91.** $x^2 - 12x + 32 = (x - 8)(x - 4)$
93. $x^2 - 2x - 35 = (x - 7)(x + 5)$ **95.** The GCF, 2, was not factored out first.   **97.** $(x + 0.4)(x + 0.2)$

99. $\left(x + \dfrac{1}{5}\right)\left(x + \dfrac{1}{5}\right) = \left(x + \dfrac{1}{5}\right)^2$ **101.** $(x + 8)(x - 32)$ **103.** 9   **104.** 19.6%   **105.** $2x^3 + x^2 - 16x + 12$

106. $3x + 2 - \dfrac{2}{x - 4}$ **107.** $(5x + 2)(4x - 3)$

Exercise Set 5.4   **1.** Factoring by grouping   **3.** Factor out the GCF   **5.** $(2x + 1)(x + 5)$ **7.** $(3x + 2)(x + 4)$
9. $(5x + 1)(x - 2)$ **11.** $(3r - 2)(r + 5)$ **13.** $(2z - 3)^2$ **15.** $(2z + 3)(3z - 4)$ **17.** Prime   **19.** $(8x + 3)(x + 2)$ **21.** Prime
23. $(5y - 1)(y - 3)$ **25.** $(7x + 1)(x + 6)$ **27.** $(2x + 5)(2x - 3)$ **29.** $(7t - 1)^2$ **31.** $(5z + 4)(z - 2)$ **33.** $(4y - 3)(y + 2)$
35. $(5x - 1)(2x - 5)$ **37.** $(5d + 4)(2d - 3)$ **39.** $2(4x + 1)(x - 6)$ **41.** $(7t + 3)(t + 1)$ **43.** $2(3x + 5)(x + 1)$

45. $x(2x + 1)(3x - 4)$ **47.** $4x(3x + 1)(x + 2)$ **49.** $2x(2x + 3)(x - 2)$ **51.** $8(2c - 1)(3c + 2)$ **53.** $4(2p + 3)(p - 1)$
55. $(8c + d)(c + 5d)$ **57.** $(5x + 3y)(3x - 2y)$ **59.** $2(2x - y)(3x + 4y)$ **61.** $(7p + 6q)(p + q)$ **63.** $(3m - 2n)(2m + n)$
65. $x(4x + 3y)(2x + y)$ **67.** $x^2(2x + y)(2x + 3y)$ **69.** $3x^2 - 20x - 7$; obtained by multiplying the factors.
71. $10x^2 + 35x + 15$; obtained by multiplying the factors.   **73.** $3t^4 + 11t^3 - 4t^2$; obtained by multiplying the factors.
75. a) Dividing the trinomial by binomial gives the second factor.   **b)** $6x + 11$ **77.** Factoring trinomials is the reverse process of
multiplying binomials.   **79.** $(6x - 5)(3x + 4)$ **81.** $(5x - 8)(3x - 20)$ **83.** $5(3a - 8)(7a + 4)$ **85.** $2x + 45$, the product of the
three first terms must equal $6x^3$, and the product of the constants must equal 2250.   **87.** 49   **88.** 155.2 mph
89. $12xy^2(3x^3y - 1 + 2x^4y^4)$ **90.** $(b + 12)(b - 8)$

Mid-Chapter Test: Sections 5.1–5.4
1. A factoring problem may be checked by multiplying the factors. [5.1]
2. $3xy^2$ [5.1]   **3.** $4a^2b(b^2 - 6a)$ [5.1]   **4.** $(d - 6)(5c - 3)$ [5.1]   **5.** $(2x + 9)(7x + 1)$ [5.1]   **6.** $(x + 4)(x + 7)$ [5.2]
7. $(x + 5)(x - 3)$ [5.2]   **8.** $(2a + 5b)(3a - b)$ [5.2]   **9.** $(5x - 2y)(x - 9)$ [5.2]   **10.** $4x(2x + 1)(x - 6)$ [5.2]
11. $(x - 3)(x - 7)$ [5.3]   **12.** $(t + 4)(t + 5)$ [5.3]   **13.** Prime [5.3]   **14.** $(x + 8)^2$ [5.3]   **15.** $(m + 5n)(m - 9n)$ [5.3]
16. $(3x + 2)(x + 5)$ [5.4]   **17.** $(4z - 3)(z - 2)$ [5.4]   **18.** Prime [5.4]   **19.** $(3x - 1)^2$ [5.4]   **20.** $3(2a - b)(a + b)$ [5.4]

Exercise Set 5.5
1. The difference of two squares   **3.** The sum of two squares   **5.** Factor out the greatest common factor
7. Prime   **9.** $9(b^2 + 9)$ **11.** $4(4m^2 + 9n^2)$ **13.** $(y + 5)(y - 5)$ **15.** $(9 + z)(9 - z)$ **17.** $(x + 7)(x - 7)$ **19.** $(x + y)(x - y)$
21. $(3y + 5z)(3y - 5z)$ **23.** $4(4a + 3b)(4a - 3b)$ **25.** $(6 + 7x)(6 - 7x)$ **27.** $(z^2 + 9x)(z^2 - 9x)$ **29.** $(5x^2 + 7y^2)(5x^2 - 7y^2)$
31. $(6m^2 + 7n)(6m^2 - 7n)$ **33.** $2(x^2 + 5y)(x^2 - 5y)$ **35.** $5(x^2 + 9)(x + 3)(x - 3)$ **37.** $(x + y)(x^2 - xy + y^2)$
39. $(x - y)(x^2 + xy + y^2)$ **41.** $(x + 4)(x^2 - 4x + 16)$ **43.** $(x - 3)(x^2 + 3x + 9)$ **45.** $(a + 1)(a^2 - a + 1)$
47. $(3x - 1)(9x^2 + 3x + 1)$ **49.** $(3a - 5)(9a^2 + 15a + 25)$ **51.** $(3 - 2y)(9 + 6y + 4y^2)$ **53.** $(4m + 3n)(16m^2 - 12mn + 9n^2)$
55. $(2a - 3b)(4a^2 + 6ab + 9b^2)$ **57.** $4(t - 3)^2$ **59.** $2(5x + 2)(5x - 3)$ **61.** $2(d + 4)^2$ **63.** $5(x - 3)(x + 1)$
65. $5(x + 2)(x - 2)$ **67.** $2(x + 5)(x - 5)$ **69.** $2y(x + 3)(x - 3)$ **71.** $3y^2(x + 1)(x^2 - x + 1)$ **73.** $2(x - 2)(x^2 + 2x + 4)$
75. $2(3x + 5)(3x - 5)$ **77.** $3r(2t^2 - 5t + 7)$ **79.** $2(3x - 2)(x + 4)$ **81.** $2r(s + 3)(s - 8)$ **83.** $(x + 2)(4x - 3)$
85. $25(b + 2)(b - 2)$ **87.** $a^3b^2(a + 2b)(a - 2b)$ **89.** $5x^2(x + 1)^2$ **91.** $x(x^2 + 25)$ **93.** $(y^2 + 4)(y + 2)(y - 2)$
95. $2(2m + 5)(4m^2 - 10m + 25)$ **97.** $(a + b)(c + 2)$ **99.** $9(1 + y^2)(1 + y)(1 - y)$ **101.** $2\blacklozenge^4(\blacklozenge^2 + 2\ast^2)$ **103.** Answers will vary.
105. $(x^2 - 3y^3)(x^4 + 3x^2y^3 + 9y^6)$ **107.** $(x - 3 + 2y)(x - 3 - 2y)$ **109.** $(x + y + 3)(x - y + 7)$
110. $x \le 1$;   **111.** 4 inches   **112.** -9 **113.** $\dfrac{8x^9}{27y^{12}}$ **114.** $\dfrac{1}{a^{11}}$

Exercise Set 5.6
1. Zero-factor property   **3.** $x = 0$ or $x = 2$ **5.** $x = -2$ or $x = 2$ **7.** $-8, 7$ **9.** $0, 8$ **11.** $-\dfrac{7}{3}, \dfrac{11}{2}$
13. $4, -4$ **15.** $0, 12$ **17.** $0, -7$ **19.** 4   **21.** $-2, -10$ **23.** $-2, -10$ **25.** $-3, 4$ **27.** $1, -24$ **29.** $-5, -6$ **31.** $5, -3$ **33.** $30, -1$
35. $-3, -\dfrac{5}{4}$ **37.** $-\dfrac{1}{3}, -2$ **39.** $\dfrac{2}{3}, -5$ **41.** $-4, 3$ **43.** $-\dfrac{3}{4}, \dfrac{1}{2}$ **45.** $8, -8$ **47.** $0, 25$ **49.** $10, -10$ **51.** $-2, 5$ **53.** $-2, \dfrac{1}{3}$ **55.** $\dfrac{3}{2}, 6$
57. $x^2 - 2x - 24 = 0$ (other answers are possible)   **59.** $x^2 - 6x = 0$ (other answers are possible)   **61. a)** $(2x - 1)$ and $(3x + 1)$
b) $6x^2 - x - 1 = 0$ **63.** They are constant multiples of one another.   **65.** $4, 5$ **67.** $0, 3, -2$ **69.** $\dfrac{17}{45}$ **70. a)** Identity
b) Contradiction   **71.** ≈ 738 people   **72.** $\dfrac{9}{p^8q^2}$ **73.** Monomial   **74.** Binomial   **75.** Not a polynomial   **76.** Trinomial

Exercise Set 5.7
1. Hypotenuse   **3.** $90°$ **5.** 8   **7.** 13   **9.** 10   **11.** 39   **13.** 13, 17   **15.** 6, 14   **17.** 16, 18   **19.** Width: 3 feet,
length: 12 feet   **21.** Width: 10 feet, length: 15 feet   **23.** 5 meters   **25.** 4 seconds   **27.** Yes   **29.** Yes   **31.** 16 feet   **33.** 41 feet
35. 6 feet, 8 feet, 10 feet   **37.** Width: 9 inches, length: 12 inches   **39.** Width: 7 feet, length: 24 feet   **41.** 30 books   **43. a)** 4   **b)** 9
45. 100 feet   **47.** 432 square feet   **49.** $0, 8, -4$ **51.** $x^3 - x^2 - 6x = 0$ **53.** 3 and 6   **55.** 20 and 50 units   **57.** $3x - 7$
58. $-x^2 + 7x - 4$ **59.** $6x^3 + x^2 - 10x + 4$ **60.** $2x - 3$ **61.** $2x - 3$

Chapter 5 Review Exercises
1. y^3 **2.** $3p$ **3.** $6c^2$ **4.** $5x^2y^2$ **5.** 1   **6.** s **7.** $x - 3$ **8.** $x + 5$ **9.** $7(x - 5)$
10. $5(7x - 1)$ **11.** $4y(6y - 1)$ **12.** $5p^2(11p - 4)$ **13.** $12ab(5a - 3b)$ **14.** $9xy(1 - 4x^2y)$ **15.** $4x^3y^2(5 + 2x^6y - 4x^2)$
16. Prime   **17.** Prime   **18.** $(5x + 3)(x - 2)$ **19.** $(t - 1)(3t + 4)$ **20.** $(4x - 3)(2x + 1)$ **21.** $(x + 6)(x + 2)$
22. $(x - 5)(x + 4)$ **23.** $(y - 6)^2$ **24.** $(y + 1)(3x + 2)$ **25.** $(a - b)(4a - 1)$ **26.** $(x + 6)(2x - 1)$ **27.** $(x + 3)(x - 2y)$
28. $(5x - y)(x + 4y)$ **29.** $(x + 3y)(4x - 5y)$ **30.** $(3a - 5b)(2a - b)$ **31.** $(p - 3)(q + 4)$ **32.** $(x - 3y)(3x + 2y)$
33. $(a + 2b)(7a - b)$ **34.** $(2x - 1)(4x + 3)$ **35.** $(x + 3)(x + 2)$ **36.** Prime   **37.** $(x + 2)(x + 9)$ **38.** $(n + 8)(n - 5)$
39. $(b + 5)(b - 4)$ **40.** $(x - 8)(x - 7)$ **41.** Prime   **42.** Prime   **43.** $x(x - 9)(x - 8)$ **44.** $t(t - 9)(t + 4)$
45. $(x + 3y)(x - 5y)$ **46.** $4x(x + 5y)(x + 3y)$ **47.** $(2x + 5)(x - 3)$ **48.** $(6x + 1)(x - 5)$ **49.** $(4x - 5)(x - 1)$
50. $(5m - 4)(m - 2)$ **51.** $(4y + 3)(4y - 1)$ **52.** $(5x - 2)(x - 6)$ **53.** Prime   **54.** $(5x - 3)(x + 8)$ **55.** $(2s + 1)(3s + 5)$
56. $(3x - 2)(2x + 5)$ **57.** $2(3x + 2)(2x - 1)$ **58.** $(5x - 3)^2$ **59.** $x(3x - 2)^2$ **60.** $2x(3x + 4)(3x - 2)$
61. $(2a - 3b)(2a - 5b)$ **62.** $(8a + b)(2a - 3b)$ **63.** $(x + 10)(x - 10)$ **64.** $(x + 6)(x - 6)$ **65.** $3(x + 4)(x - 4)$
66. $9(3x + y)(3x - y)$ **67.** $(9 + a)(9 - a)$ **68.** $(8 + x)(8 - x)$ **69.** $(4x^2 + 7y)(4x^2 - 7y)$ **70.** $(8x^3 + 7y^3)(8x^3 - 7y^3)$
71. $(a + b)(a^2 - ab + b^2)$ **72.** $(x - y)(x^2 + xy + y^2)$ **73.** $(x - 1)(x^2 + x + 1)$ **74.** $(x + 2)(x^2 - 2x + 4)$
75. $(a + 3)(a^2 - 3a + 9)$ **76.** $(b - 4)(b^2 + 4b + 16)$ **77.** $(5a + b)(25a^2 - 5ab + b^2)$ **78.** $(3 - 2y)(9 + 6y + 4y^2)$
79. $3(x - 4y)(x^2 + 4xy + 16y^2)$ **80.** $3(3x^2 + 5y)(3x^2 - 5y)$ **81.** $(x - 6)(x - 8)$ **82.** $3(x - 3)^2$ **83.** $5(q + 1)(q - 1)$

84. $8(x + 3)(x - 1)$ **85.** $4(y + 3)(y - 3)$ **86.** $(x - 9)(x + 3)$ **87.** $(3x - 1)^2$ **88.** $(7x - 3)(x + 4)$ **89.** $6(b - 1)(b^2 + b + 1)$
90. $y(x - 3)(x^2 + 3x + 9)$ **91.** $b(a + 3)(a - 5)$ **92.** $3x(2x + 3)(x + 5)$ **93.** $(x - 3y)(x - y)$ **94.** $(3m - 4n)(m + 2n)$
95. $(2x + 3y)^2$ **96.** $(5a + 7b)(5a - 7b)$ **97.** $(x + 2)(y - 7)$ **98.** $y^5(4 + 5y)(4 - 5y)$ **99.** $(2x - 3y)(3x + 7y)$

100. $2x(2x + 5y)(x + 2y)$ **101.** $x^2(4x + 1)(4x - 3)$ **102.** $(d^2 + 4)(d + 2)(d - 2)$ **103.** $0, -9$ **104.** $2, -6$ **105.** $-5, \dfrac{3}{4}$

106. $0, -7$ **107.** $0, -5$ **108.** $0, -3$ **109.** $-3, -6$ **110.** $1, 2$ **111.** $-4, 3$ **112.** $-1, -4$ **113.** $2, 4$ **114.** $3, -5$ **115.** $\dfrac{1}{4}, -\dfrac{3}{2}$

116. $-\dfrac{1}{3}, 4$ **117.** $2, -2$ **118.** $\dfrac{10}{7}, -\dfrac{10}{7}$ **119.** $\dfrac{3}{2}, \dfrac{1}{4}$ **120.** $\dfrac{3}{2}, \dfrac{5}{2}$ **121.** $a^2 + b^2 = c^2$ **122.** Hypotenuse   **123.** 10 feet   **124.** 12 meters

125. $9, 11$ **126.** $4, 14$ **127.** Width: 12 feet, length: 15 feet   **128.** 8 feet, 15 feet, 17 feet   **129.** 9 inches   **130.** 10 feet
131. 1 second   **132.** 80 dozen

Chapter 5 Practice Test   **1.** $3y^3$ [5.1]   **2.** $8p^2q^2$ [5.1]   **3.** $5x^2y^2(y - 3x^3)$ [5.1]   **4.** $4a^2b(2a - 3b + 7)$ [5.1]
5. $(x - 5)(4x + 1)$ [5.2]   **6.** $(a - 4b)(a - 5b)$ [5.2]   **7.** $(r + 8)(r - 3)$ [5.3]   **8.** $(5a - 3b)(5a + 2b)$ [5.4]   **9.** $4(x + 2)(x - 6)$ [5.4]
10. $y(2y - 3)(y + 1)$ [5.4]   **11.** $(3x + 2y)(4x - 3y)$ [5.4]   **12.** $(x + 3y)(x - 3y)$ [5.5]   **13.** $(x - 4)(x^2 + 4x + 16)$ [5.5]
14. $\dfrac{5}{6}, -3$ [5.6]   **15.** $0, 6$ [5.6]   **16.** $-8, 8$ [5.6]   **17.** -9 [5.6]   **18.** $3, 4$ [5.6]   **19.** $-2, -3$ [5.6]   **20.** 24 inches [5.7]   **21.** 34 feet [5.7]
22. $4, 9$ [5.7]   **23.** $12, 14$ [5.7]   **24.** Length: 6 meters, width: 4 meters [5.7]   **25.** 10 seconds [5.7]

Cumulative Review Test   **1.** -171 [1.9]   **2.** 9 [1.9]   **3.** $\$90$ [3.2]   **4. a)** 7   **b)** $-6, -0.2, \dfrac{3}{5}, 7, 0, -\dfrac{5}{9}, 1.34$ **c)** $\sqrt{7}, -\sqrt{2}$
d) $-6, -0.2, \dfrac{3}{5}, \sqrt{7}, -\sqrt{2}, 7, 0, -\dfrac{5}{9}, 1.34$ [1.4]   **5.** $|-8|$ [1.5]   **6.** 13 [2.5]   **7.** 19.2 [2.7]   **8.** $x \geq 5$, [2.8]

9. $y = -\dfrac{4}{3}x + \dfrac{7}{3}$ [2.6]   **10.** 6 liters [3.4]   **11.** $47, 49$ [3.2]   **12.** $\dfrac{1}{4}$ hours [3.4]   **13.** $\dfrac{16x^6}{81y^8}$ [4.1]

14. $\dfrac{16y^6}{x^3}$ [4.2]   **15.** $-3x^3 + 2x^2 + 6x - 12$ [4.4]   **16.** $3x^3 + 13x^2 - 28x + 12$ [4.5]   **17.** $x - 5 + \dfrac{21}{x + 3}$ [4.6]
18. $(r + 2)(q - 8)$ [5.2]   **19.** $(5x + 3)(x - 2)$ [5.4]   **20.** $7y(y + 3)(y - 3)$ [5.5]

Chapter 6

Exercise Set 6.1   **1.** Rational expression   **3.** Reduced to lowest terms   **5.** $x - 4$ **7.** -1 **9.** $4x - 1$ **11.** All real numbers
except 1   **13.** All real numbers except $x = 0$.   **15.** All real numbers except $n = 4$.   **17.** All real numbers except $x = 2$ and $x = -2$.
19. All real numbers except $x = \dfrac{3}{2}$ and $x = 3$.   **21.** All real numbers   **23.** All real numbers except $p = \dfrac{5}{2}$ and $p = -\dfrac{5}{2}$

25. $\dfrac{x}{3y^4}$ **27.** $\dfrac{4}{b^5}$ **29.** $\dfrac{5}{1 + y}$ **31.** 5   **33.** $\dfrac{x^2 + 6x + 7}{2}$ **35.** $r + 1$ **37.** $\dfrac{x}{x + 2}$ **39.** $\dfrac{z - 5}{z + 5}$ **41.** $\dfrac{x + 1}{x + 2}$ **43.** -1
45. $-(x + 2)$ **47.** $-\dfrac{x + 6}{2x}$ **49.** $-(x + 3)$ **51.** $\dfrac{1}{4m - 5}$ **53.** $\dfrac{x - 5}{x + 5}$ **55.** $2x - 3$ **57.** $x - 3$ **59.** $\dfrac{x - 4}{x + 4}$

61. $a^2 + 2a + 4$ **63.** $3s + 4t$ **65.** $\dfrac{3}{x - y}$ **67.** $\dfrac{☺}{5}$ **69.** $\dfrac{\Delta}{2\Delta + 9}$ **71.** -1 **73.** $x + 2; (x + 2)(x - 3) = x^2 - x - 6$

75. $x^2 + 9x + 20; (x + 5)(x + 4) = x^2 + 9x + 20$ **77.** Set the denominator equal to zero and then solve the resulting equation.

79. a) $x \neq 0, x \neq -5, x \neq \dfrac{3}{2}$ **b)** $\dfrac{1}{x(2x - 3)}$ **81.** 1, the numerator and denominator are identical.   **84.** $y = x - 4z$

85. $28°, 58°,$ and $94°$ **86.** $\dfrac{25}{81x^4y^2}$ **87.** $8x^2 - 10x - 19$ **88.** $3(a + 4)(a - 6)$ **89.** 13 inches

Exercise Set 6.2   **1.** Factor   **3.** Divide out   **5.** $x + 4$ **7.** $\dfrac{3}{19}$ **9.** $-\dfrac{15}{18}$ **11.** $\dfrac{5}{16}$ **13.** $\dfrac{3}{5}$ **15.** $-\dfrac{13}{48}$ **17.** $\dfrac{xy}{8}$ **19.** $\dfrac{70x^4}{y^6}$
21. $\dfrac{36x^9y^2}{25z^7}$ **23.** $\dfrac{-3x + 2}{3x + 2}$ **25.** 1   **27.** $\dfrac{1}{a^2 - b^2}$ **29.** 1   **31.** $\dfrac{x + 2}{x + 3}$ **33.** $x + 9$ **35.** $4x^2y$ **37.** $\dfrac{9z}{x}$ **39.** $\dfrac{11}{6ab^2}$ **41.** $6r^2$ **43.** $x + 9$
45. $\dfrac{x - 8}{x + 2}$ **47.** $\dfrac{x + 3}{x - 1}$ **49.** -1 **51.** $\dfrac{x + 1}{x - 4}$ **53.** $4x^2y^2$ **55.** $\dfrac{7c}{5ab^2}$ **57.** $\dfrac{3y^2}{a^2}$ **59.** $\dfrac{8mx^7}{3y^2}$ **61.** $\dfrac{2(x + 3)}{x(x - 3)}$ **63.** $\dfrac{7x}{y}$ **65.** $\dfrac{4}{m^4n^{11}}$
67. $\dfrac{r + 2}{r - 3}$ **69.** $\dfrac{x - 6}{x - 3}$ **71.** $\dfrac{2w - 7}{w + 1}$ **73.** $\dfrac{q - 5}{2q + 3}$ **75.** $\dfrac{2n + 3}{3n - 1}$ **77.** $\dfrac{1}{6\Delta^3}$ **79.** $\dfrac{\Delta + ☺}{9(\Delta - ☺)}$ **81.** $x^2 + 5x + 6$ **83.** $x^2 - 4x - 12$

85. $x^2 - 3x + 2$ **87.** Answers will vary.   **89.** $\dfrac{x - 1}{x - 3}$ **91.** $x^2 - 5x + 6, x^2 - x - 20$ **94.** 1 hour   **95.** $12x^4y^5z^{11}$

96. $2x^2 + x - 2 - \dfrac{2}{2x - 1}$ **97.** $6(x - 5)(x + 2)$ **98.** $5, -2$

Exercise Set 6.3 **1.** $\dfrac{3x+2}{y}$ **3.** True **5.** $x(x+6)$ **7.** $4x(x+3)$ **9. a)** The negative signs in $-(2x-9)$ was not distributed.

b) $\dfrac{4x-3-2x+9}{5x+4}$ **11. a)** The negative sign in $-(3x^2-4x+5)$ was not distributed. **b)** $\dfrac{8x-2-3x^2+4x-5}{x^2-4x+3}$ **13.** $\dfrac{5}{7}$

15. $\dfrac{5r-1}{4}$ **17.** $\dfrac{x+6}{x}$ **19.** $\dfrac{n+8}{n+1}$ **21.** $\dfrac{5x+9}{x-3}$ **23.** $\dfrac{t+3}{5t^2}$ **25.** $\dfrac{1}{x-4}$ **27.** $\dfrac{1}{m-3}$ **29.** $\dfrac{p-12}{p-5}$ **31.** $x-3$ **33.** $\dfrac{1}{2}$ **35.** 1

37. 4 **39.** $\dfrac{5}{x-2}$ **41.** $\dfrac{3}{4}$ **43.** $\dfrac{x-5}{x+2}$ **45.** $\dfrac{3x+2}{x-4}$ **47.** $\dfrac{6x+1}{x-8}$ **49.** 5 **51.** $9n$ **53.** $15x$ **55.** p^3 **57.** $3m-4$ **59.** $6t^2$ **61.** $36x^3y$

63. $18r^4s^7$ **65.** $m(m+2)$ **67.** $x(x+1)$ **69.** $4n-1$ or $1-4n$ **71.** $4k-5r$ or $-4k+5r$ **73.** $18q(q+1)$ **75.** $120x^2y^3$

77. $6(x+4)(x+2)$ **79.** $(x+1)(x+8)$ **81.** $(x-8)(x+3)(x+8)$ **83.** $(a-4)^2(a-3)$ **85.** $(x+5)(x+1)(x+3)$

87. $(x-3)^2$ **89.** $(x-6)(x-1)$ **91.** $(3t-2)(t+4)(3t-1)$ **93.** $(2x+1)^2(4x+3)$ **95.** $\dfrac{19}{35}$ **97.** $\dfrac{35}{36}$ **99.** $\dfrac{1}{18}$

101. x^2+x-9; the sum of the numerators must be $2x^2-5x-6$ **103.** $x^2+9x-10$; the sum of the numerators must be $5x-7$

105. 5☺ **107.** $(\Delta+3)(\Delta-3)$ **109.** Answers will vary. **111.** $\dfrac{-3x^2+12x}{x^2-25}$ **113.** $30x^{12}y^9$ **115.** $(x-4)(x+3)(x-2)$

117. $\dfrac{92}{45}$ or $2\dfrac{2}{45}$ **118.** $-\dfrac{1}{5}$ **119.** 2.25 ounces **120.** 70 hours **121.** 4.0×10^{11} **122.** $\dfrac{3}{2},-1$

Exercise Set 6.4 **1.** Opposites **3.** You are multiplying by 1 **5.** $12z^2$ **7.** $\dfrac{5x+2y}{xy}$ **9.** $\dfrac{t+10}{2t^2}$ **11.** $\dfrac{3x+8}{x}$ **13.** $\dfrac{3x+10}{5x^2}$

15. $\dfrac{45y+12x}{20x^2y^2}$ **17.** $\dfrac{4y^2+x}{y}$ **19.** $\dfrac{9a+7}{6a}$ **21.** $\dfrac{6x^2+2y}{xy}$ **23.** $\dfrac{45a^2-4b}{5a^2b}$ **25.** $\dfrac{13x-12}{x(x-3)}$ **27.** $\dfrac{11p+6}{p(p+3)}$ **29.** $\dfrac{-d^2+14d+25}{(d+1)(3d+5)}$

31. $\dfrac{6}{p-3}$ **33.** $\dfrac{14}{x+7}$ **35.** $\dfrac{a+16}{2(a-2)}$ **37.** $\dfrac{20x}{(x-5)(x+5)}$ **39.** $\dfrac{-7n-6}{3n(2n+1)}$ **41.** $\dfrac{15w+66}{2(w+5)(w+2)}$ **43.** $\dfrac{5z-16}{(z+4)(z-4)}$

45. $\dfrac{-x+6}{(x+2)(x-2)}$ **47.** $\dfrac{r+12}{(r-4)(r-6)}$ **49.** $\dfrac{6x-11}{(x+4)(x-2)}$ **51.** $\dfrac{x^2+3x-21}{(x+5)^2}$ **53.** $\dfrac{-a+16}{(a-8)(a-1)(a+2)}$

55. $\dfrac{9x+17}{(x+3)^2(x-2)}$ **57.** $\dfrac{3x^2-12x-5}{(2x+1)(3x-2)(x+3)}$ **59.** $\dfrac{2x^2-3x-4}{(4x+3)(x+2)(2x-1)}$ **61.** $\dfrac{1}{w-3}$ **63.** $\dfrac{6}{r-3}$ **65.** $-\dfrac{x+4}{4x}$

67. All real numbers except $x=0$. **69.** All real numbers except $x=4$ and $x=-6$. **71.** $\dfrac{7}{\Delta-2}$ **73.** All real numbers except

$a=-b$ and $a=0$. **75.** 0 **77.** $\dfrac{2x-3}{2-x}$ **79.** $\dfrac{6x+5}{(x+2)(x-3)(x+1)}$ **82.** ≈1.53 hours **83.** $x>-8$, $\xleftarrow{\ \oplus\ }{-8}\rightarrow$

84. $4x-3-\dfrac{6}{2x+3}$ **85.** -1

Mid-Chapter Test **1.** All real numbers except $x=\dfrac{2}{3}$ [6.1] **2.** All real numbers except $x=-2$ $x=7$ [6.1] **3.** 9 [6.1]

4. $\dfrac{2x+3}{3x-1}$ [6.1] **5.** $5r+6t$ [6.1] **6.** $\dfrac{6y^3}{x^3}$ [6.2] **7.** $-(m+4)$ or $-m-4$ [6.2] **8.** $x-2$ [6.2] **9.** $\dfrac{x+7}{2(x+1)}$ [6.2] **10.** $\dfrac{5x+2}{7x+3}$ [6.2]

11. $x-6$ [6.3] **12.** $x-3$ [6.3] **13.** $\dfrac{3t+2}{4t-1}$ [6.3] **14.** $3m(2m+1)$ [6.3] **15.** $(2x+3)(x-4)(x-5)$ [6.3] **16.** $\dfrac{13x-1}{10x}$ [6.4]

17. $-\dfrac{a^2+13a+23}{a^2-a-12}$ [6.4] **18.** $\dfrac{4x^2+17x-1}{2x^2+13x+6}$ [6.4] **19.** $\dfrac{x^2-7x-4}{(x+1)(x+2)(x-3)}$ [6.4]

20. Need common denominator of $x(x+1)$, $\dfrac{15x+8}{x(x+1)}$ [6.4]

Exercise Set 6.5 **1.** $\dfrac{5}{3}$ **3.** 5 **5.** $\dfrac{5}{16}$ **7.** $\dfrac{57}{32}$ **9.** $\dfrac{11}{6}$ **11.** $\dfrac{x^3y^2}{21}$ **13.** $\dfrac{2ab^3}{21c^2}$ **15.** $\dfrac{ab-a}{3+a}$ **17.** $\dfrac{3}{t}$ **19.** $\dfrac{5x-1}{4x-1}$ **21.** $\dfrac{m-n}{m}$

23. $-\dfrac{a}{b}$ **25.** -1 **27.** 1 **29.** $b-a$ **31.** $\dfrac{a^2+b}{b(b+1)}$ **33.** $\dfrac{x^2y}{y-x}$ **35.** $\dfrac{ab^2+b^2}{a^2(b+1)}$ **37. b)–c)** $-\dfrac{224}{155}$ **39. b)–c)** $\dfrac{x-y+6}{2x+2y-7}$

41. a) $\dfrac{\dfrac{5}{12x}}{\dfrac{8}{x^2}-\dfrac{4}{3x}}$ **b)** $\dfrac{5x}{96-16x}$ **43.** A complex number is a fraction that contains a fraction in its numerator or its denominator or both.

45. $\dfrac{y+x}{3xy}$ **47.** $x+y$ **49. a)** $\dfrac{2}{7}$ **b)** $\dfrac{4}{13}$ **51.** $\dfrac{a^3b+a^2b^3-ab^2}{a^3-ab^3+3b^2}$ **53.** $\dfrac{17}{2}$ **54.** A polynomial is an expression containing a finite

number of terms of the form ax^n where a is a real number and n is a whole number. **55.** $(x-5)(x-8)$ **56.** $\dfrac{x^2-9x+2}{(3x-1)(x+6)(x-3)}$

Exercise Set 6.6 **1.** Multiplied **3.** Rational expression **5.** Rational equation **7.** Yes **9.** 12 **11.** -6 **13.** 12 **15.** -4

17. -20 **19.** 30 **21.** 4 **23.** $\dfrac{25}{6}$ **25.** 36 **27.** 8 **29.** -8 **31.** 3 **33.** 4 **35.** 2 **37.** 5 **39.** No solution **41.** 7 **43.** 15

45. No solution   **47.** −3   **49.** 38   **51.** $-\frac{1}{3}, 3$ **53.** 6, −1   **55.** 4, −4   **57.** −4, −5   **59.** 4   **61.** $-\frac{5}{2}$ **63.** No solution   **65.** 24

67. −12   **69.** −3   **71.** 3   **73.** 5   **75.** 0   **77.** x can be any real number since the sum on the left is also $\frac{2x-4}{3}$.   **79.** 15 centimeters

81. −4   **83.** No, it is impossible for both sides of the equation to be equal.   **85.** More than $6\frac{1}{3}$ hours   **86.** 150 minutes   **87.** 40°, 140°
88. 6.8×10^8

Exercise Set 6.7   1. 1 complete task   **3.** $\frac{1}{5}$ **5.** length = 11 inches, width = 9 inches   **7.** base = 12 centimeters,

height = 7 centimeters   **9.** Base: 8 feet   **11.** $\frac{8}{9}, 8$ **13.** 7   **15.** 9 miles per hour   **17.** 15 miles   **19.** 150 miles per hour, 600 miles per hour

21. No wake zone: ≈ 1.83 miles, zone to Island: ≈ 34.77 miles   **23.** 3 hours at 600 miles per hour and 2 hours at 550 miles per hour

25. 1200 feet   **27.** $3\frac{3}{7}$ hours   **29.** 4 hours   **31.** 24 minutes   **33.** 120 minutes or 2 hours.   **35.** 60 minutes or 1 hour   **37.** $8\frac{3}{4}$ days

39. $\frac{6}{5}$ hours or 1 hour, 12 minutes   **41.** 300 hours   **43.** 3 or $\frac{1}{2}$ **45.** 8 pints   **47.** $-\frac{3}{2}x - \frac{27}{2}$ **48.** $(y-1)(y+6)$ **49.** 1

50. $\dfrac{3x^2 - 9x - 15}{(2x+3)(3x-5)(3x+1)}$

Exercise Set 6.8   1. $y = \frac{k}{x}$ **3.** Inversely   **5.** Direct   **7.** Inverse   **9.** Inverse   **11.** Direct   **13.** Direct   **15.** 440   **17.** $\frac{1}{5}$
19. 75   **21.** 2.5   **23.** 20   **25.** 3.5   **27.** 36   **29.** 80   **31.** It will be doubled.   **33.** It will be halved.   **35.** 110 miles   **37.** $1900
39. $57   **41.** 4.2 hours   **43.** 1000 people   **45.** 1296 hp   **47.** ≈ 452.16 square inches   **49.** ≈ 44.44 ohms   **51.** $50

53. 6400 cubic centimeters   **55.** Pounds per inch   **57. a)** $x = kyz$ **b)** 216   **59.** $2x - 3 + \frac{6}{4x+9}$ **60.** $(z-2)(y+8)$
61. −4, 2   **62.** $x + 8$

Chapter 6 Review Exercises   1. All real numbers except $x = 19$ **2.** All real numbers except $x = 3$ and $x = 5$

3. All real numbers except $x = \frac{1}{5}$ and $x = -1$ **4.** $\frac{1}{x-8}$ **5.** $x^2 + 5x + 12$ **6.** $3x + y$ **7.** $x + 4$ **8.** $a + 9$ **9.** $-(2x+1)$

10. $\frac{b-2}{b+2}$ **11.** $\frac{x-3}{x-2}$ **12.** $\frac{x-8}{2x+3}$ **13.** $\frac{5}{12b^2}$ **14.** $12xz^2$ **15.** $\frac{8b^3c^4}{a^2}$ **16.** $-\frac{2}{9}$ **17.** $-\frac{2}{3}$ **18.** 1   **19.** $\frac{36x^2}{y}$ **20.** $\frac{20z}{x^3}$ **21.** $\frac{6}{a-b}$

22. $\frac{1}{8(a+3)}$ **23.** 1   **24.** $6y(x-y)$ **25.** $\frac{n-2}{n+5}$ **26.** 4   **27.** 5   **28.** $\frac{4}{x+10}$ **29.** $4h - 3$ **30.** $3x + 4$ **31.** 24   **32.** $x + 3$

33. $20x^2y^3$ **34.** $x(x-3)$ **35.** $(n+5)(n-4)$ **36.** $x(x+2)$ **37.** $(r+s)(r-s)$ **38.** $x - 9$ **39.** $(x+7)(x-5)(x+2)$

40. $\frac{3y^2+10}{6y^2}$ **41.** $\frac{12x+y}{4xy}$ **42.** $\frac{5x^2-18y}{3x^2y}$ **43.** $\frac{7x+12}{x+2}$ **44.** $\frac{x^2-2xy-y^2}{xy}$ **45.** $\frac{9x+8}{x(x+4)}$ **46.** $\frac{-x-4}{3x(x-2)}$ **47.** $\frac{z+14}{(z+5)^2}$

48. $\frac{2x-8}{(x-3)(x-5)}$ **49.** $\frac{5x+38}{(x+6)(x+2)}$ **50.** $\frac{3x-8}{x-4}$ **51.** $\frac{5ab+10b}{a-2}$ **52.** $\frac{3x-1}{(x+3)(x-3)}$ **53.** $\frac{6p^3}{q}$ **54.** $\frac{2x+2}{(x+2)(x-3)(x-2)}$

55. $\frac{8x-29}{(x+2)(x-7)(x+7)}$ **56.** $\frac{x}{x+y}$ **57.** $\frac{3(x+3y)}{5(x-3y)}$ **58.** $a - 3$ **59.** $\frac{3a^2-8a+3}{(a+1)(a-1)(3a-5)}$ **60.** $\frac{4x-8}{x}$ **61.** $\frac{64}{9}$ **62.** $\frac{2}{3}$

63. $\frac{bc}{3}$ **64.** $\frac{8x^3z^2}{y^3}$ **65.** $\frac{ab-a}{a+1}$ **66.** $\frac{r^2s+7}{s^3}$ **67.** $\frac{3x+2}{x(5x-1)}$ **68.** $\frac{4}{x}$ **69.** x **70.** $\frac{3a+1}{4}$ **71.** $\frac{-x+1}{x+1}$ **72.** $\frac{8x^2-x^2y}{y(y-x)}$ **73.** 13

74. 6   **75.** 12   **76.** 20   **77.** −16   **78.** $\frac{1}{2}$ **79.** −6   **80.** 28   **81.** No solution   **82.** 2.4 hours   **83.** $16\frac{4}{5}$ hours   **84.** $\frac{1}{6}, 1$

85. Robert: 2.1 miles per hour, Tran: 5.6 miles per hour   **86.** 273 milligrams   **87.** 12 cubic inches

Chapter 6 Practice Test   1. 1 [6.1]   **2.** $\frac{x^2+x+1}{x+1}$ [6.1]   **3.** $\frac{8x^2z}{y}$ [6.2]   **4.** $a + 3$ [6.2]   **5.** $\frac{x^2-6x+9}{(x+3)(x+2)}$ [6.2]   **6.** −1 [6.2]

7. $\frac{x-2y}{5}$ [6.2]   **8.** $\frac{3}{y+5}$ [6.2]   **9.** $-\frac{m+6}{m-5}$ [6.2]   **10.** $\frac{3x-1}{4y}$ [6.3]   **11.** $\frac{7x^2-6x-13}{x+3}$ [6.3]   **12.** $\frac{2y^2-8}{xy^3}$ [6.4]   **13.** $-\frac{2z+15}{z-5}$ [6.4]

14. $\frac{-1}{(x+4)(x-4)}$ [6.4]   **15.** $\frac{25}{28}$ [6.5]   **16.** $\frac{x^2+x^2y}{7y}$ [6.5]   **17.** $\frac{4x+3}{9-5x}$ [6.5]   **18.** 2 [6.6]   **19.** $-\frac{12}{7}$ [6.6]   **20.** 12 [6.6]
21. 6 hours [6.7]   **22.** 1 [6.7]   **23.** Base: 6 inches, height: 10 inches [6.7]   **24.** 2 miles [6.7]   **25.** ≈ 1.13 feet [6.8]

Cumulative Review Test   1. 121 [1.9]   **2.** $\frac{17}{8}$ [2.5]   **3.** $\frac{125x^3}{y^6}$ [4.1]   **4.** $c + (c + 0.018c)$ [3.1]   **5.** $8x^2 + 5x + 14$ [4.4]

6. $6n^3 - 23n^2 + 26n - 15$ [4.5]   **7.** $(8a-5)(a-1)$ [5.2]   **8.** $13(x+3)(x-1)$ [5.3]   **9.** 36 [1.9]   **10.** $x \le -4$, ⟵━━━━⟶ [2.8]
 $\qquad\qquad\qquad\qquad\qquad\qquad\qquad\qquad\qquad\qquad\qquad\qquad\qquad\qquad\qquad\qquad\;\;-4$

11. $\frac{1}{2}x - \frac{19}{4}$ [4.6]   **12.** $4, \frac{3}{2}$ [5.6]   **13.** $\frac{x+4}{2x+1}$ [6.2]   **14.** $\frac{r^2-8r-6}{(r+2)(r-5)}$ [6.4]   **15.** $\frac{10x-18}{(x-5)(x+2)(x+3)}$ [6.4]

16. $-\frac{3}{2}$ [6.6]   **17.** No solution [6.6]   **18.** $3000 [3.2]   **19.** 20 pounds sunflower seed, 30 pounds premixed assorted seed mix; [3.4]

20. First leg: 3.25 miles, second leg: 9.5 miles; [3.4]

Chapter 7

Exercise Set 7.1 **1.** x-coordinate, y-coordinate **3.** y-axis **5.** Line **7.** Roman numerals **9.** II **11.** IV **13.** I **15.** III
17. III **19.** II **21.** $A(3,1); B(-3,0); C(1,-3);$ **23.** **25.** **27.** The points are collinear.

$D(-2, -3); E(0,3); F\left(\dfrac{3}{2}, -1\right)$

29. $(-5, -3)$ is not on the line

31. a) Point c) does not satisfy the equation.
b)

33. a) Point a) does not satisfy the equation.
b)

35. a) Point a) does not satisfy the equation.
b)

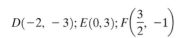

37. 2 **39.** -4 **41.** 6 **43.** $\dfrac{1}{2}$ **45. a)** Latitude, 16°N; Longitude, 56°W **b)** Latitude, 29°N; Longitude, 90.5°W **c)** Latitude 26°N; Longitude, 80.5°W **d)** Answers will vary. **47.** 0

49. To show that the line extends in both directions **55.** 21 **56.** $y = \dfrac{3x-4}{2} = \dfrac{3}{2}x - 2$ **57.** $16x^{12}$ **58.** $(x+3)(x-9)$

59. 0, 7 **60.** $\dfrac{5x+18}{3x^2}$

Exercise Set 7.2 **1.** x-axis **3.** y-intercept **5.** $(x,0)$ **7.** Horizontal **9.** 3 **11.** 5 **13.** 3 **15.** 2 **17.** $\dfrac{8}{3}$ **19.** -10

21. **23.** **25.** **27.** **29.** **31.**

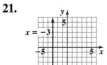
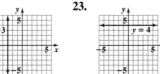
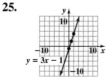
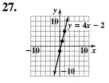

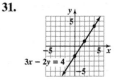

33. **35.** **37.** **39.** **41.**

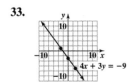

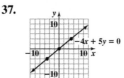
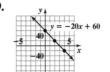

43. **45.** **47.** **49.** **51.** **53.**

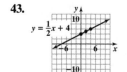

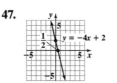
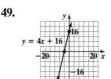
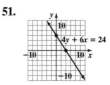
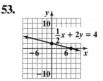

55. **57.** **59.** **61.** **63.**

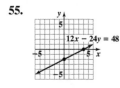
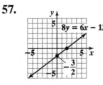
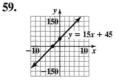
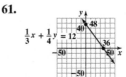
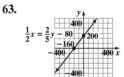

65. $x = 3$ **67.** $y = 3$ **69.** 5 **71.** 2 **73.** Yes

75. a) $C = 0.10n + 15$
b)

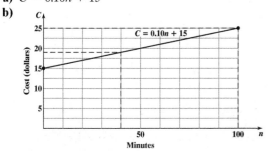

c) $19 **d)** 100 minutes

77. a) $C = m + 40$
b)

c) $100 **d)** 30 miles

79. a)

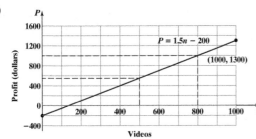

b) $550   **c)** 800 videos   **81.** 3,2   **83.** 6,4

85. a)

b) (2,3)   **c)** Yes   **d)** No

88. -57 **89.** 6.67 ounces

90. $1400   **91.** $\dfrac{15yz^2}{x}$

92. $\dfrac{2x^2 - 3x - 5}{(x-2)(x-3)}$ **93.** $5, \dfrac{7}{3}$

Exercise Set 7.3   **1.** Rise   **3.** Ratio   **5.** Horizontal   **7.** Parallel   **9.** Equal   **11.** 2   **13.** $\dfrac{1}{2}$ **15.** 0   **17.** 1   **19.** Undefined

21. $-\dfrac{3}{8}$ **23.** $\dfrac{2}{3}$ **25.** $m = 2$ **27.** $m = -2$ **29.** $m = -\dfrac{4}{7}$ **31.** $m = \dfrac{7}{4}$ **33.** $m = 0$ **35.** $m = -\dfrac{2}{3}$ **37.** Undefined

39.

41.

43.

45.

47.

49. Parallel   **51.** Neither
53. Perpendicular
55. Neither   **57.** Neither
59. Parallel   **61.** Parallel
63. Perpendicular **65.** 3

67. $\dfrac{1}{4}$ **69.** First   **71. a)** 60   **b)** 75   **73.** -4 **75.** $-\dfrac{1}{8}$ **77.** 3

79. a)
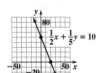

b) $AC, m = \dfrac{3}{5}; CB, m = -2; DB, m = \dfrac{3}{5}; AD, m = -2$ **c)** Yes, opposite sides are parallel.

81. a) $AB, m = 4; BC, m = -2; CD, m = 4$ **b)** $[4 + (-2) + 4]/3 = 2$
c) $AD, m = 2$ **d)** Yes   **e)** Answers will vary.

83. 2   **84. a)** -3 **b)** 0   **85.** $2x + 16$

86. -3 **87.** x-intercept: $(6, 0)$; y-intercept: $(0, -10)$

Mid-Chapter Test   **1.** IV [7.1]   **2.**

[7.1]   **3. b)** [7.1]
4. -4 [7.1]
5. 3 [7.1]
6. A graph of an equation in two variables is an illustration of a set of points whose coordinates satisfy the equation. [7.1]

7.

[7.2]   **8.**

[7.2]   **9.**

[7.2]   **10.**

[7.2]   **11.**

[7.2]

12.

[7.2]   **13.** $-\dfrac{2}{7}$ [7.3]   **16.**

[7.3]   **17.**

[7.3]   **18.** Neither [7.3]
19. Perpendicular [7.3]
20. 10 [7.3]

14. 0 [7.3]

15. Undefined [7.3]

Exercise Set 7.4   **1.** Point-slope   **3.** Slope-intercept   **5.** y-intercept   **7.** Slope   **9.** 3, (0,1)   **11.** $\dfrac{4}{3}, (0, -7)$

13. 1, (0, -3)   **15.** 3, (0, 2)   **17.** 2, (0, 0)   **19.** 2, (0, -3)

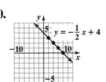

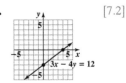

21. $\dfrac{5}{2}, (0, -5)$ **23.** $-\dfrac{1}{2}, \left(0, \dfrac{3}{2}\right)$ **25.** 3, (0, 4)   **27.** $\dfrac{3}{2}, (0, 2)$

29. $y = x - 2$ **31.** $y = -\frac{1}{3}x + 2$ **33.** $y = -3x - 5$ **35.** $y = \frac{1}{3}x + 5$ **37.** Parallel   **39.** Perpendicular   **41.** Parallel

43. Neither   **45.** Perpendicular   **47.** Neither   **49.** $y = 3x + 2$ **51.** $y = -3x - 7$ **53.** $y = \frac{1}{2}x - \frac{5}{2}$ **55.** $y = \frac{2}{3}x + 6$

57. $y = 3x + 10$ **59.** $y = -\frac{3}{2}x$ **61.** $y = \frac{1}{2}x - 2$ **63.** $y = 7.4x - 4.5$ **65. a)** $y = 5x + 60$ **b)** $210

67. a) Slope-intercept form   **b)** Point-slope form   **c)** Point-slope form
69. a) No   **b)** $y + 4 = 2(x + 5)$ **c)** $y - 12 = 2(x - 3)$ **d)** $y = 2x + 6$ **e)** $y = 2x + 6$ **f)** Yes
71. a) 1.465   **b)** $f = 1.465m$ **c)** ≈ 223.7 feet per second   **d)** 150 feet per second   **e)** 55 miles per hour

73. $y = -2x + 5$ **75.** $y = \frac{3}{4}x + 5$ **78.** $<$ **79.** $r = \dfrac{i}{pt}$ **80.** $x \le -4$, 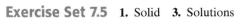   **81.** $(x - 4y)(x + 3y)$ **82.** -5

Exercise Set 7.5   **1.** Solid   **3.** Solutions

5.   **7.**   **9.**   **11.**   **13.**

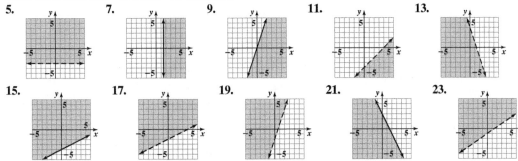

15.   **17.**   **19.**   **21.**   **23.**

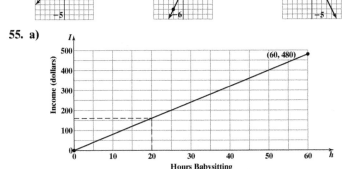

25. a) No   **b)** No   **c)** Yes   **d)** Yes   **27. a)** Less than or equal to   **b)** Greater than or equal to   **c)** Less than or equal to
d) Greater than or equal to   **29.** Points on the line satisfy the $=$ part of the inequality.   **31.** No, it could be a solution to
$ax + by = c$.   **33.** No, the location of an ordered pair which satisfies the first inequality lies on one side of the line while an ordered
pair which satisfies the other inequality lies either on the line or on the other side of the line.   **35.** Shading on opposite sides of the line

37. a) 2   **b)** $2, 0$ **c)** $2, -5, 0, \frac{2}{5}, -6.3, -\frac{23}{34}$ **d)** $\sqrt{7}, \sqrt{3}$ **e)** $2, -5, 0, \sqrt{7}, \frac{2}{5}, -6.3, \sqrt{3}, -\frac{23}{34}$ **38.** 2   **39.** $2x - 3 + \dfrac{5}{x}$ **40.** $\dfrac{1}{x + 2y}$

Exercise Set 7.6   **1.** Domain   **3.** Relation   **5.** Vertical line   **7.** x-component   **9.** Function, Domain: $\{1, 2, 3, 4, 5\}$, Range: $\{1, 2, 3, 4, 5\}$
$3, 4, 5\}$ **11.** Relation, Domain: $\{1, 2, 3, 5, 7\}$, Range: $\{-2, 0, 2, 4, 5\}$ **13.** Function, Domain: $\{0, 1, 3, 4, 5\}$, Range: $\{-4, -1, 0, 1, 2\}$
15. Relation, Domain: $\{0, 1, 3\}$, Range: $\{-3, 0, 2, 5\}$ **17.** Function, Domain: $\{0, 1, 2, 3, 4\}$, Range: $\{3\}$ **19. a)** $\{(1, 4), (2, 5), (3, 5), (4, 7)\}$
b) Function   **21. a)** $\{(-5, 4), (0, 7), (6, 9), (6, 3)\}$ **b)** Not a function   **23.** Function   **25.** Not a function   **27.** Function
29. Function   **31.** Not a Function   **33.** Function   **35. a)** 14   **b)** -2 **37. a)** 8   **b)** 8   **39. a)** 4   **b)** 6   **41. a)** 3   **b)** 8
43.   **45.**   **47.**   **49.**   **51.** $c = 0.35n$
53. Yes, it passes the vertical line test.

55. a)

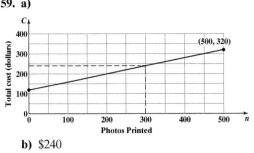

b) $160

57. a)

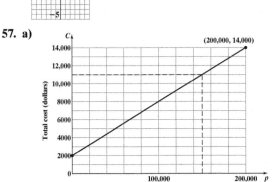

b) $11,000

59. a)

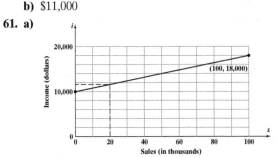

b) $240

61. a)

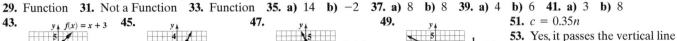

b) $11,600

63. a) No; each x must have exactly one y.   **b)** No; a y may correspond to more than one x.   **65.** Yes, it passes the vertical line test.
67. No, the vertical line $x = 1$ intersects the graph at more than one point.   **69. a)** $\dfrac{29}{8}$ **b)** $\dfrac{29}{9}$ **c)** 3.88   **73.** $\dfrac{1}{63}$ **74.** -14

75. 13 miles   **76.** $(5x + 7y)(5x - 7y)$ **77.** $\dfrac{4x^2}{y}$ **78.** A graph is an illustration of a set of points whose coordinates satisfy an equation.

Chapter 7 Review Exercises

1.
2. Not collinear

3. a), b), and **d)**

4. a) -7 **b)** -4 **c)** 6 **d)** $\dfrac{8}{3}$

5. 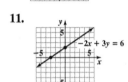   **6.**   **7.**   **8.**   **9.**   **10.**

11.   **12.**   **13.** 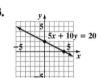   **14.** 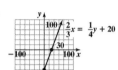   **15.** $-\dfrac{9}{5}$ **16.** $-\dfrac{1}{12}$

17. -2
18. 0
19. Undefined

20. The slope of a line is the ratio of the vertical change to the horizontal change between any two points on the line.   **21.** -2

22. $\dfrac{1}{4}$ **23.** Neither   **24.** Perpendicular   **25. a)** 18   **b)** 10   **26.** $m = -\dfrac{6}{7}, (0, 3)$ **27.** Slope is undefined, no y-intercept

28. $m = 0, (0, -3)$ **29.** $y = 3x - 3$ **30.** $y = -\dfrac{1}{2}x + 2$ **31.** Parallel   **32.** Perpendicular   **33.** $y = 3x + 1$ **34.** $y = -\dfrac{2}{3}x + 4$

35. $y = 2$ **36.** $x = 4$ **37.** $y = -\dfrac{7}{2}x - 3$ **38.** $x = -5$

39.   **40.**   **41.**   **42.** 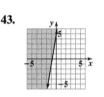   **43.**   **44.**

45. Function, Domain: $\{1, 2, 3, 4, 6\}$, Range: $\{-3, -1, 2, 4, 5\}$ **46.** Not a function, Domain: $\{3, 4, 6, 7\}$, Range: $\{0, 1, 2, 5\}$
47. Not a function, Domain: $\{3, 4, 5, 6\}$, Range: $\{-3, 1, 2\}$ **48.** Function, Domain: $\{-2, 3, 4, 5, 9\}$, Range: $\{-2\}$
49. a) $\{(1, 3), (4, 5), (7, 2), (9, 2)\}$ **b)** Function   **50. a)** $\{(4, 1)(6, 3), (6, 5), (8, 7)\}$ **b)** Not a function
51. a) Domain: $\{$Mary, Pete, George, Carlos$\}$, Range: $\{$Apple, Orange, Grape$\}$ **b)** Not a function
52. a) Domain: $\{$Sarah, Jacob, Kristen, Erin$\}$, Range: $\{$Seat 1, Seat 2, Seat 3, Seat 4$\}$ **b)** Not a function
53. a) Domain: $\{$Blue, Green, Yellow$\}$, Range: $\{$Paul, Maria, Lalo, Duc$\}$ **b)** Function
54. a) Domain: $\{1, 2, 3, 4\}$, Range: $\{A, B, C\}$ **b)** Function   **55.** Function   **56.** Function   **57.** Not a function   **58.** Function
59. a) 5   **b)** -31 **60. a)** 9   **b)** -39 **61. a)** -4 **b)** -8 **62. a)** 12   **b)** 76   **63.** Yes, it passes the vertical line test.
64. Yes, each year corresponds to exactly one y-value.   **65.**   **66.**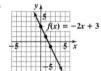

67. a)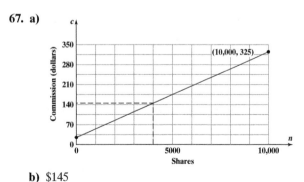

b) $145

68. a)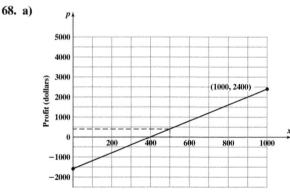

b) $400

Chapter 7 Practice Test **1.** A graph is an illustration of the set of points whose coordinates satisfy an equation. [7.1]
2. a) IV **b)** II [7.1] **3. a)** $ax + by = c$ **b)** $y = mx + b$ **c)** $y - y_1 = m(x - x_1)$ [7.1–7.4]

4. b) and d) [7.1] **5.** $-\dfrac{4}{3}$ [7.3] **6.** $\dfrac{4}{9}, \left(0, -\dfrac{5}{3}\right)$ [7.4] **7.** $y = -x - 1$ [7.4]

8. [7.2] **9.** [7.2] **10.** [7.2] **11. a)** $y = \dfrac{1}{2}x - 2$ **b)** [7.2]

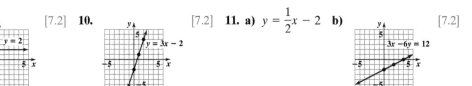

12. [7.2] **13.** $y = 4x - 13$ [7.4] **14.** $y = -\dfrac{3}{7}x + \dfrac{2}{7}$ [7.4] **15.** The lines are parallel since they have the same slope but different y-intercepts. [7.3]

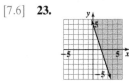

16. [7.4] **17.** [7.4] **18.** A set of ordered pairs in which each first component corresponds to exactly one second component. [7.4]
19. a) Not a function; 3, a first component, is paired with more than one value
b) Domain: $\{1, 3\,5, 6\}$, Range: $\{-4, 0, 2, 3, 5\}$ [7.6]

20. a) Function; it passes the vertical line test **b)** Not a function; a vertical line can be drawn that intersects the graph at more than one point [7.6] **21. a)** 15 **b)** 10 [7.6]

22. [7.6] **23.** [7.5] **24.** [7.5]

25. a) **b)** \$450 [7.2]

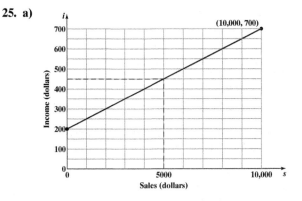

Cumulative Review Test **1. a)** $\{1, 2, 3, 4, \ldots\}$ **b)** $\{0, 1, 2, 3, 4, \ldots\}$ [1.4] **2. a)** Distributive property
b) Commutative property of addition [1.10] **3.** 20 [2.5] **4.** All real numbers [2.5]
5. $x < -5$, [2.8] **6.** \$4.00 [2.7] **7.** width: 5 feet, length: 13 feet [3.3] **8.** 2 hours [3.4]

9. $\dfrac{1}{x^{15}}$ [4.2] **10.** 6.523×10^2 [4.3] **11.** $2(x - 5)(x - 1)$ [5.3] **12.** $(2a - 5)(2a + 7)$ [5.4] **13.** 0, 7 [5.6] **14.** $-\dfrac{1}{2}$ [6.1]

15. $\dfrac{8x}{3x + 7}$ [6.2] **16.** -6 [6.6] **17.** [7.2] **18.** [7.4] **19.** $y - 2 = 3(x - 5)$ [7.4]

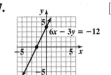

20. a) No **b)** Yes [7.6]

Applications Index

Agricultural

blueberry picking, 390
clearing a field, 401
cows at dairy, 460
insecticide application, 154
picking peaches, 388
plowing a field, 383–384

Animals/pets/nature

albino python, 29
animal art, 192
birdfood, 213–214
bird seed, 402
black bear, 184
blue heron, 154
collecting frogs, 192
dolphin, 214
exercise area, 134–135
fenced-in area, 199
Gaudy Leaf Frog, 196
horses, 184
hummingbird food, 359
oyster population, 249
poison dart frog, 196
race horse, 215
toucan, 183
water trough, 198–199

Automotive/motor vehicle

antifreeze, 214
auto exports, 194
auto loan, 133, 141
auto race, 133–134
auto registration, 453
buying tires, 17
car cost, 75, 183, 184, 185
car purchase, 497
Daytona 500 race, 312, 441
distance and speed, 429
driver education, 196
fastest car, 142
gas mileage, 17
gas needed, 220
gasoline costs, 193, 216
motorcycle sales, 18, 182
new car purchase, 194, 217
stopping distance on wet pavement, 429
taxi ride, 17, 455

tire wear, 156, 211
truck mileage, 154
truck rental, 176, 183, 193, 196, 197, 419, 502, 503
truck weight, 30
Viper cost, 185

Aviation/aeronautical

airfare, 194
airline flights, 211
commercial airlines, 18
fastest plane, 142
flight times, 215
jet flight, 387–388
jet speeds, 211
Spaceship Earth, 137

Banking

bank assets, 184
checking account, 16, 41
overdrawn checking account, 49
payroll checks, 389
savings account, 133, 141, 218
simple interest loan, 141

Business

advertising, 325
cleaning service, 385
clients, 197
commissions, 16
copy centers, 218
copy machine, 169, 193, 389
earnings, 184, 195, 250
employees, 184
hours worked, 162
minimum wage, 152
new headquarters, 194, 195
profits, 182, 183, 219, 461
restaurants, 219
salaries, 183, 193, 194, 213
salary comparison, 217
salary plans, 185, 191, 195, 197
staff increase, 218
tree chipping, 389
video store profit, 419
wage cut, 195
window cleaning, 395

Children

adoption, 18
age, 180, 182, 216
gaining height, 28
gaining weight, 27, 182
height difference, 183
model car, 169
model train, 154
newborn length, 155
weight difference, 184

Computer/technology

computer processor, 16
computer purchase, 16
computer speed, 248
computer supply, 193
fastest computer, 246–247
Internet plans, 379
laptop computer, 142, 330
laser printers, 194, 219
packaging computers, 387
photo printer, 189, 453
plasma TV, 88
processor speed, 10
spam, 184
video cassette, 185

Education

academy enrollment, 460
college tuition, 394
exams, 19
final exam review, 88
freshman majors, 88
level of education, 19
math scores, 17–18
mean grade, 15
teacher pay, 195
test grades, 16, 19, 88, 196
test score, 66
time to bachelor's degree, 29

Electronics

cable bill, 193, 213
cable laying, 154, 219
cable (television), 194, 213
circuit boards, 192–193
DVD player, 142
entertainment center, 30
plasma television, 88, 142

radio listeners, 90
satellite television, 194
television commercials, 90
television cost, 197, 218
television viewing, 193

Entertainment

Jeopardy!, 18–19
John Grisham novel, 154
kiddie train, 394
movie favorites, 144–145
movie ticket sales, 248–249
music albums, 193
Rock and Roll Hall of Fame, 213
singing sensation, 454
Spaceship Earth, 137
Wizard of Oz, 330

Environment. *See also* Weather/temperature

biggest trees, 245–246
carbon dioxide levels, 220
earthquakes, 211
energy values, 16
gravel pit volume, 75
oil consumption, 193, 195
sand and water table, 327–328

Family

stay-at-home parents, 13–14
thank-you notes, 386

Financial/investment

credit card, 49, 66
financial planning, 195
inflation, 88
interest, 395, 430
investments, 204–205
money owed, 66
net profit or loss, 47, 49
savings, 133, 141, 155, 218
simple interest, 170, 213, 241, 419
stocks, 50, 59, 154, 184, 213, 461
surplus and deficit, 49–50

Food/nutrition/cooking

apple pie, 156
bagels, 217
baking brownies, 335
baking turkey, 29, 395
beef Wellington, 214
bulk candies, 214, 219
caloric intake, 190
calories, 182
candies, 122, 197, 214
candy mixture, 294
cereal box, 143
Chesapeake Bay oysters, 249
chicken soup, 280, 462
chocolate bars, 132
chopped onion, 29
cost of meal, 185, 195
cream pie weight, 29
delivery, 389
eating out, 219
favorite doughnuts, 153
fortune cookies, 248
ground beef, 218
Hawaiian Punch, 214
holiday punch, 218
juice, 214, 496
ketchup, 169
mashed potatoes, 31
nuts, 219
onion soup, 154
orange cost, 453
peanut butter pie, 170
peanuts, 40
pizza, 136
Starbucks coffee, 214
triangles of dough, 387
tuna fish, 168

Gardening

banyan tree, 142
biggest trees, 245–246
border, 202
fertilizer, 154
flower garden, 168, 389
grass growth, 75
grass seed, 207, 213
grub problem, 189
insecticide application, 154, 214
landscaping, 217
lawn grub problem, 189
lawn mower, 23, 395
plant food, 214
plants, 184
rectangular fence, 41
rectangular garden, 217, 329, 330
soil, 183

soil delivery, 183
topsoil, 155, 184, 213
tree chipping, 389
triangular garden, 387
watering plants, 388

Geography

Death Valley, California, 58
earthquakes, 211
high mountain, 49
land area, 184
latitude and longitude, 410
Leadville, Colorado, 58
maps, 154
map scale, 169
Niagara Falls water flow, 248
population, 152, 182, 185, 192, 196, 248, 429, 453
population growth in Las Vegas, 183
population in China, 182
population median age, 183
population projection, 249

Home/home decorating

assessed value, 184
bookcase, 201, 217
charitable giving, 195
Clorox, 214
electric bills, 16, 162, 183, 454
fenced-in area, 201
fencing, 29, 142, 218
flood, 155
garage door opener, 215
garage sale, 66
grocery bills, 16
grub problem, 189
hardwood floors, 193
heating, 29
hot tub, 379, 389, 391
house cleaning, 420
jacuzzi, 142
lawn furniture, 219
leaky faucet, 17
liquid Tide, 219
living room table, 142
meter reading, 19–20
new rug, 379–380
painting a room, 388
patio resurfacing, 194
patio shape, 201
phone bills, 41
plumbing, 27
rectangular table, 335
refrigerator purchase, 420

roofing, 387, 395
sandbox construction, 197
selling a house, 453
shampoo, 29
shed construction, 241
storage shelves, 201
swimming pool, 142, 389, 394, 400
telephone plan, 419
telephone rate, 213
wallpaper, 329, 388
washing clothes, 154
washing dishes, 169
washing machines, 194
water rate, 41
water usage, 185
windows, 29

Housing/construction

assessed value, 184
corner lot, 198
designing a house, 217
Flatiron Building, 200
homes for sale, 16
house price, 217
paint, 214
painting, 147–148

Insurance

auto, 17
medical, 10–11, 17

Manufacturing

bicycles, 188
cost and revenue, 331
cost to produce vases, 434–435
pork production costs, 193
product testing, 211
water sprinklers, 330

Medical/medications

cholesterol, 145, 155
drug amount, 29
drug dosage, 30, 148–149, 155, 391–392, 401
heart rate, 66
insulin, 156
medical plans, 402
melanoma, 249
pharmacy, 214
Prader-Willi Syndrome, 155
supplies, 218
weight loss clinic, 440

Miscellaneous

advertising, 325
age, 182, 184

American consumers, 152
American flag, 201, 219
amphitheater, 142
artwork, 330
babysitting, 453
balance, 17
birthday party, 122
Blue Angels, Fat Albert, 215
Blue Angels airshow, 211
book pages, 195
brick wall, 396
butcher, 218
calling plan, 220
camera products/services, 249
charity event, 182, 195, 459
coffee bar, 49
construct data, 19
conversions, 17
conveyer belt, 212, 388
cutting wood, 27, 29, 30
daily newspaper, 395
diapers, 248
digging a trench, 389
drilling for water, 49
dropping egg, 329
electrical circuit, 395
Empire State Building, 16
estate value, 195
falling object, 335, 336, 395
falling rock, 329
fastening bolts, 30
Fat Albert (Blue Angels), 215
filling a tank, 389
film rolls, 183
gas-oil mixture, 145
gear ratio, 145–146
gift card balance, 54
gold, 155
Grisham, John novel, 154
height, 183
height of cannonball, 331
height of tree, 330
hotels, 34
house addresses, 34–35
jack, 371
Lands' End catalog, 58
life expectancy, 183
Little League, 88
mailing a letter, 152
milk tank, 278
mixing acid solutions, 208–210, 214, 218, 220, 301, 336
model car, 169
model train, 154
money, 183, 216, 219

mouthwash, 214
newsletter, 194
number problem, 324–325
oil drum, 143
panoramic photo, 135
pants inseam, 29, 59
paving roads, 204, 212
postage, 454
projectile height, 75
property crime rates, 40
reading speed, 155
rectangle dimensions, 280, 462
rectangular scrapbook, 329
retirement income, 194
road paving, 28
robberies, 217
rolling ball, 59
salt concentration, 214
salt mine, 212
salt solution, 220
sandcastles, 400
scrapbooking, 155
shopping, 90
sign dimensions, 329
skimming oil, 389
social security, 220, 278, 453
sorting mail, 390
speaker loudness, 393
speed-reading, 182
sport coat sale, 185
stationery, 122
storing wine, 384–385
submarine dive, 66
telephone lines, 330
ticket sales, 213
trapezoidal sign, 142
triangle, 327
Wall Street bull, 154
weight, 183, 184
world's richest person, 249

Retail

book store, 330
buying games, 8–9
candle shop, 192
clothing cost, 216
cost of Matchbox cars, 447
hat sale, 194
nut shop, 213
rocking chair sales, 205–206
sales increase, 183
sales price, 217
sales volume, 195, 219
shirt cost, 453
shirt sale, 183

sweater sale, 274
wind chimes sales, 218

Salary

housekeeper salaries, 193
income, 185
increase, 183, 194
salary plus commission, 416–417
wage cut, 195
weekly income, 461

Scientific/astronomical

Avogadro's Number, 250
Boyle's Law, 401
Earth's gravitational field, 326
electrical resistance, 378
half-life, 279
Hooke's Law, 396
light from the sun, 249
light through water, 394
mass earth, moon, Jupiter, 249
music soundwaves, 402
optics, 378
structure of matter, 250
submarine depth, 440
volume of gas, 396

Sports/exercise

backyard baseball, 330
baseball cards, 184, 192
baseball gate receipts, 395
Baseball Hall of Fame, 213
baseball records, 155
baseball salaries, 17
basketball, 143
bicycling, 212
bike riding, 453
boat rental, 41, 472
body mass index (BMI), 143
bowling scores, 16
calories burned by walking, 418
camel riding, 211
canoeing, 381
cross-country skiing, 336, 388
Daytona 500, 312
distance of a race, 382–383
exercise routine, 388, 401–402
football, 49, 66
golf, 58–59
gym membership, 193

health club membership, 195
home runs, 182
horseback riding, 211
ice skating rink, 450–451
ironman triathlon, 212
jet ski, 17
jogging, 185, 217
kite, 142
Little League, 88
New York Yankees, 148
Olympic gold medals, 220
PGA tour, 248
putting, 28
race horse, 215
racquet club membership, 194
rollerblading, 185, 400–401
running, 29, 212, 219, 462
sailboat charters, 392
sailboats, 136, 212
sailing, 402
season tickets, 219
ski lifts, 211
ski shop, 192
sleigh ride, 524
speedboat, 395, 495, 504
Summer Olympics, 187–188
Super Bowl, 12–13
swimming, 155, 218
tennis autographs, 194
tennis club, 197, 359, 419
tennis court, 200
walkie-talkies, 211
walking, 11–12, 141, 185, 211, 212
water bike rental, 190
water skiing, 388
white water rafting, 352

Tax

income taxes, 17
property tax, 154, 180
sales tax, 16, 75, 88
tax refund, 217

Travel/transportation.
See also **Automotive/
motor vehicle;
Aviation/aeronautical**

Amtrak, 185
average speed, 141, 280
boat trip, 169
camping trip, 203
Canadian currency exchange, 155
carry-on luggage, 387

commute times, 88
commuting to work, 153
disabled boat, 212
distance between cities, 155
distance traveled, 241, 394, 419
driving speed, 212
driving to a concert, 423
exchanging currency, 150
fastest car, 142
ferries, 211
headwind and tailwind, 388
kayak ride, 387
maps, 154
map scale, 169
Mexican peso exchange, 155
money exchange, 169
motel room cost, 336
motorcycle trip, 387
no-wake zone, 388
paddleboat ride, 387
passports processed, 153
Pittsburgh Incline, 217–218
road trip, 75
scenic route, 381–382
speed, 217, 218
spring break, 58, 168
Tail of the Dragon, 388
toll roads, 152–153
traffic jam, 212
trains, 179, 185, 211, 217, 388
travel time, 170, 212
trolley ride, 387
vacationing, 453
wagon ride, 185
White Pass Railroad, 366
yield sign, 142, 387

Weather/temperature

average daily, 182
below zero temperatures, 43
Chicago temperatures, 162
dry summers, 16
Fahrenheit *vs.* Celsius temperatures, 441
global warming, 28
lab work, 66
rainfall, 58
snowfall, 54–55
snowplowing, 212, 219
snowstorm, 389
temperature change, 58
temperature difference, 54
tornadoes, 193
wind chill, 66

Subject Index

A

Absolute value
  addition using, 45–47, 86
  explanation of, 37–38, 85
  negative of, 38
Addition
  associative property of, 77, 78, 87, 94
  commutative property of, 76, 78, 94
  of decimals, 47
  distributive property of multiplication over, 77–78, 87
  of fractions, 23–25, 84, 85, 397
  of polynomials, 252–253, 276
  of rational expressions, 352–354, 359–364, 376
  of real numbers, 42–47, 63, 85–86
  using absolute values, 45–47, 86
  words and phrases for, 172
Addition property of equality
  explanation of, 103–105, 112, 163
  mentally using, 106
  solving equations with, 123
Additive inverse
  explanation of, 45, 79
  expression divided by, 342
Algebraic expressions
  explanation of, 8, 83, 92
  translated into words, 173
Angles
  complementary, 198
  supplementary, 198
Application problem solving.
  See also Problem solving
  for application problems involving money, 188–191
  expressing relationship between two related quantities for, 173–175
  for geometry problems, 197–199
  for mixture problems, 206–210, 216
  for money problems, 204–206
  for motion problems involving two rates, 203–204
  procedure for, 186–188
  with quadratic equations, 324–328
  with rational equations, 379–386
  suggestions for, 191
  summary of, 215–216
  translating applications into equations for, 178–180
  translating phrases into mathematical expressions for, 172–173
  writing expressions involving multiplication for, 175–178
Applications, translated into equations, 178–180
Approximately equal to, 12
Area
  of circle, 136, 197
  explanation of, 134, 165
  of quadrilaterals, 134, 138, 197
  of rectangles, 134, 197
  of triangles, 134, 138, 197
Associative property
  of addition, 77, 78, 87, 94
  of multiplication, 77

B

Bar graphs, 11–12
Base, 67, 222, 275
Binomials. *See also* Polynomials
  distributive property to multiple, 259–260
  dividing polynomials by, 269–271
  explanation of, 252
  FOIL method to multiply, 260–263, 294, 295, 297
  square of, 263
  use of formulas for special products to multiply, 262–264
Braces, 72
Brackets, 72

C

Cartesian coordinate system
  explanation of, 404, 455
  plotting points in, 404–407
Checking equations, 101
Circle graphs
  explanation of, 11
  problem solving involving, 13–14
Circles, formulas for, 136, 197
Circumference, 136, 165, 197
Coefficients, 92, 163
Collinear points, 407, 408
Common denominators
  addition or subtraction of fractions with, 352
  addition or subtraction of rational expressions with, 352–354, 397
  explanation of, 23
  least, 23, 24, 43, 44, 85, 354–356, 359–360
Commutative property
  of addition, 76, 78, 87, 94
  function of, 76, 78
  of multiplication, 76, 78
Complementary angles, 198
Complex fractions
  explanation of, 367, 397
  methods to simplify, 367–370, 398
Composite numbers, 283
Conditional equations, 129, 164
Congruent triangles, 198
Consecutive integers, 179, 215, 328
Constant of proportionality, 390
Constant term, 93
Constants
  explanation of, 93, 163
  variation, 390
Contradictions, 129, 164
Counting numbers, 32
Cross-multiplication, 146, 166
Cubes, factoring sum and difference of two, 314–316, 332, 333

D

Decimals
  addition of, 47
  explanation of, 32
  solving equations containing, 117, 126–129
  subtraction of, 51, 53
  terminating or repeating, 32
Degree, of polynomials, 252
Delta (Δ), 421
Denominator. *See also* Common denominators; Least common denominator (LCD)
  explanation of, 21, 84
  negative exponents in, 234
  negative signs removed from, 62–63
  rational equations with variable appearing in, 373–376
  in rational expressions, 338–339
Descartes, René, 404
Descending order, polynomials written in, 254
Diameter, 136
Difference
  in subtraction, 51
  writing sum or, 176
Difference of two cubes, 315
Difference of two squares
  explanation of, 262–263, 313, 332
  factoring, 313–314
Direct variation
  explanation of, 390, 399
  problems involving, 391–392
Distance formula
  explanation of, 133–134, 165
  for motion problems, 203, 381
Distributive property
  explanation of, 163
  of multiplication over addition, 77–78, 87
  to multiply binomials, 259–260
  use of, 78, 95–97, 127–129, 285
Dividend, 61
Division
  of fractions, 23, 84, 397
  involving zero, 64, 86
  of polynomials, 268–272

Division *(continued)*
  of rational expressions,
    348–349, 397
  of real numbers, 61–63
  words and phrases for, 172
Divisor, 61
Domain, 445, 446, 457

E

Elements, 31, 85
Ellipsis, 22
Empty sets, 31, 85
Equality
  addition property of,
    103–106, 163
  multiplication property of,
    108–112, 164
Equations. *See also* Linear
    equations; Systems of
    linear equations
  changing application
    problems into,
    172–181 (*See also*
    Application problem
    solving)
  checking, 101
  conditional, 129, 164
  containing fractions, 436
  equivalent, 102–103, 163
  explanation of, 101
  graphs of, 407–409
  quadratic, 320–322, 333
    (*See also* Quadratic
    equations)
  solutions to, 101–102, 109,
    114–129, 163
  translating applications in,
    178–180
  use of addition property to
    solve, 103–106
  variation, 390–391
Equilateral triangles, 198
Equivalent equations
  explanation of, 163
  identification of, 102–103
Evaluation
  of expressions, 23, 119
  of formulas, 132
  of functions, 449
Exam preparation, 4–6
Expanded power rule of
    exponents, 227–229
Exponential notation, 68
Exponents
  evaluating expressions
    containing, 68, 87
  expanded power rule of,
    227–229
  explanation of, 67, 68, 222,
    275
  negative, 233–238
  parenthesis with, 68–69
  power of product rule of,
    226–227

power of quotient rule of,
    227
  power rule of, 225–227
  product rule of, 222–223
  quotient rule of, 223–224
  summary of rules for, 229,
    238, 275
  tips for writing, 228, 229
  zero exponent rule of, 225
Expressions. *See also* Rational
    expressions
  evaluation of, 119
  expansion of, 96
  explanation of, 8, 92
  exponential, 226, 229
  factoring, 282, 331
  involving multiplication,
    175–178
  simplifying, 97–98, 119,
    163
  translated into words, 173
  using parenthesis when
    writing, 177 (*See also*
    Parentheses)
Extraneous roots, 373
Extremes, 146, 166

F

Factors/factoring. *See also*
    Greatest common
    factor (GCF)
  difference of two squares,
    313–314
  dividing out common, 25
  explanation of, 21, 60, 84,
    98, 163, 182
  by grouping, 289–292,
    307–310
  of monomials from
    polynomials, 285–287
  polynomials, 316–317, 333
  solving quadratic equations
    using, 320–328, 333
  sum and difference of two
    cubes, 314–316, 332,
    333
  by trial and error, 295,
    302–307, 310
  trinomials of form $ax^2 + bx$
    $+ c, a \neq 1$, 302–310, 332
  trinomials of form $ax^2 + bx$
    $+ c$, where $a = 1$,
    294–299, 332
FOIL method
  to check factoring-by-
    grouping problem, 290
  to multiply binomials,
    260–263, 294, 295, 297
Formulas
  distance, 133–134, 165, 203
  evaluation of, 132
  explanation of, 132
  geometric, 134–137, 197
  simple interest, 132–133

solving for variable in,
    137–139, 166
Fractions
  addition of, 23–25, 43–45,
    84, 85, 397
  changing mixed numbers to
    and from, 25–27
  complex, 367–370,
    397–398
  division of, 23, 84, 397
  explanation of, 21
  multiplication of, 22–23, 84,
    345, 397
  negative, 339
  raised to negative exponent
    rule, 237, 275
  signs associated with, 339
  simplifying, 21–22, 25, 84
  simplifying equations
    containing, 436
  solving equations
    containing, 117–120,
    123, 127–129
  subtraction of, 23–25, 84,
    397
Functions
  evaluation of, 449
  explanation of, 446
  graphs of linear, 450–451
  method to determine,
    446–448
  notation for, 449, 458

G

Geometric formulas
  for areas and perimeters of
    quadrilaterals and
    triangles, 134, 197
  listing of, 197
  use of, 134–137
  for volumes of three-
    dimensional figures,
    137
Geometry. *See also specific
    geometric shapes*
  angles, 198
  facts about, 198
  parallel lines, 424, 425, 456
  perpendicular lines,
    425–426, 456
  polygons, 198
  triangles, 134, 138, 197, 198,
    216, 326–328, 333
Geometry problems
  guidelines for solving,
    197–199
  involving rational
    expressions, 379–380,
    398
  proportions to solve, 151
Golden Ratio, 156
Graphs/graphing
  bar, 11–12
  circle, 13–14

of equations, 407–409
  explanation of, 404
  line, 12–13
  of linear equations,
    407–417, 432–433,
    437–438 (*See also*
    Linear equations,
    graphs)
  of linear functions, 450–451
  of linear inequalities,
    442–444
  problem solving involving,
    11–14
Greatest common factor
    (GCF)
  explanation of, 21, 84, 282,
    331
  removed from trinomials,
    299–300
  of two or more numbers,
    283–284, 331
  of two or more terms,
    284–287, 331
Grouping
  associative property
    and, 77
  factoring by, 289–292,
    307–310
Grouping symbols
  explanation of, 69, 87
  nested, 70
  use of, 69–72

H

Horizontal lines, 415–416,
    424, 456
Hypotenuse, 326

I

Identities, 129, 164
Identity element of addition,
    79
Identity element of
    multiplication, 79
Identity property of addition,
    79
Identity property of
    multiplication, 79
Indeterminate form, 64n
Inequalities. *See also* Linear
    inequalities
  explanation of, 36–37, 156,
    167
  in one variable, 156–160
  order or sense of, 156
  properties used to solve,
    157–158
  solving, 156–160
  symbols for, 36, 57, 156,
    159, 442
  in two variables, 442–443,
    457
Integers
  consecutive, 179, 215

consecutive even and consecutive odd, 179
explanation of, 32, 85
positive, 32, 85
Interest problems, 204–205
Intersection of sets, 36
Inverse properties, 79–80, 87
Inverses
additive, 45, 79, 342
multiplicative, 79, 108
Inverse variation
explanation of, 392, 399
problems involving, 392–393
Irrational numbers
examples of, 32, 33
explanation of, 32, 33, 85
Is approximately equal to, 12, 84
Is less than, 36
Isolate the variable, 102
Isosceles triangles, 198, 216

L

Least common denominator (LCD)
addition and, 43, 44
explanation of, 23, 24, 85
method to find, 354–356, 359–360
Legs, of right triangles, 326
Like terms
explanation of, 93, 163, 252
method to combine, 93–94
solving equations with, 123
Linear equations. *See also* Equations; Systems of linear equations
explanation of, 101, 163
forms of, 435, 436
graphs
applications of, 416–417
comparing methods for, 437–438
explanation of, 407–409
of form $ax + by = 0$, 413
horizontal and vertical lines on, 415–416, 456
plotting points on, 411–412, 438, 455
using slope and y-intercept, 432–433, 457
using x- and y-intercepts, 413–415, 456
in standard form, 406
involving decimal numbers or fractions, 117–120
in one variable, 406
point-slope form of, 435–437, 457
in slope-intercept form, 431–432, 457
in two variables, 406–407, 455

with variable on both sides of equation, 123–130, 164
with variable on one side of equation, 114–116, 164
Linear inequalities. *See also* Inequalities
explanation of, 156
graphs of, 442–444
that have all real numbers as their solution, or have no solution, 160
in two variables, 442–443, 457
with variable on both sides of inequality symbol, 159
Line graphs
explanation of, 11
problem solving involving, 12–13
Lines
horizontal, 415–416, 424, 456
parallel, 56, 424, 425, 456
perpendicular, 425–426, 456
slope of, 420–426, 456
vertical, 415–416, 424, 456
Lowest terms
fractions reduced to, 21, 53, 54, 117, 118
rational expressions reduced to, 339–341

M

Mathematical expressions, translating phrases into, 172–173
Mathematical models, 47
Means
explanation of, 14
problem solving involving, 15
of proportion, 146, 166
Measurement, use of proportions to convert, 149–150
Measures of central tendency, 14
Median, 14
Metric system, base units of, 244
Minuend, 51
Mixed numbers
changing to and from fractions to, 25
explanation of, 25, 85
Mixture problems
explanation of, 206–207, 216
involving solids, 207
involving solutions, 208–210
Money applications, 188–191, 204–206

Monomials
dividing polynomials by, 268–269
explanation of, 252
factored from polynomials, 285–287, 331
multiplied by monomials, 258
multiplied by polynomials, 258–259
Motion problems
explanation of, 203
formula for, 203
involving rational expressions, 381–383, 398
involving two rates, 203–204, 216
Multiplication
associative property of, 77, 87
to clear fractions, 368–369
commutative property of, 76, 78, 87
of fractions, 22–23, 84, 345
of polynomials, 258–265
of rational expressions, 345–347, 397
of real numbers, 59–61, 63
symbols and factors for, 20–21
words and phrases for, 172
writing expressions involving, 175–178
Multiplication property of equality
explanation of, 108–111, 164
mentally using, 112
solving equations with, 123
Multiplicative inverse, 79, 108

N

Natural numbers
explanation of, 21, 85
on number line, 32
Negative exponent rule
explanation of, 233–234, 275, 553
fraction raised to, 237, 275
Negative exponents. *See also* Exponents
explanation of, 233
simplifying expressions containing, 234–238
Negative fractions, 339
Negative numbers. *See also* Signed numbers
operations with, 42, 46, 52
Negative slope, 422–423, 456
Nested grouping symbols, 70
Notation. *See* Symbols/notation

Null set. *See* Empty set
Number lines
adding real numbers using, 42–43, 85–86
explanation of, 31–32
inequalities and, 36, 37
real, 33
Numbers. *See also* Real numbers
composite, 283
counting, 32
irrational, 32, 33, 85
mixed, 25, 85
natural, 21, 22, 85
prime, 282–283
rational, 32, 33, 85
whole, 21, 22, 84, 85
Numerators, 21, 84
Numerical coefficient, 92, 163. *See also* Coefficients

O

Operations. *See also* Addition; Division; Multiplication; Subtraction
explanation of, 8, 42
order of, 69, 87
summary of, 63
Opposites, 45
Ordered pairs
components of, 445
explanation of, 405, 407, 455
functions and, 447
order of numbers in, 405
Order of operations, 69, 87
Origin, 404, 455

P

Parallel lines
explanation of, 424
slope of, 425, 456
Parallelograms, area and perimeter formulas for, 134
Parentheses
with exponents, 68–69
negative signs and, 254
preceded by plus or minus sign, 97
solving equations with, 123
use of, 69–70, 177
Percent
application problems involving, 177, 190–191
explanation of, 190
writing expressions involving, 177–178
Perimeter
explanation of, 134, 165
of quadrilaterals, 134, 197
of rectangles, 138, 197
of triangles, 134, 197

Perpendicular lines
    explanation of, 425, 456
    slope of, 425–426
Phrases, translated into
    mathematical
    expressions, 172–173
pi (π), 136
Point-slope form
    to determine equation of
        line, 435–437
    example of, 436–437
    of linear equations,
        435–437, 457
Pólya, George, 7
Polygons
    with n sides, 198
Polynomials. *See also* Rational
        expressions; Trinomials
    addition of, 252–253, 276
    degree of, 252
    descending order of, 251
    division of, 268–272, 277
    explanation of, 251
    factoring monomials from,
        285–287, 331
    factoring negative 1 from,
        341–342
    general procedure for
        factoring, 316–317,
        333
    group to factor four-term,
        289–292
    multiplication of, 258–265,
        276
    prime, 298, 306
    review of, 276
    subtraction of, 254–255,
        276
    types of, 252
    written in descending order,
        272
Positive integers, 32
Positive numbers, 42, 46. *See
        also* Signed numbers
Positive slope, 422–423, 456
Power of product rule of
        exponents, 226–227
Power of quotient rule of
        exponents, 227
Power rule of exponents
    explanation of, 225–227
    product rule vs., 226
Prime factorization
    explanation of, 283
Prime numbers, 282–283
Prime polynomials, 298, 306
Problem solving. *See also*
        Application problem
        solving
    five-step procedure for,
        7–11, 83, 186, 215
    involving bar, line, and
        circle graphs, 11–14
    involving statistics, 14–15

Product
    explanation of, 60
    of real numbers, 59–61
Product rule for exponents
    explanation of, 222–223
    power of, 226
Proportions. *See also* Ratios
    examples of problems using,
        146–149
    explanation of, 146, 166
    means of, 146
    setting up, 149, 151
    to solve problems involving
        similar figures, 151
    steps to solve problems
        using, 147, 166
    used to change units,
        149–150
Pythagorean Theorem
    explanation of, 326–327,
        333
    use of, 327–328

Q

Quadrants, 404
Quadratic equations
    applications of, 324–328
    explanation of, 320
    factoring to solve, 321–322,
        333
    in standard form, 320
Quadrilaterals
    area and perimeter
        formulas for, 134, 197
    explanation of, 134, 198
Quantities, relationship
        between related,
        173–175
Quotient
    explanation of, 61
    of positive and negative
        number, 63, 86
Quotient rule
    for exponents, 223–224

R

Radius, 136
Range, 445, 446, 457
Ranked data, 14
Rates
    in money problems, 204
    in motion problems, 203,
        216
Rational equations
    applications containing,
        379–386
    explanation of, 372
    with integer denominators,
        372–373
    solution to, 376, 398
    with variable in
        denominator,
        373–376
    variation, 390–393

when variable appears in
        denominator, 373–376
Rational expressions. *See also*
        Polynomials
    addition and subtraction of,
        352–354, 359–364, 376,
        397
    applications containing,
        379–386
    complex fractions and,
        367–370
    division of, 348–349, 397
    explanation of, 338–339, 396
    finding least common
        denominator for,
        354–356, 359–360
    in lowest terms, 339
    method to simplify,
        339–342, 396
    multiplication of, 345–347,
        397
    signs of, 339
    simplified, 339
Rational numbers
    examples of, 32, 33
    explanation of, 32, 33, 85
Ratios. *See also* Proportions
    explanation of, 144, 166
    terms of, 144
    use of, 144–146
Real number line, 33
Real numbers
    addition of, 42–47, 86
    division of, 61–63
    explanation of, 33, 85
    multiplication of, 59–61
    set of, 33
    subtraction of, 50–56, 86
    summer of operations on, 63
Real number system. *See also
        specific properties*
    associative property of, 77,
        87
    commutative property of,
        76, 87
    distributive property of,
        77–78, 87, 95–97
    identity properties of, 79, 87
    inverse properties of,
        79–80, 87
Reciprocals, 107–108, 163, 380
Rectangles, 134, 138, 197
Rectangular coordinate
        system. *See* Cartesian
        coordinate system
Relations
    domain and range of,
        445–446
    explanation of, 445, 446
Right triangles
    explanation of, 326, 333
    Pythagorean Theorem and,
        327–328
    verifying, 326–327

Rise of a line, 420
Roots
    extraneous, 373
Run of a line, 420

S

Scientific notation
    with coefficient of 1,
        244–245
    converting numbers to and
        from, 242–243
    examples of calculations
        using, 245–247
    explanation of, 242, 275
Sets, 31, 85
Signed numbers. *See also*
        Negative numbers;
        Positive numbers
    addition of, 46, 47, 63, 86
    division of, 61–63
    multiplication of, 59–61, 63
    parentheses and, 254
    subtraction of, 50–52, 63
Similar figures
    explanation of, 151
    proportions to solve
        problems involving,
        151
Similar triangles, 151, 198
Simple interest formula,
        132–133, 164, 205
Simple interest problems,
        204–205
Simplified expressions, 119
Simplified fractions, 21–22, 25
Simplify an expression, 97
Slope
    explanation of, 420–422,
        456
    formula for, 421
    graphing linear equations
        using, 432–433, 457
    of horizontal and vertical
        lines, 424
    of parallel and
        perpendicular lines,
        424–426
    positive and negative,
        422–423, 456
    undefined, 456
Slope-intercept form
    to determine equation of
        line, 434–435
    of linear equations, 431,
        435–437, 457
Solutions
    to equations, 101, 102,
        114–120
    extraneous, 373
Special products, multiplying
        binomials using
        formulas for, 262–264
Square of binomials,
        263–264

Squares
    area and perimeter
        formulas for, 134
    difference of two, 262–263,
        313–314, 332
Standard form
    linear equations in, 406,
        435, 436, 455
    quadratic equations in, 320
Statistics, problem solving
    involving, 14–15
Study skills, 2–9
Subtraction
    common errors in, 173
    computed mentally, 55–56
    of decimals, 51, 53
    of fractions, 23–25, 84, 397
    of polynomials, 254–255,
        276
    of rational expressions,
        352–354, 359–364, 376
    of real numbers, 50–56, 63,
        86
    words and phrases for, 172
Subtrahend, 51
Sum of two cubes, 315
Sum, writing, 177
Supplementary angles, 198
Symbols/notation
    approximately equal to, 12
    braces, 72
    brackets, 72
    delta (Δ), 421
    ellipsis, 22
    exponential, 68
    function, 449, 458
    grouping, 69–72, 87
    inequality, 36, 57, 156, 159,
        442
    is approximately equal to,
        12, 84

multiplication, 20, 84
parentheses, 68–70, 97, 123,
    177
pi (π), 136
ratio, 144
scientific, 242–247, 275
set of real numbers, 33
Systems of linear equations.
    See also Linear
    equations
addition method to solve,
    379–462

T

Terms
    constant, 93
    explanation of, 92, 98, 163
    like, 93–98, 163
    of the ratio, 144
Three-dimensional figures, 137
Time management, 6–7
Trapezoids, 134
Trial and error factoring,
    302–307, 310
Triangles
    area and perimeter formulas
        for, 134, 138, 197
    congruent, 198
    equilateral, 198
    isosceles, 198, 216
    right, 326–328, 333
    similar, 198
Trinomials. *See also*
    Polynomials
    explanation of, 252
    factored, 286
    of form $ax^2 + bx + c, a \neq 1$,
        302–310, 332
    of form $ax^2 + bx + c$, where
        $a = 1$, 294–299, 332

removing greatest common
    factor from, 299–300

U

Undefined number, 64
Union of sets, 36

V

Variables
    evaluating expressions
        containing, 72–73
    explanation of, 20, 92
    in formulas, 137–139
    inequities in one, 156–159
    isolation of, 105–106, 110,
        124
Variation
    direct, 390–392, 399
    inverse, 392–393, 399
Variation equations, 390–391,
    398
Venn diagrams, 35
Vertical lines, 415–416, 456
Vertical line test, 448, 457
Volume, 137, 165
Volume formulas, of three-
    dimensional figures,
    137

W

Whole numbers, 22, 31, 84,
    85
Words. *See also* Application
    problem solving
    translated into equations,
        178–180
    translated into
        mathematical
        expressions, 172–173

Work problems
    explanation of, 383
    involving rational
        expressions, 383–386

X

x-axis, 404, 455
x-coordinate
    explanation of, 405
x-intercept
    explanation of, 413, 455
    in graphs of linear
        equations, 413–415,
        438, 456
$-x = a$, solving equations of
    form, 111, 112

Y

y-axis, 404, 455
y-coordinate
    explanation of, 405
y-intercept
    explanation of, 413, 455
    in graphs of linear
        equations, 413–415,
        432–433, 438, 456, 457

Z

Zero
    division with, 64, 86
    explanation of, 31
    slope of, 456
Zero exponent rule of
    exponents, 225
Zero-factor property, 320,
    333

Chapter 1   Real Numbers

Fractions

Addition

$$\frac{a}{c} + \frac{b}{c} = \frac{a+b}{c}$$

Subtraction

$$\frac{a}{c} - \frac{b}{c} = \frac{a-b}{c}$$

Multiplication

$$\frac{a}{b} \cdot \frac{c}{d} = \frac{a \cdot c}{b \cdot d}$$

Division

$$\frac{a}{b} \div \frac{c}{d} = \frac{a}{b} \cdot \frac{d}{c} = \frac{a \cdot d}{b \cdot c}$$

Natural numbers $\{1, 2, 3, 4, \ldots\}$

Whole numbers $\{0, 1, 2, 3, \ldots\}$

Integers $\{\ldots, -3, -2, -1, 0, 1, 2, 3, \ldots\}$

Rational numbers {quotient of two integers, denominator not 0}

The sum of two positive numbers will be a positive number.
The sum of two negative numbers will be a negative number.
The sum of a positive number and a negative number can be either a positive or negative number.

The product (or quotient) of two numbers with like signs will be a positive number.
The product (or quotient) of two numbers with unlike signs will be a negative number.

$a - b$ means $a + (-b)$

$$\frac{a}{-b} = \frac{-a}{b} = -\frac{a}{b}$$

$$b^n = \underbrace{b \cdot b \cdot b \cdot \cdots \cdot b}_{n \text{ factors of } b}$$

Order of Operations

1. Evaluate expressions within parentheses.
2. Evaluate expressions with exponents.
3. Perform multiplications or divisions moving from left to right.
4. Perform additions or subtractions moving from left to right.

Properties of the Real Numbers

Commutative: $a + b = b + a, a \cdot b = b \cdot a$

Associative: $(a + b) + c = a + (b + c), (a \cdot b) \cdot c = a \cdot (b \cdot c)$

Distributive: $a(b + c) = a \cdot b + a \cdot c$

Identity: $a + 0 = 0 + a = a, 1 \cdot a = a \cdot 1 = a$

Inverse: $a + (-a) = -a + a = 0, a \cdot \dfrac{1}{a} = \dfrac{1}{a} \cdot a = 1$

Chapter 2   Solving Linear Equations and Inequalities

Addition property of equality: If $a = b$, then $a + c = b + c$ for any real numbers $a, b,$ and c.

Multiplication property of equality: If $a = b$, then $a \cdot c = b \cdot c$ for any real numbers $a, b,$ and c.

Linear equation: $ax + b = c$, for real numbers $a, b,$ and c.

To Solve Linear Equations with the Variable on Both Sides of the Equal Sign

1. If the equation contains fractions, multiply both sides of the equation by the LCD.
2. Use the distributive property to remove parentheses.
3. Combine like terms on the same side of the equal sign.
4. Use the addition property to rewrite the equation with all terms containing the variable on one side of the equal sign and all terms not containing the variable on the other side of the equal sign. Repeated use of the addition property will eventually result in an equation of the form $ax = b$.
5. Use the multiplication property to isolate the variable. This will give a solution of the form $x = $ some number.
6. Check the solution in the original equation.

Simple interest formula: $i = prt$

Distance formula: $d = rt$

Geometric formulas: See Section 2.6 and Appendix C.

Cross multiplication: If $\dfrac{a}{b} = \dfrac{c}{d}$, then $ad = bc$.

Inequalities

If $a > b$, then $a + c > b + c$.
If $a > b$, then $a - c > b - c$.
If $a > b$ and $c > 0$, then $ac > bc$.

If $a > b$ and $c > 0$, then $\dfrac{a}{c} > \dfrac{b}{c}$.

If $a > b$ and $c < 0$, then $ac < bc$.

If $a > b$ and $c < 0$, then $\dfrac{a}{c} < \dfrac{b}{c}$.

Chapter 3   Formulas and Applications of Algebra

Problem-Solving Procedure for Solving Applications Problems

1. **Understand the problem.**
   Identify the quantity or quantities you are being asked to find.
2. **Translate the problem into mathematical language (express the problem as an equation).**
   a) Choose a variable to represent one quantity, *and write down exactly what it represents.* Represent any other quantity to be found in terms of this variable.
   b) Using the information from step a) write an equation that represents the application.
3. **Carry out the mathematical calculations (solve the equation).**
4. **Check the answer (using the original application).**
5. **Answer the question asked.**

Chapter 4   Exponents and Polynomials

Rules of Exponents

1. $x^m \cdot x^n = x^{m+n}$ **product rule**

2. $\dfrac{x^m}{x^n} = x^{m-n}, x \neq 0$ **quotient rule**

3. $(x^m)^n = x^{m \cdot n}$ **power rule**

4. $x^0 = 1, x \neq 0$ **zero exponent rule**

5. $x^{-m} = \dfrac{1}{x^m}, x \neq 0$ **negative exponent rule**

6. $\left(\dfrac{ax}{by}\right)^m = \dfrac{a^m x^m}{b^m y^m}, b \neq 0, y \neq 0$ **expanded power rule**

7. $\left(\dfrac{a}{b}\right)^{-m} = \left(\dfrac{b}{a}\right)^m, a \neq 0, b \neq 0$ **a fraction raised to a negative exponent rule**

FOIL method (*First, Outer, Inner, Last*) of multiplying binomials:
$(a + b)(c + d) = ac + ad + bc + bd$

Product of the sum and difference of the same two terms:
$(a + b)(a - b) = a^2 - b^2$

Squares of binomials:
$(a + b)^2 = a^2 + 2ab + b^2$
$(a - b)^2 = a^2 - 2ab + b^2$

Chapter 5   Factoring

If $a \cdot b = c$, then a and b are **factors** of c.
Difference of two squares: $a^2 - b^2 = (a + b)(a - b)$
Sum of two cubes: $a^3 + b^3 = (a + b)(a^2 - ab + b^2)$
Difference of two cubes: $a^3 - b^3 = (a - b)(a^2 + ab + b^2)$

To Factor a Polynomial

1. If all the terms of the polynomial have a greatest common factor other than 1, factor it out.
2. If the polynomial has two terms, determine if it is a difference of two squares or a sum or a difference of two cubes. If so, factor using the appropriate formula.
3. If the polynomial has three terms, factor the trinomial using one of the procedures discussed.
4. If the polynomial has more than three terms, try factoring by grouping.

5. As a final step, examine your factored polynomial to see if the terms in any factors listed have a common factor. If you find a common factor, factor it out at this point.

Quadratic equation: $ax^2 + bx + c = 0, a \neq 0$

Zero-factor property: If $ab = 0$, then $a = 0$ or $b = 0$.

To Solve a Quadratic Equation by Factoring

1. Write the equation in standard form with the squared term positive. This will result in one side of the equation being 0.
2. Factor the side of the equation that is not 0.
3. Set each factor containing a variable equal zero and solve each equation.
4. Check the solution found in step 3 in the original equation.

Pythagorean Theorem: $a^2 + b^2 = c^2$

Chapter 6   Rational Expressions and Equations

To Simplify Rational Expressions

1. Factor both the numerator and denominator as completely as possible.
2. Divide out any factors common to both the numerator and denominator.

To Multiply Rational Expressions

1. Factor all numerators and denominators completely.
2. Divide out common factors.
3. Multiply the numerators together and multiply the denominators together.

To Add or Subtract Two Rational Expressions

1. Determine the least common denominator (LCD).
2. Rewrite each fraction as an equivalent fraction with the LCD.
3. Add or subtract numerators while maintaining the LCD.

4. When possible, factor the remaining numerator and simplify the fraction.

To Solve Rational Expressions

1. Determine the LCD of all fractions in the equation.
2. Multiply both sides of the equation by the LCD. This will result in every term in the equation being multiplied by the LCD.
3. Remove any parentheses and combine like terms on each side of the equation.
4. Solve the equation.
5. Check your solution in the original equation.

Variation

Direct Variation: $y = kx$

Inverse Variation: $y = \dfrac{k}{x}$

Chapter 7   Graphing Linear Equations

Linear equation in two variables: $ax + by = c$

A **graph** is an illustration of the set of points whose coordinates satisfy the equation.

Every **linear equation** of the form $ax + by = c$ will be a straight line when graphed.

To find the y-intercept (where the graph crosses the y-axis) set $x = 0$ and solve for y.

To find the x-intercept (where the graph crosses the x-axis) set $y = 0$ and solve for x.

slope $(m) = \dfrac{\text{change in } y}{\text{change in } x} = \dfrac{y_2 - y_1}{x_2 - x_1}$

Positive slope
(rises to right)

Negative slope
(falls to right)

Slope is 0.
(horizontal line)

Slope is undefined.
(vertical line)

Linear Equations

Standard form of a linear equation: $ax + by = c$

Slope–intercept form of a linear equation: $y = mx + b$, where m is the slope and $(0, b)$ is the y-intercept.

Point–slope form of a linear equation: $y - y_1 = m(x - x_1)$, where m is the slope and (x_1, y_1) is a point on the line.

A **relation** is any set of ordered pairs.

A **function** is a set of ordered pairs in which each first component corresponds to exactly one second component.